PROBLEMS AND SOLUTIO

Merrill

Physics

Principles and Problems

AUTHORS

Paul Zitzewitz
Professor of Physics
University of Michigan-Dearborn
Dearborn, Michigan

Donald Wilke
Physics Teacher
Worthington High School
Worthington, Ohio

Daniel Spears
Physics Teacher, Principal
Tree of Life Christian School
Columbus, Ohio

GLENCOE

Macmillan/McGraw-Hill

New York, New York Columbus, Ohio Mission Hills, California Peoria, Illinois

A Glencoe/McGraw-Hill Program

Merrill Physics: Principles & Problems

Student Edition
Teacher Wraparound Edition
Problems and Solutions Manual
Teacher Resource Package
Transparency Package
Laboratory Manual:
 Student and Teacher Editions
Study Guide, Student Edition
Lesson Plan Booklet
English/Spanish Glossary
Computer Test Bank

The Problems and Solutions Manual is a supplement of Merrill's *Physics: Principles and Problems,* published by Glencoe. The Manual is a Comprehensive resource of all student text problems and solutions.

Chapter 1 of *Physics: Principles and Problems* is an introductory chapter and contains no mathematical problems. For Chapters 2 through 31, there are three sources of problems to reinforce the quantitative concepts introduced in each chapter.

Practice Problems follow most Example Problems. Answers to these problems are found in the margin of the Teacher Wraparound Edition. Complete solutions to these problems are available to the student in Appendix A of the student text. Each Practice Problem with the solution is restated in this manual.

Chapter Review Problems are a part of each Chapter Review. Answers to these problems are found in the margins of the Teacher Wraparound Edition. Each problem with the solution is included in this Manual.

Supplemental Problems are listed in Appendix B of the student edition, with answers in the margin of the Teacher Wraparound Edition. Each supplemental problem with the solution is included in this Manual.

ISBN 0-02-826726-5

Send all inquiries to: **GLENCOE DIVISION, Macmillan/McGraw-Hill**
936 Eastwind Drive
Westerville, Ohio 43081

Printed in the United States of America

1 2 3 4 5 6 7 8 9 BAW 99 98 97 96 95 94

Table of Contents

Chapter 2: A Mathematical Toolkit

2

Practice Problems

page 16

Express the following measurements in scientific notation

1. **a.** 5800 m

   5.8×10^3 m

   b. 450 000 m

   4.5×10^5 m

   c. 302 000 000 m

   3.02×10^8 m

   d. 86 000 000 000 m

   8.6×10^{10} m

2. **a.** 0.000 508 kg

   5.08×10^{-4} kg

   b. 0.000 000 45 kg

   4.5×10^{-7} kg

   c. 0.003600 kg

   3.600×10^{-3} kg

   d. 0.004 kg

   4×10^{-3} kg

3. **a.** 300 000 000 s

   3×10^8 s

   b. 186 000 s

   1.86×10^5 s

   c. 93 000 000 s

   9.3×10^7 s

Practice Problems

page 17

4. Convert each of the following length measurements to its equivalent in meters.

   a. 1.1 cm

   $$(1.1\ \text{cm})\frac{(1 \times 10^{-2}\ \text{m})}{(1\ \text{cm})} = 1.1 \times 10^{-2}\ \text{m}$$

   b. 76.2 pm

   $$(76.2\ \text{pm})\frac{(1 \times 10^{-12}\ \text{m})}{(1\ \text{pm})} = 76.2 \times 10^{-12}\ \text{m}$$

   $$= 7.62 \times 10^{-11}\ \text{m}$$

   c. 2.1 km

   $$(2.1\ \text{km})\frac{(1 \times 10^{3}\ \text{m})}{(1\ \text{km})} = 2.1 \times 10^{3}\ \text{m}$$

   d. 0.123 Mm

   $$(0.123\ \text{Mm})\frac{(1 \times 10^{6}\ \text{m})}{(1\ \text{Mm})} = 0.123 \times 10^{6}\ \text{m}$$

   $$= 1.23 \times 10^{5}\ \text{m}$$

5. Convert each of these mass measurements to its equivalent in kilograms.

   a. 147 g

   $$1\ \text{kg} = 1 \times 10^3 g \text{ so } 147 g \left[\frac{1\ \text{kg}}{1 \times 10^3 g}\right]$$

   $$= 147 \times 10^{-3}\ \text{kg}$$
   $$= 1.47 \times 10^{-1}\ \text{kg}$$

   b. 11 μg

   $$1 \mu g = 1 \times 10^{-6} g \text{ and } 1\ \text{kg} = 1 \times 10^3 g \text{ so}$$

   $$11 \mu g \left[\frac{1 \times 10^{-6} g}{1 \mu g}\right]\left[\frac{1\ \text{kg}}{1 \times 10^3 g}\right]$$

   $$= 11 \times 10^{-6} \times 10^{-3}\ \text{kg}$$
   $$= 1.1 \times 10^{-8}\ \text{kg}$$

Practice Problems

c. 7.23 Mg

$$7.23\ \text{Mg}\left[\frac{1\times10^6\text{g}}{1\ \text{Mg}}\right]\left[\frac{1\ \text{kg}}{1\times10^3\text{g}}\right]$$

$= 7.23 \times 10^3$ kg

d. 478 mg

$$478\ \text{mg}\left[\frac{1\times10^{-3}\text{g}}{1\ \text{mg}}\right]\left[\frac{1\ \text{kg}}{1\times10^3\text{g}}\right]$$

$= 4.78 \times 10^{-4}$ kg

page 18

Solve the following problems. Express your answers in scientific notation.

6. a. 5×10^{-7} kg + 3×10^{-7} kg

8×10^{-7} kg

b. 4×10^{-3} kg + 3×10^{-3} kg

7×10^{-3} kg

c. 1.66×10^{-19} kg + 2.30×10^{-19} kg

3.96×10^{-19} kg

d. 7.2×10^{-12} kg − 2.6×10^{-12} kg

4.6×10^{-12} kg

7. a. $6 \times 10^{-8}\ \text{m}^2 - 4 \times 10^{-8}\ \text{m}^2$

$2 \times 10^{-8}\ \text{m}^2$

b. $3.8 \times 10^{-12}\ \text{m}^2 - 1.90 \times 10^{-11}\ \text{m}^2$

$-1.52 \times 10^{-11}\ \text{m}^2$

c. $5.8 \times 10^{-9}\ \text{m}^2 - 2.8 \times 10^{-9}\ \text{m}^2$

$3.0 \times 10^{-9}\ \text{m}^2$

d. $2.26 \times 10^{-18}\ \text{m}^2 - 1.80 \times 10^{-18}\ \text{m}^2$

$0.46 \times 10^{-18}\ \text{m}^2 = 4.6 \times 10^{-19}\ \text{m}^2$

8. a. 5.0×10^{-7} mg + 4×10^{-8} mg

5.0×10^{-7} mg + 4×10^{-8} mg
$= 5.0 \times 10^{-7}$ mg + 0.4×10^{-7} mg
$= 5.4 \times 10^{-7}$ mg

Practice Problems

b. 6.0×10^{-3} mg + 2×10^{-4} mg

6.0×10^{-3} mg + 2×10^{-4} mg
$= 6.0 \times 10^{-3}$ mg + 0.2×10^{-3} mg
$= 6.2 \times 10^{-3}$ mg

c. 3.0×10^{-2} pg − 2×10^{-6} ng

3.0×10^{-2} pg − 2×10^{-6} ng
$= 3.0 \times 10^{-2} \times 10^{-12}\text{g} - 2 \times 10^{-6} \times 10^{-9}\text{g}$
$= 3.0 \times 10^{-14}\text{g} - 0.2 \times 10^{-14}\text{g}$
$= 2.8 \times 10^{-14}\text{g}$

d. 8.2 km − 3×10^2 m

8.2 km − 3×10^2 m
$= 8.2 \times 10^3$ m − 0.3×10^3 m
$= 7.9 \times 10^3$ m

page 19

Find the value of each of the following quantities.

9. a. $(2 \times 10^4\ \text{m})(4 \times 10^8\ \text{m})$

$(2 \times 10^4\ \text{m})(4 \times 10^8\ \text{m}) = 8 \times 10^{4+8}\ \text{m}^2$
$= 8 \times 10^{12}\ \text{m}^2$

b. $(3 \times 10^4\ \text{m})(2 \times 10^6\ \text{m})$

$(3 \times 10^4\ \text{m})(2 \times 10^6\ \text{m}) = 6 \times 10^{4+6}\ \text{m}^2$
$= 6 \times 10^{10}\ \text{m}^2$

c. $(6 \times 10^{-4}\ \text{m})(5 \times 10^{-8}\ \text{m})$

$(6 \times 10^{-4}\ \text{m})(5 \times 10^{-8}\ \text{m})$
$= 30 \times 10^{-4-8}\ \text{m}^2$
$= 3 \times 10^{-11}\ \text{m}^2$

d. $(2.50 \times 10^{-7}\ \text{m})(2.50 \times 10^{16}\ \text{m})$

$(2.50 \times 10^{-7}\ \text{m})(2.50 \times 10^{16}\ \text{m})$
$= 6.25 \times 10^{-7+16}\ \text{m}^2$
$= 6.25 \times 10^9\ \text{m}^2$

10. a. $\dfrac{6 \times 10^8\ \text{kg}}{2 \times 10^4\ \text{m}^3}$

$$\frac{6 \times 10^8\ \text{kg}}{2 \times 10^4\ \text{m}^3} = 3 \times 10^{8-4}\ \text{kg/m}^3$$

$$= 3 \times 10^4\ \text{kg/m}^3$$

Practice Problems

b. $\dfrac{6 \times 10^{8}\ \text{kg}}{2 \times 10^{-4}\ \text{m}^3}$

$$\frac{6 \times 10^{8}\ \text{kg}}{2 \times 10^{-4}\ \text{m}^3} = 3 \times 10^{8-(-4)}\ \text{kg/m}^3$$

$$= 3 \times 10^{12}\ \text{kg/m}^3$$

c. $\dfrac{6 \times 10^{-8}\ \text{m}}{2 \times 10^{4}\ \text{s}}$

$$\frac{6 \times 10^{-8}\ \text{m}}{2 \times 10^{4}\ \text{s}} = 3 \times 10^{-8-4}\ \text{m/s}$$

$$= 3 \times 10^{-12}\ \text{m/s}$$

d. $\dfrac{6 \times 10^{-8}\ \text{m}}{2 \times 10^{-4}\ \text{s}}$

$$\frac{6 \times 10^{-8}\ \text{m}}{2 \times 10^{-4}\ \text{s}} = 3 \times 10^{-8-(-4)}\ \text{m/s}$$

$$= 3 \times 10^{-4}\ \text{m/s}$$

11. a. $\dfrac{(3 \times 10^{4}\ \text{kg})(4 \times 10^{4}\ \text{m})}{6 \times 10^{4}\ \text{s}}$

$$\frac{(3 \times 10^{4}\ \text{kg})(4 \times 10^{4}\ \text{m})}{6 \times 10^{4}\ \text{s}}$$

$$= \frac{12 \times 10^{4+4}\ \text{kg} \cdot \text{m}}{6 \times 10^{4}\ \text{s}}$$

$$= 2 \times 10^{8-4}\ \text{kg} \cdot \text{m/s} = 2 \times 10^{4}\ \text{kg} \cdot \text{m/s}$$

The evaluation may be done in several other ways. For example

$$\frac{(3 \times 10^{4}\ \text{kg})(4 \times 10^{4}\ \text{m})}{6 \times 10^{4}\ \text{s}}$$

$$= (0.5 \times 10^{4-4}\ \text{kg/s})(4 \times 10^{4}\ \text{m})$$
$$= (0.5\ \text{kg/s})(4 \times 10^{4}\ \text{m})$$
$$= 2 \times 10^{4}\ \text{kg} \cdot \text{m/s}$$

b. $\dfrac{(2.5 \times 10^{6}\ \text{kg})(6 \times 10^{4}\ \text{m})}{5 \times 10^{-2}\text{s}^2}$

$$\frac{(2.5 \times 10^{6}\ \text{kg})(6 \times 10^{4}\ \text{m})}{5 \times 10^{-2}\text{s}^2}$$

$$= \frac{15 \times 10^{6+4}\ \text{kg} \cdot \text{m}}{5 \times 10^{-2}\text{s}^2}$$

$$= 3 \times 10^{10-(-2)}\ \text{kg} \cdot \text{m/s}^2$$
$$= 3 \times 10^{12}\ \text{kg} \cdot \text{m/s}^2$$

Practice Problems

page 24

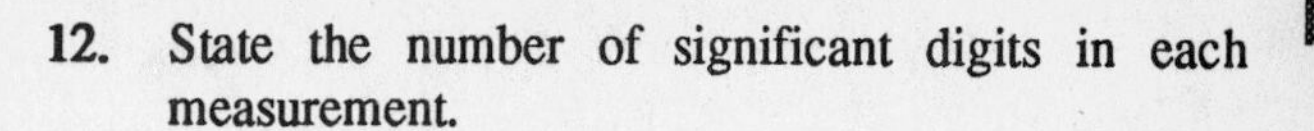

12. State the number of significant digits in each measurement.

a. 2804 m 4

b. 2.84 m 3

c. 0.0029 m 2

d. 0.003 068 m 4

e. 4.6×10^{5} m 2

f. 4.06×10^{5} m 3

13. State the number of significant digits for each measurement.

a. 75 m 2

b. 75.00 mm 4

c. 0.007 060 kg 4

d. 1.87×10^{6} ml 3

e. 1.008×10^{8} m 4

f. 1.20×10^{-4} m 3

page 25

14. Add 6.201 cm, 7.4 cm, 0.68 cm, and 12.0 cm.

26.3 cm (rounded from 26.281 cm)

15. Subtract

a. 8.264 g from 10.8 g.

2.5 g (rounded from 2.536 g)

b. 0.4168 m from 475 m.

475 m (rounded from 474.5832 m)

16. Perform the following multiplications.

a. 131 cm × 2.3 cm

3.0×10^{2} cm^2 (the result 301.3 cm^2 expressed to two significant digits. Note that the expression in the form 300 cm^2 would not indicate how many of the digits are significant.)

Practice Problems

b. 3.2145 km × 4.23 km

13.6 km² (the result 13.597335 expressed to three significant digits)

17. Perform the following divisions.

a. 20.2 cm ÷ 7.41 s

2.73 cm/s (the result 2.726045...cm/s expressed to three significant digits)

b. 3.1416 cm ÷ 12.4 s

0.253 cm/s (the result 0.253354...cm/s expressed to three significant digits)

page 33

18. Solve the following equation for b.

$y = mx + b$

$mx + b = y,\ b = y - mx$

19. Solve the following equations for v.

a. $d = vt$

$vt = d,\ v = \frac{d}{t}$

b. $t = \frac{d}{v}$

$t = \frac{d}{v},\ tv = d,\ v = \frac{d}{t}$

c. $a = \frac{v^2}{2d}$

$\frac{v^2}{2d} = a,\ v^2 = 2ad,\ v = \pm\sqrt{2ad}$

d. $\frac{v}{a} = \frac{b}{c}$

$\frac{v}{a} = \frac{b}{c},\ v = \frac{ab}{c}$

Practice Problems

20. Solve each of these equations for E.

a. $f = \frac{E}{s}$

$\frac{E}{s} = f,\ E = fs$

b. $m = \frac{2E}{v^2}$

$\frac{2E}{v^2} = m,\ 2E = mv^2,\ E = \frac{mv^2}{2}$

c. $\frac{E}{c^2} = m$

$\frac{E}{c^2} = m,\ E = mc^2$

21. Solve the equation $v^2 = v_0^2 + 2ad$ for d.

$v_0^2 + 2ad = v^2,\ 2ad = v^2 - v_0^2,\ d = \frac{(v^2 - v_0^2)}{2a}$

22. Solve each of these equations for a.

a. $v = v_0 + at$

$at = v - v_0;\ a = \frac{v - v_0}{t}$

b. $y = v_0t + \frac{1}{2}at^2$

$\frac{1}{2}at^2 = y - v_0t;\ a = \frac{2(y - v_0t)}{t^2}$

c. $v^2 = v_0^2 + 2ay$

$2ay = v^2 - v_0^2;\ a = \frac{v^2 - v_0^2}{2y}$

d. $v = \sqrt{2as}$

$v^2 = 2as;\ a = \frac{v^2}{2s}$

Practice Problems

23. Identify the answers to these exercises using consistent units.

 a. Find the area of a rectangle 2 mm by 30 cm.

 $A = (0.2 \text{ cm})(30 \text{ cm}) = 6 \text{ cm}^2$

 b. Find the perimeter of a rectangle 25 cm by 2.00 m.

 $P = 0.25 \text{ m} + 0.25 \text{ m} + 2.00 \text{ m} + 2.00 \text{ m}$
 $= 4.50 \text{ m}$

24. Find which of the following equations are incorrect.

 a. area = (length)(width)(height)

 incorrect; area has units m^2 and (length)(width)(height) has units m^3

 b. $\text{time} = \dfrac{\text{distance}}{\text{speed}}$

 correct since $\dfrac{\text{distance}}{\text{speed}}$ has units $\dfrac{\text{m}}{(\text{m/s})} = \text{s}$

 c. distance = (speed)(time)^2

 incorrect since (speed)(time)^2 has units $(\text{m/s})(\text{s})^2 = m \cdot s$

Chapter Review Problems

pages 37–39

1. Express the following numbers in scientific notation.

 a. 5 000 000 000 000 000 000 000 000 m

 5×10^{24} m

 b. 0.000 000 000 000 000 000 166 m

 1.66×10^{-19} m

 c. 2 033 000 000 m

 2.033×10^{9} m

Chapter Review Problems

 d. 0.000 000 103 0 m

 1.030×10^{-7} m

2. Convert each of the following measurements into meters.

 a. 42.3 cm

 $$\frac{42.3 \text{ cm}}{1}\left[\frac{1 \times 10^{-2} \text{ m}}{1 \text{ cm}}\right] = 0.423 \text{ m}$$

 b. 6.2 pm

 $$\frac{6.2 \text{ pm}}{1}\left[\frac{1 \times 10^{-12} \text{ m}}{1 \text{ pm}}\right] = 6.2 \times 10^{-12} \text{ m}$$

 c. 21 km

 $$\frac{21 \text{ km}}{1}\left[\frac{1 \times 10^{3} \text{ m}}{1 \text{ km}}\right] = 2.1 \times 10^{4} \text{ m}$$

 d. 0.023 mm

 $$\frac{0.023 \text{ mm}}{1}\left[\frac{1 \times 10^{-3} \text{ m}}{1 \text{ mm}}\right] = 2.3 \times 10^{-5} \text{ m}$$

 e. 214 μm

 $$\frac{214 \ \mu\text{m}}{1}\left[\frac{1 \times 10^{-6} \text{ m}}{1 \ \mu\text{m}}\right] = 2.14 \times 10^{-4} \text{ m}$$

 f. 570 nm

 $$570 \text{ nm}\left[\frac{1 \times 10^{-9} \text{ m}}{1 \text{ nm}}\right] = 5.70 \times 10^{-7} \text{ m}$$

3. Rank the following mass measurements from smallest to largest: 11.6 mg, 1021 μg, 0.000 006 kg, 0.31 mg.

 $$\frac{11 \text{ mg}}{1}\left[\frac{1 \times 10^{-3} \text{ g}}{1 \text{ mg}}\right] = 1.1 \times 10^{-2} \text{ g}$$

 $$\frac{1021 \ \mu\text{g}}{1}\left[\frac{1 \times 10^{-6} \text{ g}}{1 \mu\text{g}}\right] = 1.021 \times 10^{-3} \text{ g}$$

$$\frac{0.000\ 006\ \text{kg}}{1}\left[\frac{10^3\ \text{g}}{1\ \text{ky}}\right] = 6 \times 10^{-3}\ \text{g}$$

$$\frac{0.31\ \text{mg}}{1}\left[\frac{1 \times 10^{7-}\ \text{g}}{1\ \text{mg}}\right] = 3.1 \times 10^{-4}\ \text{g}$$

0.31 mg, 1021 μg, 0.000 006 kg, 11 mg

4. Add or subtract as indicated.

a. 5.80×10^9 s + 3.20×10^9 s

5.80×10^9 s + 3.20×10^8 s = 6.12×10^9 s

b. 4.87×10^{-6} m − 1.93×10^{-6} m

4.87×10^{-6} m − 1.93×10^{-6} m
= 2.94×10^{-6} m

c. 3.14×10^{-5} kg + 9.36×10^{-5} kg

3.14×10^{-5} kg + 9.36×10^{-5} kg
= 12.50×10^{-5} kg = 1.250×10^{-4} kg

d. 8.12×10^7 g − 6.20×10^6 g

8.12×10^7 g − 6.20×10^6 g
= 7.50×10^7 g

5. State the number of significant digits in each measurement.

a. 248 m 3

b. 0.000 03 m 1

c. 64.01 m 4

d. 80.001 m 5

6. State the number of significant digits in the following measurements.

a. 2.40×10^6 kg 3

b. 6×10^8 kg 1

c. 4.07×10^{16} m 3

Chapter Review Problems

7. Many labels give metric equivalents of English quantities. Examples are: 12 fluid ounces (9345.66 mL), 353 ft (107.59 m), 2.0 inches (50.80 mm). Report each metric equivalent using the correct number of significant digits.

9.4×10^3 mL, 108 m, 51 mm

8. Add or subtract as indicated and state the answer with the correct number of significant digits.

a. 16.2 m + 5.008 m + 13.48 m

$$\begin{array}{r} 16.2\ \ \ \ \text{m} \\ 5.008\ \text{m} \\ \underline{13.48\ \ \text{m}} \\ 34.688\ \text{m} \end{array} = 34.7\ \text{m}$$

b. 5.006 m + 12.0077 m + 8.0084 m

$$\begin{array}{r} 5.006\ \ \text{m} \\ 12.0077\ \text{m} \\ \underline{8.0084\ \text{m}} \\ 25.0221\ \text{m} \end{array} = 25.022\ \text{m}$$

c. 78.05 cm² − 32.046 cm²

$$\begin{array}{r} 78.05\ \ \text{cm}^2 \\ \underline{-32.046\ \text{cm}^2} \\ 46.004\ \text{cm}^2 \end{array} = 46.00\ \text{cm}^2$$

d. 15.07 kg − 12.0 kg

$$\begin{array}{r} 15.07\ \text{kg} \\ \underline{-12.0\ \ \text{kg}} \\ 3.07\ \text{kg} \end{array} = 3.1\ \text{kg}$$

9. Multiply or divide as indicated watching significant digits.

a. $(6.2 \times 10^{18}\ \text{m})(4.7 \times 10^{-10}\ \text{m})$

$2.9 \times 10^9\ \text{m}^2$

b. $(5.6 \times 10^{-7}\ \text{m}) \div (2.8 \times 10^{-12}\ \text{s})$

2.0×10^5 m/s

c. $(8.1 \times 10^{-4}\ \text{km})(1.6 \times 10^{-3}\ \text{km})$

$1.3 \times 10^{-6}\ \text{km}^2$

d. $(6.5 \times 10^5\ \text{kg}) \div (3.4 \times 10^3\ \text{m}^3)$

$1.9 \times 10^2\ \text{kg/m}^3$

10. Tom did the following problems on his calculator, reporting results shown. Give the answer to each using the correct number of significant digits.

a. 5.32 mm + 2.1 mm = 7.4200000 mm

7.4 mm

b. $13.597\ \text{m} \times 3.65\ \text{m} = 49.6290500\ \text{m}^2$

$49.6\ \text{m}^2$

c. 83.2 kg − 12.804 kg = 70.3960000 kg

70.4 kg

11. A rectangular floor has a length of 15.72 m and a width of 4.40 m. Calculate the area of the floor to the best possible value using these measurements.

$69.2\ \text{m}^2$

12. A yard is 33.21 m long and 17.6 m wide.

a. What length of fence must be purchased to enclose the entire yard?

Perimeter = $2\ell + 2w$
= 2(33.21 m) + 2(17.6 m)
= 66.42 m + 35.2 m
= 101.6 m

b. What area must be covered if the yard is to be fertilized?

Area= ℓw = (33.21 m)(17.6 m)
= $584\ \text{m}^2$

13. The length of a room is 16.40 m, its width is 4.5 m, and its height is 3.26 m. What volume does the room enclose?

V = ℓwh = (16.40 m)(4.5 m)(3.26 m)
= $2.4 \times 10^2\ \text{m}^3$

Chapter Review Problems

14. The sides of a quadrangular plot of land are 132.68 m, 48.3 m, 132.736 m, and 48.37 m. What is the perimeter of the plot as can best be determined from these measurements?

Perimeter
= 132.68 m + 48.3 m + 132.736 m + 48.37 m
= 362.1 m

15. A water tank has a mass of 3.64 kg when empty and a mass of 51.8 kg when filled to a certain level. What is the mass of the water in the tank?

51.8 kg
−3.64 kg
48.16 kg = 48.2 kg

16. Figure 2–18 shows the mass of three substances for volumes between 0 and 60 cm^3.

a. What is the mass of 30 cm^3 of each substance?

(a) 80 g, (b) 260 g, (c) 400 g.

b. If you had 100 g of each substance, what would their volumes be?

(a) 37 cm^3, (b) 11 cm^3, (c) 7 cm^3.

c. Describe the meaning of the steepness of the lines in this graph (a single word is not a sufficient answer!).

The steepness represents the increased mass of each additional cubic centimeter of the substance.

17. During an experiment, a student measured the mass of 10.0 cm^3 of alcohol. The student then measured the mass of 20.0 cm^3 of alcohol. In this way the data in Table 2–3 were collected.

Table 2–3

Volume (cm^3)	Mass (g)
10.0	7.9
20.0	15.8
30.0	23.7
40.0	31.6
50.0	39.6

a. Plot the values given in the table and draw the curve that best fits all points.

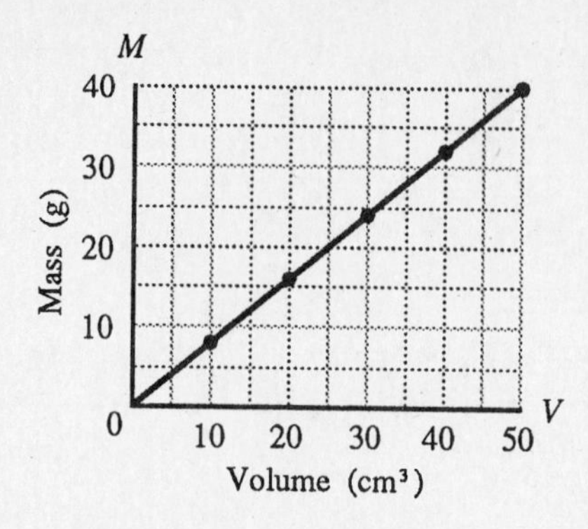

b. Describe the resulting curve.

A straight line

c. Use the graph to write an equation relating the volume to the mass of the alcohol.

$M = mV$, where m is the slope

d. Find the units of the slope of the graph. What is the name given to this quantity?

mass/volume; density

18. During a class demonstration, an instructor placed a 1.0-kg mass on a horizontal table that was nearly frictionless. The instructor then applied various horizontal forces to the mass and measured the rate at which the mass gained speed (was accelerated) for each force applied. The results of the experiment are shown in Table 2-4.

Table 2-4

Force (N)	Acceleration (m/s²)
5.0	4.9
10.0	9.8
15.0	15.2
20.0	20.1
25.0	25.0
30.0	29.9

Chapter Review Problems

a. Plot the values given in the table and draw the curve that best fits all points.

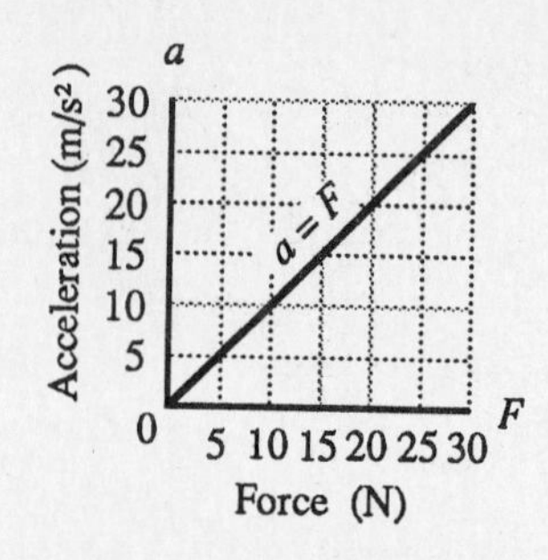

b. Describe, in words, the relationship between force and acceleration according to the graph.

The acceleration varies directly with the force

c. Write the equation relating the force and the acceleration that results from the graph.

$F = ka$

d. Find the units of the slope of the graph.

$k = a/F$ so the units of k are $(m/s^2)/N$
$= m/s^2 \cdot N$

19. The teacher who performed the experiment in the previous problem then changed the procedure. The mass was varied while the force was kept constant. The acceleration of each mass was then recorded. The results are shown in Table 2-5.

Table 2-5

Mass (kg)	Acceleration (m/s²)
1.0	12.0
2.0	5.9
3.0	4.1
4.0	3.0
5.0	2.5
6.0	2.0

a. Plot the values given in the table and draw the curve that best fits all points.

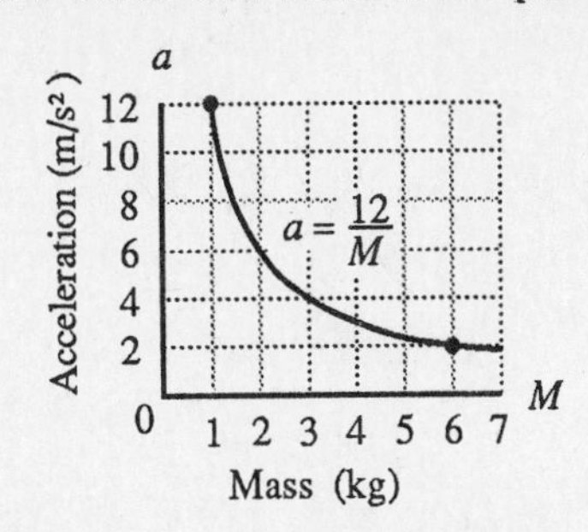

b. Describe the resulting curve.

Hyperbola

c. According to the graph, what is the relationship between mass and the acceleration produced by a constant force?

Acceleration varies inversely with the mass.

d. Write the equation relating acceleration to mass given by the data in the graph.

$a = c/M$, c = constant = 12

e. Find the units of the constant in the equation.

$c = Ma$, so the units of c are (kg)(m/s²)
= kg · m/s²

20. Each cubic centimeter of gold has a mass of 19.3 g. A cube of gold measures 4.23 cm on each edge.

a. What is the volume of the cube?

(4.23 cm)³ = 75.7 cm³

b. What is its mass?

M = (density)(V) = (19.3 g/cm³)(75.7 cm³)
= 1.46×10^3 g

Chapter Review Problems

21. Solve the equation

$$T = 2\pi\sqrt{\frac{\ell}{g}}$$

for

a. ℓ

$T = 2\pi\sqrt{\frac{\ell}{g}}$, so $\frac{T}{2\pi} = \sqrt{\frac{\ell}{g}}$ square both sides

$\frac{T^2}{4\pi^2} = \frac{\ell}{g}$, so $\ell = \frac{gT^2}{4\pi^2}$

b. g

from above $-\ \frac{T^2}{4\pi^2} = \frac{\ell}{g}$, so $\frac{gT^2}{4\pi^2} = \ell$,

or $gT^2 = 4\pi^2\ell$, or $g = \frac{4\pi^2\ell}{T^2}$

22. Each cubic centimeter of silver has a mass of 10.5 g.

a. What is the mass of 65.0 cm³ of silver?

density of silver = D = 10.5 g/cm³.
Since $D = M/V$,
$M = DV$ = (10.5 g/cm³)(65.0 cm³)
= 683 g

b. When placed on a beam balance, the 65.0 cm³ piece of silver has a mass of only 616 g. What volume of the piece is hollow?

actual volume of silver
= $V = M/D$ = (616 g)/(10.5 g/cm³)
= 58.7cm³.
Hollow volume = given volume − actual volume
= 65.0 cm³ − 58.7 cm³ = 6.3 cm³

23. Assume that a small sugar cube has sides 1.0 cm long. If you had a box containing 1 mole of sugar cubes and lined them up side by side, how long would the line be? 1 mole = 6.02×10^{23} units.

$(6.02 \times 10^{23})(1 \text{ cm}) = 6.02 \times 10^{23}$ cm or
$(6.02 \times 10^{23} \text{ cm})/(100 \text{ cm/m})(1000 \text{ m/km})$
$= 6.02 \times 10^{18}$ km

24. The average distance between Earth and the sun is 1.50×10^8 km.

a. Calculate the average speed, in km/h, of Earth assuming a circular path about the sun. Use the equation $v = \frac{2\pi r}{t}$.

$$v = \frac{2\pi r}{t} = \frac{2\pi(1.50 \times 10^8 \text{ km})}{365 \text{ dy}\left[\frac{24 \text{ k}}{1 \text{ dy}}\right]}$$

$= 1.08 \times 10^5$ km/h

b. Convert your answer from km/h to m/s. Show all units.

$$\frac{1.08 \times 10^5 \text{ km}}{\text{h}}\left[\frac{1000 \text{ m}}{1 \text{ km}}\right]\left[\frac{1 \text{ h}}{3600 \text{ s}}\right]$$

$= 3.00 \times 10^4$ m/s

25. The radius of Earth is 6.37×10^3 km.

a. Find the speed, in km/h, resulting from the rotation of Earth, of a person standing on the equator.

$$v = \frac{2\pi r}{t} = \frac{2\pi(6.37 \times 10^3 \text{ km})}{24 \text{ h}}$$

$= 1.67 \times 10^3$ km/h

b. Convert your answer to m/s.

$$\frac{1.67 \times 10^3 \text{ km}}{\text{h}}\left[\frac{1 \text{ h}}{3600 \text{ s}}\right]\left[\frac{1000 \text{ m}}{1 \text{ km}}\right]$$

= 464 m/s

Chapter Review Problems

26. A child rides a merry-go-round horse that is 5.4 m from the center. The rides lasts 10 minutes. During this time the ride makes 24 revolutions. Find the speed of the child in meters/second. Use the equation $v = \frac{2\pi r}{t}$.

$$t = \frac{10 \text{ min}}{24 \text{ rev}} = 0.42 \frac{\text{min}}{\text{rev}}, \text{ and}$$

$$v = \frac{2\pi r}{t} = \frac{2\pi(5.4 \text{ m})}{\left[\frac{0.42 \text{ min}}{1}\right]\left[\frac{60 \text{ s}}{1 \text{ min}}\right]} = 1.4 \text{ m/s}$$

27. Manipulate the equation v = d/t and find the answers to these problems using consistent units.

a. Find the distance a bike travels in 1.5 minutes, if it is traveling at a constant speed of 20 km/hr.

$v = \frac{d}{t}$,

$$\text{so } d = vt = \left[\frac{20 \text{ km}}{\text{h}}\right]\left[\frac{1 \text{ h}}{60 \text{ min}}\right]\left[\frac{1.5 \text{ min}}{1}\right]$$

= 0.50 km

b. How long would it take a car to travel 6000 m if its speed is a constant 30 km/hr?

$v = \frac{d}{t}$, so vt = d, and $t = \frac{d}{v}$

$$= \frac{\left[\frac{6000 \text{ m}}{1}\right]\left[\frac{1 \text{ km}}{1000 \text{ m}}\right]}{30 \frac{\text{km}}{\text{h}}} = 0.20 \text{ h}$$

28. Water drips from a faucet into a flask at the rate of two drops every 3 seconds. A cubic centimeter (cm^3) contains 20 drops.
What volume of water, in cubic decimeters (dm^3), will be collected in 1 hour?

$$V = \left[\frac{2 \text{ drops}}{30 \text{ s}}\right]\left[\frac{1 \text{ cm}^3}{20 \text{ drops}}\right]\left[\frac{\text{dm}^3}{1000 \text{ cm}^3}\right]$$

$$= \left[\frac{3600 \text{ s}}{1 \text{ h}}\right] = 0.12 \frac{\text{dm}^3}{\text{h}}$$

Chapter Review Problems

29. Tony's Pizza Shop ordered new 23 cm pizza pans (9–inch pans). By mistake, 26 cm (10–inch) pans were delivered. Tony says that the difference is too small to worry about. As Tony's accountant, what would you say knowing materials cost about 0.25 cents per square centimeter?

The area of each pan is given by $A = \pi r^2$ or $\pi\left[\frac{d}{2}\right]^2$, so the difference in area for the pans is

$$\pi\left[\frac{26\text{ cm}}{2}\right]^2 - \left[\frac{23\text{ cm}}{2}\right]^2 = 120\text{ cm}^2$$

$(120\text{ cm}^2)(0.25¢/\text{cm}^2) = \$0.30$
Each pizza costs 30 cents more.

Supplemental Problems

1. Express the following numbers in scientific notation.

   a. 810 000 g 8.1×10^5 g

   b. 0.000634 g 6.34×10^{-4} g

   c. 60 000 000 g 6×10^7 g

   d. 0.0000010 g 1.0×10^{-6} g

2. Convert each of the following time measurements to its equivalent in seconds.

   a. 58 ns 5.8×10^{-8} s

   b. 0.046 Gs 4.6×10^7 s

   c. 9270 ms 9.27 s

   d. 12.3 ks 1.23×10^4 s

Supplemental Problems (Appendix B)

3. Solve the following problems. Express your answers in scientific notation.

   a. 6.2×10^{-4} m + 5.7×10^{-3}

   6.32×10^{-3} m

   b. 8.7×10^8 km – 3.4×10^7 km

   8.36×10^8 km

   c. $(9.21 \times 10^{-5}$ cm$)(1.83 \times 10^8$ cm$)$

   1.69×10^4 cm^2

   d. $(2.63 \times 10^{-6}$ m$) \div (4.08 \times 10^6$ s$)$

   6.45×10^{-13} m/s

4. State the number of significant digits in the following measurements.

   a. 3218 kg 4

   b. 60.080 kg 5

   c. 801 kg 3

   d. 0.000534 kg 3

5. State the number of significant digits in the following measurements.

   a. 5.60×10^8 m 3

   b. 3.0005×10^{-6} m 5

   c. 8.0×10^{10} m 2

   d. 9.204×10^{-3} m 4

6. Add or subtract as indicated and state the answer with the correct number of significant digits.

   a. 85.26 g + 4.7 g = 90.0 g

   b. 1.07 km + 0.608 km = 1.68 km

   c. 186.4 kg − 57.83 kg = 128.6 kg

   d. 60.08 s − 12.2 s = 47.9 s

7. Multiply or divide as indicated using significant digits correctly.

   a. $(5 \times 10^8 \text{ m})(4.2 \times 10^7 \text{ m})$

   $2 \times 10^{16} \text{ m}^2$

   b. $(1.67 \times 10^{-2} \text{ km})(8.5 \times 10^{-6} \text{ km})$

   $1.4 \times 10^{-7} \text{ km}^2$

   c. $(2.6 \times 10^4 \text{ kg}) \div (9.4 \times 10^3 \text{ m}^3)$

   2.8 kg/m^3

   d. $(6.3 \times 10^{-1} \text{ m}) \div (3.8 \times 10^2 \text{ s})$

   $1.7 \times 10^{-3} \text{ m/s}$

8. A rectangular room is 8.7 m by 2.41 m.

   a. What length of baseboard molding must be purchased to go around the perimeter of the floor?

   $P = 2\ell + 2w$

   2(8.7 m) + 2(2.41 m) = 22.2 m

   b. What area must be covered if tiles are layed?

   $A = \ell w$ = (8.7 m)(2.41 m) = 21 m²

Supplemental Problems

9. The following data table was established showing the total distances an object fell during various lengths of time.

Time (s)	Distance (m)
1	5
2	20
3	44
4	78
5	123

   a. Plot distance versus time from the values given in the table and draw a curve that best fits all points.

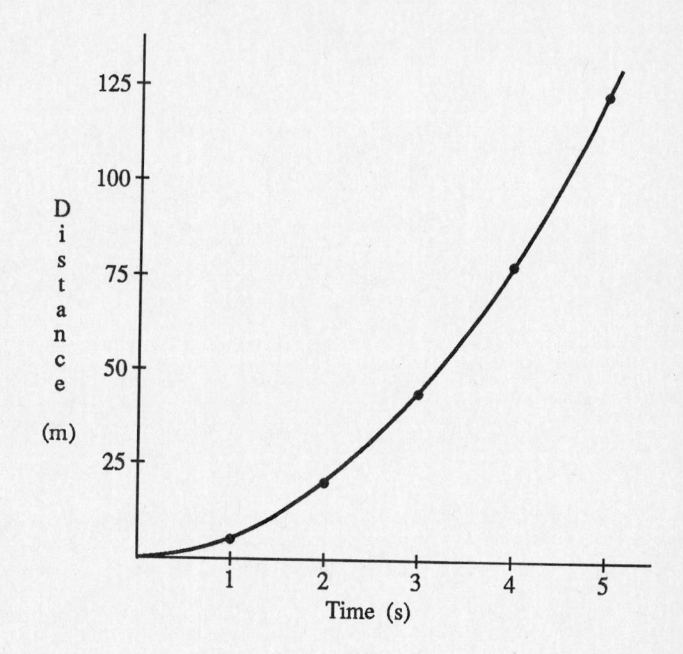

   b. Describe the resulting curve.

   Parabola; curve starts at origin and is concave upward

   c. According to the graph, what is the relationship between distance and time for a free–falling object?

   The distance increases faster and faster with time.

10. The total distance a lab cart travels during specified lengths of time is given in the following table.

Time (s)	Distance (m)
1	0.32
2	0.60
3	0.95
4	1.18
5	1.45

a. Plot distance versus time from the values given in the table and draw the curve that best fits all points.

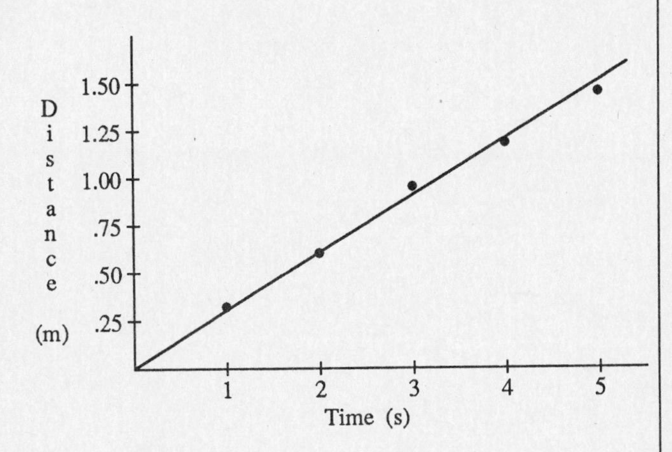

b. Describe the resulting curve.

Straight Line

c. According to the graph, what type of relationship exists between the total distance traveled by the lab cart and time?

Linear Relationship

d. What is the slope of this graph?

$$M = \frac{\Delta y}{\Delta x} = \frac{1.5 - .60}{5 - 2} = \frac{.90}{3} = .30 \text{ m/s}$$

Supplemental Problems

e. Write an equation relating distance and time for this data.

$d = .30(t)$

11. Solve the equation $F = \dfrac{mv^2}{r}$

a. For m, $m = \dfrac{Fr}{v^2}$

b. For r, $r = \dfrac{Mv^2}{F}$

c. For v, $v^2 = \dfrac{Fr}{M}$

$$v = \sqrt{\frac{Fr}{M}}$$

12. Solve the equation:

$$\frac{1}{f} = \frac{1}{d_o} + \frac{1}{d_i}$$

for d_o.

$$\frac{1}{d_o} = \frac{1}{f} - \frac{1}{d_i}$$

$$d_o = \frac{1}{\frac{1}{f} - \frac{1}{d_i}} = \frac{1}{\frac{d_i - f}{d_i f}} = \frac{d_i f}{d_i - f}$$

13. A cube has an edge of length 5.2 cm.

a. Find its surface area.

Area of one side

$A = s^2 = (5.2)^2 = 27 \text{ cm}^2$

Total surface Area

$(27 \text{ cm}^2)(6) = 160 \text{ cm}^2$

b. Find its volume.

$V = s^3 = (5.2)^3 = 140 \text{ cm}^3$

Supplemental Problems

14. A truck is traveling at a constant velocity of 70 km/hr. Convert the velocity to m/s.

70 km/hr · 1000 m/km · hr/3600 s = 19m/s

15. The density of gold is 19.3 g/cm³. A gold washer has an outside radius of 4.3 cm and an inside radius of 2.1 cm. Its thickness is 0.14 cm. What is the mass of the washer?

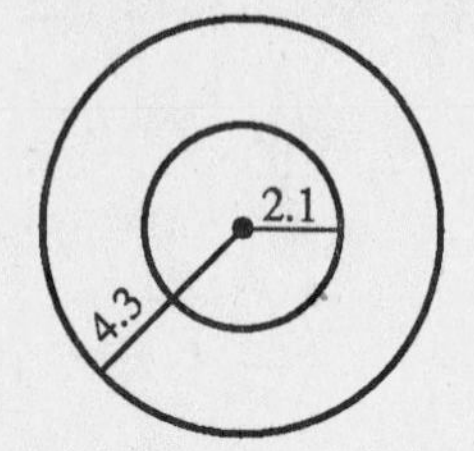

Volume of outside cylinder:

$V = \pi R^2 h = \pi(4.3)^2(0.14) = 8.1\ \text{cm}^3$

Volume of inside cylinder:

$V = \pi R^2 h = \pi(2.1)^2(0.14) = 1.9\ \text{cm}^3$

Volume of washer:

$8.1\ \text{cm}^3 - 1.9\ \text{cm}^3 = 6.2\ \text{cm}^3$

$M = DV = (19.3\ \text{g/cm}^3)(6.2\ \text{cm}^3) = 120\ \text{g}$

Chapter 3: Describing Motion: Velocity

Practice Problems

page 45

1. A high school athlete runs 1.00×10^2 m in 12.20 s. What is the velocity in m/s and km/h?

$\bar{v} = \frac{\Delta d}{\Delta t} = (1.00 \times 10^2 \text{ m})(12.20 \text{ s})$

$= 8.20$ m/s;

(8.20 m/s)(1 km/1000 m)(3600 s/1 h)

$= 29.5$ km/h

or

(8.20 m/s)(3600 s/h)(1000 m/km)

$= 29.5$ km/h

2. A person walks 13 km in 2.0 h. What is the person's average velocity in km/h and m/s?

$\bar{v} = \frac{\Delta d}{\Delta t} = (13 \text{ km})/(2.0\text{h})$

$= 6.5$ km/h;

(6.5 km/h)(1 h/3600 s)(1000 m/1 km)

$= 1.8$ m/s

or

(6.5 km/h)(1000 m/km)/(3600 s/h)

$= 1.8$ m/s

page 46

3. Using the data in Table 3–1, during what one–second–long time interval is the car moving slowest? The fastest?

Slowest between 0.0 and 1.0 s (0 m/s). Fastest between 3.0 and 4.0 s (15 m/s).

4. Using the data in Table 3–1, find the average velocity of the car in the time interval between 0.0 and 2.0 seconds.

Practice Problems

$\bar{v} = (d_2 - d_1)/(t_2 - t_1)$
$= (35 \text{ m} - 30 \text{ m})/(2.05 - 0.05)$
$= 2.5$ m/s

page 47

5. Suppose a car travels at a constant 10 m/s. How far would it move in 1 hour? In 1 minute? In 1 second? In 1 millisecond? In 1 microsecond? In 1 nanosecond?

Using $d = vt$ with $v = 10$ m/s:

t	d
1 h = 3600 s	3.6×10^4 m
1 min = 60 s	6.0×10^2 m
1 s	10 m
1 ms = 10^{-3} s	10×10^{-3} m = 10 mm
1 μs = 10^{-6} s	10×10^{-6} m = 10 μm
1 ns = 10^{-9} s	10×10^{-9} m = 10 nm

6. A train leaves the station at the 0.0–m marker traveling with a constant velocity of 36.0 m/s.

a. How many seconds later will the train pass the 1620.0 m marker?

$v = \frac{d}{t}$ so $t = \frac{d}{v} = \frac{(1620.0 \text{ m})}{(36.0 \text{ m/s})} = 45.0$ s

b. What is the velocity of the train in km/h?

$v =$ (36.0 m/s)(1 km/1000 m)(3600 s/1 h)

$= 130$ km/h

7. At 1:00 p.m. a car, traveling at a constant velocity of 94 km/h toward the west, is 17 km to the west of your school. Where will it be at 3:30 p.m.?

$\bar{v} = \frac{(d_2 - d_1)}{(t_2 - t_1)}$ with $t_2 - t_1 = 2.5$ h.

$d_2 = d_1 + \bar{v}(t_2 - t_1)$

$= 17$ km + (94 km/h)(2.5 h)

$= 252$ km west of school.

Practice Problems

8. Suppose the car in Problem 7 started 17 km east of your school at the same time, moving in the same direction at the same velocity.

   a. Where would it be at 3:30 pm?

   Same displacement, but position is –17 km +235 km = 218 km west of school.

   b. When would it be at your school?

   $$\Delta t = \frac{\Delta d}{\bar{v}} = \frac{(17\ \text{km})}{(94\ \text{km/h})} = 11\ \text{min},$$

   so t = 1:11 pm.

page 53

9. Describe in your own words the motion of the four walkers shown in the four curves in Figure 3–10. Assume the positive direction is east and the reference point is the corner of High Street.

   a. Starts at High St., walking east at constant velocity.
   b. Starts west of High St., walking east at slower constant velocity.
   c. Walks west from High St., first fast, but slowing to a stop.
   d. Starts east of High St., walking west at constant velocity.

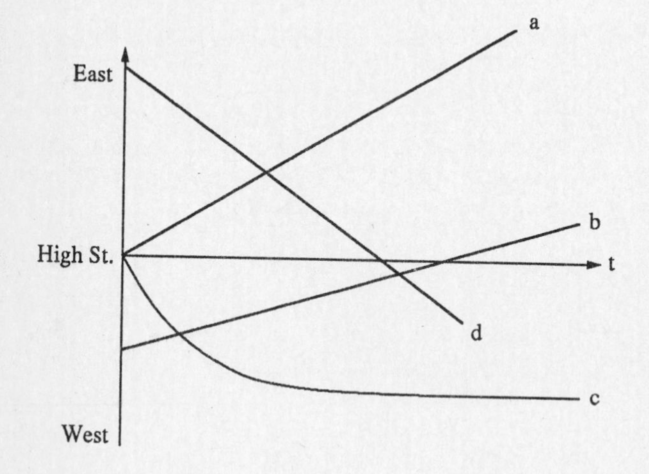

Practice Problems

10. Sketch position–time graphs for these four motions:

    a. starting at a positive position with a positive velocity

    b. starting at a negative position with a smaller positive velocity

    c. remaining at a negative position

    d. starting at a positive position with a negative velocity.

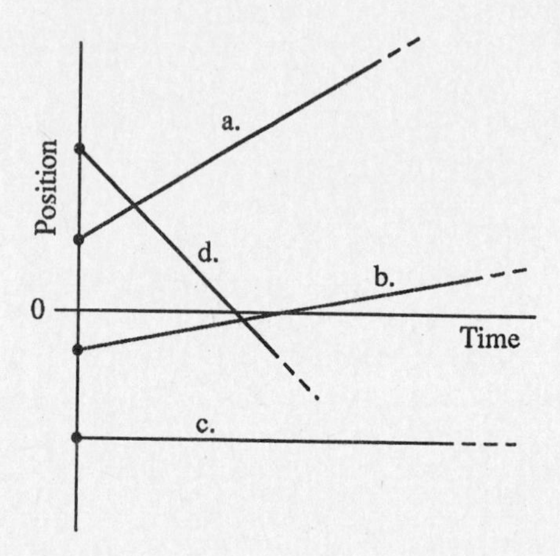

11. Find the average velocities shown in Figure 3–11.

    a. between t = 10 and 12 s.

    $$\bar{v} = \frac{\Delta d}{\Delta t} = \frac{+5\ \text{m}}{2\ \text{s}} = 2.5\ \text{m/s}$$

    b. between t = 14 and 18 s.

    $$\bar{v} = \frac{\Delta d}{\Delta t} = \frac{0\ \text{m}}{4\ \text{s}} = 0\ \text{m/s}$$

    c. between t = 20 and 24 s.

    $$\bar{v} = \frac{\Delta d}{\Delta t} = \frac{-15\ \text{m}}{4\ \text{s}} = -3.75\ \text{m/s}$$

    d. between t = 26 and 20 s.

    $$\bar{v} = \frac{\Delta d}{\Delta t} = \frac{+5\ \text{m}}{4\ \text{s}} = 1.25\ \text{m/s}$$

Practice Problems

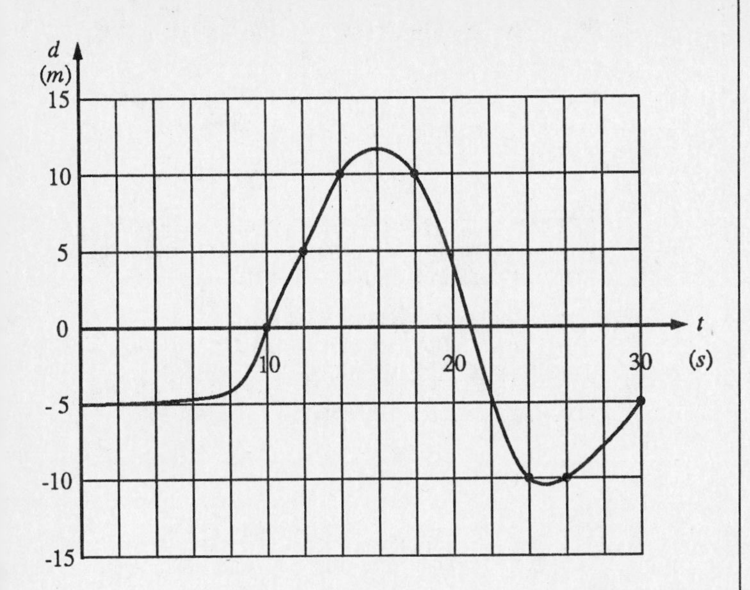

12. Draw a position–time graph of a moving elevator. Use the first floor as reference point and up as positive. The elevator waits on the first floor for 30 s, rises to the third floor in 20 s, where it stops for 30 s, before going to the basement, which it reaches in 40 s.

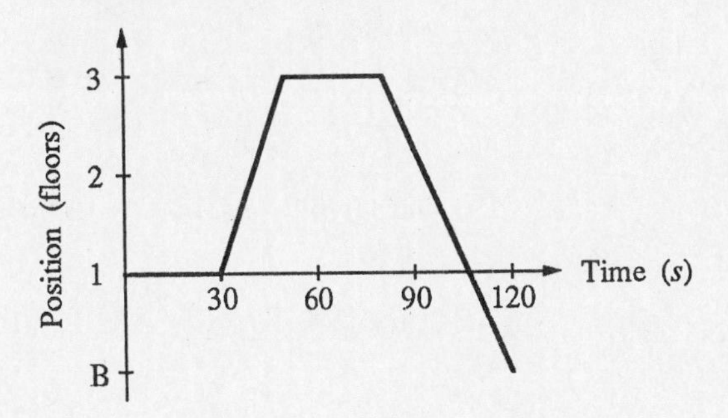

page 55

13. Using Figure 3–15c, find the sprinter's velocity at 2.0 seconds.

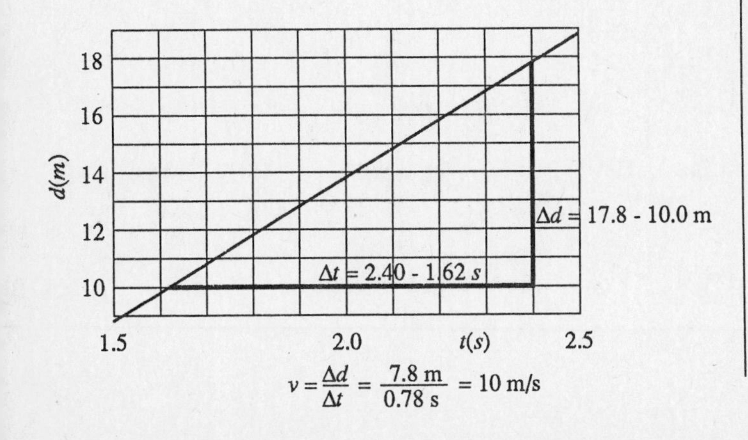

$$v = \frac{\Delta d}{\Delta t} = \frac{7.8 \text{ m}}{0.78 \text{ s}} = 10 \text{ m/s}$$

Practice Problems

14. Use your hand on your desk to model the motion shown by the curves in Figure 3–16a below. Describe in words the motions.

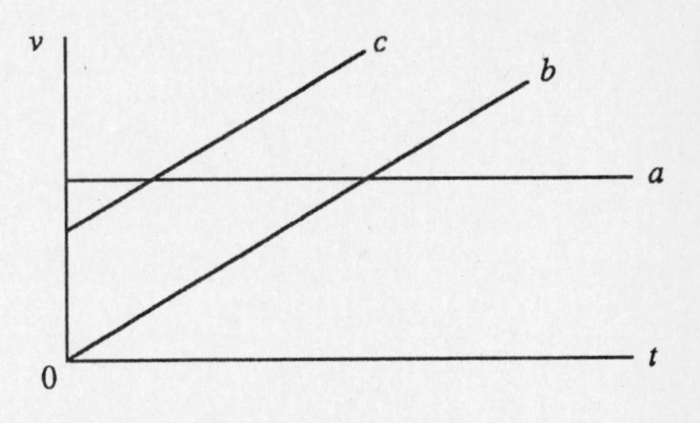

a. Moves to right at constant speed.

b. Moves to right from rest at constantly increasing speed.

c. Has an initial non–zero velocity to the right and continues to move to right at constantly increasing speed.

15.

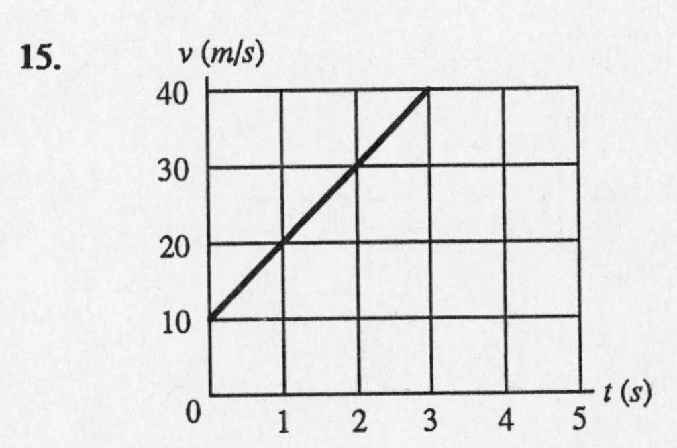

Figure 3–16b is the velocity–time graph of an object. What is its velocity at

a. 0 seconds?

10 m/s

b. 1 second?

20 m/s

c. 2 seconds?

30 m/s

Practice Problems

16. Using the graph in Figure 3–16b describe how the instantaneous velocity changes with time.

Each second it increases 10 m/s.

17.

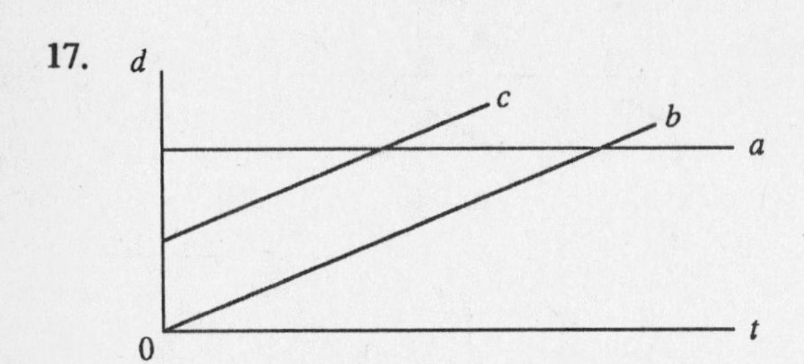

Sketch velocity–time graphs for the position–time graphs in Figure 3–16c.

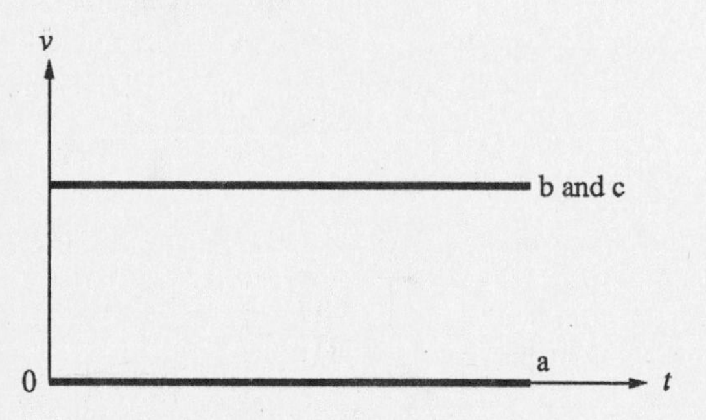

18. A car moves along a straight road at a constant velocity of +75 km/h for 4.0 hours, stops for 2.0 hours, and then drives in the reverse direction at the original speed for 3.0 hours.

a. Plot a velocity–time graph for the car.

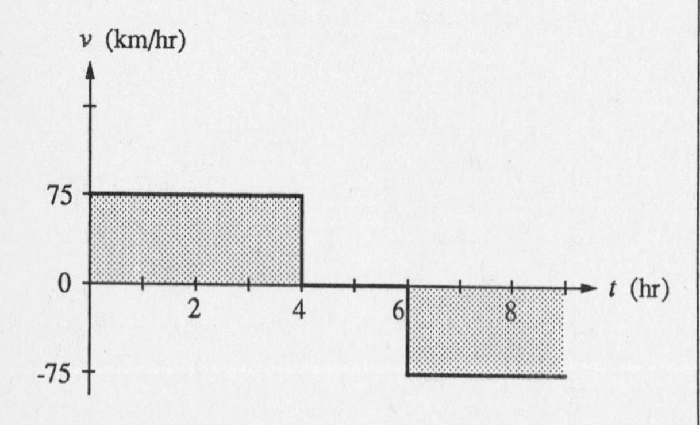

Practice Problems

b. Find the area under curve for the first four hours. What does this represent?

Area is (75 km/h)(4 h) = 300 km, the distance travelled in that time.

c. Explain how to use the graph to find the distance the car is from its starting point at the end of 9.0 hours.

Find total area under curve for all three segments of trip, which is
300 km + 0 km + (–225 km) = 75 km.

19. A person drives a car at a constant +25 m/s for 10.0 minutes. The car runs out of gas, so the driver, carrying an empty gasoline can, walks at +1.5 m/s for 20.0 minutes to the nearest gas station. After the 10.0 minutes needed to fill the can, the driver walks back to the car at a slower –1.2 m/s. The car is then driven back home at –25 m/s.

a. Draw a velocity–time graph for the driver, using seconds as your time unit. You will have to calculate the distance the driver walked to the station in order to find the time needed to walk back to the car.

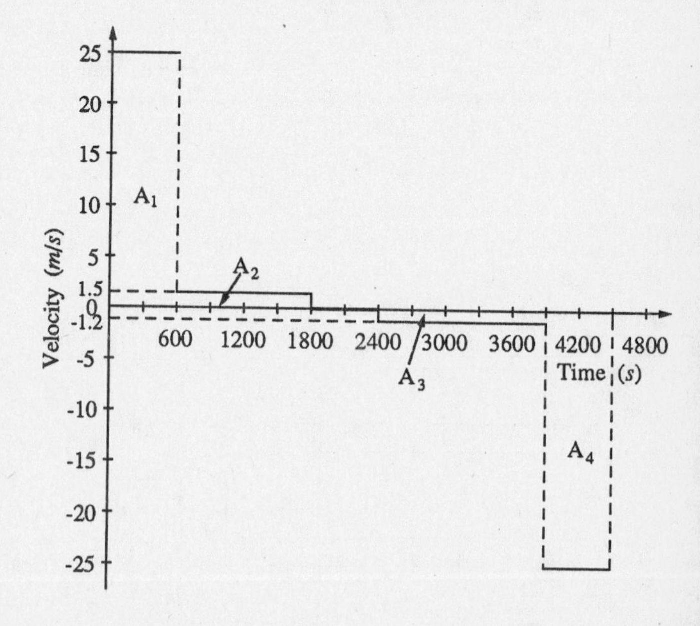

Practice Problems

Distance walked to station
= (1.5 m/s)(20.0 min)(60 s/min)
= 1800 m.

Time for walk back to car
$= \frac{(1800 \text{ m})}{(1.2 \text{ m/s})}$
= 1500 s.

b. Draw a position–time graph for the problem from the areas under the curves of the velocity–time graph.

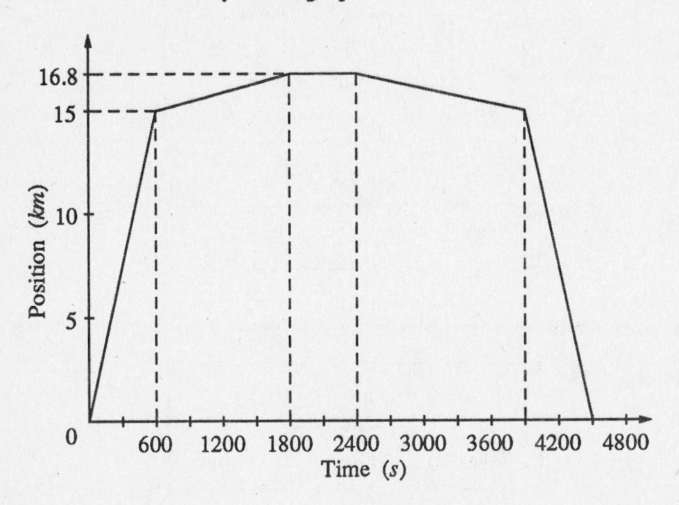

From the graph in part a, the changes in position are:

$\Delta d_1 = A_1$ = (25 m/s)(600 s)
= 15 000 m = 15 km

$\Delta d_2 = A_2$ = (1.5 m/s)(1200 s)
= 1800 m = 1.8 km

$\Delta d_3 = A_3$ = (–1.2 m/s)(1500 s)
= –1800 m = –1.8 km

$\Delta d_4 = A_4$ = (–25 m/s)(600 s)
= –15 000 m = –15 km

page 56

20. From the reference frame of a stationary observer, a car, traveling at a constant speed of 92 km/h, is passed by a truck moving at 105 km/h.

Practice Problems

a. From the point of view of the car, what is the truck's speed?

If $V_B = V_A + V_{BA}$, where V_A, V_B are velocities relative to Earth and V_{BA} is the velocity of B relative to A, then $V_{BA} = V_B - V_A$.

$V_{tc} = V_t - V_c$ = 105 km/h – 92 km/h
= 13 km/h

b. From the point of view of the truck, what is the car's speed?

$V_{ct} = V_c - V_t$ = 92 km/h – 105 km/h
= –13 km

21. As you travel at a constant 95 km/h, a car that you know to be 3.5 m long, passes you in 1.8 s. How fast is it going relative to Earth?

The relative speed is $\frac{(3.5 \text{ m})}{(1.8 \text{ s})}$ = 1.9 m/s = 7.0 km/h, so its speed is 102 km/h.

Chapter Review Problems

pages 59–61

1. While John is traveling along an interstate highway he noticed a mile marker read 160 as he passed through town. Later John passed another mile marker, 115.

a. What is the distance between town and John's current location?

45 miles

b. What is John's current position?

+115

2. While John is traveling along a straight interstate highway he noticed that the mile marker reads 260. John traveled until he reached the 150 mile marker and then retraced his path to the 175 mile marker. What is the magnitude of John's resultant displacement from the 260 mile marker?

$\Delta d = d_2 - d_1$ = 175 mi – 260 mi = –85 mi

3. A physics book is moved once around the perimeter of a table of dimensions 1.0 m by 2.0 m.

   a. If the book ends up at its initial position, what is its displacement?

   Any time a book ends up where it started its displacement is zero.

   b. What is the distance traveled?

   The distance is equal to the perimeter of the table, 6.0 m.

4. Light from the sun reaches Earth in 8.3 min. The velocity of light is 3.00×10^8 m/s. How far is Earth from the sun?

Time = 8.3 min = 498 = 5.0×10^2 s

$$\bar{v} = \frac{\Delta d}{\Delta t},$$

so $\Delta d = \bar{v}\Delta t = (3.00 \times 10^8 \text{ m/s})(5.0 \times 10^2 \text{ s}) = 1.5 \times 10^{11}$ m

5. You and a friend each drive 50 km. You travel at 90 km/h, your friend at 95 km/h. How long will your friend wait for you at the end of the trip?

It takes your friend $\frac{(50 \text{ km})}{(95 \text{ km/h})}$ = 31.6 minutes, and takes you $\frac{(50 \text{ km})}{(90 \text{ km/h})}$ = 33.3 minutes, so your friend waits 1.8 minutes.

6. From the list of winning times from the 1988 Summer Olympics, in Table 3–2, calculate the average speeds for each race. Assume the length of each event is known to the nearest 0.1 m.

Chapter Review Problems

Length of event (m)	Time (min:sec) Men	Women
100	9.92	10.54
200	19.75	21.34
400	43.87	48.65
800	1:44.06	1:56.10
1 500	3:35.96	3:53.96
3 000		8:26.53
5 000	13:11.70	
10 000	27:21.46	31:05.21

Length of event (m)	Velocity (m/s) Men	Women
10.1	10.1	9.488
200	10.13	9.372
400	9.118	8.222
800	7.688	6.891
1 500	6.9457	6.411
3 000		5.9227
5 000	6.3155	
10 000	6.09214	5.36133

7. Construct a table similar to Table 3–2 listing average speeds for track events in your school, district, or state.

   Students answers will vary.

Chapter Review Problems

8. Construct an average speed table similar to Problem 6 for swimming events at your school, district, or state. Compare times for swimming to those for running. Explain.

Student answers will vary.
Students can run faster than they can swim.

9. Two cars approach each other; both cars are moving westward, one at 78 km/h, the other at 64 km/h.

a. What is the velocity of the first relative to (in the frame of reference of) the second?

Let east be the positive direction.

Initially car 1 is going –78 km/h and car 2 is going –64 km/h. To use car 2 as our reference point add the opposite of its current velocity, +64 km/h, to give it a zero speed. Add +64 km/h to car 1's velocity also; –78 km/h + (+64 km/h) = –14 km/h or 14 km/h, west.

b. After they pass, will their relative velocity change?

No

10. Ann is driving down a street in a car at 55 km/h. Suddenly a child runs into the street. If it takes Ann 0.75 s to react and apply the brakes, how many meters will she have moved before she begins to slow down?

$$\bar{v} = \frac{\Delta d}{\Delta t}, \text{ so}$$

$$\Delta d = \bar{v}\Delta t = \frac{(55 \text{ km/h})(0.75 \text{ s})(1000 \text{ m/km})}{(3600 \text{ s/h})}$$

$$= 11 \text{ m}$$

11. You plan a trip on which you want to average 90 km/h. You cover the first half of the distance at an average speed of only 48 km/h.

a. What must your average speed be in the second half of the trip to meet your goal? Note that velocities are based on half the distance, not half the time.

$$\bar{v} = \frac{\Delta d}{\Delta t}, \text{ so } \Delta t = \frac{\Delta d}{\bar{v}}$$

Let $d = \frac{1}{2}d + \frac{1}{2}d$ and $t_{total} = t_1 + t_2$,

$$\text{so } \frac{d}{v} = \frac{\frac{1}{2}d}{v_1} + \frac{\frac{1}{2}d}{v_2} \text{ multiply by } 2d$$

$$\frac{2}{v} = \frac{1}{v_1} + \frac{1}{v_2},$$

$$\text{so } \frac{1}{v_2} = \frac{2}{v} - \frac{1}{v_1}$$

$$= \frac{2}{90 \text{ km/h}} - \frac{1}{48 \text{ km/h}}$$

so $v_2 = 720$ km/h

b. Is this a reasonable speed?

No

12. You drive a car 2.0 hours at 40 km/h, then 2.0 hours at 60 km/h.

a. What is your average velocity?

Total distance: 80 km + 120 km = 200 km. Total time 4.0 hours, so,

$$v = \frac{\Delta d}{\Delta t} = \frac{200 \text{ km}}{4.0 \text{ h}} = 50 \text{ km/h}.$$

b. Do you get the same answer if you drive 100 km at each of the two speeds above?

No. Total distance 200 km;

$$\text{total time} = \frac{(100 \text{ km})}{(40 \text{ km/h})} + \frac{(100 \text{ km})}{(60 \text{ km/h})}$$

= 2.5 h + 1.7 h = 4.2 h.

$$\text{So } v = \frac{\Delta d}{\Delta v} = \frac{200 \text{ km}}{4.2 \text{ h}} = 48 \text{ km/h}.$$

13. The total distance a steel ball rolls down an incline at the end of each second of travel is given in Table 3–3.

a. Draw a position–time graph of the motion of the ball. When setting up the axes use five divisions for each 10 m of travel on the d–axis. Use five divisions for each second of time on the t–axis.

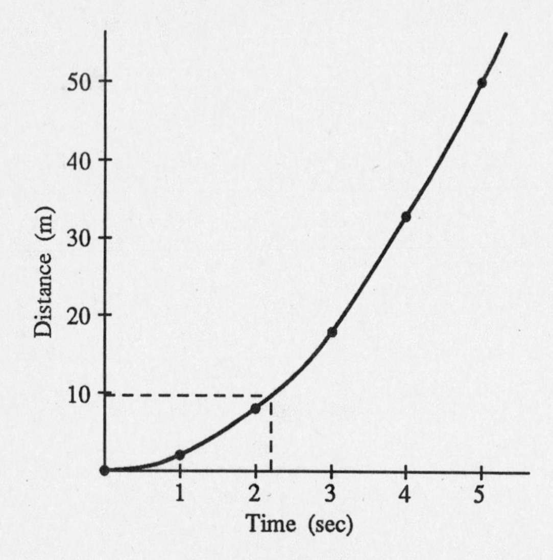

b. What type of curve is the line of the graph?

The curve is a parabola.

c. What distance has the ball rolled at the end of 2.2 s?

After 2.2 seconds the ball has rolled approximately 10 m.

14. Use the position–time graph in Figure 3–24 to find

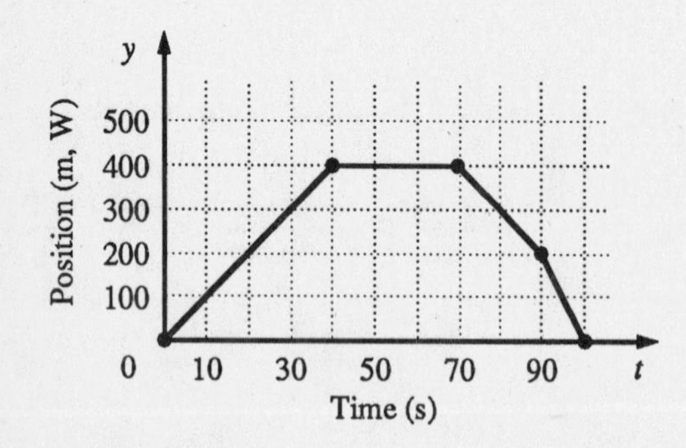

Chapter Review Problems

a. How far the object travels between t = 0 s and t = 40 s.

$$\Delta d = d_{40} - d_0 = 400\text{ m} - 0\text{ m} = 400\text{ m}$$

b. How far it travels between t = 40 s and t = 70 s.

$$\Delta d = d_{70} - d_{40} = 400\text{ m} - 400\text{ m} = 0$$

c. How far it travels between t = 90 s and t = 100 s.

$$\Delta d = d_{100} - d_{90} = 0 - 200\text{ m} = -200\text{ m}$$

15. Both car A and car B leave school when a clock reads zero. Car A travels at a constant 75 km/h, while car B keeps its velocity 85 km/h.

a. Draw a position–time graph showing the motion of both cars.

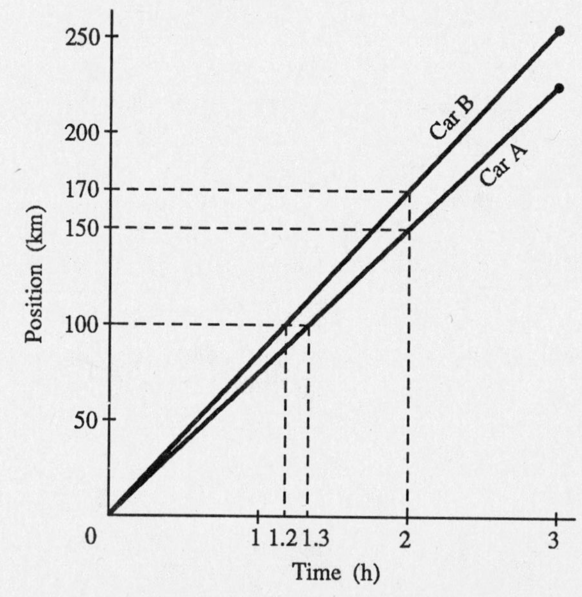

b. How far are the two cars from school when the clock reads 2.0 hours? Calculate the distances using the equation of motion and show them on your graph.

$$d_A = v_A t = (75\text{ km/h})(2.0\text{ h}) = 150\text{ km}$$

$$d_B = v_B t = (85\text{ km/h})(2.0\text{ h}) = 170\text{ km}$$

c. Both cars passed a gas station 100 km from the school. When did each car pass the station? Calculate the times and show them on your graph.

$d = vt$, so $t = \frac{d}{v}$

$t_A = \frac{d}{v_A} = \frac{100 \text{ km}}{75 \text{ km/h}} = 1.3 \text{ h}$

$t_B = \frac{d}{v_B} = \frac{100 \text{ km}}{85 \text{ km/h}} = 1.2 \text{ h}$

16. Draw a position–time graph for two cars driving to the beach, 50 km from school. Car A leaves a store 10 km from school closer to the beach at noon, and drives at 40 km/h. Car B starts from school at 12:30 pm and drives at 100 km/h. At what time does each get to the beach?

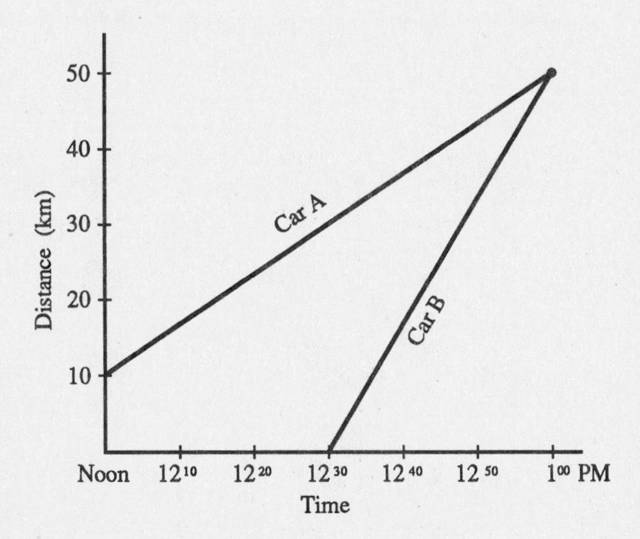

Both cars arrive at the beach at 1:00.

Chapter Review Problems

17. Plot the data in Table 3–1 on a position–time graph. Find the average velocity in the time interval between 0.0 and 5.0 seconds.

Table 3–1

Clock Readings, t in s	Positions, d, in m
0.0	30
1.0	30
2.0	35
3.0	45
4.0	60
5.0	70

$$\text{slope} = \frac{\Delta d}{\Delta t} = \frac{70 \text{ m} - 30 \text{ m}}{5.0 \text{ s} - 0.0 \text{ s}} = 8.0 \text{ m/s}$$

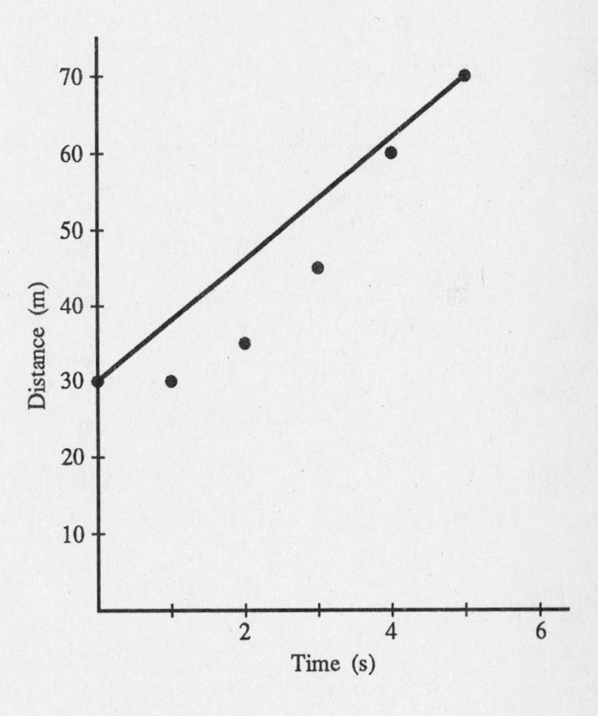

18. A cyclist maintains a constant velocity of +5.0 m/s. At time t = 0, the cyclist is +250 m from point A.

a. Plot a position–time graph of the cyclist's location from point A at 10.0 second intervals for 60.0 s.

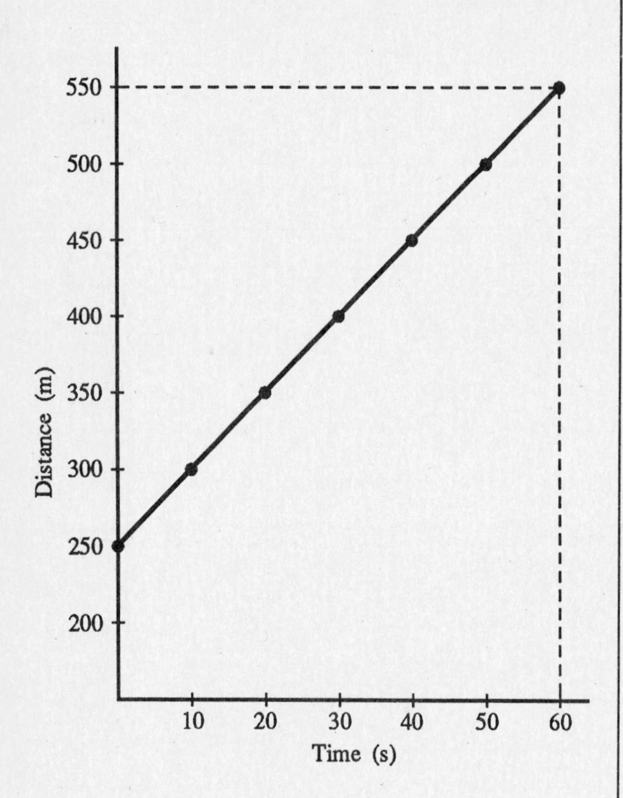

b. What is the position from point A at 60.0 s?

550 m

c. What is the displacement from the starting position at 60.0 s?

550 m − 250 m = 300 m

Chapter Review Problems

19. From the position–time graph, Figure 3–24, construct a table showing the average velocity of the object during each 10–s interval over the entire 100 s.

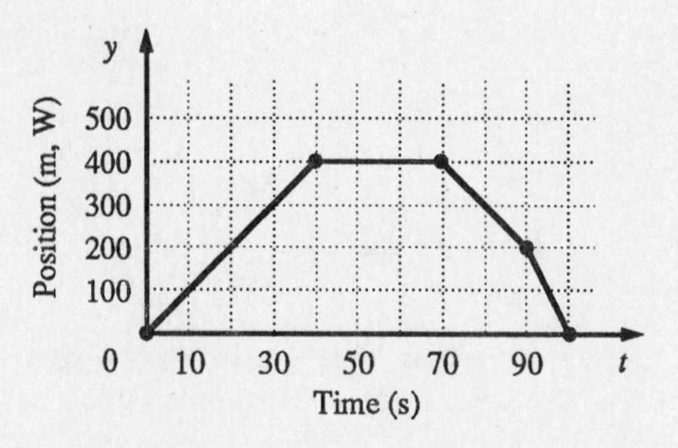

Time interval (s)	Average Velocity (m/s)
0–10	10
10–20	10
20–30	10
30–40	10
40–50	0
50–60	0
60–70	0
70–80	–10
80–90	–10
90–100	–20

20. Two cars travel along the same straight road. When a stopwatch reads t = 0.0 hr car A is at d_A = 48.0 km moving at a constant 36.0 km/h. Later, when the watch reads t = 0.50 hr car B is at d_B = 0.00 km moving at 48.0 km/h. Solve the following questions first graphically by creating a postion–time graph, second algebraically by writing down equations for the positions d_A and d_B as a function of the stopwatch time t.

a. What will the watch read when car B passes car A?

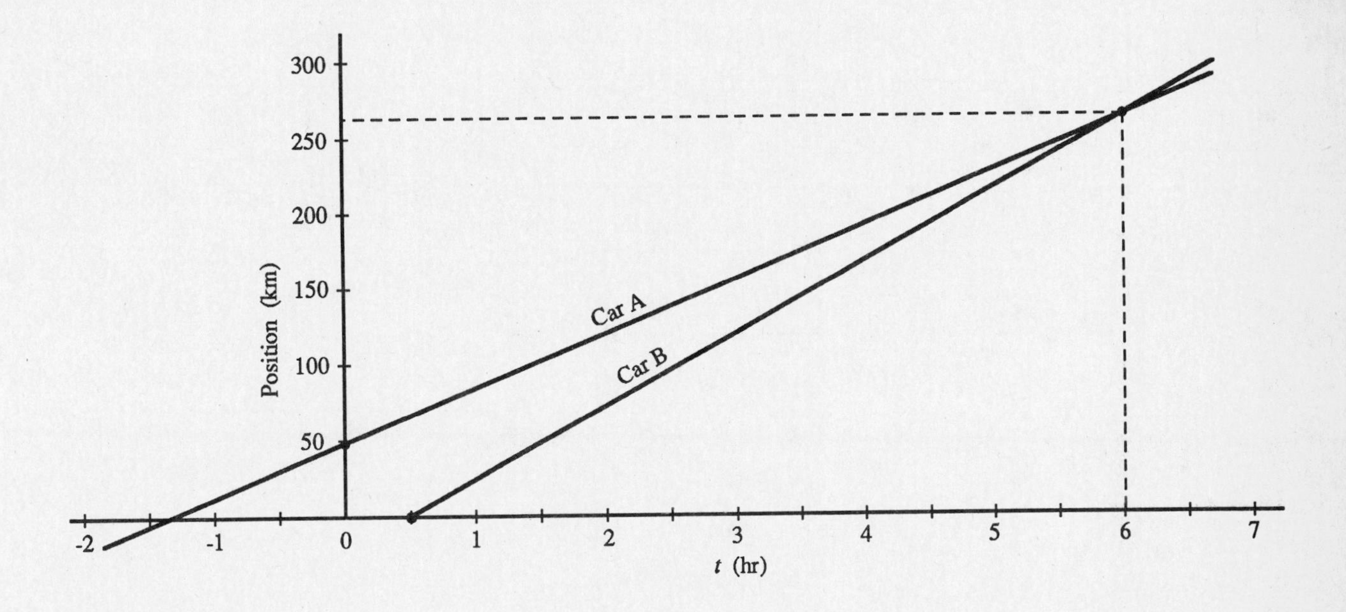

6.00 h

Cars pass when the distances are equal, $d_A = d_B$.

d_A = 48.0 km + (36.0 km/h)t and d_B = 0 + (48.0 km/h)(t – 0.50 h), so

$$48.0\text{ km} + (36.0\text{ km/h})t = (48.0\text{ km/h})(t - 0.50\text{ h})$$
$$48.0\text{ km} + (36.0\text{ km/h})t = (48.0\text{ km/h})t - 24\text{ km}$$
$$72\text{ km} = (12.0\text{ km/h})t$$
$$t = 6.0\text{ h}$$

b. At what position will the passing occur?

d_A = 48.0 km + (36.0 km/h)(6.0 h) = 2.6×10^2 km

c. When the cars pass, how long will it have been since car A was at the reference point?

$$d = vt, \text{ so } t\,\frac{d}{v} = \frac{-48.0\text{ km}}{36.0\text{ km/h}} = -1.33\text{ h}$$

Car A started 1.33 h before the clock started.

t = 6.0 h + 1.3 h = 7.3 h

21.

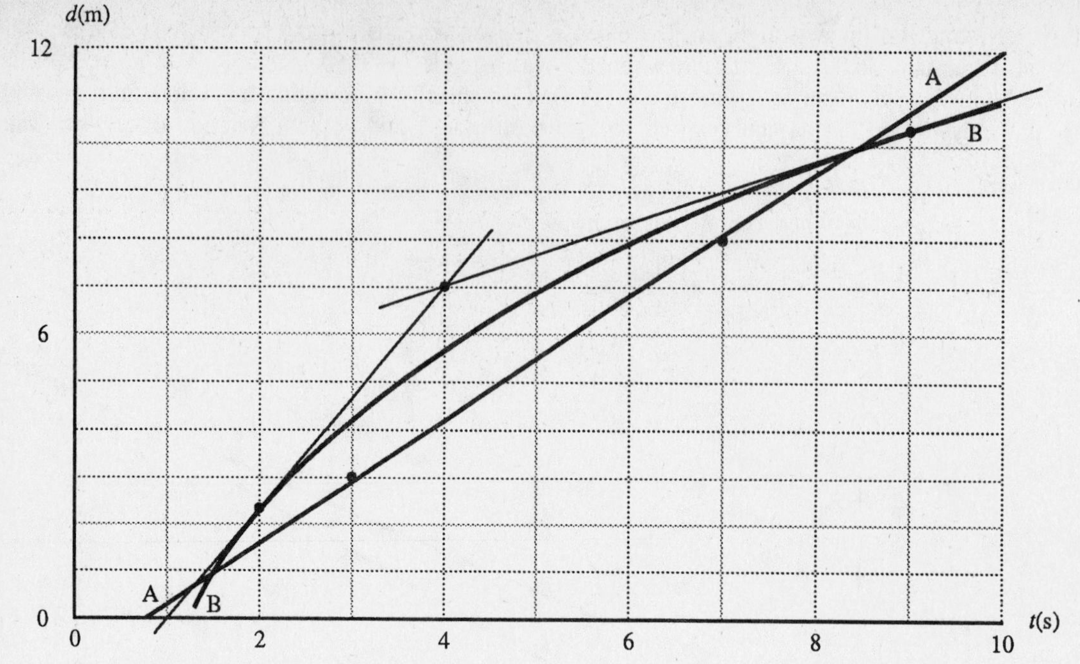

Refer to Figure 3–22 to find the instantaneous speed for

a. car B at 2.0 s

$$\text{slope} = \frac{\Delta d}{\Delta t} = \frac{7\text{ m} - 0\text{ m}}{4\text{ s} - 1\text{ s}} = 2.3\text{ m/s}$$

b. car B at 9.0 s

$$\text{slope} = \frac{\Delta d}{\Delta t} = \frac{11\text{ m} - 7\text{ m}}{10\text{ s} - 4\text{ s}} = 0.67\text{ m/s}$$

c. car A at 2.0 s

$$\text{slope} = \frac{\Delta d}{\Delta t} = \frac{8\text{ m} - 3\text{m}}{7\text{ s} - 3\text{ s}} = 1.25\text{ m/s}$$

Student answers will vary.

22. Find the instantaneous speed of the car at 15 s from Figure 3–19.

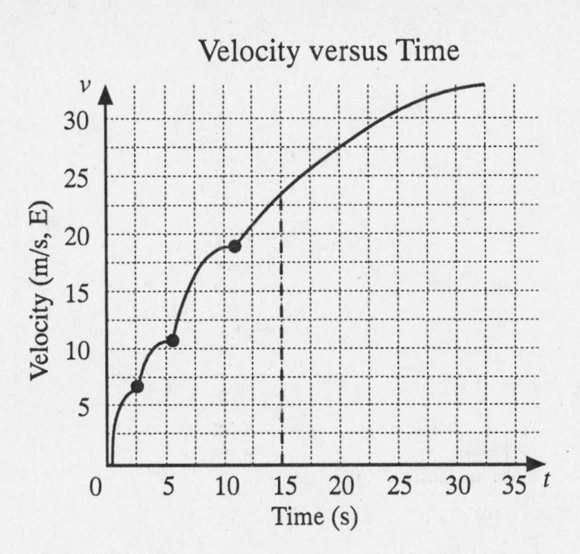

Student answer will vary.

Approximately 23 m/s

23. Plot a velocity–time graph using the information in Table 3–4.

Time (s)	Velocity (m/s)	Time (s)	Velocity (m/s)
0.0	4.0	7.0	12.0
1.0	8.0	8.0	8.0
2.0	12.0	9.0	4.0
3.0	14.0	10.0	0.0
4.0	16.0	11.0	–4.0
5.0	16.0	12.0	–8.0
6.0	14.0		

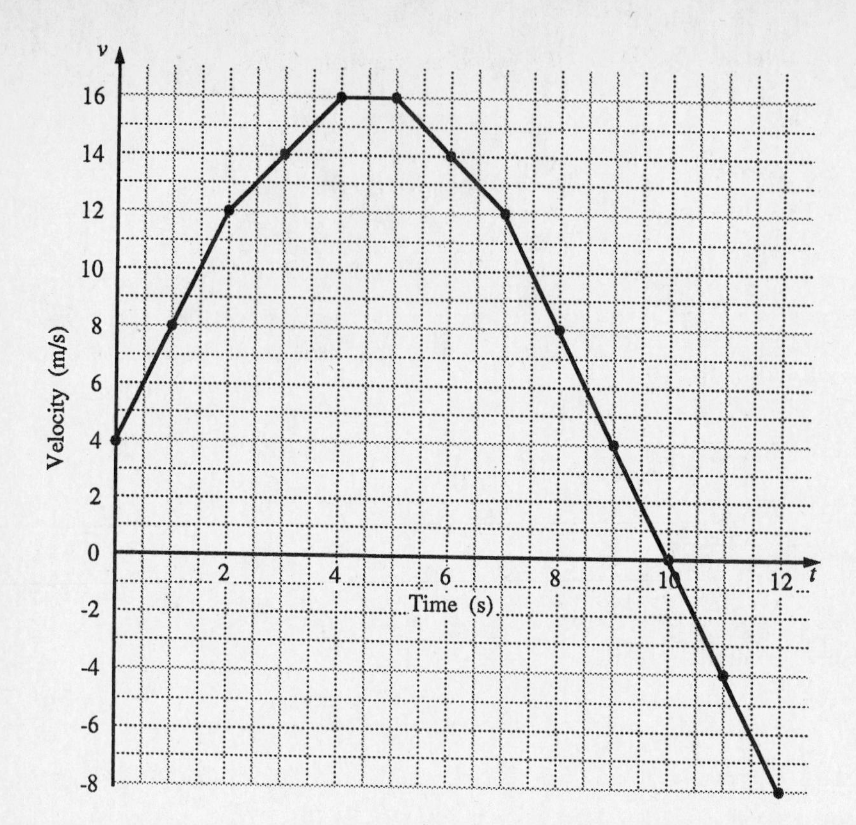

24. Refer to Figure 3–25 to find the distance the moving object travels

a. between t = 0 s and t = 5 s.

$$\text{Area I} = \frac{1}{2}bh = \frac{1}{2}(5\text{s})(30\text{ m/s}) = 75\text{ m}$$

b. between t = 5 s and t = 10 s.

$$\text{Area II} = bh = (10\text{ s} - 5\text{ s})(30\text{ m/s}) = 150\text{ m}$$

c. between t = 10 s and t = 15 s.

$$\text{Area III} + \text{Area IV} = bh + \frac{1}{2}bh = (15\text{ s} - 10\text{ s})(20\text{ m/s}) + \frac{1}{2}(15\text{ s} - 10\text{ s})(10\text{ m/s})$$
$$= 100\text{ m} + 25\text{ m} = 125\text{ m}$$

d. between t = 0 s and t = 25 s.

75 m + 150 m + 125 m + 100 m + 50 m = 500 m

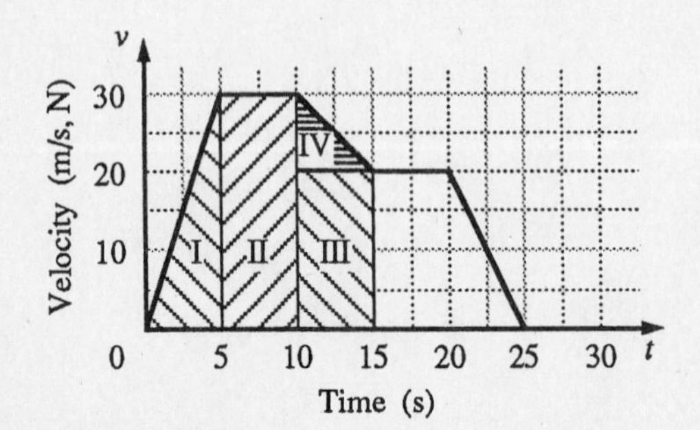

Chapter Review Problems

25. The velocity of an automobile changes over an 8.0–s time period as shown in Table 3–5.

Time (s)	Velocity (m/s)	Time (s)	Velocity (m/s)
0.0	0.0	5.0	20.0
1.0	4.0	6.0	20.0
2.0	4.0	7.0	20.0
3.0	8.0	8.0	20.0
4.0	16.0		

a. Plot the velocity–time graph of the motion.

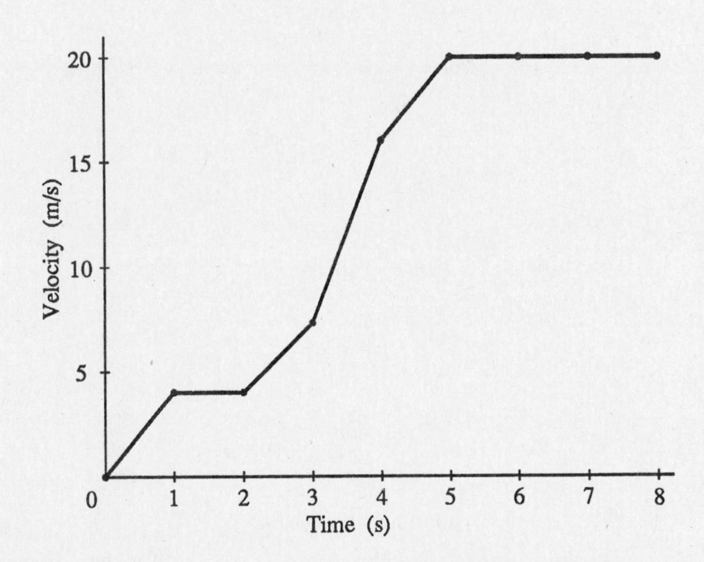

b. Determine the distance the car travels during the first 2.0 s.

$$\Delta d = \frac{1}{2}(1.0 \text{ s})(4.0 \text{ m/s}) + (1.0 \text{ s})(4.0 \text{ m/s}) = 6.0 \text{ m}$$

c. What distance does the car travel during the first 4.0 s?

$$\Delta d = 6.0 \text{ m} + \frac{1}{2}(1.0 \text{ s})(8.0 \text{ m/s} - 4.0 \text{ m/s}) + (1.0 \text{ s})(4.0 \text{ m/s}) + \frac{1}{2}(1.0 \text{ s})(16.0 \text{ m/s} - 8.0 \text{ m/s})$$
$$+ (1.0 \text{ s})(8.0 \text{ m/s}) = 24 \text{ m}$$

d. What distance does the car travel during the entire 8.0 s?

$$\Delta d = 24 \text{ m} + (1.0 \text{ s})(16.0 \text{ m/s}) + \frac{1}{2}(1.0 \text{ s})(20.0 \text{ m/s} - 16.0 \text{ m/s}) + (3.0 \text{ s})(20.0 \text{ m/s})$$
$$= 102 \text{ m}$$

1. Bob walks 80 m and then he walks 125 m.

   a. What is Bob's displacement if he walks east both times?

   205 m

   b. What is Bob's displacement if he walks east then west?

   –45 m

   c. What distance does Bob walk in each case?

   205 m

2. A cross country runner runs 5.0 km east along the course, then turns around and runs 5.0 km west along the same path. She returns to the starting point in 40 min. What is her average speed? Her average velocity?

   average speed
   = (distance traveled during time interval)(time)

   $$= \frac{(5.0\text{ km} + 5.0\text{ km})}{(40\text{ min})}$$

   = (0.25 km/min)(60 min/h)
   = 15 km/h, average velocity

   $$= \frac{(\text{displacement during time interval})}{(\text{time})}$$

   $$= \frac{(+5.0\text{ km} - 5.0\text{ km})}{(40\text{ min})} = 0$$

3. 0.30 s after seeing a puff of smoke rise from the starter's pistol, the sound of the firing of the pistol is heard by the track timer 100 m away. What is the velocity of sound?

   $$v = \frac{d}{t} = \frac{100}{0.30} = 330\text{ m/s}$$

4. The radius of the tires on a particular vehicle is 0.62 m. If the tires are rotating 5 times per second, what is the velocity of the vehicle?

   $$C = 2\pi R = 2\pi(0.62) = 3.9\text{ m}$$

   $$V = \left[\frac{3.9\text{ m}}{\text{Rotation}}\right]\left[\frac{5\text{ Rotations}}{\text{s}}\right] = 20\text{ m/s}$$

5. A bullet is fired with a speed of 720.0 m/s.

   a. What time is required for the bullet to strike a target at a position +324 m?

   $$t = \frac{d}{v} = \frac{(324\text{ m})}{(720.0\text{ m/s})} = 0.450\text{ s}$$

   b. What is the velocity in km/h?

   $$v = \frac{(720.0\text{ m/s})(3600\text{ s/h})}{(1000\text{ m/km})} = 2592\text{ km/h}$$

6. Light travels at 3.0×10^8 m/s. How many seconds go by from the moment the starter's pistol is shot until the smoke is seen by the track timer 100 m away?

   $$t = \frac{d}{v} = \frac{100}{3.0 \times 10^8} = 3.3 \times 10^{-7}\text{ s}$$

7. You drive your car from home at an average velocity of 80 km/h for 3 hours. Being halfway to your destination you develop some engine problems, and for 5 hours you nurse the car the rest of the way. What is your average velocity for the entire trip?

   $$d = \bar{v}t = (80)(3) = 240\text{ km}$$

   Total distance traveled is 480 km.
   Total time is 8 hours.

   $$\bar{v} = \frac{d}{t} = \frac{480}{8} = 60\text{ km/h}$$

8. The total distance a ball is off the ground when thrown vertically is given for each second of flight by the following table:

Time (s)	Distance (m)
0.0	0.0
1.0	24.5
2.0	39.2
3.0	44.1
4.0	39.2
5.0	24.5
6.0	0.0

a. Draw a position–time graph of the motion of the ball.

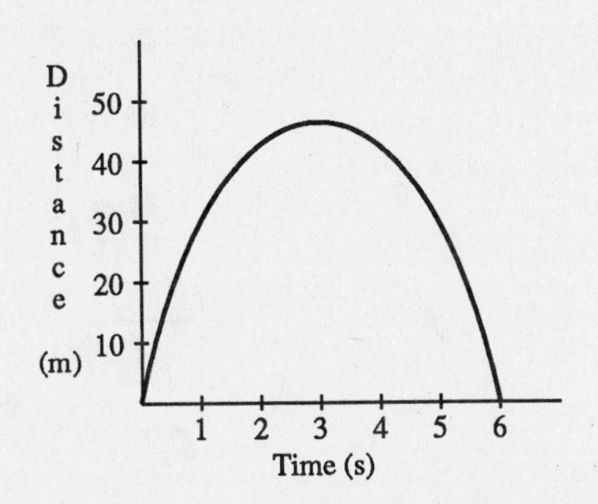

b. How far off the ground is the ball at the end of 0.5 s? When would the ball again be this distance from the ground?

13.5 m, 5.5 s

Supplemental Problems

9. Use the following position–time graph to find how far the object travels:

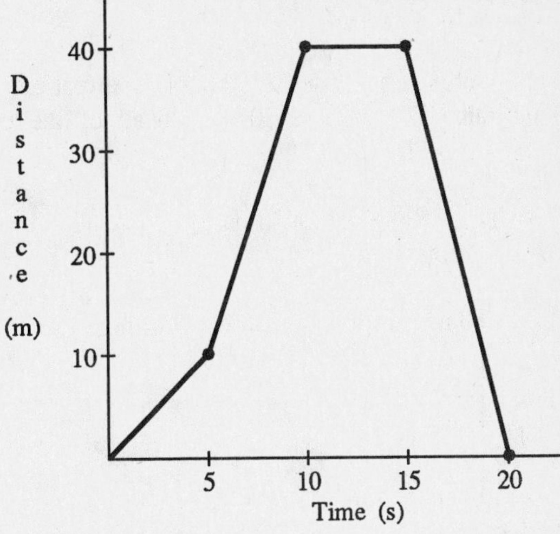

a. between t = 0 s to t = 5 s

10 m

b. between t = 0 s to t = 10 s

30 m

c. between t = 10 s to t = 15 s

0 m

d. between t = 15 s to t = 20 s

–40 m

e. between t = 0 s to t = 20 s

80 m of distance, but 0 displacement

10. Use the position–time graph from problem 9 to find the object's velocity:

a. between t = 0 s to t = 5 s

$$v = \frac{\Delta y}{\Delta x} = \frac{10}{5} = 2 \text{ m/s}$$

b. between t = 5 s to t = 10 s

$$v = \frac{30}{5} = 6 \text{ m/s}$$

c. between t = 10 s to t = 15 s

$$v = \frac{0}{5} = 0 \text{ m/s}$$

d. between t = 15 s to t = 20 s

$$v = \frac{-40}{5} = -8 \text{ m/s}$$

11. Two cars are headed in the same direction; one traveling 60 km/h is 20 km ahead of the other traveling 80 km/h.

a. Draw a position–time graph showing the motion of the cars.

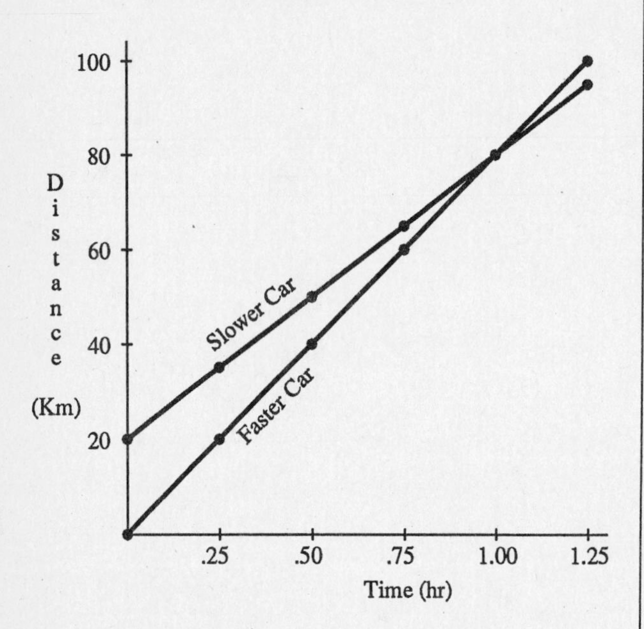

b. Using your graph show the time when the faster car overtakes the slower one.

1 hr

12. Use the graph from Problem 8 to calculate the ball's instantaneous velocity at:

a. t = 2 s

≈ 10 m/s

b. t = 3 s

0 m/s

c. t = 4 s

≈ –10 m/s

Supplemental Problems

13. A plane flies in a straight line at a constant speed of +75 m/s. Assume that it is at the reference point when the clock reads t = 0.

a. Construct a table showing the position or displacement of the plane at the end of each second for a 10 s period.

Clock Reading t, in s	Position, d, in m
0	0
1	75
2	150
3	225
4	300
5	375
6	450
7	525
8	600
9	675
10	750

b. Use the data from the table to plot a position–time graph.

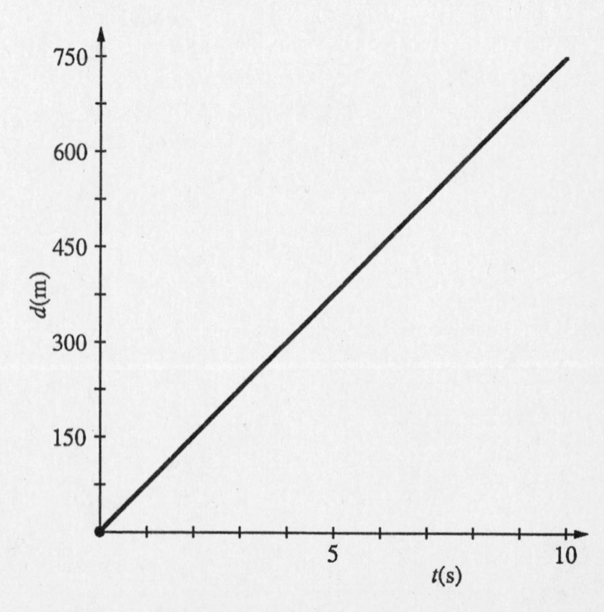

c. Show that the slope of the line is the velocity of the plane. Use at least two different sets of points along the line.

From d–t graph:

$$\text{slope 1} = \frac{(450\text{ m})}{(6\text{ s} - 0\text{ s})} = 75\text{ m/s},$$

$$\text{slope 2} = \frac{(600\text{ m} - 200\text{ m})}{(8\text{ s} - 2.67\text{ s})} = 75\text{ m/s}$$

d. Plot a velocity–time graph of the plane's motion for the first 6 s of the 10–s interval.

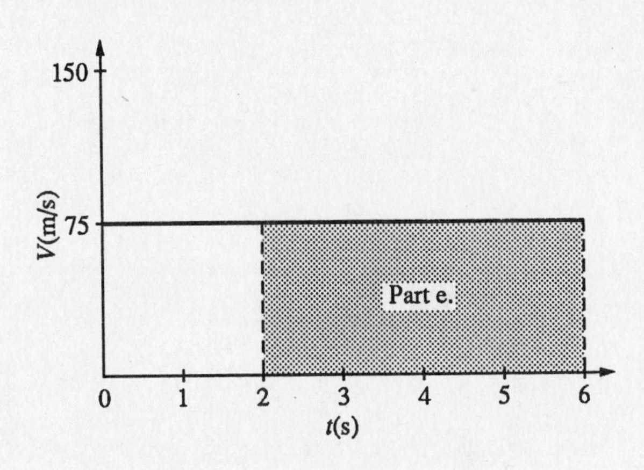

e. From the velocity–time graph, find the displacement of the plane between the second and sixth seconds.

Shaded area under v – t graph = d

= (75 m/s)(4 s) = 300 m

14. Mary jogs for 15 minutes at 240 m/min, walks the next 10 minutes at 90 m/min, rests for 5 minutes, and jogs back to where she started at –180 m/min.

Supplemental Problems

a. Plot a velocity–time graph for Mary's exercise run.

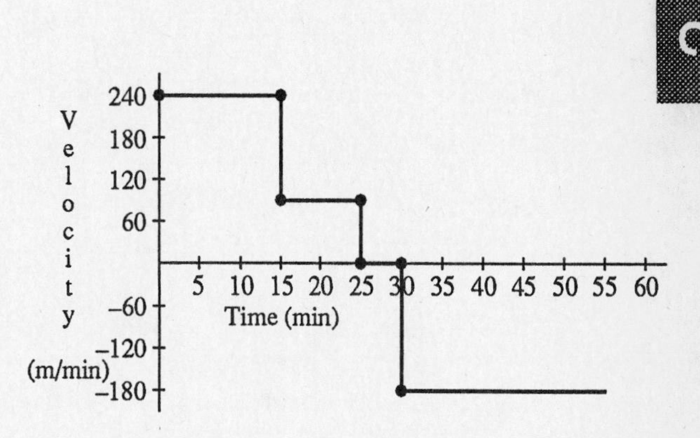

b. Find the area under the curve for the first 15 minutes. What does this represent?

Area = 240(15) = 3600 m
The distance jogged.

c. What is the total distance traveled by Mary?

3600 + 900 + 4500 = 9000 m

d. What is Mary's displacement from start to finish?

4500 – 4500 = 0 m

15. Car A is traveling at 85 km/h while car B is at 60 km/h. What is the relative velocity of car A to Car B:

a. If they both are traveling in the same direction?

85 – 60 = 25 km/h

b. If they are headed towards each other?

85 + 60 = 145 km/h

Chapter 4: Acceleration

Practice Problems

page 46

1. An Indy–500 race car's velocity increases from +4.0 m/s to +36 m/s over a 4.0–second period. What is its acceleration?

$$a = \frac{\Delta v}{\Delta t} = \frac{(36 \text{ m/s} - 4.0 \text{ m/s})}{(4.0 \text{ s})} = 8.0 \text{ m/s}^2$$

2. The same race car slows from +36 m/s to +15 m/s over 3.0 s. What is its average acceleration over this time interval?

$$a = \frac{(v_2 - t_1)}{(t_2 - t_1)} = \frac{(15 \text{ m/s} - 36 \text{ m/s})}{(3.0 \text{ s})} = -7.0 \text{ m/s}^2$$

3. A car is coasting backwards down a hill at –3.0 m/s when the driver gets the engine started. After 2.5 s the car is moving uphill at a velocity of +4.5 m/s. What is the car's average acceleration?

$$a = \frac{(v_2 - v_1)}{(t_2 - t_1)} = \frac{(4.5 \text{ m/s} - (-3.0 \text{ m/s}))}{(2.5 \text{ s})} = 3.0 \text{ m/s}^2$$

4. A bus is moving at 25 m/s. The driver steps on the brakes, and the bus stops in 3.0 s.

   a. What is the average acceleration of the bus while braking?

$$a = \frac{(v_2 - v_1)}{(t_2 - t_1)} = \frac{(0 \text{ m/s} - 25 \text{ m/s})}{(3.0 \text{ s})} = -8.3 \text{ m/s}^2$$

   b. Suppose the bus took twice as long to stop. How would the acceleration compare to the acceleration you found above?

   Half as great (–4.2 m/s²).

page 68

5. Describe, in your own words, the velocity of the toy train shown in Figure 4–6 between 0 and 20 s.

   Starting from rest, it accelerates to 10 m/s in the first five seconds. It remains at this speed for 10 s, before slowing to 4 m/s over the last 5 s.

Practice Problems

6. Figure 4–6 shows a velocity–time graph of a toy train.

   a. During which time interval or intervals is the speed constant?

   5 to 15 s and 21 to 28 s.

   b. During which interval or intervals is the train's acceleration positive?

   0 to 6 s.

   c. During which interval or intervals is its acceleration less than zero?

   15 to 20 s, 28 s to 40 s.

   d. During which time interval is the acceleration most negative?

   16 to 19 s.

7. For Figure 4–6 find the average acceleration over the given time intervals.

   a. 0 to 5 s.

   2 m/s².

   b. 0 to 10 s.

   1 m/s².

   c. 15 to 20 s.

   –1.2 m/s².

   d. 0 to 40 s.

   0 m/s².

Practice Problems

8. **a.** Draw a velocity–time graph for an object whose velocity is constantly decreasing from 10 m/s at t = 0.0 s to –10 m/s at t = 2.0 s. Assume it has constant acceleration.

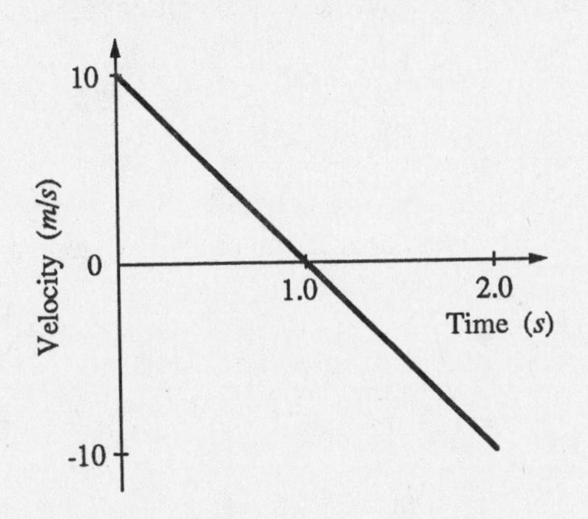

b. What is its average acceleration between 0.0 s and 2.0 s?

$$a = \frac{\Delta v}{\Delta t} = \frac{(-10\text{ m/s} - 10\text{ m/s})}{(2\text{ s})} = -10\text{ m/s}^2.$$

c. What is its acceleration when its velocity is 0 m/s?

The same, –10 m/s².

page 69

9. A golf ball rolls up a hill on a Putt–Putt hole.

a. If it starts with a velocity of +2.0 m/s and accelerates at a rate of –0.50 m/s², what is its velocity after 2.0 s?

$$v_f = v_i + at = 2.0\text{ m/s} + (-0.50\text{ m/s}^2)(2.0\text{ s}) = 1.0\text{ m/s}$$

b. If the acceleration occurs for 6.0 s, what is its final velocity?

$$v_f = v_i + at = 2.0\text{ m/s} + (-0.50\text{ m/s}^2)(6.0\text{ s}) = -1.0\text{ m/s}$$

c. Describe, in words, the motion of the golf ball.

The ball velocity simply decreased in the first case. In the second case the ball slowed to a stop and then began rolling back down the hill.

Practice Problems

10. A bus traveling at +30 km/h accelerates at +3.5 m/s² for 6.8 s. What is its final velocity in km/h?

$$a = (3.5\text{ m/s}^2)(1\text{ km}/1000\text{ m})(3600\text{ s}/1\text{ h}) = 12.6\text{ (km/h)/s}$$

$$v_f = v_i + at = 30\text{ km/h} + (12.6\text{(km/h)/s})(6.8\text{ s}) = 30\text{ km/h} + 86\text{ km/h} = 116\text{ km/h}$$

11. If a car accelerates from rest at a constant 5.5 m/s², how long will be required to reach 28 m/s?

$$v_f = v_i + at \text{ so } t = \frac{(v_f - v_i)}{a} = \frac{(28\text{ m/s} - 0\text{ m/s})}{(5.5\text{ m/s}^2)} = 5.1\text{ s}$$

12. A car slows from 22 m/s to 3 m/s with a constant acceleration of –2.1 m/s². How long does it require?

$$v_f = v_i + at$$

$$\text{so } t = \frac{(v_f - v_i)}{a} = \frac{(3\text{ m/s} - 22\text{ m/s})}{(-2.1\text{ m/s}^2)} = 9.0\text{ s}$$

page 72

13. A race car traveling at +44 m/s is uniformly accelerated to a velocity of +22 m/s over an 11–s interval. What is its displacement during this time?

$$d = \frac{1}{2}(v_f + v_i)t = \frac{1}{2}(22\text{ m/s} + 44\text{ m/s})(11\text{ s}) = 3.6 \times 10^2\text{ m}$$

14. A rocket traveling at +88 m/s is accelerated uniformly to +132 m/s over a 15–s interval. What is the rocket's displacement during this time?

$$d = \frac{1}{2}(v_f + v_i)t = \frac{1}{2}(132\text{ m/s} + 88\text{ m/s})(15\text{ s}) = 1.7 \times 10^3\text{ m}$$

Practice Problems

15. A car accelerates at a constant rate from 15 m/s to 25 m/s while it travels 125 m. How long does this motion take?

$$d = \frac{1}{2}(v_f + v_i)t$$

$$\text{so } t = \frac{2d}{(v_f + v_i)}$$

$$= \frac{2(125 \text{ m})}{(25 \text{ m/s} + 15 \text{ m/s})} = 6.3 \text{ s.}$$

16. A bike rider accelerates constantly to a velocity of 7.5 m/s during 4.5 s. The bike's displacement is +19 m. What was the initial velocity of the bike?

$$d = \frac{1}{2}(v_f + v_i)t,$$

$$\text{so } v_i = \frac{2d}{t} - v_f$$

$$= \frac{2(19 \text{ m})}{(4.5 \text{ s}) - 7.5 \text{ m/s}} = 0.9 \text{ m/s}$$

page 74

17. An airplane starts from rest and accelerates at a constant +3.00 m/s^2 for 30.0 s before leaving the ground. What is its displacement during this time?

$$d = v_i t + \frac{1}{2}at^2$$

$$= (0 \text{ m/s})(30.0 \text{ s}) + \frac{1}{2}(3.00 \text{ m/s}^2)(30.0 \text{ s})^2$$

$$= 0 \text{ m} + 1350 \text{ m} = 1.35 \times 10^3 \text{ m}$$

18. Starting from rest, a race car moves 110 m in the first 5.0 s of uniform acceleration. What is the car's acceleration?

Using $d = v_i t + \frac{1}{2}at^2$ with $v_i = 0$,

$$a = \frac{2d}{t^2} = \frac{2(110 \text{ m})}{(5.0 \text{ s})^2} = 8.8 \text{ m/s}^2$$

Practice Problems

19. A driver brings a car traveling at +22 m/s to a full stop in 2.0 s. Assume its acceleration is constant.

a. What is the car's acceleration?

$$a = \frac{(v_1 - v_2)}{(t_2 - t_1)} = \frac{(0 \text{ m/s} - 22 \text{ m/s})}{(2.0 \text{ s})}$$

$$= -11 \text{ m/s}^2$$

b. How far does it travel before stopping?

$$d = v_i t + \frac{1}{2}at^2$$

$$= (22 \text{ m/s})(2.0 \text{ s}) + \frac{1}{2}(-11 \text{ m/s}^2)(2.0 \text{ s})^2$$

$$= 44 \text{ m} - 22 \text{ m}$$

$$= 22 \text{ m}$$

20. A biker passes a lamp post at the crest of a hill at +4.5 m/s. She accelerates down the hill at a rate of +0.40 m/s^2 for 12 s. How far does she move down the hill during this time?

$$d = v_i t + \frac{1}{2}at^2$$

$$= (4.5 \text{ m/s})(12 \text{ s}) + \frac{1}{2}(0.40 \text{ m/s}^2)(12 \text{ s})^2$$

$$= 54 \text{ m} + 29 \text{ m} = 83 \text{ m}$$

page 75

21. An airplane accelerates from a velocity of 21 m/s at the constant rate of 3.0 m/s^2 over a distance of 535 m. What is its final velocity?

$$v_f^2 = v_i^2 + 2ad$$

$$= (21 \text{ m/s})^2 + 2(3.0 \text{ m/s}^2)(535 \text{ m})$$

$$= 3651 \text{ m}^2/\text{s}^2.$$

$$v_f = 60 \text{ m/s.}$$

22. The pilot stops the same plane in 484 m using a constant acceleration of -8.0 m/s^2. How fast was the plane moving before braking began?

$$v_f^2 = v_i^2 + 2ad$$

$$\text{so } v_i^2 = v_f^2 - 2ad$$

$$= (0 \text{ m/s})^2 - 2(-8.0 \text{ m/s}^2)(484 \text{ m})$$

$$= 7744 \text{ m}^2/\text{s}^2,$$

$$v_i = 88 \text{ m/s}$$

Practice Problems

23. A person with shoulder harness can survive a car crash if the acceleration is smaller than $-300\ m/s^2$. Assuming constant acceleration, how far must the front end of the car collapse if it crashes at 101 km/h?

Using $v_f^2 = v_i^2 + 2ad$ with
$v_i = 101$ km/h
$= 28.1$ m/s and $v_f = 0$,

$$d = \frac{(v_f^2 - v_i^2)}{2a} = \frac{((0\ m/s)^2 - (28.1\ m/s)^2)}{2(-300\ m/s^2)}$$

$$= 1.32\ m$$

24. A car is initially sliding backwards down a hill at −25 km/h. The driver guns the car. By the time the car's velocity is +35 km/h, it is +3.2 m from its starting point. Assuming the car was uniformly accelerated, find the acceleration.

Convert speeds to m/s.

$v_i = -6.9$ m/s, $v_f = 9.7$ m/s,

$$d = \frac{(v_f^2 - v_i^2)}{2a},$$

$$\text{so } a = \frac{(v_f^2 - v_i^2)}{2d}$$

$$= \frac{((9.7\ m/s)^2 - (-6.9\ m/s)^2)}{2(3.2\ m)}$$

$$= 7.3\ m/s^2.$$

page 77

25. A brick falls freely from a high scaffold.

a. What is its velocity after 4.0 s?

$v_f = v_i + gt$
$= 0\ m/s + (-9.80\ m/s^2)(4.0\ s)$
$v_i = -39$ m/s (downward)

b. How far does the brick fall during the first 4.0 s?

$$d = v_i t + \frac{1}{2}gt^2$$

$$= 0 + \frac{1}{2}(-9.80\ m/s^2)(4.0\ s)^2$$

$$= \frac{1}{2}(-9.81\ m/s^2)(16\ s^2)$$

$$d = -78\ m \text{ (downward)}$$

Practice Problems

26. Now that you know about acceleration, test your reaction time. Ask a friend to hold a ruler just even with the top of your fingers. Then have your friend drop the ruler. Taking the number of centimeters that the ruler falls before you can catch it, calculate your reaction time. An average of several trials will give more accurate results. The reaction time for most people is more than 0.15 seconds.

Using $d = \frac{1}{2}gt^2$ the reaction time can be calculated from $t = \sqrt{\frac{2d}{g}}$

page 79

27. If you drop a golf ball, how far does it fall in $\frac{1}{2}$ s?

$$d = v_i t + \frac{1}{2}gt^2 = 0 + \frac{1}{2}(-9.80\ m/s^2)(0.50\ s)^2$$

$$= -1.2\ m.$$

28. A spacecraft traveling at a velocity of +1210 m/s is uniformly accelerated at $-150\ m/s^2$. If the acceleration lasts for 8.68 seconds, what is the final velocity of the craft? Explain your results in words.

$v_f = v_i + at = 1210\ m/s + (-150\ m/s^2)(8.68\ s)$
$= 1210\ m/s - 1300\ m/s$
$= -90\ m/s$

Spacecraft slows to a stop then reverses motion.

29. A man falls 1.0 m to the floor.

a. How long does the fall take?

Using $d = v_i t + \frac{1}{2}gt^2$ with $v_i = 0$,

$$t = \sqrt{\frac{2d}{g}} = \sqrt{\frac{2(-1.0\ m)}{(-9.80\ m/s^2)}} = 0.45\ s$$

b. How fast is he going when he hits the floor?

$v_f = v_i + gt = 0\ m/s + (-9.80\ m/s^2)(0.45\ s)$
$= -4.4\ m/s$

Practice Problems

30. On wet pavement a car can be accelerated with a maximum acceleration $a = 0.20g$ before its tires slip.

a. Starting from rest, how fast is it moving after 2.0 seconds?

$v_i = 0$ m/s,
so $v_f = at = (0.2)(9.80 \text{ m/s}^2)(2.0 \text{ s})$
$= 3.9$ m/s

b. How far has it moved after 4.0 seconds?

$$d = \frac{1}{2}at^2 = \frac{1}{2}(0.2)(9.8 \text{ m/s}^2)(4.0 \text{ s})^2 = 16 \text{ m}.$$

page 80

31. A pitcher throws a baseball straight up with an initial speed of 27 m/s.

a. How long does it take the ball to reach its highest point?

Since $v_f = 0$ at high point, $v_f = v_i + gt$

becomes $t = \frac{-v_i}{g} = \frac{-(27 \text{ m/s})}{(-9.80 \text{ m/s}^2)} = 2.8$ s

b. How high does the ball rise above its release point?

$$d = v_i t + \frac{1}{2}gt^2$$

$$= (27 \text{ m/s})(2.8 \text{ s}) + \frac{1}{2}(-9.80 \text{ m/s}^2)(2.8 \text{ s})^2$$

$$= 75.6 \text{ m} - 38.4 \text{ m} = 37 \text{ m}$$

32. A motor of a certain elevator gives it a constant upward acceleration of 46 m/min/s. The elevator starts from rest, accelerates for 2.0 s, then continues with constant speed.

a. Explain what this statement of acceleration means

$a = 46$ m/min/s can be interpreted as a speed change of either 46 m/min each second or 46 m/s each minute.

Practice Problems

b. What is the final speed after 2 s?

$v_f = v_i + at$
$= 0 \text{ m/min} + (46 \text{ m/min/s})(2.0 \text{ s})$
$= 92$ m/min

c. Calculate speed after 0.5, 1.0, 1.5, 2.0, 3.0, 4.0, and 5.0 s. Sketch graph showing speed vs time.

Speeds before 2.0 s are given by $v_f = at$; speeds after are 92 m/min

t(s)	v_f(m/min)
0.5	23
1.0	46
1.5	69
2.0	92
3.0	92
4.0	92
5.0	92

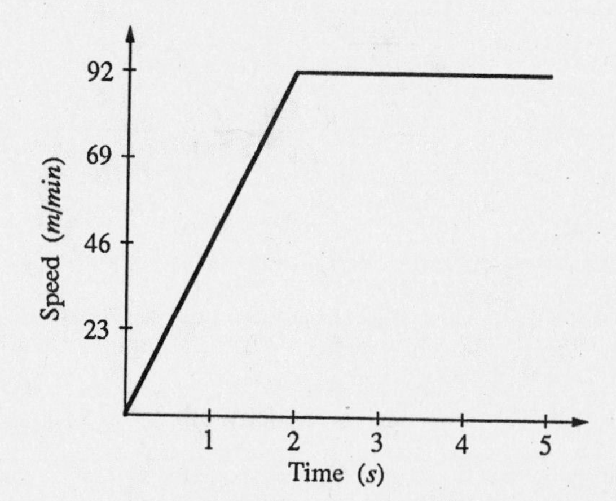

Practice Problems

d. How far has it risen 1.0, 2.0, 3.0, 4.0, and 5.0 s after start? Sketch graph.

For first 2 seconds $d = \frac{1}{2}at^2$ where

a = (46 m/min/s)(1 min/60 s)
= 0.767 m/s^2
and after 2 seconds it continues to rise (92 m/min)(1/60 min) = 1.5 m each second

t(s)	d(m)
1.0	0.4
2.0	1.5
3.0	3.0
4.0	4.5
5.0	6.0

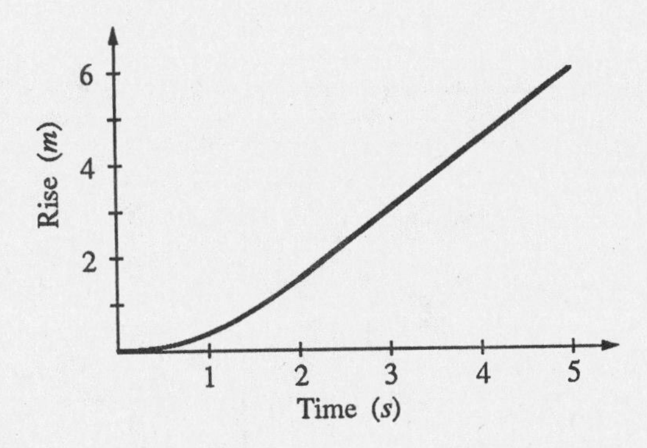

Chapter Review Problems

pages 105–107

1. Find the uniform acceleration that causes a car's velocity to change from 32 m/s to 96 m/s in an 8.0–s period.

$$a = \frac{\Delta v}{\Delta t} = \frac{v_2 - v_1}{\Delta t} = \frac{96 \text{ m/s} - 32 \text{ m/s}}{8.0 \text{ s}} = 8.0 \text{ m/s}^2$$

Chapter Review Problems

2. Rocket–powered sleds are used to test the responses of humans to acceleration. Starting from rest, one sled can reach a speed of 444 m/s in 1.80 s and can be brought to a stop again in 2.15 s.

a. Calculate the acceleration of the sled when starting and compare it to the acceleration due to gravity, 9.80 m/s^2.

$$a = \frac{\Delta v}{\Delta t} = \frac{v_2 - v_1}{\Delta t} = \frac{444 \text{ m/s} - 0}{1.80 \text{ s}}$$

$$= 247 \text{ m/s}^2$$

$$\frac{247 \text{ m/s}^2}{9.80 \text{ m/s}^2} = 25.2$$

b. Find the acceleration of the sled when braking and compare it to the magnitude of the acceleration due to gravity.

$$a = \frac{\Delta v}{\Delta t} = \frac{v_2 - v_1}{\Delta t} = \frac{0 - 444 \text{ m/s}}{2.15 \text{ s}} = -207 \text{ m/s}^2$$

$$\frac{207 \text{ m/s}^2}{9.80 \text{ m/s}^2} = 21.1$$

3. Use Figure 4–18 to find the acceleration of the moving object

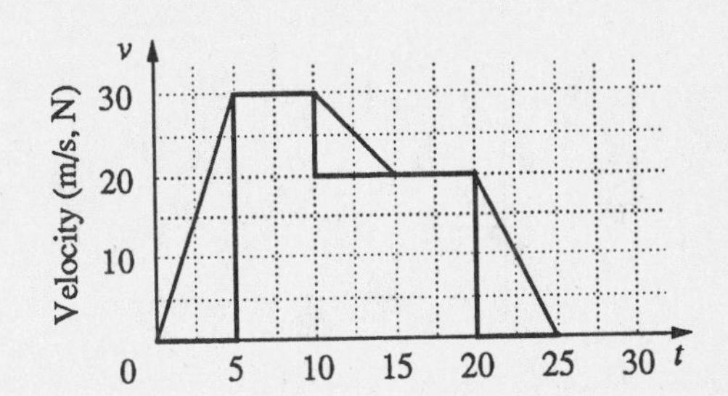

a. during the first five seconds of travel.

$$a = \frac{\Delta v}{\Delta t} = \frac{30 \text{ m/s} - 0 \text{ m/s}}{5 \text{ m/s}} = 6 \text{ m/s}^2$$

b. between the fifth and the tenth second of travel.

$$a = \frac{\Delta v}{\Delta t} = \frac{30 \text{ m/s} - 30 \text{ m/s}}{5 \text{ s}} = 0$$

c. between the tenth and the fifteenth second of travel.

$$a = \frac{\Delta v}{\Delta t} = \frac{20\ \text{m/s} - 30\ \text{m/s}}{5\ \text{s}} = -2\ \text{m/s}^2$$

d. between the twentieth and twenty–fifty second of travel.

$$a = \frac{\Delta v}{\Delta t} = \frac{0 - 20\ \text{m/s}}{5\ \text{s}} = -4\ \text{m/s}^2$$

4. To accompany each of the graphs in Figure 4–19, draw

a. a velocity–time graph.

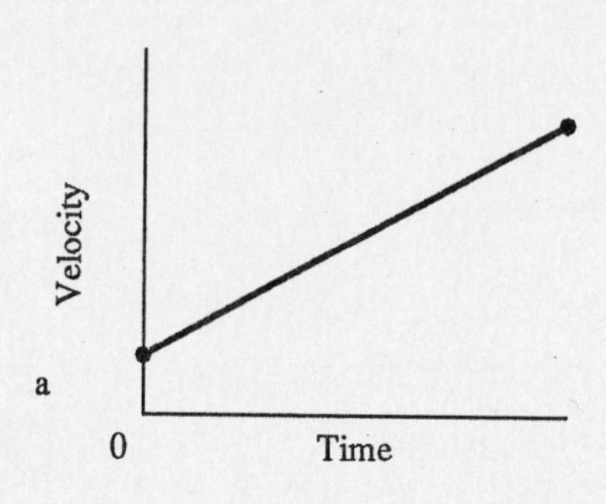

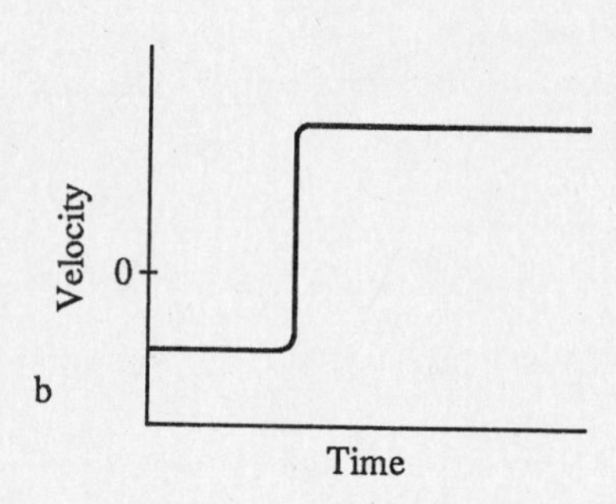

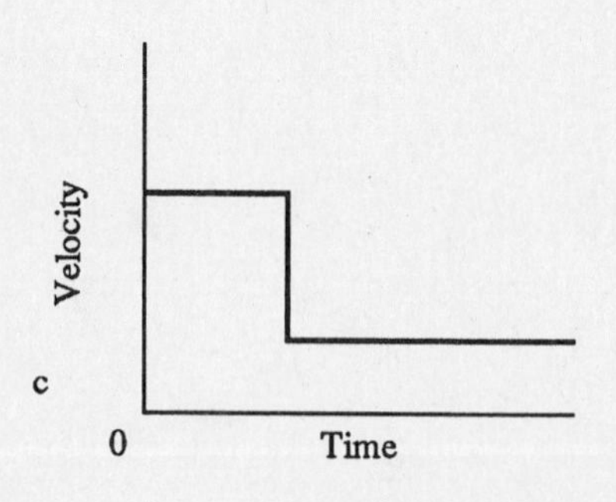

Chapter Review Problems

b. an acceleration–time graph.

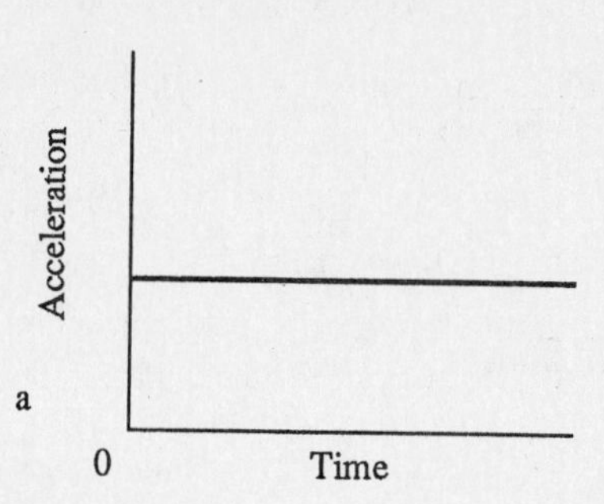

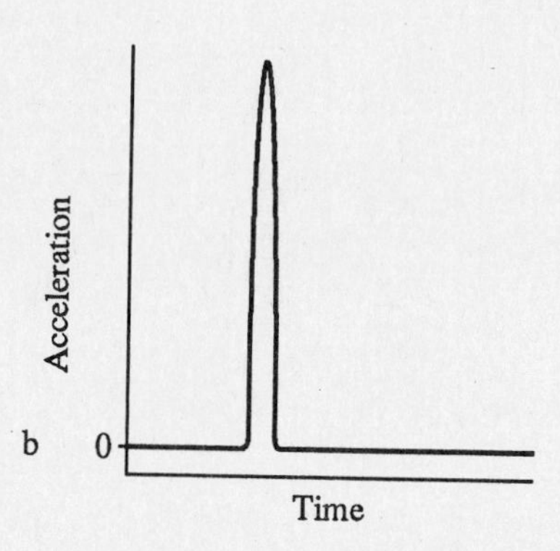

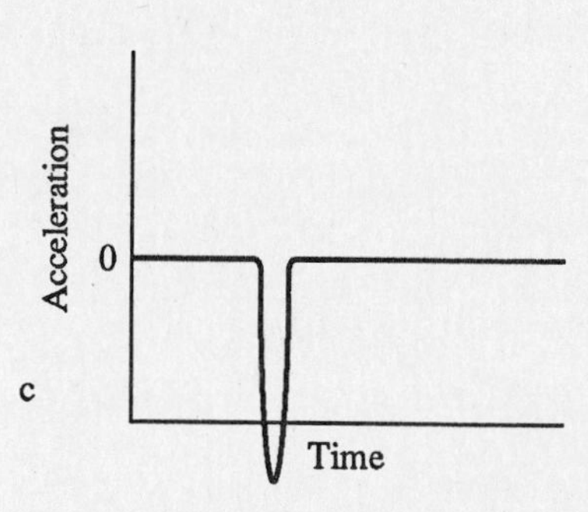

5. A car with a velocity of 22 m/s is accelerated uniformly at the rate of 1.6 m/s² for 6.8 s. What is its final velocity?

$$v_f = v_i + at = 22\ \text{m/s} + (1.6\ \text{m/s}^2)(6.8\ \text{s}) = 33\ \text{m/s}$$

6. The velocity of an automobile changes over an 8.0–s time period as shown in Table 4–3.

Time (s)	Velocity (m/s)	Time (s)	Velocity (m/s)
0.0	0.0	5.0	20.0
1.0	4.0	6.0	20.0
2.0	8.0	7.0	20.0
3.0	12.0	8.0	20.0
4.0	16.0		

a. Plot the velocity–time graph of the motion.

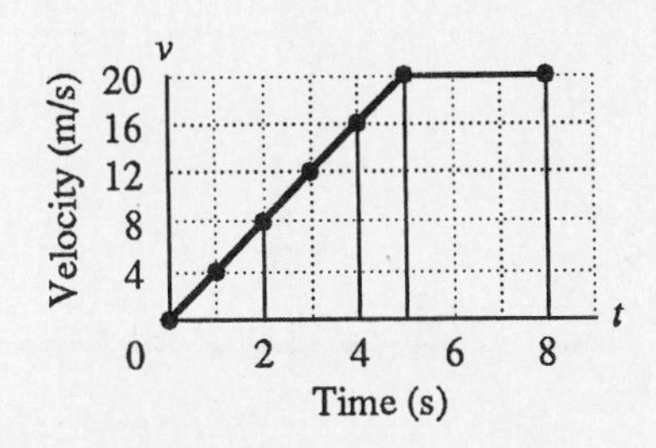

b. Determine the displacement of the car during the first 2.0 s.

$$d = \frac{1}{2}bh = \frac{1}{2}(2.0 \text{ s})(8.0 \text{ m/s} - 0) = 8.0 \text{ m}$$

c. What displacement does the car have during the first 4.0 s?

$$d = \frac{1}{2}bh = \frac{1}{2}(4.0 \text{ s})(16.0 \text{ m/s} - 0) = 32 \text{ m}$$

d. What displacement does the car have during the entire 8.0 s?

$$d = \frac{1}{2}bh + bh$$

$$= \frac{1}{2}(5.0 \text{ s})(20.0 \text{ m/s} - 0)$$

$$+ (8.0 \text{ s} - 5.0 \text{ s})(20.0 \text{ m/s}) = 110 \text{ m}$$

e. Find the slope of the line between t = 0 s and t = 4.0 s. What does this slope represent?

$$a = \frac{\Delta v}{\Delta t} = \frac{16 \text{ m/s} - 0 \text{ m/s}}{4 \text{ s} - 0 \text{ s}}$$

$$= 4 \text{ m/s}^2 \text{ acceleration}$$

Chapter Review Problems

f. Find the slope of the line between t = 5.0 s and t = 7.0 s. What does this slope indicate?

$$a = \frac{\Delta v}{\Delta t} = \frac{20 \text{ m/s} - 20 \text{ m/s}}{7 \text{ s} - 5 \text{ s}}$$

$$= 0 \text{ constant velocity}$$

7. Figure 4–20 shows the position–time and velocity–time graphs of a karate expert using a fist to break wooden boards.

a. Use the velocity–time graph to describe the motion of the expert's fist during the first 10 ms.

The fist moves downward at about –13 m/s for about 5 ms. It then suddenly comes to a halt (accelerates).

b. Estimate the slope of the velocity–time graph to determine the acceleration of the fist when it suddenly stops.

$$a = \frac{\Delta v}{\Delta t} = \frac{0 - (-13 \text{ m/s})}{7.5 \text{ ms} - 5.0 \text{ ms}}$$

$$= 5.2 \times 10^3 \text{ m/s}^2$$

c. Express the acceleration as a multiple of the gravitational acceleration, g = 9.80 m/s^2.

$$\frac{5.2 \times 10^3 \text{ m/s}^2}{9.80 \text{ m/s}^2} = 5.3 \times 10^2$$

the acceleration is about 530 g

d. Determine the area under the velocity–time curve to find the displacement of the fist in the first 6 ms. Compare with the position–time graph.

The area is almost rectangular:

(–13 m/s)(0.006 s) = –8 cm. This is in agreement with the position–time graph where the hand moves from +8 cm to 0 cm, for a net displacement of –8 cm.

Chapter Review Problems

8. A supersonic jet that is flying at 145 m/s is accelerated uniformly at the rate of 23.1 m/s² for 20.0 s.

a. What is its final velocity?

$$v_f = v_i + at$$
$$= 145 \text{ m/s} + (23.1 \text{ m/s}^2)(20.0 \text{ s})$$
$$= 607 \text{ m/s}$$

b. The speed of sound in air is 331 m/s. How many times the speed of sound is the plane's final speed?

$$N = \frac{607 \text{ m/s}}{331 \text{ m/s}}$$
$$= 1.83 \text{ times the speed of sound}$$

9. Determine the final velocity of a proton that has an initial velocity of 2.35×10^5 m/s and then is accelerated uniformly in an electric field at the rate of -1.10×10^{12} m/s² for 1.50×10^{-7} s.

$$v_f = v_i + at$$
$$= 2.35 \times 10^5 \text{ m/s}$$
$$+ (-1.10 \times 10^{12} \text{ m/s}^2)(1.50 \times 10^{-7} \text{ s})$$
$$= 2.35 \times 10^5 \text{ m/s} - 1.65 \times 10^5 \text{ m/s}$$
$$= 7.0 \times 10^4 \text{ m/s}$$

10. Determine the displacement of a plane that is uniformly accelerated from 66 m/s to 88 m/s in 12 s.

$$d = \frac{(v_f + v_i)t}{2} = \frac{(88 \text{ m/s} + 66 \text{ m/s})(12 \text{ s})}{2}$$
$$= 9.2 \times 10^2 \text{ m}$$

11. How far does a plane fly in 15 s while its velocity is changing from +145 m/s to +75 m/s at a uniform rate of acceleration?

$$d = \frac{(v_f + v_i)t}{2} = \frac{(75 \text{ m/s} + 145 \text{ m/s})(15 \text{ s})}{2}$$
$$= 1.7 \times 10^3 \text{ m}$$

12. A car moves at 12 m/s and coasts up a hill with a uniform acceleration of −1.6 m/s².

a. How far has the car traveled after 6.0 s?

$$d = v_i t + \frac{1}{2}at^2$$
$$= (12 \text{ m/s})(6.0 \text{ s}) + \frac{1}{2}(-1.6 \text{ m/s}^2)(6.0 \text{ s})^2$$
$$= 43 \text{ m}$$

b. How far has it gone after 9.0 s?

$$d = v_i t + \frac{1}{2}at^2$$
$$= (12 \text{ m/s})(9.0 \text{ s}) + \frac{1}{2}(-1.6 \text{ m/s}^2)(6.0 \text{ s})^2$$
$$= 43 \text{ m}$$

the car is on the way back down the hill.

13. Four cars start from rest. Car A accelerates at 6.0 m/s²; car B at 5.4 m/s²; car C at 8.0 m/s², and car D at 12 m/s².

a. In the first column of a table, show the velocity of each car at the end of 2.0 s.

b. In the second column, show the displacement of each car travels during the same 2.0 s.

c. What conclusions do you reach about the velocity attained and the displacement of a body starting from rest at the end of the first 2.0 s of acceleration?

Tables should indicate that, for a body accelerating uniformly from rest, displacement traveled and velocity attained are numerically the same at the end of two seconds.

Car	Velocity (m/s)	Displacement (m)
A	12	12
B	11	11
C	16	16
D	24	24

Chapter Review Problems

14. An astronaut drops a feather from 1.2 m above the surface of the moon. If the acceleration of gravity on the moon is 1.62 m/s², how long does it take the feather to hit the surface?

$$d = v_i t + \frac{1}{2}at^2$$

$$t = \sqrt{\frac{2d}{g}} = \sqrt{\frac{(2)(-1.2\ \text{m})(6)}{(-9.8\ \text{m/s}^2)}} = 1.2\ \text{s}$$

15. Table 4–4 is a table of the displacements and velocities of a ball at the end of each second for the first 5.0 s of free-fall from rest.

Table 4–4

Time (s)	Displacement (m)	Velocity (m/s)
0.0	0.0	0.0
1.0	–4.9	–9.8
2.0	–19.6	–19.6
3.0	–44.1	–29.4
4.0	–78.4	–39.2
5.0	–122.5	–49.0

a. Use the data in the table to plot a velocity–time graph.

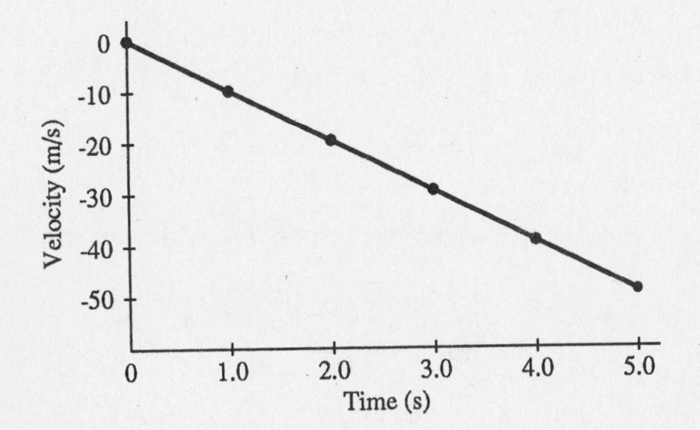

b. Use the data in the table to plot a position–time graph.

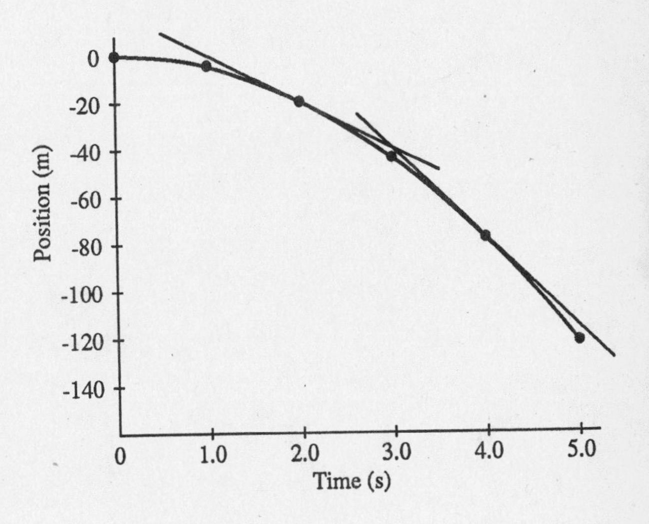

c. Find the slope of the curve at the end of 2.0 and 4.0 s on the position–time graph. What are the approximate slopes? Do these values agree with the table of velocity?

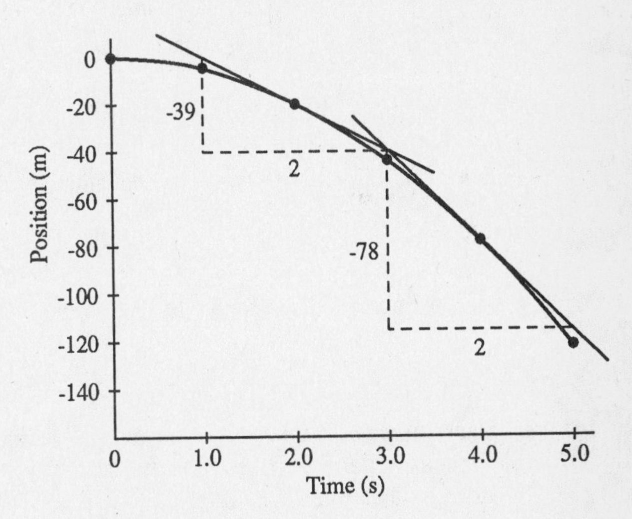

At t = 2.0 s,

$$\text{slope} = \frac{-40\ \text{m} - (-1\ \text{m})}{3.0\ \text{s} - 1.0\ \text{s}} = -20\ \text{m/s}$$

At t= 4.0 s,

$$\text{slope} = \frac{-118\ \text{m} - (-40\ \text{m})}{5.0\ \text{s} - 3.0\ \text{s}} = -39\ \text{m/s}$$

Yes, the values agree.

d. Use the data in the table to plot a position versus time–squared graph. What type of curve is obtained?

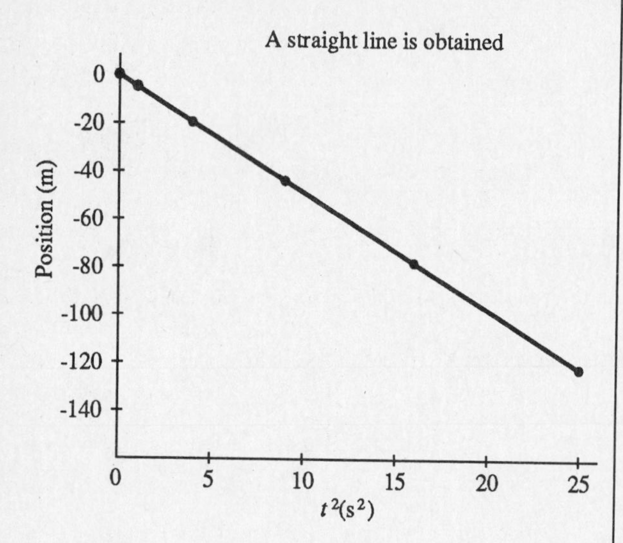

e. Find the slope of the line at any point. Explain the significance of the value you obtain.

$$\text{slope} = \frac{-122.5\text{ m} - 0}{25\text{ s}^2 - 0} = -4.9\text{ m/s}^2$$

The slope is $\frac{1}{2}g$.

f. Does this curve agree with the equation $d = \frac{1}{2}gt^2$?

Yes. Since it is a straight line $y = mx + b$ where y is d, m is $\frac{1}{2}g$, x is t^2 and b is 0.

16. A plane travels 5.0×10^2 m while being accelerated uniformly from rest at the rate of 5.0 m/s². What final velocity does it attain?

$$v_f^2 = v_i^2 + 2ad$$

$$v_f = \sqrt{v_i^2 + 2ad}$$

$$= \sqrt{0 + 2(5.0\text{ m/s}^2)(5.0 \times 10^2\text{ m})} = 71\text{ m/s}$$

Chapter Review Problems

17. A race car can be slowed with a constant acceleration of −11 m/s².

a. If the car is going 55 m/s, how many meters will it take to stop?

$$v_f^2 = v_i^2 + 2ad$$

$$d = \frac{v_f^2 - v_i^2}{2a} = \frac{0 - (+55\text{ m/s})^2}{(2)(-11\text{ m/s}^2)} = 1.4 \times 10^2\text{ m}$$

b. Repeat for a car going 110 m/s.

$$d = \frac{v_f^2 - v_i^2}{2a} = \frac{0 - (110\text{ m/s})^2}{(2)(-11\text{ m/s}^2)} = 5.5 \times 10^2\text{ m}$$

18. An engineer must design a runway to accommodate airplanes that must reach a ground velocity of 61 m/s before they can take off. These planes are capable of being accelerated uniformly at the rate of 2.5 m/s².

a. How long will it take the planes to reach takeoff speed?

$$v_f = v_i + at,$$

$$\text{so } t = \frac{v_f - v_i}{a} = \frac{61\text{ m/s} - 0}{2.5\text{ m/s}^2} = 24\text{ s}$$

b. What must be the minimum length of the runway?

$$v_f^2 = v_i^2 + 2ad,$$

$$\text{so } d = \frac{v_f^2 - v_i^2}{2a}$$

$$= \frac{(61\text{ m/s})^2 - 0}{2(2.5\text{ m/s}^2)} = 7.4 \times 10^2\text{ m}$$

19. A rocket traveling at 155 m/s is accelerated at a rate of −31.0 m/s².

a. How long will it take before the instantaneous speed is 0 m/s?

$$v_f = v_i + at$$

$$t = \frac{v_f - v_i}{a} = \frac{0 - (+155\text{ m/s})}{-31.0\text{ m/s}^2} = 5.00\text{ s}$$

Chapter Review Problems

b. How far will it travel during this time?

$$d = v_i t + \frac{1}{2}at^2$$
$$= (+155 \text{ m/s})(5.00 \text{ s}) + \frac{1}{2}(-31.0 \text{ m/s})(5.00 \text{ s})^2$$
$$= 388 \text{ m}$$

c. What will be its velocity after 8.00 s?

$$v_f = v_i + at$$
$$= (+155 \text{ m/s}) + (-31.0 \text{ m/s}^2)(8.00 \text{ s})$$
$$= -93 \text{ m/s}$$

The rocket is moving in a direction opposite to its original direction.

20. Engineers are developing new types of guns that might someday be used to launch satellites as if they were bullets. One such gun can give a small object a velocity of 3.5 km/s moving it through only 2.0 cm.

a. What acceleration does the gun give this object?

$$v_f^2 = v_i^2 + 2ad, \text{ or } v_f^2 = 2ad$$

$$a = \frac{v_f^2}{2d} = \frac{(3.5 \times 10^3 \text{ m/s})^2}{2(0.020 \text{ m})} = 3.1 \times 10^8 \text{ m/s}^2$$

b. Over what time interval does the acceleration take place?

$$d = \frac{(v_f + v_i)t}{2}$$

$$t = \frac{2d}{(v_f + v_i)} = \frac{2(2.0 \times 10^{-2} \text{ m})}{(3.5 \times 10^3 \text{ m/s} + 0)}$$
$$= 11 \times 10^{-6} \text{ s}$$
$$= 11 \text{ microseconds}$$

21. An express train, traveling at 36.0 m/s, is accidentally sidetracked onto a local train track. The express engineer spots a local train exactly 1.00×10^2 m ahead on the same track and traveling in the same direction. The engineer jams on the brakes and slows the express at a constant rate of -3.00 m/s^2. The local engineer is unaware of the situation. If the speed of the local is 11.0 m/s, will the express be able to stop in time or will there be a collision? To solve this problem take the position of the express when it first sights the local as a point of origin. Next, keeping in mind that the local has exactly a 1.00×10^2 m lead, calculate how far each train is from the origin at the end of the 12.0 s it would take the express to stop.

a. On the basis of your calculations, would you conclude that there is or is not a collision?

$$d_{\text{Express}} = v_i t + \frac{1}{2}at^2$$
$$= (36.0 \text{ m/s})(12.0 \text{ s}) + \frac{1}{2}(-3.00 \text{ m/s}^2)(12.0 \text{ s})^2$$
$$= 432 \text{ m} - 216 \text{ m} = 216 \text{ m}$$
$$d_{\text{Local}} = 100 \text{ m} + v_i t + \frac{1}{2}at^2$$
$$= 100 \text{ m} + (11.0 \text{ m/s})(12.0 \text{ s}) + 0$$
$$= 100 \text{ m} + 132 \text{ m} = 232 \text{ m}$$

On this basis no collision will occur.

b. The calculations you made in part **a** do not allow for the possibility that a collision might take place before the end of the twelve seconds required for the express to come to a halt. To check on this, take the position of the express when it first sights the local as the point of origin and calculate the position of each train at the end of each second after sighting. Make a table showing the distance of each train from the origin at the end of each second. Plot these positions on the same graph and draw two lines.

t (s)	d(Local) (m)	d(Express) (m)
1	111	35
2	122	66
3	133	95
4	144	120
5	155	143
6	166	162
7	177	179
8	188	192
9	199	203
10	210	210
11	221	215
12	232	216

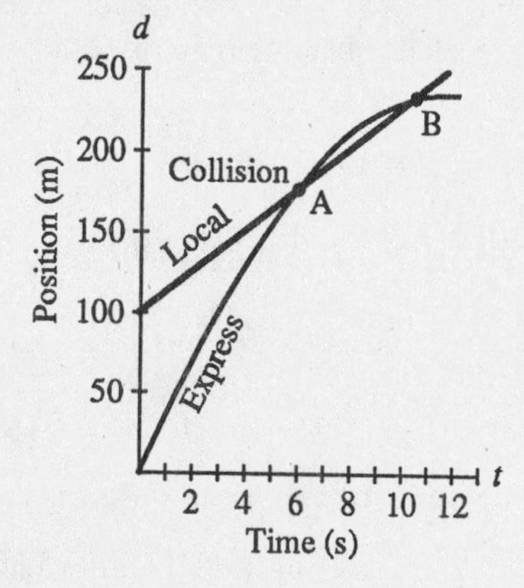

c. Use your graph to check your answer to part a.

The collision occurs at point A (not B).

22. Highway safety engineers build soft barriers so that cars hitting them will slow down at a safe rate. A person wearing a safety belt can withstand an acceleration of –300 m/s². How thick should barriers be to safely stop a car that hits a barrier at 110 km/h?

$$v_i = \frac{(110\text{ km/h})(1000\text{ m/km})}{3600\text{ s/h}} = 31\text{ m/s}$$

$v_f^2 = v_i^2 + 2ad$ with $v_f = 0$, $v_i^2 = -2\,ad$, or

$$d = \frac{-v_i^2}{2a} = \frac{-(31\text{ m/s})^2}{2(-300\text{ m/s}^2)} = 1.6\text{ m thick}$$

Chapter Review Problems

23. A baseball pitcher throws a fastball at a speed of 44 m/s. The acceleration occurs as the pitcher holds the ball in his hand and moves it through an almost straight–line distance of 3.5 m. Calculate the acceleration, assuming it is uniform. Compare the acceleration to the acceleration due to gravity, 9.80 m/s².

$$v_f^2 = v_i^2 + 2ad$$

$$a = \frac{v_f^2 - v_i^2}{2d}$$

$$= \frac{(44\text{ m/s})^2 - 0}{2(3.5\text{ m})} = 2.8 \times 10^2\text{ m/s}^2,$$

$$\frac{2.8 \times 10^2\text{ m/s}^2}{9.80\text{ m/s}^2} = 29,\text{ or } 29\text{ times } g$$

24. If a bullet leaves the muzzle of a rifle with a speed of 600 m/s, and the barrel of the rifle is 0.9 m long, what is the acceleration of the bullet while in the barrel?

$$v_f^2 = v_i^2 + 2ad$$

$$a = \frac{v_f^2 - v_i^2}{2d} = \frac{(600\text{ m/s})^2 - 0}{(2)(0.9\text{ m})}$$

$$= \frac{3.6 \times 10^5\text{ m}^2/\text{s}^2}{1.8\text{ m}}$$

$$= 2 \times 10^5\text{ m/s}^2$$

25. A driver of a car going 90.0 km/h suddenly sees the lights of a barrier 40.0 m ahead. It takes the driver 0.75 s before he applies the brakes, and the average acceleration during braking is –10.0 m/s².

a. Determine if the car hits the barrier.

$$v_i = \frac{(90.0\text{ km/h})(1000\text{ m/km})}{(3600\text{ s/h})} = 25.0\text{ m/s}$$

$$v_f = v_i + at$$

$$t = \frac{v_f - v_i}{a} = \frac{0 - (25.0\text{ m/s})}{-10.0\text{ m/s}^2} = 2.50\text{ s}$$

The car will travel

$d. = vt = (25.0\text{ m/s})(0.75\text{ s})$

$= 18.75\text{ m} = 19\text{ m}$

before the driver applies the brakes. The total distance the car must travel to stop is

$$d = 19\text{ m} + v_i t + \frac{1}{2}at^2$$

$$= 19\text{ m} + (25.0\text{ m/s})(2.50\text{ s}) + \frac{1}{2}(-10.0\text{ m/s}^2)(2.50\text{ s})^2$$

$= 50$ m, yes it hits the barrier.

b. What is the maximum speed at which the car could be moving and not hit the barrier 40.0 m ahead? Assume the acceleration rate doesn't change. Hint: The displacement at constant speed plus the displacement while decelerating equals the total displacement.

$d_{total} = d_{constant\ v} + d_{decelerating} = 40.0$ m

$d_c = vt = (0.75\ s)v$

$$d_d = \frac{-v^2}{2a} = \frac{-v^2}{2(-10.0\ m/s^2)} = \frac{v^2}{20.0\ m/s^2}$$

$$40\ m = (0.75\ s)v + \frac{v^2}{20.0\ m/s^2}$$

$v^2 + 15v - 800 = 0$

Using the quadratic equation:

$v = 22$ m/s (The sense of the problem excludes the negative value.)

26. Data in Table 4–5, taken from a driver's handbook, show the distance a car travels when it brakes to a halt from a specific initial velocity.

Initial Velocity (m/s)	Braking distance (m)
11	10
15	20
20	34
25	50
29	70

a. Plot the braking distance versus the initial velocity. Describe the shape of the curve you obtain.

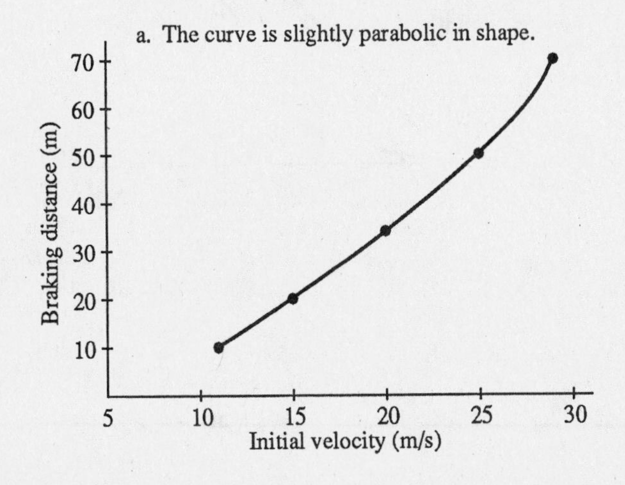

b. Plot the braking distance versus the square of the initial velocity. Describe the shape of the curve you obtain.

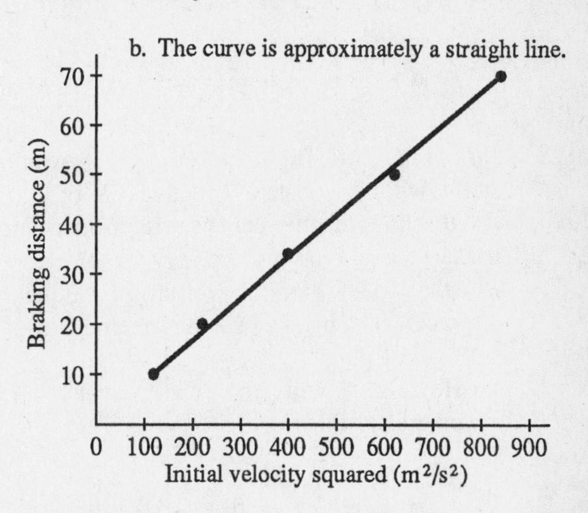

c. Calculate the slope of your graph from part **b.** Find the value and units of the quantity 1/slope of the curve.

$$\text{slope} = \frac{70\ m - 10\ m}{(29\ m/s)^2 - (11\ m/s)^2}$$

$$= 0.083\ s^2/m$$

$$\frac{1}{\text{slope}} = 12\ m/s^2$$

d. Does this curve agree with the equation $v_i^2 = -2ad$? What is the value of a?

yes, -6 m/s^2

27. A car moving with a constant acceleration covers the distance between two points 60 m apart in 6.0 s. Its velocity as it passes the second point is 15 m/s.

a. What was the speed at the first point?

$$d = \left[\frac{v_i + v}{2}\right]t, \text{ so } v_i + v = \frac{2d}{t}, \text{ and}$$

$$v_i = \frac{2d}{t} - v = \frac{2(60\ m)}{6.0\ s} - 15\ m/s = 5\ m/s$$

b. What is the constant acceleration?

$$a = \frac{\Delta v}{t} = \frac{v - v_i}{t} = \frac{15\ m/s - 5\ m/s}{6.0\ s} = 1.7\ m/s^2$$

c. How far behind the first point was the car at rest?

$v^2 = v_i^2 + 2ad,$

$$\text{so } d = \frac{v^2 - v_i^2}{2a} = \frac{(5\ \text{m/s})^2 - 0}{2(1.7\ \text{m/s}^2)} = 7.5\ \text{m}$$

28. Just as a traffic light turns green, a waiting car starts with a constant acceleration of 6.0 m/s². At the instant the car begins to accelerate, a truck with a constant velocity of 21 m/s passes in the next lane. Hint: Equate the displacements in the two displacement equations.

a. How far will the car travel before it overtakes the truck?

$$d_{car} = v_i t + \frac{1}{2}at^2 = 0 + \frac{1}{2}(6.0\ \text{m/s}^2)t^2$$

$$= 3.0\ t^2\ \text{m/s}^2$$

$$d_{truck} = v_i t + \frac{1}{2}at^2 = (21\ \text{m/s})t$$

$d_{car} = d_{truck}$, when the truck overtakes the car
$3.0\ t^2\ \text{m/s}^2 = (21\ \text{m/s})t$
$t = 7.0\ \text{s}$
$d_{car} = (3.0\ \text{m/s}^2)(7.0\ \text{s})^2 = 1.5 \times 10^2\ \text{m}$

b. How fast will the car be traveling when it overtakes the truck?

$$v_f = v_i + at = 0 + (6.0\ \text{m/s}^2)(7.0\ \text{s}) = 42\ \text{m/s}$$

Chapter Review Problems

page 15

29. Use the information from the previous problem.

a. Draw velocity–time and position–time graphs for the car and truck.

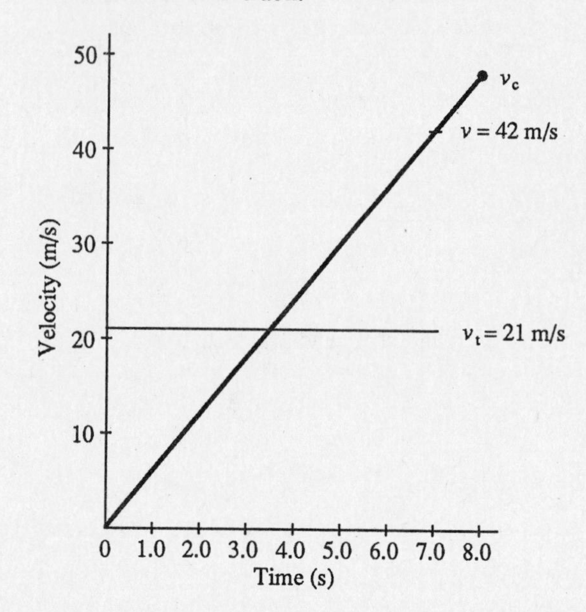

b. Do the graphs confirm the answer you calculated for the exercise?

b. The graphs confirm the calculated answer.

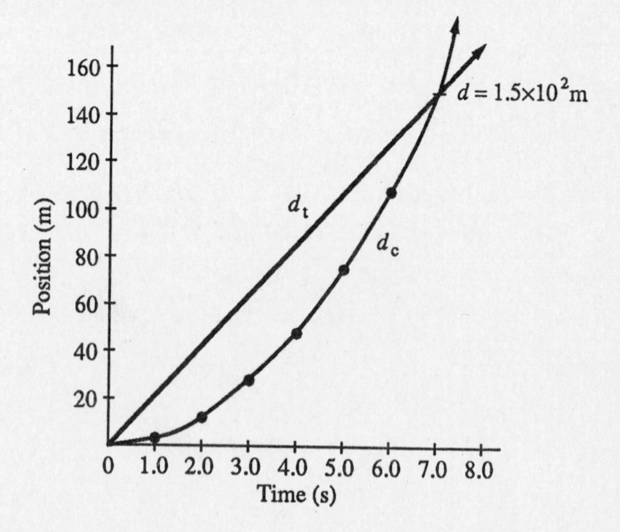

Yes

30. A stone falls from rest for 8.0 s.

a. Calculate the stone's velocity after 8.0 s.

$$v_f = v_i + gt = 0 + (-9.8\ \text{m/s}^2)(8.0\ \text{s}) = -78\ \text{m/s (downward)}$$

b. What is the stone's displacement during this time?

$d = v_i t + \frac{1}{2}gt^2 = 0 + \frac{1}{2}(-9.8\ m/s^2)(8.0\ s)^2$

$= -3.1 \times 10^2\ m$

31. A student drops a rock from a bridge to the water 12.0 m below. With what speed does the rock strike the water?

$v_f^2 = v_i^2 + 2gd$

$v_f = \sqrt{v_i^2 + 2gd}$

$= \sqrt{0 + (2)(-9.80\ m/s^2)(-12.0\ m)}$

$= \sqrt{235.2\ m^2/s^2} = 15.3\ m/s$

32. Kyle is flying a helicopter when he drops a bag. When the bag has fallen 2.0 s,

a. What is the bag's velocity?

$v_f = v_i + gt = 0 + (-9.80\ m/s^2)(2.0\ s)$
$= -20\ m/s$

b. How far has the bag fallen?

$d = v_i t + \frac{1}{2}gt^2 = 0 + \frac{1}{2}(-9.80\ m/s^2)(2.0\ s)^2$

$= -20\ m$

33. Kyle is flying the same helicopter and it is rising at 5.0 m/s when he releases the bag. After 2.0 s,

a. What is the bag's velocity?

$v_f = v_i + gt = 5.0\ m/s + (-9.80\ m/s)(2.0\ s)$
$= -15.\ m/s$

b. How far has the bag fallen?

$d = v_i t + \frac{1}{2}gt^2$

$= (5.0\ m/s)(2.0\ s)$

$+ \frac{1}{2}(-9.80\ m/s)(2.0\ s)^2$

$= -10\ m$

Chapter Review Problems

c. How far below the helicopter is the bag?

The helicopter has risen
$d = v_i t = (5.0\ m/s)(2.0) = 10\ m$
The bag is 10 m below the origin and 20 m below the helicopter.

34. Now Kyle's helicopter is falling at 5.0 m/s as he releases the bag. After 2.0 s,

a. What is the bag's velocity?

$v_f = v_i + gt$
$= -5.0\ m/s + (-9.80\ m/s^2)(2.0\ s)$
$= 25\ m/s$

b. How far has the bag fallen?

$d = v_i t + \frac{1}{2}gt^2$

$= (-5.0\ m/s)(2.0) + \frac{1}{2}(-9.80\ m/s^2)(2.0\ s)^2$

$= -30\ m$

c. How far below the helicopter is the bag?

The helicopter has fallen
$d = vt = (-5.0\ m/s)(2.0\ s) = -10\ m$ and the bag is 20 m below the helicopter.

d. What is common to the three answers above?

The bag is 20 m below the helicopter after 2.0 s.

35. A weather balloon is floating at a constant height above Earth when it releases a pack of instruments.

a. If the pack hits the ground with a velocity of –73.5 m/s, how far does the pack fall?

$v_f^2 = v_i^2 + 2gd$

$d = \frac{v_f^2 - v_i^2}{2g} = \frac{(-73.5\ m/s)^2 - 0}{(2)(-9.80\ m/s^2)}$

$= \frac{5402\ m^2/s^2}{-19.6\ m/s^2} = -276\ m$

b. How long does the pack fall?

$v_f = v_i + gt$

$t = \frac{v_f - v_i}{g} = \frac{-73.5\ \text{m/s} - 0}{-9.80\ \text{m/s}^2} = 7.50\ \text{s}$

36. During a baseball game, a batter hits a high pop-up. If the ball remains in the air for 6.0 s, how high does it rise? Hint: Calculate the height using the second half of the trajectory.

Let the time be 3.0 s

$d = v_i t + \frac{1}{2}gt^2$

$= 0 + \frac{1}{2}(-9.8\ \text{m/s}^2)(3.0\ \text{s})^2 = -44\ \text{m}$

The ball rises 44 m, the same distance it falls.

37. A tennis ball is dropped from 1.20 m above the ground. It rebounds to a height of 1.00 m.

a. With what velocity does it hit the ground?

Using $v_f^2 = v_i^2 + 2gd$,
$v_f^2 = 2gd$
$= 2(-9.80\ \text{m/s}^2)(1.20\ \text{m})$
$v_f = -4.85\ \text{m/s}$ (downward)

b. With what velocity does it leave the ground?

Using $v_f^2 = v_i^2 + 2gd$,
$v_i^2 = -2gd$
$= -2(-9.80\ \text{m/s}^2)(1.00\ \text{m})$,
$v_i = 4.43\ \text{m/s}$

c. If the tennis ball were in contact with the ground for 0.010 s, find its acceleration while touching the ground. Compare to g.

$a = \frac{(v_f - v_i)}{t} = \frac{(4.43\ \text{m/s} - (-4.85\ \text{m/s}))}{0.010\ \text{s}}$

$= +930\ \text{m/s}^2$, or some 95 times g

Chapter Review Problems

Supplemental Problems (Appendix B)

1. From the moment a 40 m/s fastball touches the catcher's glove until it is completely stopped takes 0.012 s. Calculate the average acceleration of the ball as it is being caught.

$a = \frac{v_f - v_i}{t} = \frac{0 - 40}{0.012} = -3.3 \times 10^3\ \text{m/s}^2$

2. The following velocity–time graph describes a familiar motion of a car traveling during rush hour traffic.

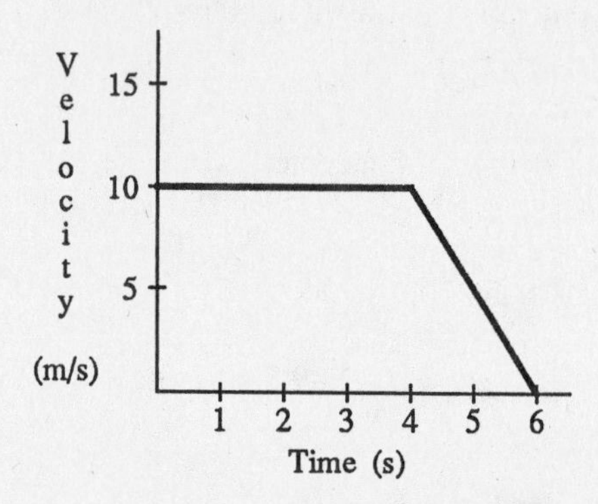

a. Describe the car's motion from $t = 0$ s to $t = 4$ s.

Constant velocity of 10 m/s.

b. Describe the car's motion from $t = 4$ s to $t = 6$ s.

Slowing down to a stop.

c. What is the average acceleration for the first 4 seconds?

0 m/s²

d. What is the average acceleration from $t = 4$ s to $t = 6$ s?

$\frac{-10\ \text{m/s}}{2\ \text{s}} = -5\ \text{m/s}^2$

3. Given the following table:

Time (s)	Velocity (m/s)
0.0	0.0
1.0	5.0
2.0	20.0
3.0	45.0
4.0	80.0

a. Plot a velocity–time graph for this motion.

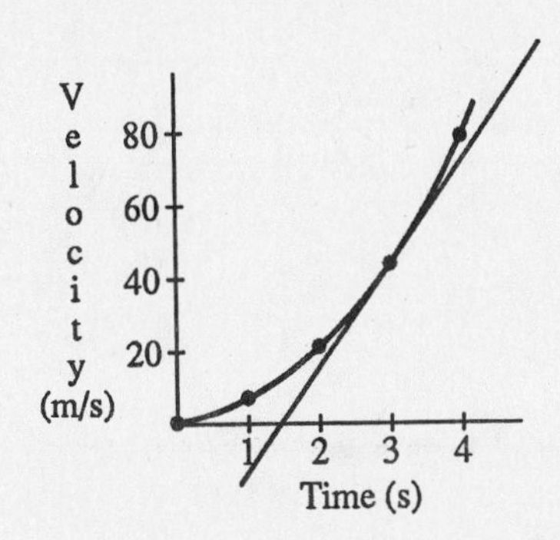

b. Is this motion constant velocity? uniform acceleration?

No, No

c. Calculate the instantaneous acceleration at $t = 3.0$ s.

Slope of the tangent is ≈ 30 m/s²

4. Top fuel drag racers are able to uniformly accelerate at 12.5 m/s² from rest to 100 m/s before crossing the finish line. How much time elapses during the run?

$$t = \frac{v_f - v_i}{a} = \frac{100 \text{ m/s} - 0}{12.5 \text{ m/s}^2} = 8.00 \text{ s}$$

Supplemental Problems

5. A race car accelerates from rest at +7.5 m/s² for 4.5 s. How fast will it be going at the end of that time?

$$v_f = v_i + at = 0 + (7.5 \text{ m/s}^2)(4.5 \text{ s}) = 34 \text{ m/s}$$

6. A race car starts from rest and is accelerated uniformly to +41 m/s in 8.0 s. What is the car's displacement?

$$d = \frac{(v_f + v_i)t}{2} = \frac{(41 \text{ m/s} + 0)(8.0 \text{ s})}{2} = 160 \text{ m}$$

7. A jet plane traveling at +88 m/s lands on a runway and comes to rest in 11 s.

a. Calculate its uniform acceleration.

$$a = \frac{(v_f - v_i)}{t} = \frac{(0 - 88 \text{ m/s})}{(11 \text{ s})} = -8.0 \text{ m/s}^2$$

b. Calculate the distance it travels.

$$d = v_i t + \frac{1}{2}at^2$$
$$= (88 \text{ m/s})(11 \text{ s}) + \left[\frac{1}{2}\right](-8.0 \text{ m/s}^2)(11 \text{ s})^2$$
$$= 480 \text{ m}$$

8. A bullet accelerates at 6.8 × 10⁴ m/s² from rest as it travels the 0.80 m of the rifle barrel.

a. How long was the bullet in the barrel?

$$d = v_i t + \frac{1}{2}at^2$$

$$0.80 = (0 \text{ m/s})t + \frac{1}{2}(6.8 \times 10^4 \text{ m/s}^2)t^2$$

$$t = \sqrt{\frac{2(0.80 \text{ m})}{6.8 \times 10^4 \text{ m/s}}} = 4.9 \times 10^{-3} \text{ s}$$

b. What velocity does the bullet have as it leaves the barrel?

$$v_f = v_i + at$$
$$= 0 + (6.8 \times 10^4 \text{ m/s})(4.9 \times 10^{-3} \text{ s})$$
$$= 3.3 \times 10^2 \text{ m/s}$$

9. A car traveling at 14 m/s encounters a patch of ice and takes 5.0 s to stop.

a. What is the car's acceleration?

$$a = \frac{v_f - v_i}{t} = \frac{0 - 14 \text{ m/s}}{5.0 \text{ s}} = -2.8 \text{ m/s}^2$$

b. How far does it travel before stopping?

$$d = \left[\frac{v_f + v_i}{2}\right]t = \left[\frac{0 + 14 \text{ m/s}}{2}\right]5.0 \text{ s} = 35 \text{ m}$$

10. A motorcycle traveling at 16 m/s accelerates at a constant rate of 4.0 m/s² over 50 m. What is its final velocity?

$$v_f^2 = v_i^2 + 2ad = (16 \text{ m/s})^2 + 2(4.0 \text{ m/s})(50 \text{ m})$$
$$= 656 \text{ m}^2/\text{s}^2$$
$$v_f = 26 \text{ m/s}$$

11. A hockey player skating at 18 m/s comes to a complete stop in 2.0 m. What is the acceleration of the hockey player?

$$a = \frac{v_f^2 - v_i^2}{2d} = \frac{0^2 - (18 \text{ m/s})^2}{2(2.0 \text{ m})} = -81 \text{ m/s}^2$$

12. Police find skid marks 60 m long on a highway showing where a car made an emergency stop. Assuming that the acceleration was –10 m/s² (about the maximum for dry pavement), how fast was the car going? Was the car exceeding the 80 km/h speed limit?

$v_f^2 = v_i^2 + 2ad.$
Since $v_f = 0$, $v_i^2 = -2ad$
$= -2(-10 \text{ m/s}^2)(60 \text{ m})$
$= 1200 \text{ m}^2/\text{s}^2,$
$v_i = 35 \text{ m/s} = 130 \text{ km/h}.$
Yes, the car was exceeding the speed limit.

13. An accelerating lab cart passes through two photo gate timers 3.0 m apart in 4.2 s. The velocity of the cart at the second timer is 1.2 m/s.

a. What is the cart's velocity at the first gate?

$$d = \left[\frac{v_f + v_i}{2}\right]t$$

$$3.0 = \left[\frac{1.2 + v_i}{2}\right]4.2$$

$$\frac{6.0}{4.2} = 1.2 + v_i$$

$$v_i = 0.2 \text{ m/s}$$

Supplemental Problems

b. What is the acceleration?

$$a = \frac{v_f - v_i}{t}$$

$$a = \frac{1.2 \text{ m/s} - .23 \text{ m/s}}{4.2 \text{ s}}$$

$$a = 0.24 \text{ m/s}^2$$

14. A camera is accidentally dropped from the edge of a cliff and 6.0 s later reaches the bottom.

a. How fast was it going just before it hit?

$$v_f = v_i + at$$
$$= 0 + 9.8 \text{ m/s}^2(6.0 \text{ s}) = 59 \text{ m/s}$$

b. How high is the cliff?

$$d = v_i t + \frac{1}{2}at^2$$

$$= 0(6.0 \text{ s}) + \frac{1}{2}(9.8 \text{ m/s}^2)(6.0 \text{ s})^2$$

$$= 1.8 \times 10^2 \text{ m}$$

15. A rock is thrown vertically with a velocity of 20 m/s from the edge of a bridge 42 m above a river. How long does the rock stay in the air?

To get back to bridge height

$$t = \frac{v_f - v_i}{a} = \frac{-20 - 20}{-9.8} = 4.1 \text{ s}$$

Velocity before going into river

$$v_f^2 = v_i^2 + 2ad$$
$$= (20 \text{ m/s})^2 + 2(9.8 \text{ m/s}^2)(42 \text{ m})$$
$$= 1223.2 \text{ m}^2/\text{s}^2$$
$$v_f = 35 \text{ m/s}$$

Time to fall from bridge to river

$$t = \frac{v_f - v_i}{a} = \frac{35 \text{ m/s} - 20 \text{ m/s}}{9.8 \text{ m/s}^2} = 1.5 \text{ s}$$

Total time

4.1 s + 1.5 s = 5.6 s

Supplemental Problems

16. A platform diver jumps vertically with a velocity of 4.2 m/s. 2.5 s later the diver enters the water. How high is the platform above the water?

$$d = v_i t + \frac{1}{2}at^2$$

$$= (4.2\ \text{m/s})(2.5\ \text{s}) + \frac{1}{2}(-9.8\ \text{m/s}^2)(2.5\ \text{s})^2$$

$$= -20\ \text{m}$$

Diver is 20 m below starting point platform is 20 m high.

Chapter 5: Forces

Practice Problems

page 92

1. When a shot–putter exerts a net force of 140 N on a shot, the shot has an acceleration of 19 m/s². What is the mass of the shot?

$$m = \frac{F}{a} = \frac{+140 \text{ N}}{+19 \text{ m/s}^2} = 7.4 \text{ kg}$$

2. Together a motorbike and rider have a mass of 275 kg. The motorbike is slowed down with an acceleration of – 4.50 m/s². What is the net force on the motorbike? Describe the direction of this force and the meaning of the negative sign.

$F = ma = (275 \text{ kg})(-4.50 \text{ m/s}^2)$
$= -1.24 \times 10^3 \text{ N}$
The negative sign of the acceleration slowing down the motorbike tells us that the motorbike has a velocity in the positive direction. The negative sign on the force indicates that it is directed opposite to the motorbike velocity.

3. A car, mass 1225 kg, traveling at 105 km/h, slows to a stop in 53 m. What is the size and direction of the force that acted on the car? What provided the force?

Given: $v_i = 105 \text{ km/h} = 29.2 \text{ m/s}$,
$v_f = 0$, $d = 53 \text{ m}$,

$$a = \frac{(v_f^2 - v_i^2)}{2d} = -8.0 \text{ m/s}^2.$$

$F = ma = (1225 \text{ kg})(-8.0 \text{ m/s}^2) = -9.8 \times 10^3 \text{ N}$
The force is directed opposite to the car motion and is provided by the road surface pushing against the car tires.

4. Imagine a spider with mass 7.0×10^{-5} kg moving downward on its thread. The thread exerts a force that results in a net upward force on the spider of 1.2×10^{-4} N.

a. What is the acceleration of the spider?

$$a = \frac{F}{m} = \frac{(+1.2 \times 10^{-4} \text{ N})}{(7.0 \times 10^{-5} \text{ kg})} = +1.7 \text{ m/s}^2$$

Practice Problems

b. Explain the sign of the velocity and describe in words how the thread changes the velocity of the spider.

The upward force being given as a positive number means that the downward motion of the spider is represented as a negative velocity. The positive acceleration is opposed to this negative velocity and gives rise to a slowing down of the spider.

page 94

In these problems, use $g = 9.80 \text{ m/s}^2$.

5. What is the weight of each of the following objects?

a. 0.133–kg hockey puck

$W = mg = (0.133 \text{ kg})(9.8 \text{ m/s}^2) = 1.11 \text{ N}$

b. 108–kg football player

$W = mg = (108 \text{ kg})(9.80 \text{ m/s})^2$
$= 1.06 \times 10^3 \text{ N}$

c. 870–kg automobile

$W = mg = (870 \text{ kg})(9.80 \text{ m/s}^2)$
$= 8.50 \times 10^3 \text{ N}$

6. Find the masses of each of these weights.

a. 98 N

$$m = \frac{W}{g} = \frac{98 \text{ N}}{9.80 \text{ m/s}^2} = 10 \text{ kg}$$

b. 80 N

$$m = \frac{W}{g} = \frac{80 \text{ N}}{9.80 \text{ m/s}^2} = 8.2 \text{ kg}$$

c. 0.98 N

$$m = \frac{W}{g} = \frac{0.98 \text{ N}}{9.80 \text{ m/s}^2} = 0.10 \text{ kg}$$

Practice Problems

page 95

7. A 20–N stone rests on a table. What is the force the table exerts on the stone? In what direction?

   20 N, upward

8. An astronaut with mass 75 kg travels to Mars. What is his weight

   a. on Earth?

   $W = mg = (75 \text{ kg})(9.80 \text{ m/s}^2)$
   $= 7.4 \times 10^2$ N

   b. on Mars, where $g = 3.8 \text{ m/s}^2$?

   $W = mg = (75 \text{ kg})(3.8 \text{ m/s}^2) = 2.9 \times 10^2$ N

   c. What is the value of g on top of a mountain if the astronaut weighs 683 N?

   $$g = \frac{W}{m} = \frac{683 \text{ N}}{75 \text{ kg}} = 9.1 \text{ m/s}^2$$

page 99

9. Suppose Joe, who weighs 625 N, stands on a bathroom scale calibrated in newtons.

   a. What force would the scale exert on Joe? In what direction?

   625 N, upward

   b. If Joe now holds a 50–N cat in his arms, what force would the scale exert on him?

   675 N

   c. After Joe puts down the cat, his father comes up behind him and lifts upward on his elbows with a 72–N force. What force does the scale now exert on Joe?

   Since $F_{\text{father on Joe}} + F_{\text{scale on Joe}} = W_{\text{Joe}}$,
   $F_{\text{scale on Joe}} = W_{\text{Joe}} - F_{\text{father on Joe}}$
   $= 625 \text{ N} - 72 \text{ N}$
   $= 553$ N, upward.

Practice Problems

10. **a.** A 52–N sled is pulled across a cement sidewalk at a constant speed. A horizontal force of 36 N is exerted. What is the coefficient of sliding friction between the sidewalk and the metal runners of the sled?

   $F_f = \mu F_N$ with $F_N = W$, so

   $$\mu = \frac{F_f}{F_N} = \frac{36 \text{ N}}{52 \text{ N}} = 0.69$$

page 100

   b. Suppose the sled now runs on packed snow. The coefficient of the friction is now only 0.12. If a person weighing 650 N sits on the sled, what force is needed to slide the sled across the snow at constant speed?

   The force must equal the friction force.
   $F_f = \mu F_N = \mu(W + W_1)$
   $= (0.12)(52 \text{ N} + 650 \text{ N}) = 84$ N

11. The coefficient of sliding friction between rubber tires and wet pavement is 0.50. The brakes are applied to a 750–kg car traveling 30 m/s, and the car skids to a stop.

   a. What is the size and direction of the force of friction that the road exerts on the car?

   $F_f = \mu F_N$ where $F_N = W = mg$, so
   $F_f = -(0.50)(750 \text{ kg})(9.80 \text{ m/s}^2)$
   $= -3.7 \times 10^3$ N

   b. What would be the size and direction of the acceleration of the car? Why would it be constant?

   $$a = \frac{F_f}{m} = \frac{(-3.7 \times 10^3 \text{ N})}{750 \text{ kg}} = -4.9 \text{ m/s}^2$$

   directed opposite car velocity and constant because F_f is constant.

   c. How far would the car travel before stopping?

   $v_f^2 = v_i^2 + 2ad$, so

   $$d = \frac{(v_f^2 - v_i^2)}{2a} = \frac{(0 - (30 \text{ m/s})^2)}{-9.8 \text{ m/s}^2}$$

   $= 92$ m

5

Practice Problems

12. If the tires of the car in Practice Problem 11 did not skid, the coefficient of friction would have been 0.70. Would the force of friction have been larger, smaller, or the same? Would the car have come to a stop in a shorter, the same, or a longer distance?

Larger, since F_f is proportional to μ; shorter distance since, from the solution to Practice Problem 11, d is inversely proportional to a, and a is proportional to F_f.

page 102

13. A rubber ball weighs 49 N.

a. What is the mass of the ball?

$$m = \frac{W}{g} = \frac{49 \text{ N}}{9.80 \text{ m/s}^2} = 5.0 \text{ kg}$$

b. What is the acceleration of the ball if an upward force of 69 N is applied?

$$ma = F_{net} = F_{appl} + W = 69 \text{ N} + (-49 \text{ N}) = 20 \text{ N}$$

$$\text{So, } a = \frac{F_{net}}{m} = \frac{20 \text{ N}}{5.0 \text{ kg}} = 4.0 \text{ m/s}^2$$

14. A small weather rocket weighs 14.7 N.

a. What is its mass?

$$m = \frac{W}{g} = \frac{14.7 \text{ N}}{9.80 \text{ m/s}^2} = 1.50 \text{ kg}$$

b. The rocket is carried up by a balloon. The rocket is released from the balloon and fired, but its engine exerts an upward force of 10.2 N. What is the acceleration of the rocket?

$$ma = F_{net} = F_{appl} + W = 10.2 \text{ N} + (-14.7 \text{ N}) = -4.50 \text{ N}$$

$$\text{Thus, } a = \frac{F_{net}}{m} = \frac{-4.50 \text{ N}}{1.5 \text{ kg}} = -3.00 \text{ m/s}^2$$

Practice Problems

15. The space shuttle has a mass of 2.0×10^6 kg. At lift–off the engines generate an upward force of 30×10^6 N.

a. What is the weight of the shuttle?

$$W = mg = (2 \times 10^6 \text{ kg})(9.80 \text{ m/s}^2) = 20 \times 10^6 \text{ N}$$

b. What is the acceleration of the shuttle when launched?

$$ma = F_{net} = F_{appl} + W = 30 \times 10^6 \text{ N} + (-20 \times 10^6 \text{ N}) = 10 \times 10^6 \text{ N}$$

$$\text{Thus, } a = \frac{F_{net}}{m} = \frac{(10 \times 10^6 \text{ N})}{(2 \times 10^6 \text{ kg})} = 5.0 \text{ m/s}^2$$

c. The average acceleration of the shuttle during its 10 minute launch is 13 m/s². What velocity does it attain?

$$v = at = (13 \text{ m/s}^2)(600 \text{ s}) = 7.8 \times 10^3 \text{ m/s} = 7.8 \text{ km/s}$$

d. As the space shuttle engines burn, the mass of the fuel becomes less and less. Assuming the force extered by the engines remains the same, would you expect the acceleration to increase, decrease, or remain the same? Why?

It would increase.

$a = \frac{F}{m}$. F is constant, m decreases, so a increases.

16. A certain sports car accelerates from 0 to 60 mph in 9.0 s (average acceleration = 3.0 m/s²). The mass of the car is 1354 kg. The average backward force due to air drag during acceleration is 280 N. Find the force required to give the car this acceleration.

$$F_{net} = ma = (1354 \text{ kg})(3.0 \text{ m/s}^2) = 4.1 \times 10^3 \text{ N}$$

$$F_{net} = F_{appl} + F_{drag}, \text{ so}$$

$$F_{appl} = F_{net} - F_{drag} = 4.1 \times 10^3 \text{ N} - (-280 \text{ N}) = 4.4 \times 10^3 \text{ N}$$

Chapter Review Problems

pages 105–107

1. A 873–kg (1930 lb) dragster, starting from rest, attains a speed of 26.3 m/s (58.9 miles/hour) in 0.59 s.

a. Find the average acceleration of the dragster during this time interval.

$$a = \frac{\delta v}{\delta t} = \frac{(26.4 \text{ m/s} - 0)}{0.59 \text{ s}} = 45 \text{ m/s}^2$$

b. What is the size of the average force on the dragster during this time interval?

$F = ma = (873 \text{ kg})(45 \text{ m/s}^2) = 3.9 \times 10^4 \text{ N}$

c. Assume the driver has a mass of 68 kg. What horizontal force does the seat exert on the driver?

$F = ma = (68 \text{ kg})(45 \text{ m/s}^2) = 3.1 \times 10^3 \text{ N}$

d. Is the driver's mass in part c an inertial mass or a gravitational mass?

Inertial mass.

2. The dragster in Problem 1 completed the 402.3 m (0.2500 mile) run in 4.936 s. If the car had constant acceleration, what would be its acceleration and final velocity?

$d = \frac{1}{2}at^2$, so

$a = 2d/t^2 = 2(402.3 \text{ m})/(4.936 \text{ s})_2 = 33.02 \text{ m/s}$

$d = \frac{1}{2}vt$, so

$v = 2d/t = 2(402.3 \text{ m})/4.936 \text{ s}) = 163.0 \text{ m/s}$

3. The dragster crossed the finish line going 126.6 m/s (283.1 mph). Is the assumption of constant acceleration good? What other piece of evidence could you use to see if the acceleration is constant?

126.6 m/s is slower than found in Problem 2, so the acceleration cannot be constant. Further, we found that the acceleration in the first half–second was 45 m/s², which is not equal to 33.02 m/s².

4. In Chapter 4 you found that when a karate strike hits wooden blocks, the hand undergoes an acceleration of – 6500 m/s². Medical data indicates the mass of the forearm and hand to be about 0.7 kg. What is the force exerted on the hand by the blocks? What is its direction?

$F = ma = (0.7 \text{ kg})(-6500 \text{ m/s}^2)$
$= -5 \times 10^3 \text{ N}$ (upward)

5. After a day of testing race cars, you decide to take your own 1550–kg car out onto the test track. While moving down the track at 10 m/s, you suddenly accelerate to 30 m/s in 10 s. What is the net average force that you have applied to the car during the 10–s interval?

$F = ma = m\Delta v/t$
$= (1550 \text{ kg})(30 \text{ m/s} - 10 \text{ m/s})/10 \text{ s} =$
$= 3.1 \times 10^3 \text{ N}$

6. A race car has a mass of 710 kg. It starts from rest and travels 40 m in 3.0 s. The car is uniformly accelerated during the entire time. What net force is applied to it?

$F = ma$, where, since d and t are known, a can be found from $d = v_i t + (1/2)at^2$. Since $v_i = 0$, $a = 2d/t^2 = 2(40 \text{ m})/(3.0 \text{ s})^2 = 8.9 \text{ m/s}^2$, so $F = (710 \text{ kg})(8.9 \text{ m/s}^2) = 6.3 \times 10^3 \text{ N}$.

7. A force of – 9000 N is used to stop a 1500–kg car traveling at 20 m/s. What braking distance is needed to bring the car to a halt?

$a = F/m = (-9.0 \times 10^3 \text{ N})/(1.5 \times 10^3 \text{ kg})$
$= -6.0 \text{ m/s}^2$
Use $v_f^2 = v_i^2 + 2ad$,
so $d = (v_f^2 - v_i^2)/2a$.
$= (0 - (20 \text{ m/s})^2)/(2)(-6.0 \text{ m/s}^2)$
$= 33 \text{ m}$

8. A 65–kg swimmer jumps off a 10–m high tower.

a. Find the swimmer's velocity when hitting the water.

$v_f^2 = v_i^2 + 2gd$. $v_i = 0$,
so $v_f^2 = 2gd = 2(9.80 \text{ m/s}^2)(10 \text{ m})$
so $v_f = 14 \text{ m/s}$.

b. The swimmer comes to a stop 2.0 m below the surface. Find the net force exerted by the water.

$v_f^2 = v_i^2 + 2ad$, or

$$a = \frac{v_f^2 - v_i^2}{2d} = \frac{0^2 - (14 \text{ m/s})^2}{2(2.0 \text{ m})} = -49 \text{ m/s}^2$$

and

$F = ma = (65 \text{ kg})(-49 \text{ m/s}) = 3.2 \times 10^3 \text{ N}$

9. When you drop a 0.40-kg apple, Earth exerts a force on it which accelerates it at 9.8 m/s² towards Earth's surface. According to Newton's Third Law of Motion, the apple must exert an equal and opposite force on Earth. If the mass of Earth is 5.85 × 10^{24} kg, what's the magnitude of Earth's acceleration?

$F_{a \text{ on } E} = -F_{E \text{ on } a}$, $m_a a_a = -m_E a_E$,

$a_E = -(m_a a_a)/m_E$

$= -(4.0 \text{ kg})(-9.8 \text{ m/s}^2)/(5.98 \times 10^{24} \text{ kg})$

$= 6.6 \times 10^{-25} \text{ m/s}^2$

10. A 60.0-kg boy and a 40.0-kg girl use an elastic rope while engaged in a tug-of-war on an icy frictionless surface. If the acceleration of the girl toward the boy is 3.0 m/s², determine the magnitude of the acceleration of the boy toward the girl.

$F_{1,2} = -F_{2,1}$ so $m_1 a_1 = -m_2 a_2$, and

$$a_1 = \frac{-(m_2 a_2)}{m_1}$$

$$= \frac{(40.0 \text{ kg})(3.0 \text{ m/s}^2)}{(60.0 \text{ kg})}$$

$= -2.0 \text{ m/s}^2$

11. A 95.0-kg (209 lb) boxer has his first match in the Canal Zone (g = 9.782 m/s²) and his second match at the North Pole (g = 9.832 m/s²).

a. What is his mass in the Canal Zone?

95.0 kg

b. What is his weight in the Canal Zone?

$W = mg = (95.0)(9.782 \text{ m/s}^2) = 929 \text{ N}$

c. What is his mass at the North Pole?

95.0 kg

Chapter Review Problems

d. What is his weight at the North Pole?

$W = mg = (95.0)(9.832 \text{ m/s}^2) = 934 \text{ N}$

e. Does he 'weigh-in' or does he really 'mass-in'?

Mass-in. We sometimes use the word weight when we mean mass.

12. Your new motorcycle weighs 2450 N. What is its mass in kilograms?

$W = mg$, so

$m = W/g = (-2450 \text{ N})/(-9.80 \text{ m/s}^2)$

$= 250 \text{ kg}$

13. You place a 7.50-kg television set on a spring scale. If the scale reads 78.4 N, what is the acceleration of gravity at that location?

$W = mg$, so

$g = W/m = (78.4 \text{ N})(7.50 \text{ kg})$

$= 10.5 \text{ m/s}^2$, downward

14. In Chapter 4 you calculated the braking acceleration for a car based on data in a drivers' handbook. The acceleration was − 12.2 m/s².

If the car has a mass of 925 kg, find the frictional force and state the direction.

$F_f = ma = (925 \text{ kg})(-12.2 \text{ m/s}^2)$

$= 1.13 \times 10^4$ N, opposite direction of motion

15. If you use a horizontal force of 30.0 N to slide a 12.0-kg wooden crate across a floor at a constant velocity, what is the coefficent of sliding friction between crate and floor?

$$\mu = \frac{F_f}{F_N}$$

$$= \frac{F_f}{W} = \frac{F_f}{mg}$$

$$= \frac{(30.0 \text{ N})}{(12.0 \text{ kg})(9.80 \text{ m/s}^2)} = 0.255$$

Chapter Review Problems

16. You are driving a 2500.0-kg car at a constant speed of 14.0 m/s along an icy, but straight and level, road. While approaching a traffic light, it turns red. You slam on the brakes. Your wheels lock, the tires begin skidding and the car slides to a halt in a distance of 25.0 m. What is the coefficient of sliding friction (μ) between your tires and the icy roadbed?

$F_f = \mu F_N = ma$
$-\mu mg = m(v_f^2 - v_i^2)/2d$ where $v_f = 0$.
(The − sign indicates the force is acting opposite to the direction of motion.)
$\mu = v_i^2/2dg = (14.0\text{ m/s})^2/2(25.0\text{ m})(9.80\text{ m/s}^2)$
$= 0.400$

17. A person fishing hooks a 2.0-kg fish on a line that can only sustain a maximum of 38 N of force before breaking. At one point while reeling in the fish, it fights back with a force of 40 N. What is the minimum acceleration with which he must play out line during this time in order to keep the line from breaking?

Take the direction from the fish to the person as positive. The acceleration of the fish, and hence the line, will be obtained from
$ma = F_{net} = F_{appl} + F_{fish}$.
Thus, $a = (F_{appl} + F_{fish})/m$
$= (38\text{ N} - 40\text{ N})/(2.0\text{ kg})$
$= -1.0\text{ m/s}^2$.

18. A 4500-kg helicopter accelerates upward at 2 m/s². What lift force is exerted by the air on the propellers?

$ma = F_{net} = F_{appl} + W = F_{appl} + mg$, so
$F_{appl} = ma - mg$
$= (4500\text{ kg})(2\text{ m/s}^2)$
$- (4500\text{ kg})(-9.8\text{ m/s}^2)$
$= 5.3 \times 10^4\text{ N}$.

19. The maximum force a grocery sack can withstand and not rip is 250 N. If 20 kg of groceries are lifted from the floor to a table with an acceleration of 5 m/s², will the sack hold?

$ma = F_{net} = F_{appl} + W = F_{appl} + mg$, so
$F_{appl} = ma - mg$
$= (20\text{ kg})(5\text{ m/s}^2) - (20\text{ kg})(-9.8\text{ m/s}^2)$
$= 300\text{ N}$.
No, this force is greater than 250 N, hence the sack rips.

20. A student stands on a bathroom scale in an elevator at rest on the 64th floor of a building. The scale reads 836 N.

The basic equation to be applied is $ma = F_{net} = F_{appl} - W$, where the positive direction is taken upward and F_{appl} is the force exerted by the scale. The mass of the student is $m = W/g = (836\text{ N})/(9.80\text{ m/s}^2) = 85.3\text{ kg}$.

a. As the elevator moves up, the scale reading increases to 935 N, then decreases back to 836 N. Find the acceleration of the elevator.

$a = (F_{appl} - W)/m$
$= (935\text{ N} - 836\text{ N})/(85.3\text{ kg})$
$= 1.2\text{ m/s}^2$

b. As the elevator approaches the 74th floor, the scale reading drops as low as 782 N. What is the acceleration of the elevator?

$a = (F_{appl} - W)/m$
$= (782\text{ N} - 836\text{ N})/(85.3\text{ kg})$
$= -0.63\text{ m/s}^2$

c. Using your results from parts **a** and **b**, explain which change in velocity, starting or stopping, would take the longer time.

Stopping, because the acceleration is less and $t = -v_i/a$

d. Explain the changes in the scale you would expect on the ride back down.

$F_{appl} = W + ma = 836\text{ N} + ma$. As the elevator starts to descend a is negative and the scale reads less than 836 N. When constant downward velocity is reached, the scale reads 836 N since the acceleration is then zero. When the elevator is slowing at the bottom, the acceleration is positive and the scale reads more than 836 N.

21. A 2.1×10^{-4}–kg spider is suspended from a thin strand of spider web. The greatest tension the strand can withstand without breaking is 2.2×10^{-3} N. What is the maximum acceleration with which the spider can safely climb up the strand?

$ma = F_{net} = F_{appl} + W$
The tension (T) is F_{appl}. Take up as positive. Therefore $ma = T - W$.

$$\frac{((2.2 \times 10^{-3}\ \text{N}) - (2.1 \times 10^{-4})(9.8\ \text{m/s}^2))}{2.1 \times 10^{-4}\ \text{kg}}$$

$= 0.68\ \text{m/s}^2$

22. A sled of mass 50 kg is pulled along snow–covered, flat ground. The static friction coefficient is 0.30, and the sliding friction coefficient is 0.10.

a. What does the sled weigh?

$W = mg = (50\ \text{kg})(9.8\ \text{m/s}^2) = 4.9 \times 10^2\ \text{N}$

b. What force will be needed to start the sled moving?

$F_i = \mu F_N = \mu W = (0.30)(490\ \text{N}) = 150\ \text{N}$, static friction.

c. What force is needed to keep the sled moving at a constant velocity?

$F_i = \mu F_N = \mu W = (0.10)(490\ \text{N}) = 49\ \text{N}$, sliding friction.

d. Once moving, what total force must be applied to the sled to accelerate it 3.0 m/s²?

$ma = F_{net} = F_{appl} - Fi$ so
$F_{appl} = ma + F_i$
$= (50\ \text{kg})(3.0\ \text{m/s}^2) + 49\ \text{N}$
$= 2.0 \times 10^2$

23. A force of 40 N accelerates a 5.0–kg block at 6.0 m/s² along a horizontal surface.

a. How large is the frictional force?

$ma = F_{net} = F_{appl} - F_i$, so
$F_f = F_{appl} - ma$
$= 40\ \text{N} - (5.0\ \text{kg})(6.0\ \text{m/s}^2) = 10\ \text{N}$

b. What is the coefficient of fricion?

$F_i = \mu F_N = \mu mg$ so
$\mu = F_f/mg = (10\ \text{N})/(5.0\ \text{kg})(9.8\ \text{m/s}^2)$
$= 0.20$

24. A 200–kg crate is pushed horizontally with a force of 700 N. If the coefficient of friction is 0.20, calculate the acceleration of the crate.

$ma = F_{net} = F_{appl} - F_i$ where $F_i = \mu F_N = \mu mg$.
Therefore
$a = (F_{appl} - \mu mg)/m$

$$= \frac{(700\ \text{N} - (0.20)(200\ \text{kg})(9.8\ \text{m/s}^2)}{200\ \text{kg}}$$

$= 1.5\ \text{m/s}^2$.

25. Safety engineers estimate that an elevator can hold 20 persons of 75–kg average mass. The elevator itself has a mass of 500 kg. Tensile strength tests show that the cable supporting the elevator can tolerate a maximum force of 2.96×10^4 N. What is the greatest acceleration that the elevator's motor can produce without breaking the cable?

$m = (20)(75\ \text{kg}) + 500\ \text{kg} = 2.0 \times 10^3\ \text{kg}$.
$W = mg = (2.0 \times 10^3\ \text{kg})(9.8\ \text{m/s}^2)$
$= 2.0 \times 10^4\ \text{N}$.
$ma = F_{net} = F_{appl} - W$,
$a = (F_{appl} - W)/m$
$= (2.96 \times 10^4\ \text{N} - 2.0 \times 10^4)/(2.0 \times 10^3)$
$= 4.8\ \text{m/s}^2$.

26. The instruments attached to a weather balloon have a mass of 5.0 kg.

a. The balloon is released, and exerts an upward force of 98 N on the instruments. What is the acceleration of the balloon and instruments?

$ma = F_{net} = F_{appl} + W = 98\ \text{N} + (-49\ \text{N})$
$= +49\ \text{N}$ (up)
$a = (+49\ \text{N})/(5.0\ \text{kg}) = +9.8\ \text{m/s}^2$ (up)

b. After the balloon has been accelerating for 10.0 seconds, the instruments are released. What is the velocity of the instruments at the moment of their release?

$v = at = (+9.80\ \text{m/s}^2)(10\ \text{s}) = +98\ \text{m/s}$ (up)

c. What net force acts on the instruments after their release?

Just the instrument weight, – 49 N (down)

d. When does the direction of their velocity first become downward?

The velocity becomes negative after it passes through zero. Thus, use $v_f = v_i + gt$, where $v_f = 0$, or

$t = -v_i/g = -(+98\text{ m/s})/(-9.80\text{ m/s}^2)$
$= 10\text{ s}.$

27. A 2.0-kg mass (m_1) and a 3.0-kg mass (m_2) are attached to a lightweight cord that passes over a frictionless pulley, as diagrammed. The hanging masses are free to move. Take the direction of the physical motion, smaller mass upward and larger mass downward, to be the positive direction of motion.

a. Draw the situation, showing all forces.

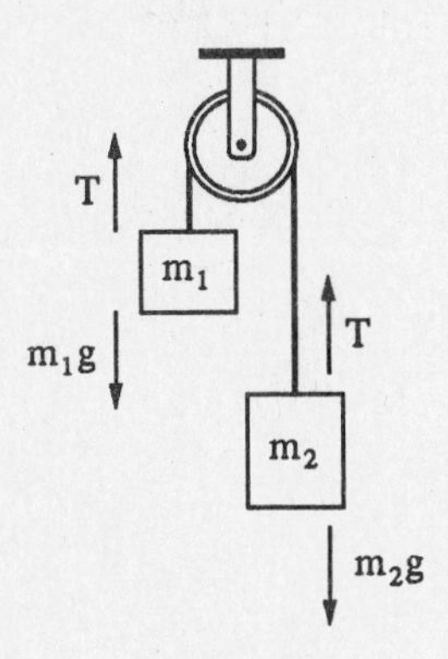

b. In what direction does the smaller mass move?

upward

c. What is its acceleration?

$ma = F_{net}$ where m is the total mass being accelerated.
For m_1, $m_1a = T - m_1g$
For m_2, $m_2a = -T + m_2g$ or $T = m_2g - m_2a$
Substituting into the equation for m_1 gives
$m_1a = m_2g - m_2a - m_1g$ or
$(m_1 + m_2)a = (m_2 - m_1)g$
Therefore $a = ((m_2 - m_1)/(m_1 + m_2))g$
$= ((3.0 - 2.0)/(3.0 + 2.0))9.80$
$= (1.0/5.0)9.80 = 2.0\text{ m/s}^2$

Chapter Review Problems

28. You change the masses in Figure 5–18 to 1.00 kg and 4.00 kg.

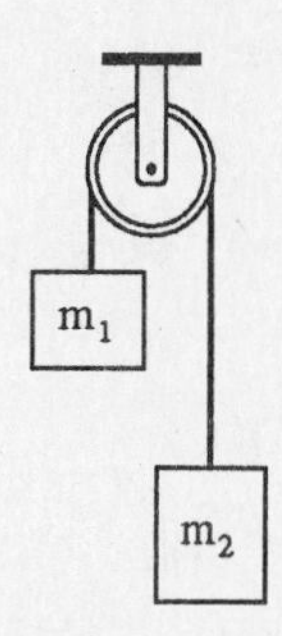

5

a. What can you expect the acceleration of the 4.00-kg mass to be?

Take the direction of the physical motion, smaller mass upward and larger mass downward, to be the positive direction of motion.
For m_1, $m_1a = T - m_1g$
For m_2, $m_2a = -T + m_2g$ or $T = m_2g - m_2a$
Substituting into the equation for m_1 gives
$m_1a = m_2g - m_2a - m_1g$ or
$(m_1 + m_2)a = (m_2 - m_1)g$
Therefore,
$a = ((m_2 - m_1)/(m_1 + m_2))g$
$= ((4.00 - 1.00)/(4.00 + 1.00))9.80$
$= (3.00/5.00)(9.80) = 5.9\text{ m/s}^2$

b. What is the tension force acting on the cord?

$T = m_2g - m_2a = m_1(g - a)$
$= 4.00(9.80 - 5.9) = 16\text{ N}$

29. You then decide to replace the 1.00-kg object from Problem 28 with a 2.00-kg object.

a. What is the acceleration of the 2.00-kg object?

The acceleration will be the same for both masses. From Problem 28,
$a = ((m_2 - m_1)/(m_2 + m_1))g$
$= ((4.00 - 2.00)/(4.00 + 2.00))9.80$
$= (2.00/6.00)9.80 = 3.3\text{ m/s}^2$

b. What is the new tension force acting on the cord?

From Problem 28,
$T = m_2(g - a) = 4.00(9.80 - 3.27) = 26.1$ N

Supplemental Problems

1. A towrope is used to pull a 1750–kg car, giving it an acceleration of 1.35 m/s². What force does the rope exert?

$F = ma = (1750 \text{ kg})(1.35 \text{ m/s}^2)$
$= 2.36 \times 10^3$ N, in the direction of the acceleration.

2. A race car undergoes a uniform acceleration of 4.00 m/s². If the net force causing the acceleration is 3.00×10^3 N, what is the mass of the car?

$m = F/a = (3.00 \times 10^3 \text{ N})/(4.00 \text{ m/s}^2)$
$= 750$ kg

3. A 5.2–kg bowling ball is accelerated from rest to a velocity of 12 m/s as the bowler covers 5.0 m of approach before releasing the ball. What average force is exterted on the ball during this time?

$v_f^2 - v_i^2 = 2ad$

$$a = \frac{v_f^2 - vi^2}{2d} = \frac{(12 \text{ m/s})^2 - 0^2}{2(5.0 \text{ m})} = 14.4 \text{ m/s}^2$$

$F = ma = (5.2 \text{ kg})(14.4 \text{ m/s}^2) = 75$ N.

4. A high jumper falling at 4.0 m/s lands on a foam pit and comes to rest, compressing the pit .40 m. If the pit is able to exert an average force of 1200 N on the high jumper in breaking the fall, what is the jumper's mass?

$v_f^2 - v_i^2 = 2ad$

$$a = \frac{v_f^2 - v_i^2}{2d} = \frac{0^2 - (4.0 \text{ m/s}^2)}{2(0.40 \text{ m})} = -20 \text{ m/s}^2$$

where the positive direction is downward.
$F = ma$

$$m = \frac{F}{a} = \frac{-1200}{-20} = 60 \text{ kg}$$

Supplemental Problems (Appendix B)

5. When a 20–kg child steps off a 3.0–kg stationary skateboard with an acceleration of .50 m/s², with what acceleration will the skateboard travel in the opposite direction?

$F_{child} = ma = (20 \text{ kg})(0.50 \text{ m/s}^2) = 10$ N
$F_{child} = F_{skateboard}$ so for skateboard
$F = ma$, or

$$a = \frac{F}{m} = \frac{10 \text{ N}}{3.0 \text{ kg}} = 3.3 \text{ m/s}^2$$

6. On planet X a 50–kg barbell can be lifted by only exerting a force of 180 N.

a. What is the acceleration of gravity on planet X?

$W = mg$

$$g = \frac{W}{m} = \frac{180 \text{ N}}{50 \text{ kg}} = 3.6 \text{ m/s}^2$$

b. If the same barbell was lifted on earth, what minimal force is needed?

$W = mg$
$= (50 \text{ kg})(9.8 \text{ m/s}^2)$
$= 4.9 \times 10^2$ N

7. A proton has a mass of 1.672×10^{-27} kg. What is its weight?

$W = mg$
$= (1.672 \times 10^{-27} \text{ kg})(9.8 \text{ m/s}^2)$
$= 1.6 \times 10^{-26}$ N

8. A force of 20 N accelerates a 9.0–kg wagon at 2.0 m/s² along the sidewalk.

a. How large is the frictional force?

$F_{net} = ma = (9.0 \text{ kg})(2.0 \text{ m/s}^2) = 18$ N
$F_f = F_{appl} - F_{net} = 20 \text{ N} - 18 \text{ N} = 2$ N

b. What is the coefficient of friction?

$F_N = W = mg = (9.0 \text{ kg})(9.8 \text{ m/s}^2) = 88$ N

$$\mu = \frac{F_f}{F_N} = \frac{2 \text{ N}}{88 \text{ N}} = 0.02$$

9. A 2.0-kg brick has a sliding coefficient of friction of .38. What force must be applied to the brick for it to move at a constant velocity?

$F_f = \mu F_N$ where
$F_N = W = mg = (2.0 \text{ kg})(9.8 \text{ m/s}^2) = 19.6 \text{ N}$ so
$F_f = \mu F_N = (0.38)(19.6 \text{ N}) = 7.4 \text{ N}$

10. In bench pressing 100 kg, a weight lifter applies a force of 1040 N. How large is the upward acceleration of the weights during the lift?

$W = mg = (100 \text{ kg})(9.80 \text{ m/s}^2) = 980 \text{ N}$
$F_{net} = F_{appl} - W = 1040 \text{ N} - 980 \text{ N} = 60 \text{ N}$
$F_{net} = ma$

$$a = \frac{F_{net}}{m} = \frac{60 \text{ N}}{100 \text{ kg}} = 0.60 \text{ m/s}^2$$

11. An elevator that weighs 3.0×10^3 N is accelerated upward at 1.0 m/s². What force does the cable exert to give it this acceleration?

The mass of the elevator is
$m = W/g = (-3.0 \times 10^3 \text{ N})/(-9.8 \text{ m/s}^2)$
$= 3.1 \times 10^2$ kg.
Now $ma = F_{net} = F_{appl} + W$ so that
$F_{appl} = ma - W$
$= (3.1 \times 10^2 \text{ kg})(1.0 \text{ m/s}^2) - (-3.0 \times 10^3 \text{ N})$
$= 3.3 \times 10^3$ N.

12. A person weighing 490 N stands on a scale in an elevator.

The basic equation to be applied is $ma = F_{net} = F_{appl} - W$, where the positive direction is taken upward and F_{appl} is the force exerted by the scale. The mass of the person is $m = W/g = (490 \text{ N})/(9.8 \text{ m/s}^2) = 50$ kg.

a. What does the scale read when the elevator is at rest?

$a = 0$ so $F_{appl} = W = 490$ N

b. What is the reading on the scale when the elevator rises at a constant velocity?

$a = 0$ so $F_{appl} = W = 490$ N

c. The elevator slows down at -2.2 m/s² as it reaches the desired floor. What does the scale read?

$F_{appl} = ma + W$
$= (50 \text{ kg})(-2.2 \text{ m/s}^2) + 490 \text{ N}$
$= 3.8 \times 10^2$ N

d. The elevator descends, accelerating at -2.7 m/s². What does the scale read?

$F_{appl} = ma + W$
$= (50 \text{ kg})(-2.7 \text{ m/s}^2) + 490 \text{ N}$
$= 3.6 \times 10^2$ N

e. What does the scale read when the elevator descends at a constant velocity?

$a = 0$ so $F_{appl} = W = 490$ N

f. Suppose the cable snapped and the elevator fell freely. What would the scale read?

$a = -g$ so
$F_{appl} = ma + W = m(-g) + mg = 0$

13. A 10.0-kg mass (m_1) on a frictionless table is accelerated by a 5.0-kg mass (m_2) hanging from the table as shown below. What is the acceleration of the mass along the table?

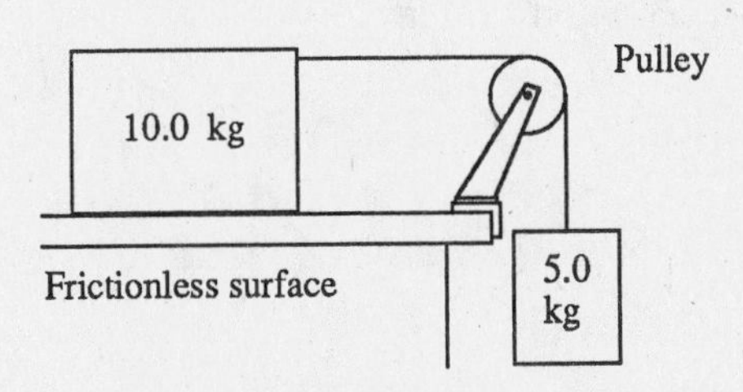

$F = ma$ where
$m = m_1 + m_2$ = the total mass being accelerated and $F = m_2 g$ = the applied force. Thus,
$m_2 g = (m_1 + n_2)a$ or
$a = m_2 g/(m_1 + m_2)$
$= (5.0 \text{ kg})(9.80 \text{ m/s}^2)/(5.0 \text{ kg} + 10.0 \text{ kg})$
$= 3.3$ m/s², to the right.

5

Chapter 6: Vectors

Practice Problems

page 112

Draw vector diagrams to solve each problem.

1. After walking 11 km due north from camp, a hiker then walks 11 km due east.

   a. What is the total distance walked by the hiker?

   11 km + 11 km = 22 km

   b. Determine the total displacement from the starting point.

   16 km

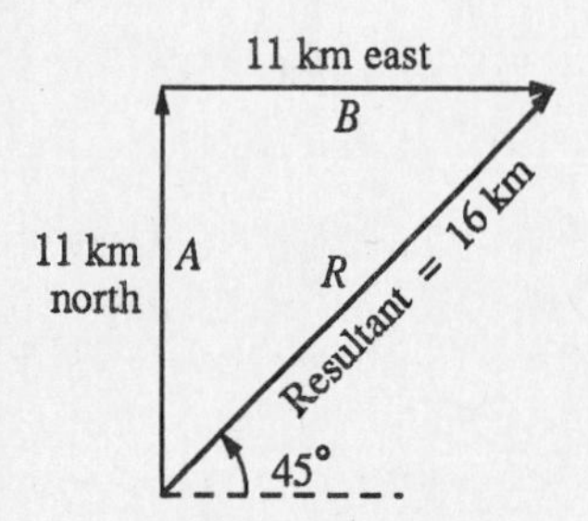

2. Two boys push on a box. One pushes with a force of 125 N to the east. The other exerts a force of 165 N to the north. What is the size and direction of the resultant force on the box?

   207 N, 53°, north of east

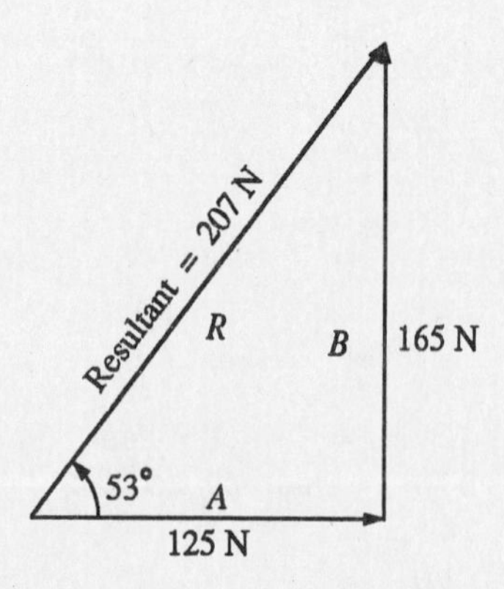

Practice Problems

3. An explorer walks 13 km due east, then 18 km north, and finally 3 km west.

   a. What is the total distance walked?

   13 km + 18 km + 3 km = 34 km

   b. What is the resulting displacement of the explorer from the starting point?

   21 km, 61°, north of east

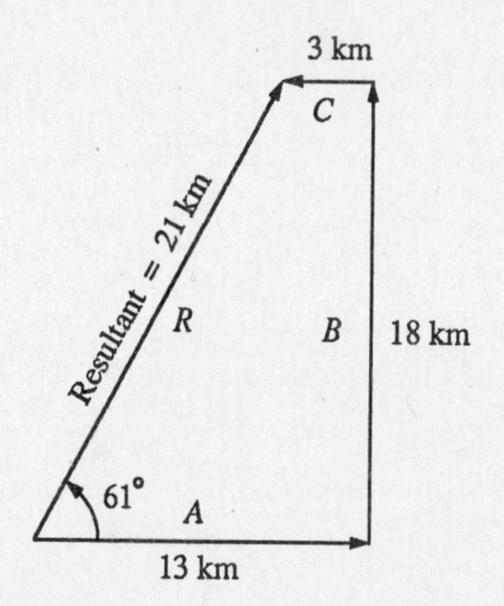

Draw vector diagrams to solve each problem.

4. A motorboat heads due east at 16 m/s across a river that flows due north at 9.0 m/s.

   a. What is the resultant velocity (speed and direction) of the boat?

   18 m/s, 29°, north of east

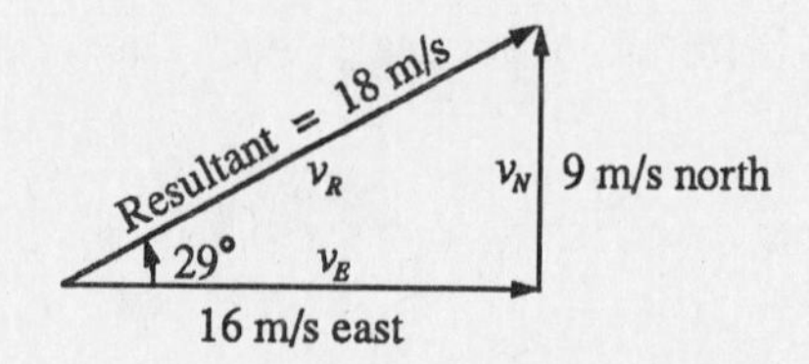

   b. If the river is 136 m wide, how long does it take the motorboat to reach the other side?

$$t = \frac{d}{v_E} = \frac{136 \text{ m}}{16 \text{ m/s}} = 8.5 \text{ s}$$

c. How far downstream is the boat when it reaches the other side of the river?

$d = v_N t = (9.0\ \text{m/s})(8.5\ \text{s}) = 77\ \text{m}$

5. While flying due east at 120 km/h, an airplane is also carried northward at 45 km/h by the wind blowing due north. What is the plane's resultant velocity?

130 km/h, 21°, north of east

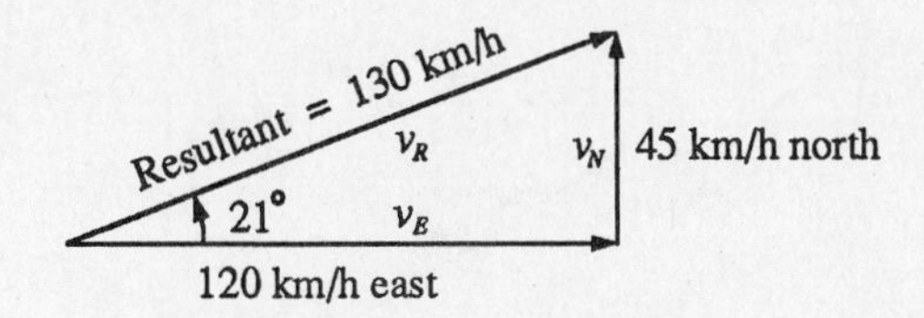

page 113

6. Three teenagers push a heavy crate across the floor. Dion pushes with a force of 185 N at 0°. Shirley exerts a force of 165 N at 30°, while Joan pushes with a 195 N force at 300°. What is the resultant force on the crate?

434 N, 11.5°, south of east

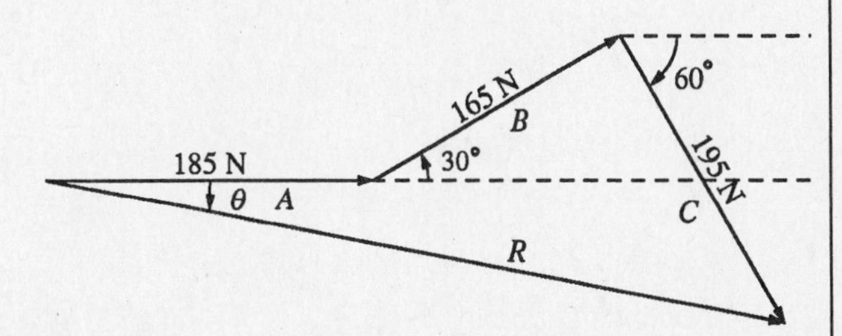

page 115

7. A 110-N force and a 55-N force both act on an object point *P*. The 110-N force acts at 90°. The 55-N force acts at 0°. What is the magnitude and direction of the resultant force?

$$F_R^2 = F_A^2 + F_B^2$$

$$F_R = \sqrt{(55\ \text{N})^2 + (110\ \text{N})^2} = 120\ \text{N}$$

$$\tan\theta = \frac{110}{55} = 2.0$$

$$\theta = 63°$$

Practice Problems

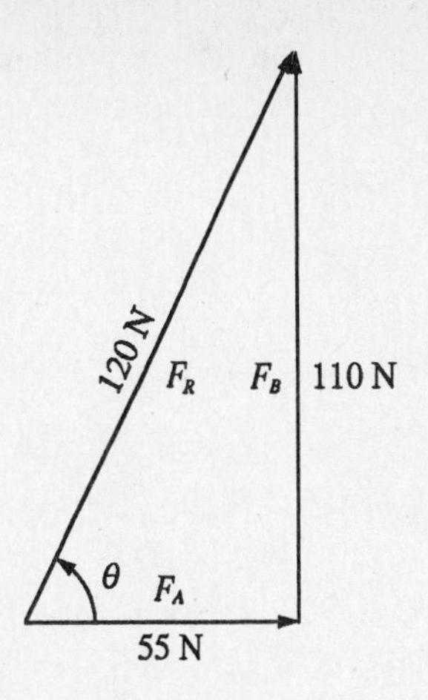

page 116

8. A motorboat travels at 8.5 m/s. It heads straight across a river 110 m wide.

a. If the water flows downstream at a rate of 3.8 m/s, what is the boat's resultant velocity?

$$v_R = \sqrt{(8.5\ \text{m/s})^2 + (3.8\ \text{m/s})^2} = 9.3\ \text{m/s}$$

$$\tan\theta = \frac{3.8}{0.5} = 0.45,\ \theta = 24°$$

$$v_R = 9.3\ \text{m/s at } 24°$$

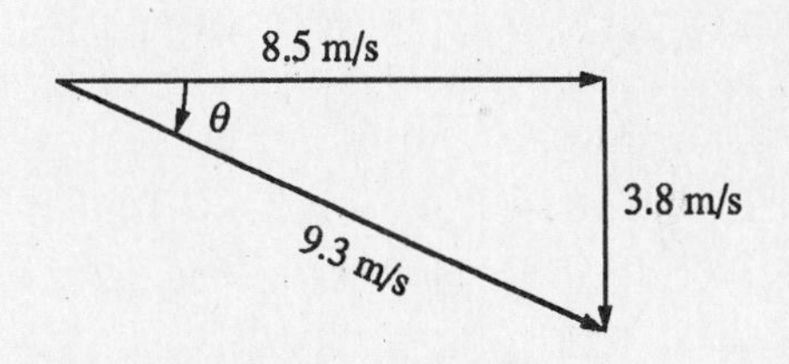

b. How much time does it take the boat to reach the opposite shore?

$$t = \frac{d}{v} = \frac{110\ \text{m}}{8.5\ \text{m/s}} = 13\ \text{s}$$

6

Practice Problems

9. A boat heads directly across a river 41 m wide at 3.8 m/s. The current is flowing downstream at 2.2 m/s.

a. What is the resultant velocity of the boat?

$$v_R = \sqrt{(3.8\text{ m/s})^2 + (2.2\text{ m/s})^2} = 4.4\text{ m/s}$$

$$\tan\theta = \frac{2.2}{3.8} = 0.58,\ \theta = 30°$$

$$v_R = 4.4\text{ m/s at }30°$$

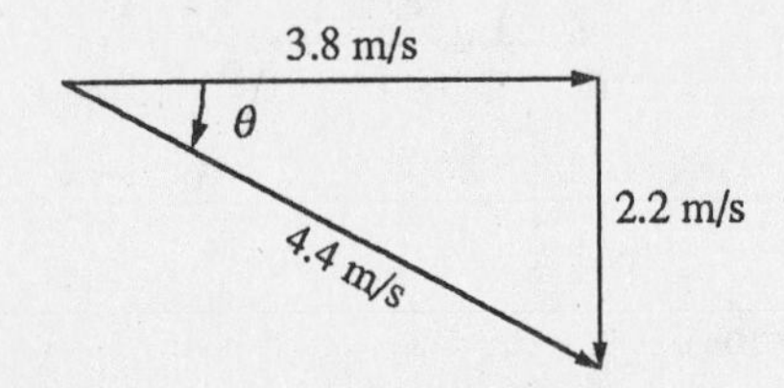

b. How much time does it take the boat to cross the river?

$$t = \frac{d}{v} = \frac{41\text{ m}}{3.8\text{ m/s}} = 11\text{ s}$$

c. How far downstream is the boat when it reaches the other side?

$$d = vt = (2.2\text{ m/s})(11\text{ s}) = 24\text{ m}$$

10. A 42-km/h wind blows toward 215°, while a plane heads toward 125° at 152 km/h. What is the resultant velocity of the plane?

$$v_R = \sqrt{(152\text{ km/h})^2 + (42\text{ km/h})^2} = 160\text{ km/h}$$

$$\tan\theta = \frac{42}{152} = 0.276$$

$$\theta = 15°$$

$$\theta_R = 125° + 15° = 140°$$

$$v_R = 160\text{ km/h at }140°$$

Practice Problems

page 118

11. A heavy box is pulled across a wooden floor with a rope. The rope makes an angle of 60° with the floor. A force of 75 N is exerted on the rope. What is the component of the force parallel to the floor?

$$F_h = (75\text{ N})\cos 60° = 38\text{ N}$$

12. An airplane flies toward 149° at 525 km/h.

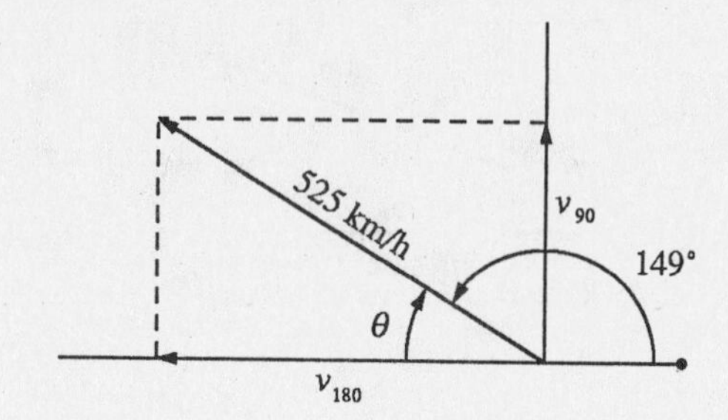

$$\theta = 180° - 149° = 31°$$

What is the component of the plane's velocity

a. toward 90°?

$$v_{90} = v\sin\theta = (525\text{ km/h})\sin 31° = 270\text{ km/h}$$

b. toward 180°?

$$v_{180} = v\cos\theta = (525\text{ km/h})\cos 31° = 450\text{ km/h}$$

13. A student exerts a force of 72 N along the handle of a lawn mower to push it across the lawn. Find the horizontal component of this force when the handle is held at an angle with the lawn of

a. 60.0°.

$$F_h = (72\text{ N})\cos 60° = 36\text{ N}$$

b. 40.0°.

$$F_h = (72\text{ N})\cos 40° = 55\text{ N}$$

c. 30.0 °.

$$F_h = (72\text{ N})\cos 30° = 62\text{ N}$$

Practice Problems

14. A hiker walks 14.7 km at an angle of 305° from east. Find the east–west and north–south components of this walk.

$\theta = 360° - 305° = 55°$ south of east

east – west component = (14.7 km) cos 55° = 8.43 km, east

north – south component = (14.7 km) sin 55° = 12.0 km, south.

page 120

15. Find the resultant force on the log in the last Example Problem if F_1 remains the same and F_2 is changed to 14.0 N at 310.0°.

$F_{1x} = (12.0\text{ N})\cos 10.0° = 11.8\text{ N}$
$F_{1y} = (12.0\text{ N})\sin 10.0° = 2.0\text{ N}$
$F_{2x} = (14.0\text{ N})\cos 310.0° = 9.0\text{ N}$
$F_{2y} = (14.0\text{ N})\sin 310.0° = -10.7\text{ N}$

where $\cos 310.0° = \cos(-50.0°) = \cos 50.0°$
$\sin 310.0° = \sin(-50.0°) = -\sin 50.0°$

$$F_{net} = \sqrt{(F_{1x} + F_{2x})^2 + (F_{1y} + F_{2y})^2}$$
$$= \sqrt{(11.8\text{ N} + 9.0\text{ N})^2 + (2.0\text{ N} - 10.7\text{ N})^2}$$
$$= \sqrt{(20.8\text{ N})^2 + (-8.7\text{ N})^2} = 22.5\text{ N}$$

$$\tan\theta = \frac{F_y}{F_x} = \frac{-8.7\text{ N}}{20.8\text{ N}} = -0.418$$
$$\theta = -22.7° \text{ or } 337.3°$$

16. Three people are pulling on a tree. The first person pulls with 15 N at 65.0°; the second with 16 N at 135°; the third with 11 N at 195°. What is the magnitude and direction of the resultant force of the tree?

$F_{1x} = (15\text{ N})\cos 65.0° = 6.3\text{ N}$
$F_{1y} = (15\text{ N})\sin 65.0° = 13.6\text{ N}$
$F_{2x} = (16\text{ N})\cos 135° = -11.3\text{ N}$
$F_{2y} = (16\text{ N})\sin 135° = 11.3\text{ N}$
$F_{3x} = (11\text{ N})\cos 195° = -10.6\text{ N}$
$F_{3y} = (11\text{ N})\sin 195° = -2.8\text{ N}$

$F_x = F_{1x} + F_{2x} + F_{3x}$
$= 6.3\text{ N} + (-11.3\text{ N}) + (-10.6\text{ N})$
$= -15.6\text{ N}$

$F_y = F_{1y} + F_{2y} + F_{3y}$
$= 13.6\text{ N} + 11.3\text{ N} + (-2.8\text{ N}) = 22.1\text{ N}$

$$F_{net} = \sqrt{F_x^2 + F_y^2}$$
$$= \sqrt{(-15.6\text{ N})^2 + (22.1\text{ N})^2} = 27.1\text{ N}$$

$$\tan\theta = \frac{F_y}{F_x} = \frac{22.1\text{ N}}{-15.6\text{ N}} = -1.42$$

Since, from signs of F_x and F_y, θ is second quadrant angle $\theta = 180° - 54.8° = 125°$

Practice Problems

page 123

17. A net force of 55 N acts due west on an object. What added single force on the object produces equilibrium?

55 N, due east

18. Two forces act on an object. One force is 6.0 N horizontally. The second force is 8.0 N vertically.

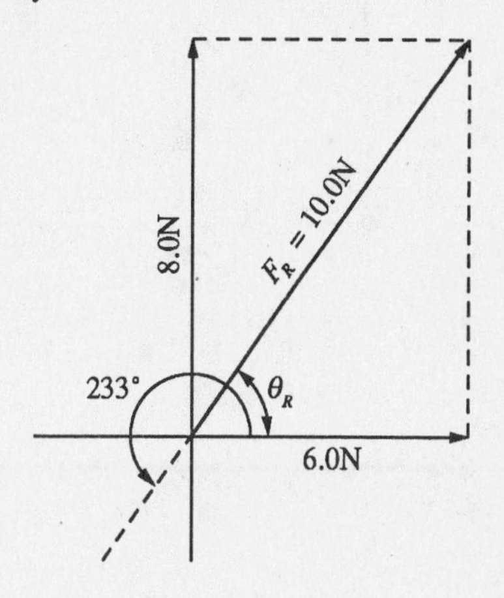

a. Find the magnitude and direction of the resultant.

$F_R = \sqrt{(6.0\text{ N})^2 + (8.0\text{ N})^2}$
$= 10.0\text{ N}$

$$\tan\theta_R = \frac{8.0}{6.0} = 1.33$$

$\theta_R = 53°$
$F_R = 10.0\text{ N at } 53°$

b. If the object is in equilibrium, find the magnitude and direction of the force that produces equilibrium.

$F_E = 10.0\text{ N at } 53° + 180° = 233°$

Practice Problems

19. A 62–N force acts at 30.0° and a second 62–N force acts at 60.0°.

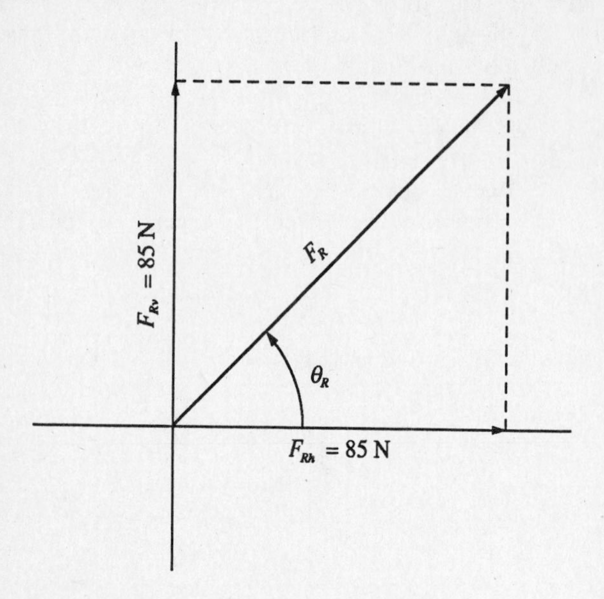

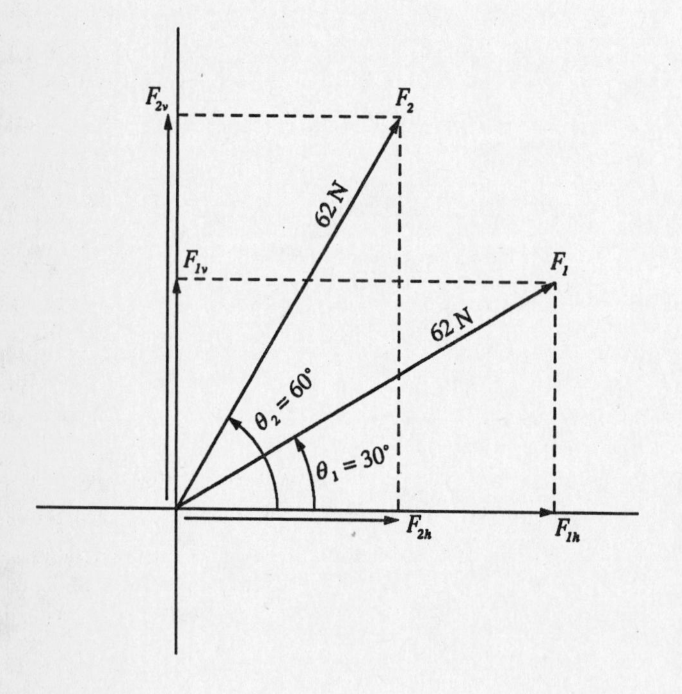

Practice Problems

a. Determine the resultant force.

Vector addition is most easily carried out by using the method of addition by components. The first step in this method is the resolution of the given vectors into their horizontal and vertical components.

$$F_{1h} = F_1 \cos\theta_1 = (62\text{ N})\cos 30° = 54\text{ N}$$
$$F_{1v} = F_1 \sin\theta_1 = (62\text{ N})\sin 30° = 31\text{ N}$$

$$F_{2h} = F_2 \cos\theta_2 = (62\text{ N})\cos 60° = 31\text{ N}$$
$$F_{2v} = F_2 \sin\theta_2 = (62\text{ N})\sin 60° = 54\text{ N}$$

At this point, the two original vectors have been replaced by four components, vectors that are much easier to add. The horizontal and vertical components of the resultant vector are found by simple addition.

$$F_{Rh} = F_{1r} + F_{2h} = 54\text{ N} + 31\text{ N} = 85\text{ N}$$
$$F_{Rv} = F_{1v} + F_{2v} = 31\text{ N} + 54\text{ N} = 85\text{ N}$$

The magnitude and direction of the resultant vector are found by the usual method.

$$F_R = \sqrt{(F_{Rh})^2 + (F_{Rv})^2}$$
$$= \sqrt{(85\text{ N})^2 + (85\text{ N})^2}$$
$$= 120\text{ N}$$

$$\tan\theta_R = \frac{F_{RV}}{F_{Rh}} = \frac{85\text{ N}}{85\text{ N}} = 1,\ \theta_R = 45°$$

$$F_R = 120\text{ N at } 45°$$

b. What is the magnitude and direction of the force that produces equilibrium?

F_E = 120 N, 225°

Practice Problems

20. Two forces act on an object. A 36-N force acts at 225°. A 48-N force acts at 315°. What would be the magnitude and direction of their equilibrant?

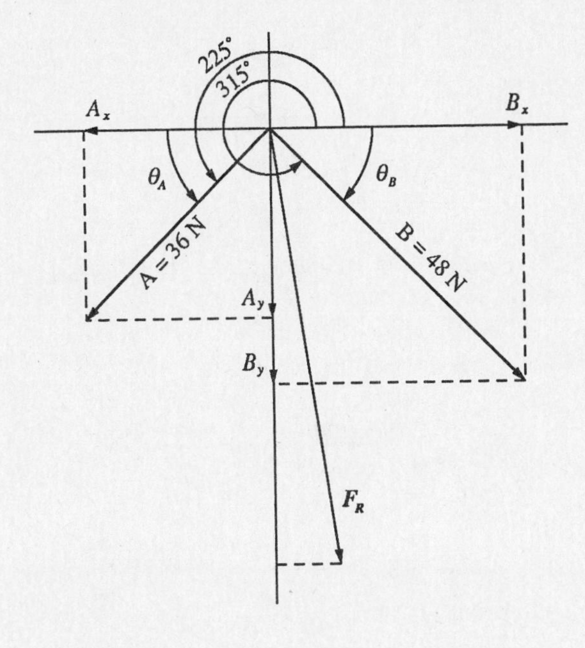

$\theta_A = 225° - 180° = 45°$
$\theta_B = 360° - 315° = 45°$
$A_x = -A \cos \theta_A = -(36 \text{ N}) \cos 45° = -25 \text{ N}$
$A_y = -A \sin \theta_A = (-36 \text{ N}) \sin 45° = -25 \text{ N}$
$B_x = B \cos \theta_B = (48 \text{ N}) \cos 45° = 34 \text{ N}$
$B_y = -B \sin \theta_B = -(48 \text{ N}) \sin 45° = -34 \text{ N}$
$F_x = A_x + B_x = -25 \text{ N} + 34 \text{ N} = 9 \text{ N}$
$F_y = A_y + B_y = -25 \text{ N} - 34 \text{ N} = -59 \text{ N}$

$$F_R = \sqrt{F_x^2 + F_y^2} = \sqrt{(-9 \text{ N})^2 + (-59 \text{ N})^2} = 60 \text{ N}$$

$$\tan \theta_R = \frac{9}{59} = 0.153, \ \theta = 9°$$

$\theta_R = 270° + 9° = 279°$
$F_R = 60 \text{ N at } 279°$
$F_E = 60 \text{ N}$
$\theta_E = 279° - 180° = 99°$

Practice Problems

21. The sign in the last Example Problem is now hung by ropes that each make an angle of 42° with the horizontal. What force does each rope exert?

Following the method of the Example Problem, the vertical component of the force exerted by each rope must support half of the sign weight.

$$A_v = B_v = \frac{168 \text{ N}}{2} = 84 \text{ N}$$

$$\frac{A_v}{\sin 42°} = A = \frac{84 \text{ N}}{\sin 42°} = 126 \text{ N}$$

$$B = A = 126 \text{ N}$$

22. The people who hung the sign decided to raise it higher by pulling the two ropes more horizontal. They increase the force on each rope to 575 N and keep the angles equal. What angle does each rope make with the horizontal now?

Since $A_v = A \sin \theta$, and $A_v = 84$ N and $A = 575$ N,

$$\sin \theta = \frac{84}{575} = 0.146$$

$$\theta = 8.4°.$$

page 126

23. The 562-N trunk is placed on an inclined plane that forms a 66° angle with the horizontal.

a. Calculate the values of $F_\perp$ and $F_\parallel$.

$F_\perp = (562 \text{ N}) \cos 66° = 229 \text{ N}$
$F_\parallel = (562 \text{ N}) \sin 66° = 513 \text{ N}$

b. Compare your results with those given above for the same trunk on a 30° incline.

The perpendicular force is less and the parallel force is greater on the 66° incline than in the case of the 30° incline.

6

Practice Problems

24. A car weighing 1.2×10^4 N is parked on a 36° slope.

  a. Find the force tending to cause the car to roll down the hill.

  $F_{||} = (1.2 \times 10^4 \text{ N}) \sin 36° = 7.1 \times 10^3$ N

  b. What is the force the car exherts perpendicular to the hill?

  $F_{\perp} = (1.2 \times 10^4 \text{ N}) \cos 36° = 9.7 \times 10^3$ N

25. The brakes in the car in Problem 24 fail, and the car starts to roll down the hill. Assume there is no friction.

  a. What is the acceleration of the car?

  $$a = \frac{F}{m} = \frac{F_{||}}{m} = \frac{mg \sin \theta}{m^2}$$

  $g \sin \theta = 5.8 \text{ m/s}^2$

  b. After it has moved 30 m, how fast is it moving?

  $v^2 = 2ad = 2(5.8 \text{ m/s}^2)(30 \text{ m})$, so
  $v = 19$ m/s

  c. Could a sprinter run this fast?

  No. A sprinter can run about 10 m/s.

26. The roof on a house rises 1.00 m over a horizontal distance of 3.50 m. A 71.0-kg roofer stands on the roof. Is the frictional force that keeps the roofer from slipping equal in magnitude to $F_{\perp}$ or $F_{||}$? What is its magnitude?

  $F_{||} = W \sin \theta$, where we find θ from

  $\tan \theta = (1.00 \text{ m})/(3.50 \text{ m}) = 0.286$, so
  $\theta = 16.0°$
  $W = (71.0 \text{ kg})(9.80 \text{ m/s}^2) = 969$ N,
  so $F_{||} = 191$ N.

Chapter Review Problems

page 129–131

1. What is the vector sum of a 65–N force acting due east and a 32–N force acting due west?

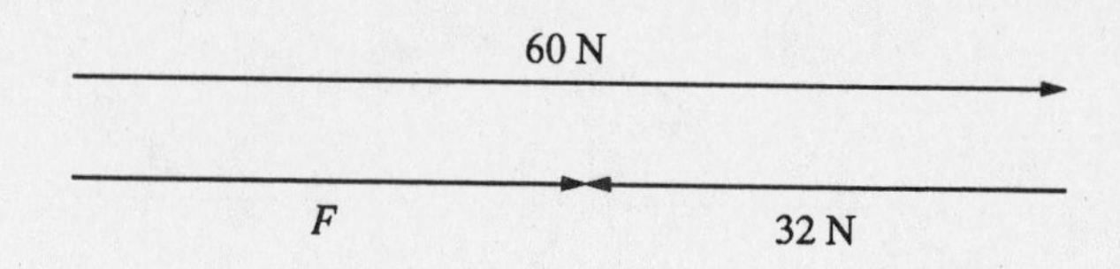

$F = 33$ N, due east

2. Graphically find the sum of the following pairs of vectors in Figure 6–25.

  a. D and C

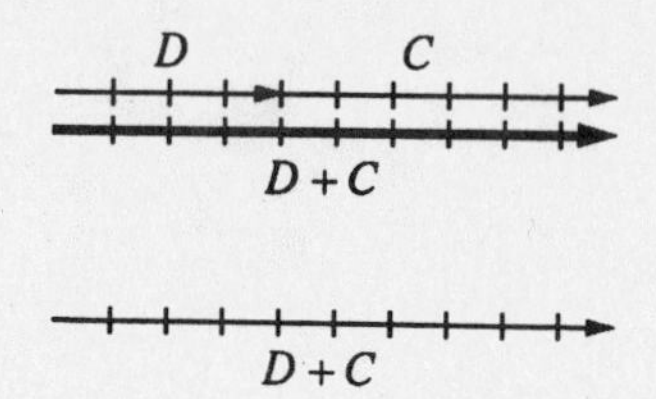

  b. A and D

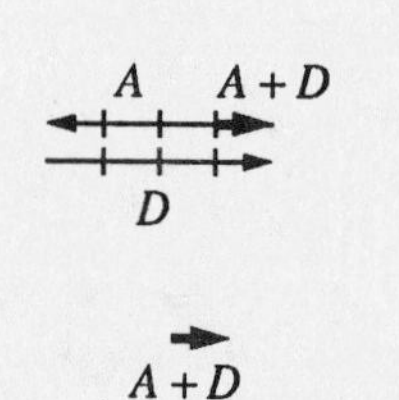

  c. C and A

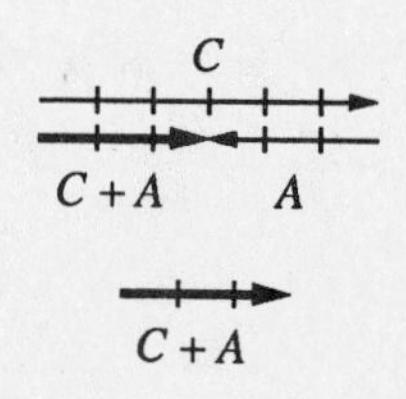

  d. A and C

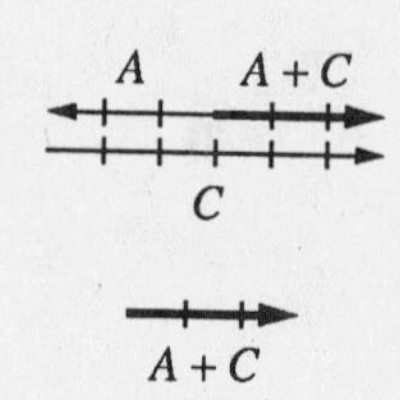

  e. E and F

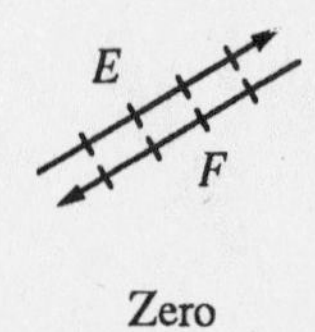

Zero

3. a. What is the resultant of a pair of forces, 100 N, upward and 75 N, downward?

   25 N, upward

   b. What is their resultant if they both act downward?

   175 N, downward

4. An airplane normally flies at 200 km/h. What is the resultant velocity of the airplane if

   a. it experiences a 50-km/h tail wind?

   Tail wind is in the same direction as the airplane;
   200 km/h + 50 km/h = 250 km/h.

   b. it experiences a 50-km/h head wind?

   Head wind is in the opposite direction of the airplane;
   200 km/h − 50 km/h = 150 km/h

5. Graphically add the following pairs of vectors in Figure 6–25.

   a. B and D

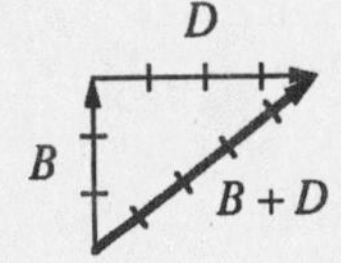

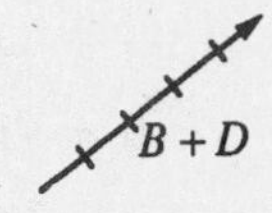

   b. C and E

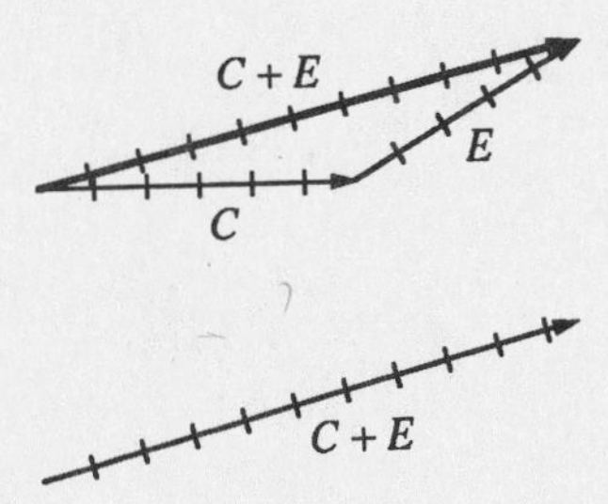

Chapter Review Problems

   c. D and E

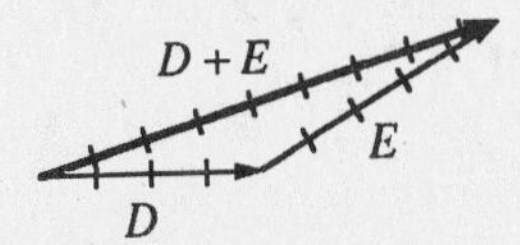

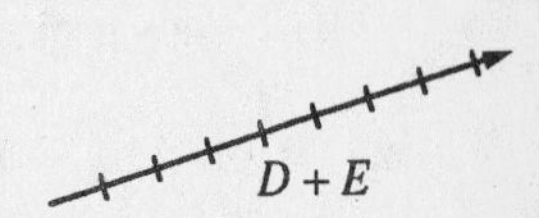

6. Graphically add the following vectors in Figure 6–25.

   a. A + C + D

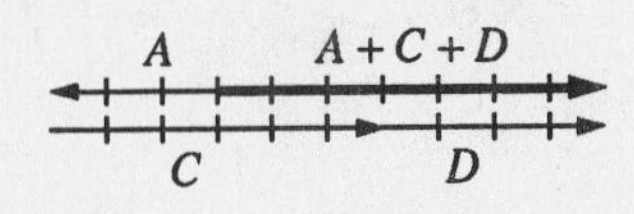

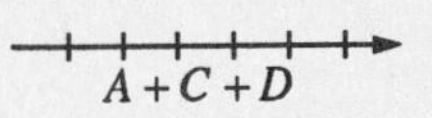

   b. D + E + B

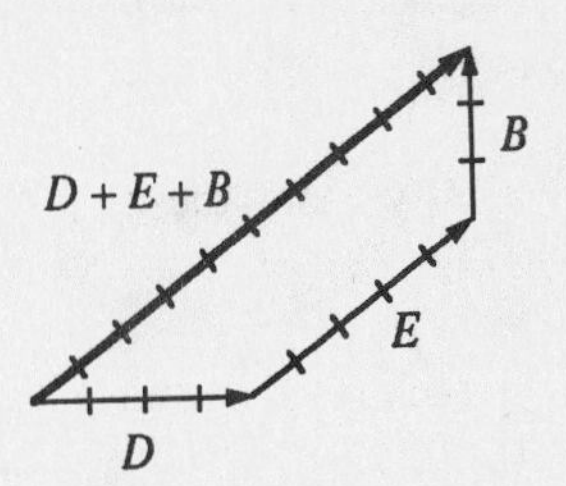

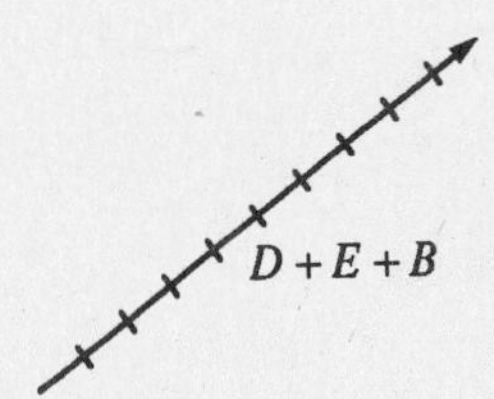

   c. B + D + F

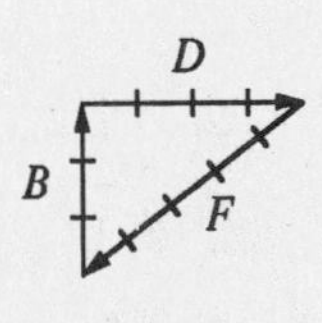

Zero

7. Three forces act on point *P*. Force *A* has a magnitude of 80.0 N and is directed at 60.0°. Force *B* has a magnitude of 70.0 N and is directed at 0.0°. Force *C* has a magnitude of 40.0 N and is directed at 315°.

a. Graphically add these three forces in the order A + B + C.

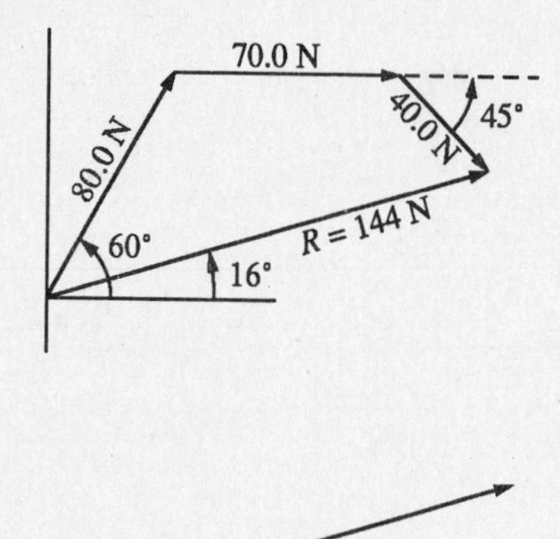

144 N, 16°

b. Graphically add these three forces in the order C + B + A.

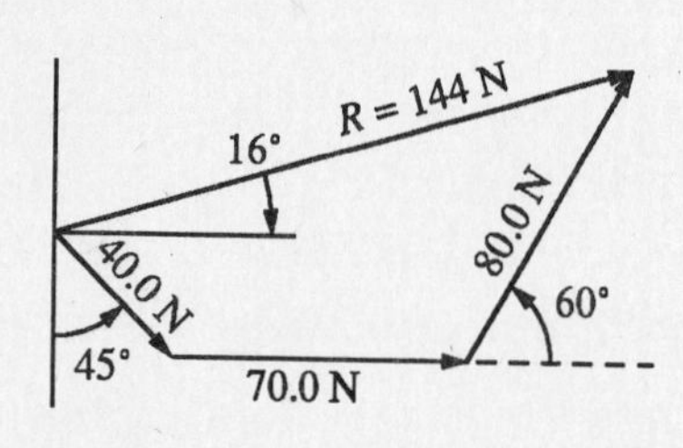

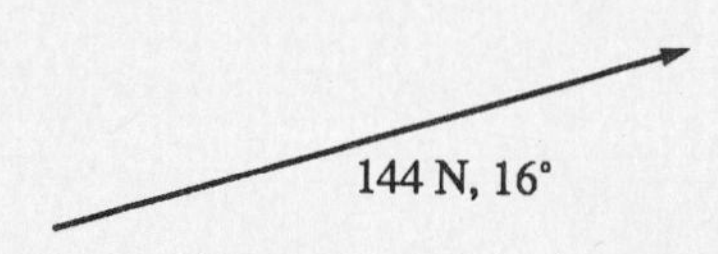

c. What is noted about the solutions in each case?

Added head to tail, each arrangement of the vectors should give the same resultant. This is about 144 N at 16°.

Chapter Review Problems

8. You head downstream on a river in a canoe. You can paddle at 5.0 km/h and the river is flowing at 2.0 km/h. How far downstream will you be in 30 minutes?

5 2

7

$d = vt =$ (7.0 km/h)(0.50 h) = 3.5 km

9. You walk 30 m south and 30 m east. Draw and add vectors for these two displacements. Compute the resultant.

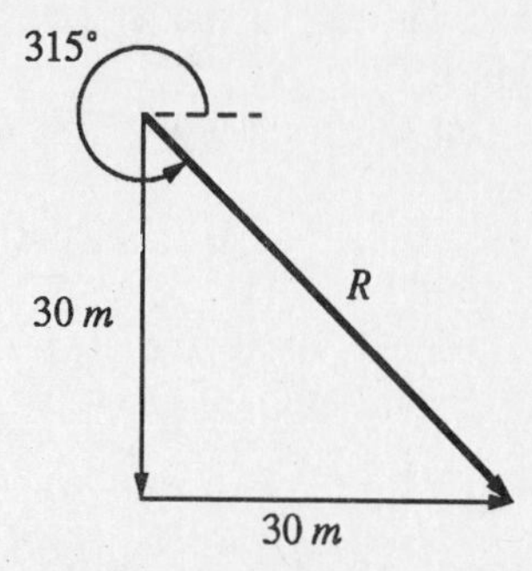

$$R^2 = A^2 + B^2$$

$$R = \sqrt{(30\ \text{m})^2 + (30\ \text{m})^2}$$

$$= \sqrt{1800\ \text{m}^2} = 42\ \text{m}$$

$$\tan\theta = \frac{30\ \text{m}}{30\ \text{m}} = 1$$

$$\theta = 45°$$

$$R = 42\ \text{m},\ 315°$$

Chapter Review Problems

10. A ship leaves its home port expecting to travel to a port 500 km due south. Before it can move, a severe storm comes up and blows the ship 100 km due east. How far is the ship from its destination? In what direction must the ship travel to reach its destination?

$R^2 = A^2 + B^2$

$R = \sqrt{(100 \text{ km})^2 + (500 \text{ km})^2} = \sqrt{260\,000 \text{ km}^2}$
$= 509 \text{ km}$

$\tan \theta = \dfrac{500 \text{ km}}{100 \text{ km}} = 5$

$\theta = 79°$
$R = 509 \text{ km}, 259°$

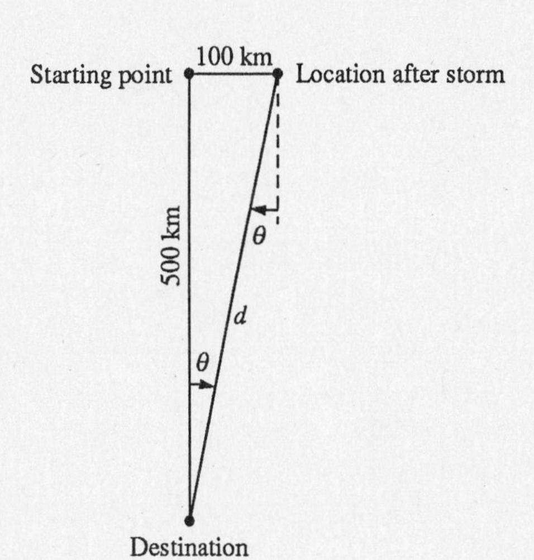

11. A hiker leaves camp and, using a compass, walks 4 km E, 6 km S, 3 km E, 5 km N, 10 km W, 8 km N, and 3 km S. At the end of three days, the hiker is lost. By drawing a diagram, compute how far the hiker is from camp and which direction should be taken to get back to camp.

Take north and east to be positive directions.
North: $-6 \text{ km} + 5 \text{ km} + 8\text{km} - 3 \text{ km} = 4 \text{ km}$
East: $4 \text{ km} + 3 \text{ km} - 10 \text{ km} = -3 \text{ km}$

The hiker is 4 km north and 3 km west of camp. To return to camp, the hiker must go 3 km east and 4 km south.

$R^2 = A^2 + B^2$

$R = \sqrt{(3 \text{ km})^2 + (4 \text{ km})^2} = \sqrt{25 \text{ km}^2} = 5 \text{ km}$

$\tan \theta = \dfrac{3 \text{ km}}{4 \text{ km}} = 0.75$

$\theta = 37°$
$R = 5 \text{ km}, 307°$

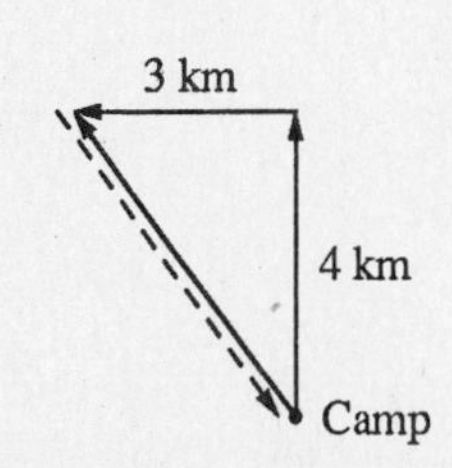

4 km E + 3 km E + 10 km W = 3 km W
6 km S + 5 km N + 8 km + 3 km S = 4 km N

Chapter Review Problems

12. Three forces act simultaneously on point J. One force is 10.0 N north; the second is 15.0 N west; the third is 15.0 N 30.0° east of north. Determine the magnitude and direction of the resultant force.

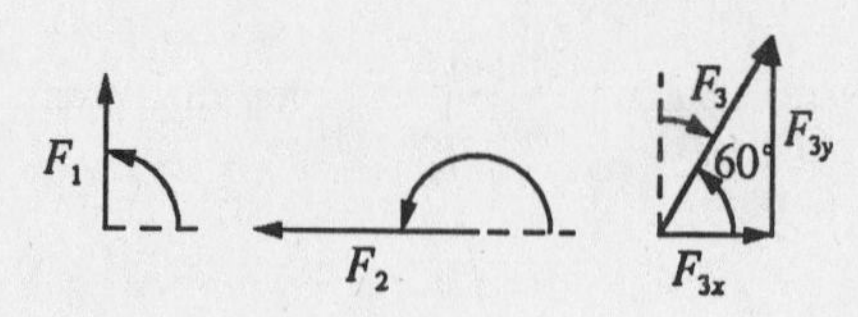

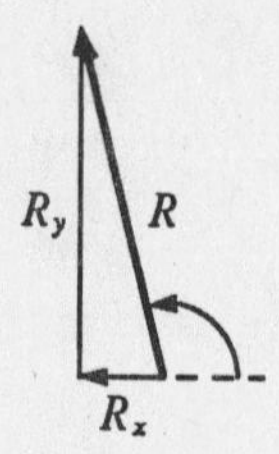

F_1 = 10.0 N north (90°)
F_2 = 15.0 N west (180°)
F_3 = 15.0 N, 60°

$F_{1x} = 10.0 \cos 90 = 0.0$
$F_{2x} = 15.0 \cos 180 = -15.0$
$F_{3x} = 15.0 \cos 60 = 7.5$

$F_{1y} = 10.0 \sin 90 = 10.0$
$F_{2y} = 15.0 \sin 180 = 0.0$
$F_{3y} = 15.0 \sin 60 = 13.0$

$R_x = 0.0 + (-15.0) + 7.5 = -7.5$ N
$R_y = 10.0 + 0.0 + 13.0 = 23.0$ N

$R^2 = \sqrt{R^2_x + R^2_y} = \sqrt{(-7.5\text{ N})^2 + (23.0\text{ N})^2} = \sqrt{585.3\text{ N}^2} = 24$

$\tan\theta = \dfrac{7.5}{23.0} = 0.326$

$\theta = 18°$
$R = 24.2$ N, 108°

13. Diane rows a boat at 8.0 m/s directly across a river that flows at 6.0 m/s.

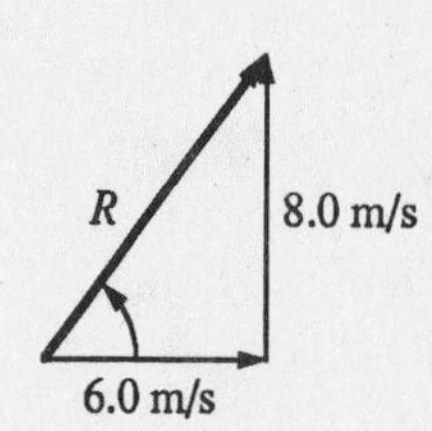

a. What is the resultant speed of the boat?

$R^2 = A^2 + B^2$

$R = \sqrt{(8.0\text{ m/s})^2 + (6.0\text{ m/s}^2)} = \sqrt{100\text{ m}^2/\text{s}^2} = 10$ m/s

$\tan\theta = \dfrac{8.0\text{ m/s}}{6.0\text{ m/s}} = 1.33$

$\theta = 53°$
$R = 10$ m/s, 53°, as measured from the bank

b. If the stream is 240 m wide, how long will it take Diane to row across?

$v = \dfrac{d}{t}$, so $t = \dfrac{d}{v} = \dfrac{240\text{ m}}{8.0\text{ m/s}} = 30$ s

c. How far downstream will Diane be?

$d = vt = (6.0\ \text{m/s})(30) = 1.8 \times 10^2\ \text{m}$

14. Dave rows a boat across a river at 4.0 m/s. The river is flowing at 6.0 m/s and it is 360 m across.

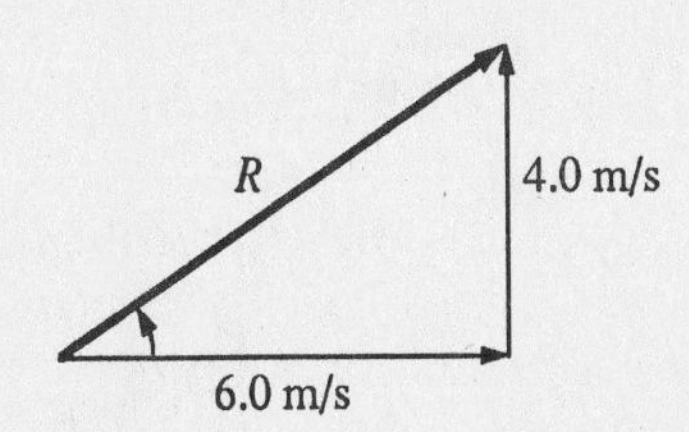

a. In what direction, relative to the shore, does Dave's boat go?

$\tan\theta = \frac{4.0}{6.0} = 0.67$

$\theta = 34°$

b. How long does it take Dave to cross the river?

$v = \frac{d}{t}$, so $t = \frac{d}{v} = \frac{360\ \text{m}}{4.0\ \text{m/s}} = 90\ \text{s}$

c. How far downstream is Dave's landing point?

$d = vt = 6.0(90) = 5.4 \times 10^2\ \text{m}$

d. How long would it take Dave to cross the river if there were no current?

90 s

15. Kyle is flying a plane due north at 225 km/h as a wind carries it due east at 55 km/h. Find the magnitude and direction of the plane's resultant velocity analytically.

$R^2 = A^2 + B^2$

$v = \sqrt{(55\ \text{km/h})^2 + (225\ \text{km/h})^2}$
$= 230\ \text{km/h}$

$\tan\theta = \frac{225\ \text{km/h}}{55\ \text{km/h}} = 4.09$

$\theta = 76°$
$v = 230\ \text{km/h},\ 76°$

Chapter Review Problems

16. Sue and Jenny kick a soccer ball at exactly the same time. Sue's foot exerts a force of 66 N north. Jenny's foot exerts a force of 88 N east. What is the magnitude and direction of the resultant force on the ball?

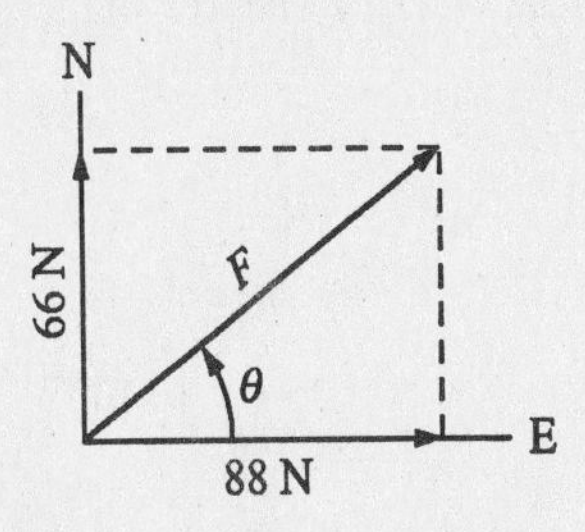

$R^2 = A^2 + B^2$

$R = \sqrt{(66\ \text{N})^2 + (88\ \text{N})^2} = \sqrt{12\,100\ \text{N}^2} = 110\ \text{N}$

$\tan\theta = \frac{66\ \text{N}}{88\ \text{N}} = 0.75$

$\theta = 37°$
$F = 1.1 \times 10^2\ \text{N},\ 37°$

17. Kym is in a boat traveling 3.8 m/s straight across a river 240 m wide. The river is flowing at 1.6 m/s.

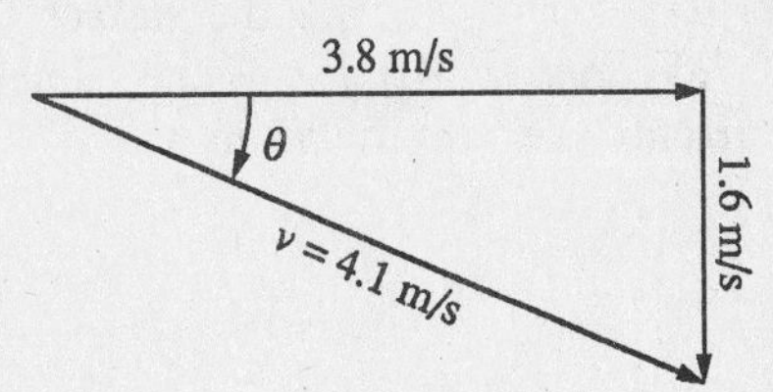

a. What is Kym's resultant velocity?

$R^2 = A^2 + B^2$

$R = \sqrt{(3.8\ \text{m/s})^2 + (1.6\ \text{m/s})^2} = 4.1\ \text{m/s}$

$\tan\theta = \frac{3.8\ \text{m/s}}{1.6\ \text{m/s}} = 2.38$
$\theta = 67°$ from bank

b. How long does it take Kym to cross the river?

$v = \frac{d}{t}$, so $t = \frac{d}{v} = \frac{2.40\ \text{m}}{3.8\ \text{m/s}} = 63\ \text{s}$

c. How far is Kym downstream when Kym reaches the other side?

$d = vt = (1.6\ \text{m/s})(63\ \text{s}) = 1.0 \times 10^2\ \text{m}$

18. A weather station releases a weather balloon. The balloon's buoyancy accelerates it straight up at 15 m/s². At the same time, a wind accelerates it horizontally at 6.5 m/s². What is the magnitude and direction (with reference to the horizontal) of the resultant acceleration?

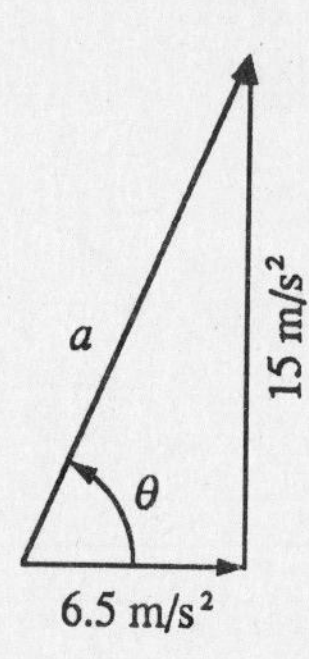

$a = \sqrt{(6.5\ \text{m/s}^2)^2 + (15\ \text{m/s}^2)^2} = 16\ \text{m/s}^2$

$\tan\theta = \dfrac{15\ \text{m/s}^2}{6.5\ \text{m/s}^2} = 2.31$

$\theta = 67°$

$a = 16\ \text{m/s}^2,\ 67°$

19. A descent vehicle landing on the moon has a vertical velocity toward the surface of the moon of 35 m/s. At the same time, it has a horizontal velocity of 55 m/s.

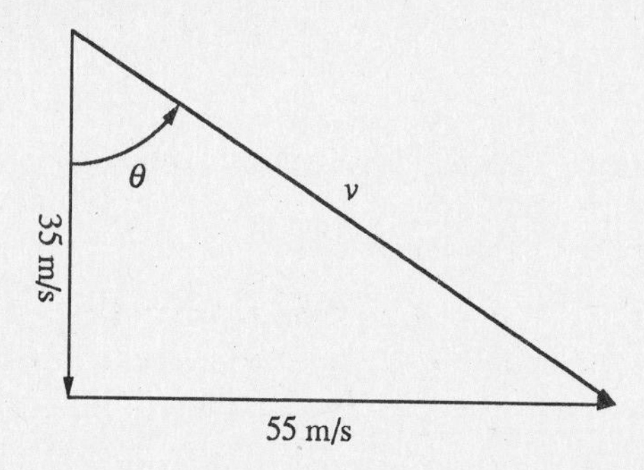

a. At what speed does the vehicle move along its descent path?

$R^2 = A^2 + B^2$

$R = \sqrt{(55\ \text{m/s})^2 + (35\ \text{m/s})^2} = 65\ \text{m/s}$

b. At what angle with the vertical is this path?

$\tan\theta = \dfrac{55\ \text{m/s}}{35\ \text{m/s}} = 1.57$

$\theta = 58°$

Chapter Review Problems

20. Kyle wishes to fly to a point 450 km due south in 3.00 hours. A wind is blowing from the west at 50 km/h. Compute the proper heading and speed that Kyle must choose in order to reach his destination on time.

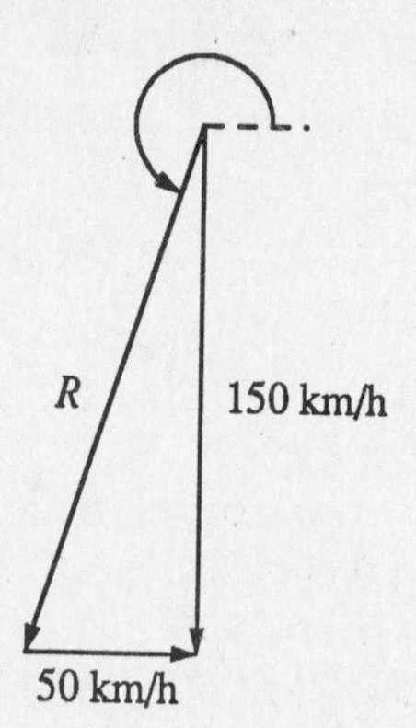

With no wind, $v = \dfrac{d}{t} = \dfrac{450\ \text{km}}{3.00\ \text{h}} = 150\ \text{km/h}$

Kyle's velocity and the wind must add to 150 km/h

$R^2 = A^2 + B^2$

$R = \sqrt{(50\ \text{km/h})^2 + (150\ \text{km/h})^2}$
$= 158\ \text{km/h}$

$\tan\theta = \dfrac{50\ \text{km/h}}{150\ \text{km/h}} = 0.333$

$\theta = 18°$

$R = 158$ km/h, 18° west of south

21. Dan applies a force of 92 N on a heavy box by using a rope held at an angle of 45° with the horizontal. What are the vertical and horizontal components of the 92–N force?

$F_h = F\cos\theta = (92\ \text{N})\cos 45 = 65\ \text{N}$

$F_v = F\sin\theta = (92\ \text{N})\sin 45 = 65\ \text{N}$

22. Beth, a construction worker, attempts to pull a stake out of the ground by pulling on a rope that is attached to the stake. The rope makes an angle of 60.0° with the horizontal. Beth exerts a force of 125 N on the rope. What is the magnitude of the upward component of the force acting on the stake?

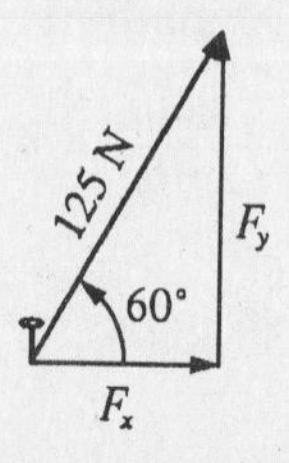

$F_v = F\sin\theta = (125\ \text{N})\sin 60 = 108\ \text{N}$

Chapter Review Problems

23. A 40-kg crate is pulled across the ice with a rope. A force of 100 N is applied at an angle of 30° with the horizontal.

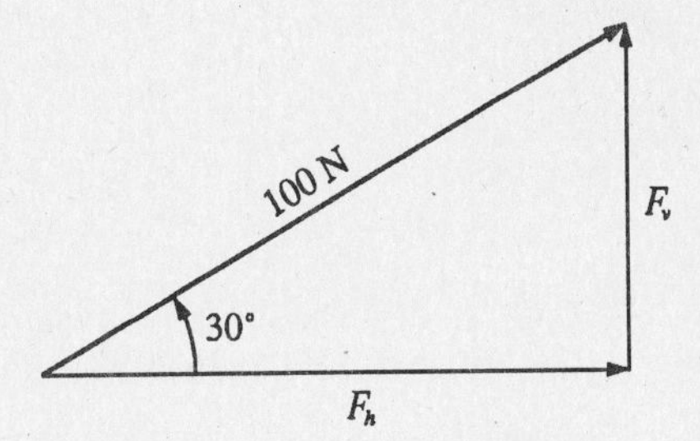

Calculate

a. the acceleration of the crate.

$$F_h = F \cos \theta$$

$$a = \frac{F_h}{m} = \frac{F \cos \theta}{m} = \frac{(100 \text{ N}) \cos 30}{40 \text{ kg}} = 2.2 \text{ m/s}^2$$

b. the upward force the ice exerts on the crate as it is pulled. Neglect friction.

$$F_v = F \sin \theta = (100 \text{ N}) \sin 30 = 50 \text{ N, up}$$

$$W = mg = (40 \text{ kg})(9.80 \text{ m/s}^2) = 390 \text{ N, down}$$

$$F_{ice} = W - F_v = 390 \text{ N} - 50 \text{ N} = 340 \text{ N, up}$$

24. Joe pushes on the handle of a 10-kg lawn spreader. The handle makes a 45° angle with the horizontal. Joe wishes to accelerate the spreader from rest to 1.39 m/s in 1.5 s. What force must Joe apply to the handle? Neglect friction.

$a = \frac{v}{t}$ and $F_h = ma = F \cos \theta$ so,

$$F = \frac{ma}{\cos \theta} = \frac{mv}{t \cos \theta} = \frac{(10 \text{ kg})(1.39 \text{ m/s})}{(1.5 \text{ s})(\cos 45)} = 13 \text{ N}$$

25. Tammy leaves the office, drives 26 km due north, then turns onto a second highway and continues in a direction of 30.0° north of east for 62 km. What is her total displacement from the office? Add displacements by components.

$d_1 = 26$ km, north $d_{1h} = (26 \text{ km}) \cos 90 = 0$ $d_{1v} = (26 \text{ km}) \sin 90 = 26$ km

$d_2 = 62$ km, 30.0° $d_{2h} = (62 \text{ km}) \cos 30 = 54$ km $d_{2v} = (62 \text{ km}) \sin 30 = 31$ km

$$R_h = 0 + 54 \text{ km} = 54 \text{ km}$$
$$R_v = 26 \text{ km} + 31 \text{ km} = 57 \text{ km}$$
$$R^2 = R^2_h + R^2_v$$
$$R = \sqrt{(54 \text{ km})^2 + (57 \text{ km})^2} = 79 \text{ km}$$

$$\tan \theta = \frac{57 \text{ km}}{54 \text{ km}} = 1.056,$$

so $\theta = 47°$
$R = 79$ km, 47°

Chapter Review Problems

26. Find the magnitude of the resultant of a 40–N force and a 70–N force acting concurrently when the angle between them is

a. 0.0°

40 N + 70 N = 110 N

b. 30.0°

R_h = 40 N + 70 cos 30 = 10 N R_v = 70 sin 30 = 35 N

$R = \sqrt{(101\ \text{N})^2 + (35\ \text{N})^2} = 107\ \text{N}$

c. 60.0°

R_h = 40 N + 70 cos 60 = 75 N R_v = 70 sin 60 = 61 N

$R = \sqrt{(75\ \text{N})^2 + (70\ \text{N})^2} = 97\ \text{N}$

d. 90.0°

R_h = 40 N R_v = 70 N

$R = \sqrt{(40\ \text{N})^2 + (70\ \text{N})^2} = 81\ \text{N}$

e. 180.0°

70 N − 40 N = +30 N

27. Three people attempt to haul a heavy sign to the roof of a building by using three ropes attached to the sign. Abby stands directly above the sign and pulls straight up on a rope. Eric and Kim stand on either side of Abby. Their ropes form 30.0° angles with Abby's rope. A force of 102 N is applied on each rope. What is the net upward force acting on the sign? See Figure 6–26.

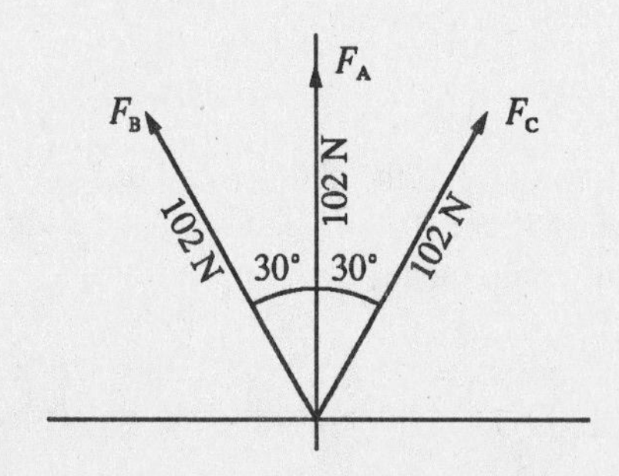

Eric: F_{eh} = (102 N) cos 60.0 = − 51.0 N F_{ev} = (102 N) sin 60.0 = 88.3 N

Abby: F_{ah} = (102 N) cos 90.0 = 0.0 F_{ah} = (102 N) sin 90.0 = 102 N

Kim: F_{kh} = (102 N) cos 60.0 = 51.0 N F_{kv} = (102 N) sin 60.0 = 88.3 N

R_h = − 51.0 N + 0 + 51.0 N = 0

R_v = 88.3 N + 102 N + 88.3 N = 279 N, up

28. A river flows toward 90°. Mark, a riverboat pilot, heads the boat at 297° and is able to go straight across the river at 6.0 m/s.
See Figure 6–27.

a. What is the velocity of the current?

$$\tan\theta = \frac{v_c}{6.0\ \text{m/s}},\ \text{so } v_c = (6.0\ \text{m/s})\tan 63° = 12\ \text{m/s, } 90°$$

b. What is the velocity of the boat as seen from the river bank?

6.0 m/s, 0°
Note: v_c is the velocity of the boat in still water.

29. An object in equilibrium has three forces exerted on it. A 33–N force acts at 90°, and a 44–N force acts at 60°. What is the magnitude and direction of the third force?
Solution by components.

F_1 = 33 N, 90° $\quad F_{1h}$ = (33 N) cos 90 = 0 $\quad F_{1v}$ = (33 N) sin 90 = 33 N
F_2 = 44 N, 60° $\quad F_{2h}$ = (44 N) cos 60 = 22 N $\quad F_{2v}$ = (44 N) sin 60 = 38 N
F_3 = ? $\quad F_{3h} = x \quad F_{3v} = y$

For equilibrium, the sum of the components must equal zero, so

$0 + 22\ \text{N} + x = 0$ and $x = -22\ \text{N}$
$33\ \text{N} + 38\ \text{N} + y = 0$ and $y = -71\ \text{N}$

$$R = \sqrt{(-22\ \text{N})^2 + (-71\ \text{N})^2} = 74\ \text{N}$$

$$\tan\theta = \frac{-71\ \text{N}}{-22\ \text{N}} = 3.23,\ \text{so } \theta = 73°$$

F_3 = 74 N, 253°

30. Five forces act on an object: the first, 60 N at 90°; the second, 40 N at 0°; the third, 80 N at 270°; the fourth, 40 N at 180°; and the fifth, 50 N at 60°. What is the magnitude and direction of a sixth force that produces equilibrium of the object?

Solutions by components

F_1 = 60 N, 90° $\quad F_{1h}$ = (60 N) cos 90 = 0 $\quad F_{1v}$ = (60 N) sin 90 = 60 N
F_2 = 40 N, 0° $\quad F_{2h}$ = (40 N) cos 0 = 40 N $\quad F_{2v}$ = (40 N) sin 0 = 0
F_3 = 80 N, 270° $\quad F_{3h}$ = (80 N) cos 270 = 0 $\quad F_{3v}$ = (80 N) sin 270 = – 80 N
F_4 = 40 N, 180° $\quad F_{4h}$ = (40 N) cos 180 = – 40 N $\quad F_{4v}$ = (40 N) sin 180 = 0
F_5 = 50 N, 60° $\quad F_{5h}$ = (50 N) cos 60 = 25 N $\quad F_{5v}$ = (50 N) sin 60 = 43 N
F_6 = ? $\quad F_{6h} = x \quad F_{6v} = y$

$0 + 40\ \text{N} + 0 + (-40\ \text{N}) + 25\ \text{N} + x = 0$, so $x = -25\ \text{N}$
$60\ \text{N} + 0 + (-80\ \text{N}) + 0 + 43\ \text{N} + y = 0$, so $y = -23\ \text{N}$

$$R = \sqrt{(-25\ \text{N})^2 + (-23\ \text{N})^2} = 34\ \text{N}$$

$$\tan\theta = \frac{-23\ \text{N}}{-25\ \text{N}} = 0.92,\ \text{so } \theta = 43°$$

F_6 = 34 N, 223°

31. A street lamp weighs 150 N. It is supported equally by two wires that form an angle of 120° with each other.

Solution by components.

a. What is the tension of these wires?

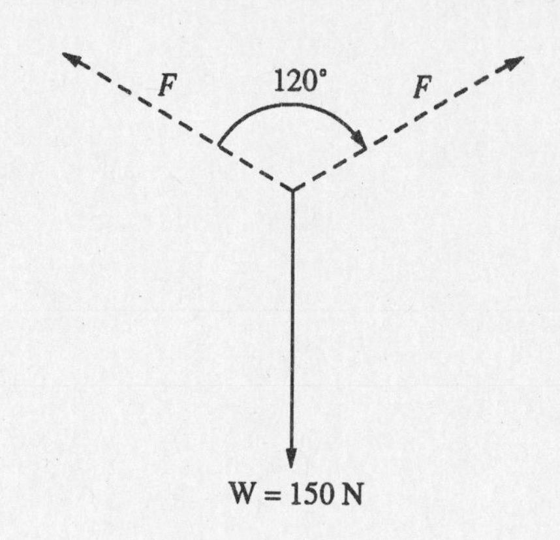

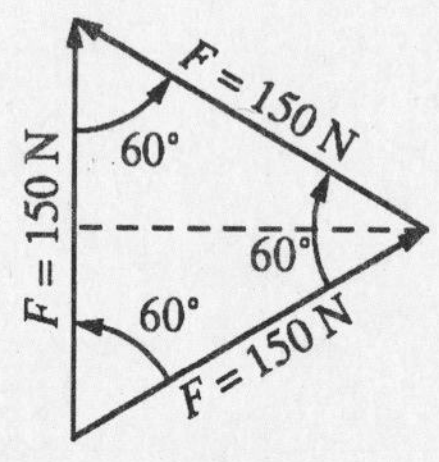

Horizontal $-T_{1h} + T_{2h} = 0$,
so $T_{1h} = T_{1v}$ and $T_1 \cos 30 = T_2 \cos 30$,
so $T_1 = T_2$
Vertical, $T_{1v} + T_{2v} - 150 \text{ N} = 0$,
so $T_1 \sin 30 + T_1 \sin 30 = 150$

$$T_1 = T_2 = \frac{150}{2 \sin 30} = 150 \text{ N}$$

b. If the angle between the wires is reduced to 90.0°, what new force does each wire exert?

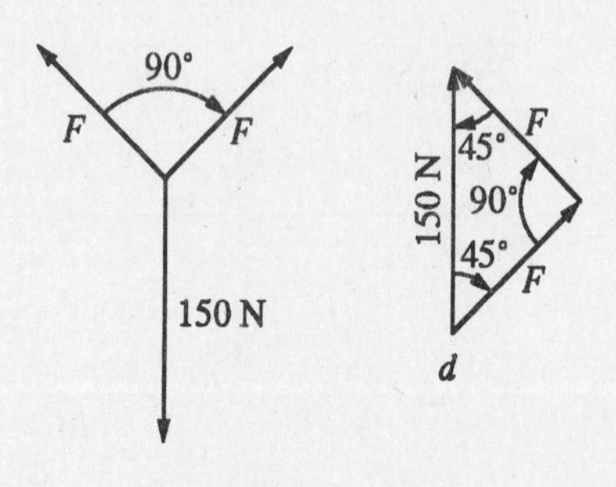

$$T_1 = T_2 = \frac{150}{2 \sin 45} = 106 \text{ N}$$

Chapter Review Problems

c. As the angle between the wire decreases, what happens to the force on the wire?

decreases toward 75 N

32. Joe wishes to hang a sign weighing 750 N so that cable A attached to the store makes a 30° angle as shown in Figure 6–28. Cable B is attached to an adjoining building. Calculate the necessary tension in cable B.

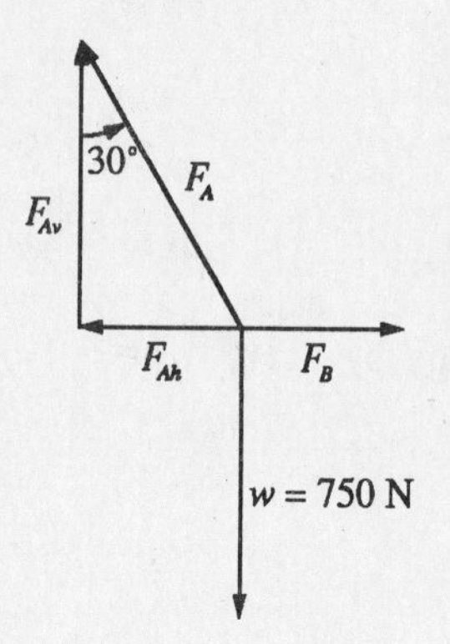

Solution by components.

The sum of the components must equal zero, so $F_{Av} - W = 0$ and $F_{Av} = F \sin 60.0 = 750$ N

$$F = \frac{750 \text{ N}}{\sin 60} = 866 \text{ N}$$

Also, $F_B - F_{Ah} = 0$,
so $F_B - F_{Ah} = (866 \text{ N}) \cos 60 = 433$ N, right

33. Rachel pulls her 18–kg suitcase at a constant speed by pulling on a handle that makes an angle θ with the horizontal. The frictional force on the suitcase is 27 N and Rachel exerts a 43–N force on the handle.

Rachel pulls at constant speed, so the suitcase is at equilibrium and the sum of components equals zero.

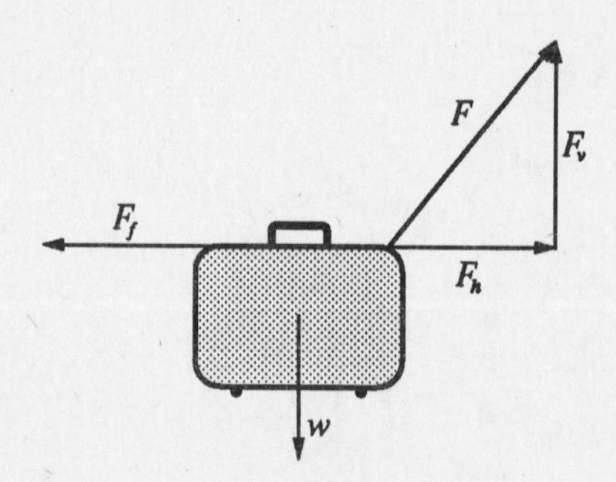

Chapter Review Problems

a. What angle does the handle make with the horizontal?

$F_h - F_f = 0$, so $F_h = F_f = 27$ N and

$\cos\theta = \frac{F_h}{F} = \frac{27 \text{ N}}{43 \text{ N}}$, so $\theta = 51°$.

b. What is the normal force exerted on the suitcase?

$Fn + Fv - W = 0$, so
$F_N = W - Fv = mg - F \sin\theta$
$= (18 \text{ kg})(9.80 \text{ m/s}^2) - 43 \sin 51°$
$= 1.4 \times 10^2$ N, up

34. You place a box weighing 215 N on an inclined plane that makes a 35.0° angle with the horizontal. Compute the component of the gravitational force acting down the inclined plane.

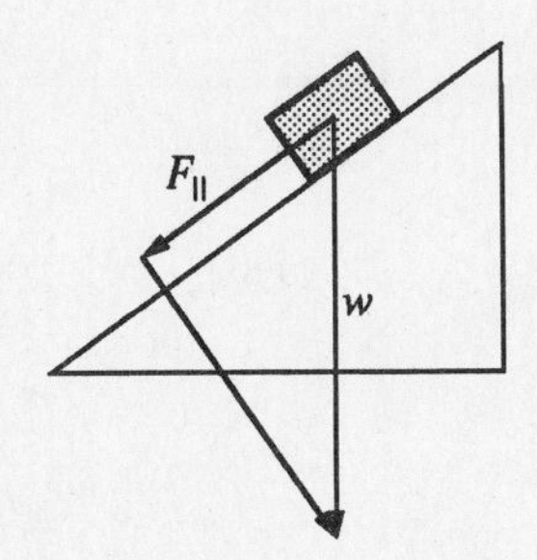

$F_{||} = W \sin\theta$
$= (215 \text{ N}) \sin 35°$
$= 123$ N

35. You slide a 325-N trunk up a 20.0° inclined plane with a constant velocity by exerting a force of 211 N parallel to the inclined plane.

a. What is the component of the trunk's weight parallel to the plane?

$F_{||} = W \sin\theta = (325 \text{ N}) \sin 20 = 111$ N

b. What is the sum of your applied force, friction, and the parallel component of the trunk's weight? Why?

zero, because the velocity is constant

c. What is the size and direction of the friction force?

Let up plane be positive, then
$F - F_{||} - F_f = 0$

$211 \text{ N} - 111 \text{ N} - F_f = 0$, so
$F_f = 100$ N, downward along the plane

d. What is the coefficient of friction?

$$\mu = \frac{F_f}{F_N} = \frac{100 \text{ N}}{325 \cos 20} = 0.327$$

36. What force would you have to exert on the trunk in Problem 35 so that it would side down the plane with a constant velocity? What would be the direction of the force? Positive direction still up plane.

$F - F_{||} + F_f = 0$, so

$F = F_{||} - F_f = W \sin\theta - \mu W \cos\theta$
$= (325 \text{ N}) \sin 20$
$- (0.327)(325) \cos 20$
$= 11$ N, up plane

37. A 2.5-kg block slides down a 25° inclined plane with constant acceleration. The block starts from rest at the top. At the bottom, its velocity reaches 0.65 m/s. The length of the incline is 1.6 m.

a. What is the acceleration of the block?

$v^2 = v_0^2 + 2ad$, but $v_0 = 0$,

so $a = \frac{v^2}{2d} = \frac{(0.65 \text{ m/s})^2}{2(1.6 \text{ m})} = 0.13 \text{ m/s}^2$

b. What is the coefficient of friction between the plane and block?

Let up plane be positive. Then,
$F_f - F_{||} = -(ma)$, so $Ff = F_{||} - (ma)$

$$\mu = \frac{F_f}{F_N} = \frac{F_{||} - (ma)}{F_N} = \frac{W \sin\theta - (ma)}{W \cos\theta}$$
$$= \frac{mg \sin\theta - ma}{mg \cos\theta} = \frac{m(g \sin\theta - a)}{mg \cos\theta}$$
$$= \frac{(9.80 \text{ m/s}^2) \sin 25 - (0.13 \text{ m/s}^2)}{(9.80 \text{ m/s}^2) \cos 25}$$
$$= \frac{4.01 \text{ m/s}^2}{8.88 \text{ m/s}^2}$$
$$= 0.452$$

c. Does the result of either **a** or **b** depend on the mass of the block?

No. In part b, the mass divides out.

Supplemental Problems (Appendix B)

1. Find θ if

a. $\tan \theta = 9.5143$. $\theta = 84.000°$

b. $\sin \theta = .4540$. $\theta = 27.00°$

c. $\cos \theta = .8192$. $\theta = 35.00°$

d. $\tan \theta = .1405$. $\theta = 7.998°$

e. $\sin \theta = .7547$. $\theta = 49.00°$

f. $\cos \theta = .9781$. $\theta = 12.01°$

2. Find the value of:

a. $\tan 28° = 0.53$

b. $\sin 86° = 1.0$

c. $\cos 2° = 1$

d. $\tan 58° = 1.6$

e. $\sin 40° = 0.64$

f. $\cos 71° = 0.33$

3. Solve for all sides and all angles for the following right triangles.

a.

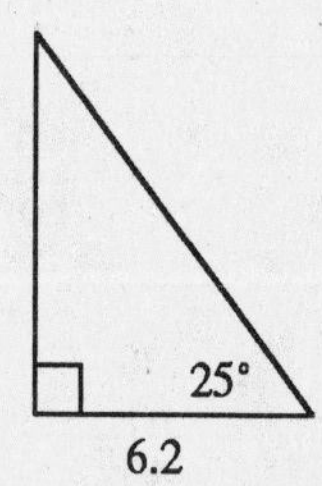

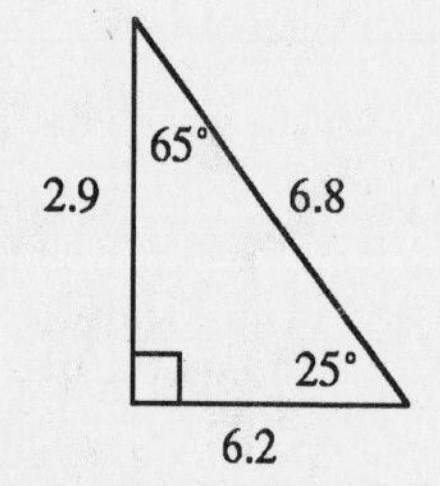

Supplemental Problems (Appendix B)

b.

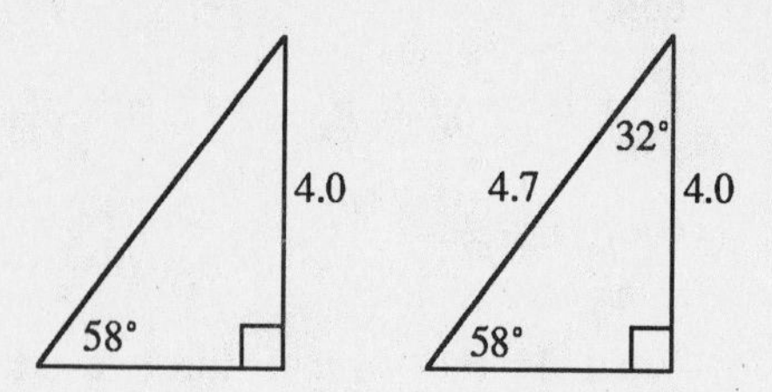

c.

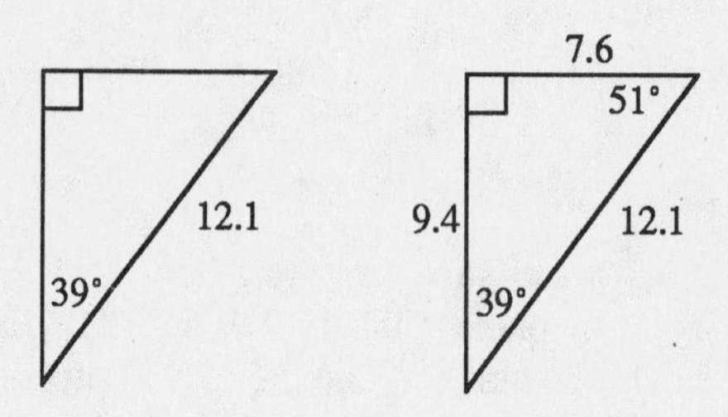

d.

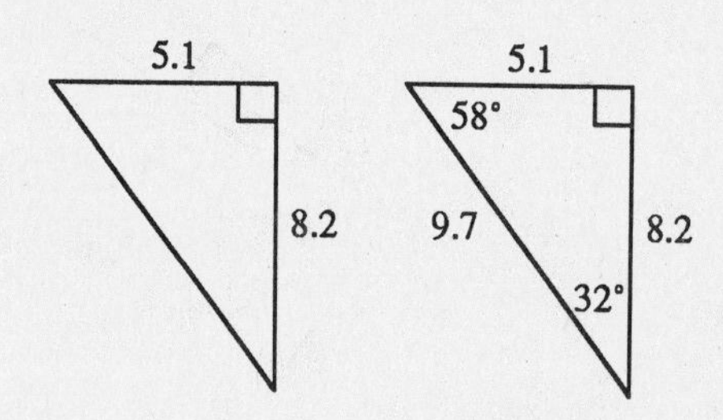

e.

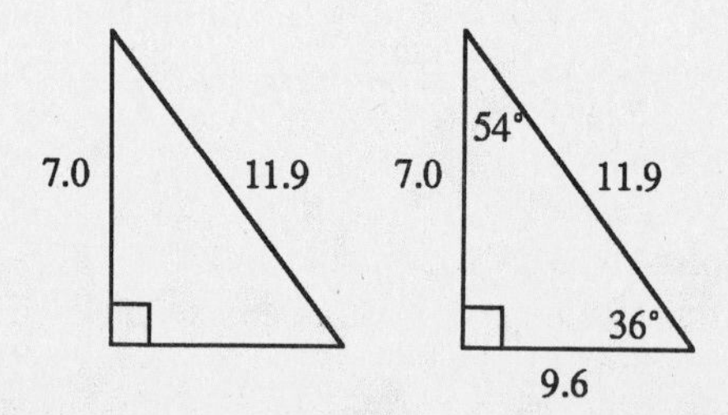

4. An 80–N and a 60–N force act concurrently on a point. Find the magnitude of the vector sum if the forces pull

a. in the same direction.

60 N

80 N

140 N

b. in opposite directions.

20 N

c. at a right angle to each other.

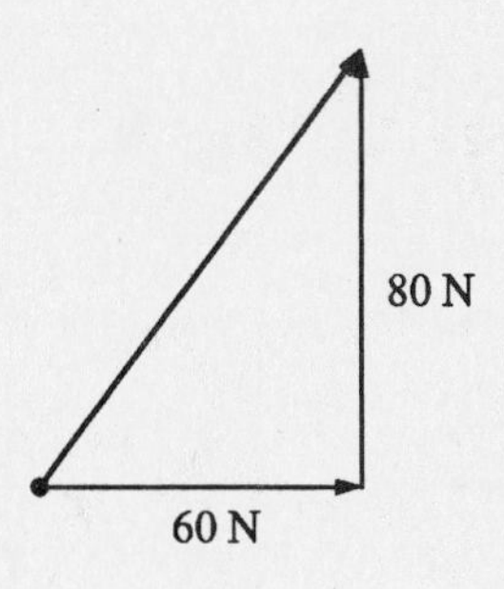

100 N

5. You head downstream on a river in an outboard. The current is flowing at a rate of 1.50 m/s. After 30.0 min, you find that you have traveled 24.3 km. How long will it take you to trave back upstream to your original point of departure?

Downstream:

$$v_{down} = \frac{(24.3\text{ km})(1.00 \times 10^3\text{ m/km})}{(30.0\text{ min})(60.0\text{ s/min})}$$

$= 13.5$ m/s

$v_{boat} = v_{down} - v_{current} = 13.5$ m/s $- 1.50$ m/s

$v_{boat} = 12.0$ m/s

Upstream:

$v_{up} = v_{boat} - v_{current} = 12.0$ m/s $- 1.50$ m/s

$= 10.5$ m/s

$v_{up} = d/t$; so $t = d/v_{up} = 2.43 \times 10^4$ m/10.5 m/s

$t = 2.31 \times 10^3$ s $= 38.5$ min

Supplemental Problems

6. One force of 60 N and a second of 30 N act on an object at point P. Graphically add the vectors and find the magnitude of the resultant when the angle between them is as follows.

a. 0°

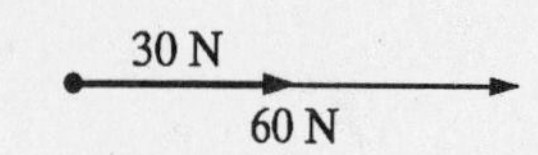

90 N

b. 30°

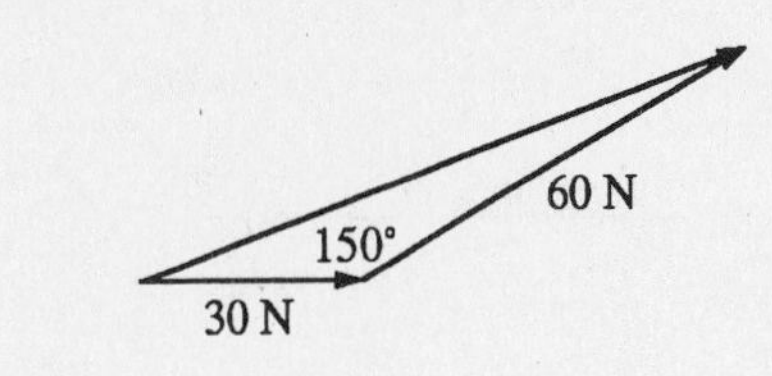

87 N

c. 45°

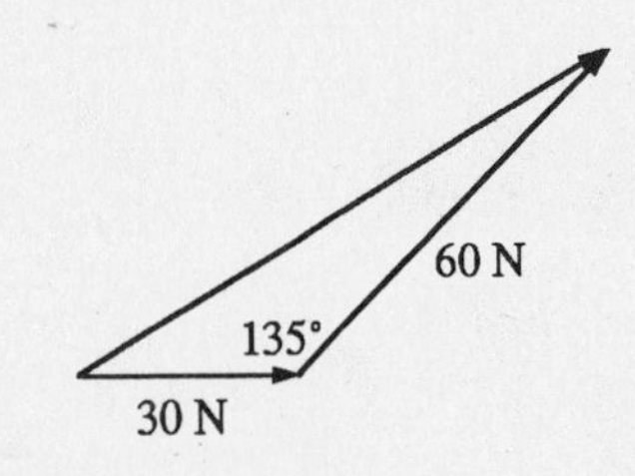

84 N

d. 60°

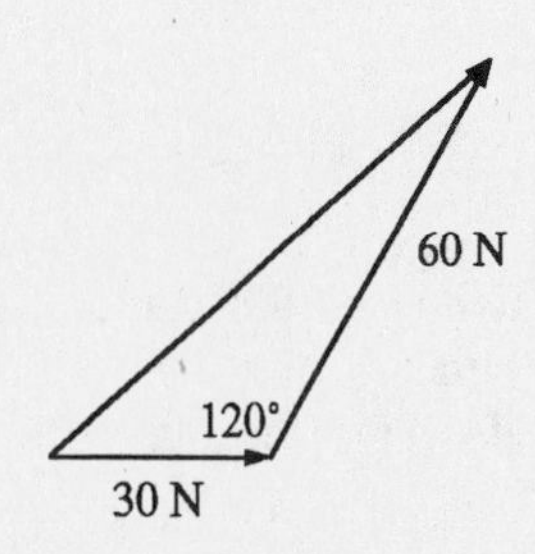

79 N

6

Supplemental Problems

e. 90°

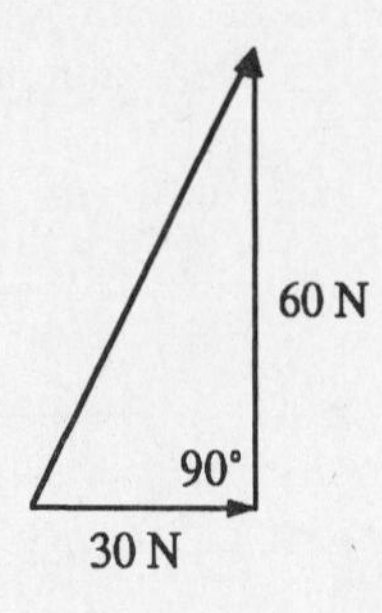

67 N

f. 180°

30 N

7. You walk 30 m south and 30 m east. Draw and add vectors representing these two displacements.

$R^2 = (30\text{ m})^2 + (30\text{ m})^2$
$R = 42\text{ m}, 315°$

$\tan\theta = \frac{30\text{ m}}{30\text{ m}} = 1$

$\theta = 45°$

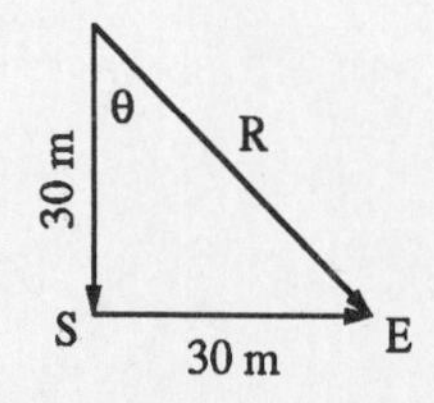

8. A plane flying at 90° at 1.00 × 10² m/s is blown toward 180° at 5.0 × 10¹ m/s by a strong wind. Find the plane's resultant velocity and direction.

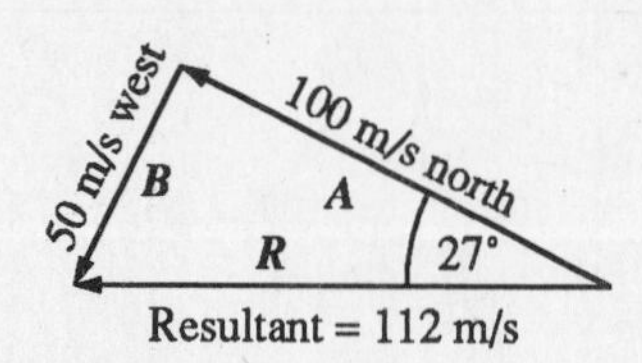

$v = 112\text{ m/s}, 117°$

9. In tackling a running back from the opposing team, a defensive lineman exerts a force of 500 N at 180°, while a linebacker simultaneously applies a force of 650 N at 270°. What is the resultant force on the ball carrier?

$R^2 = 650^2 + 500^2$
$R = 820\text{ N}$

$\tan\theta = \frac{650}{500}$

$\theta = 52°$
$180° + 52 = 232°$
$F = 820\text{ N}, 232°$

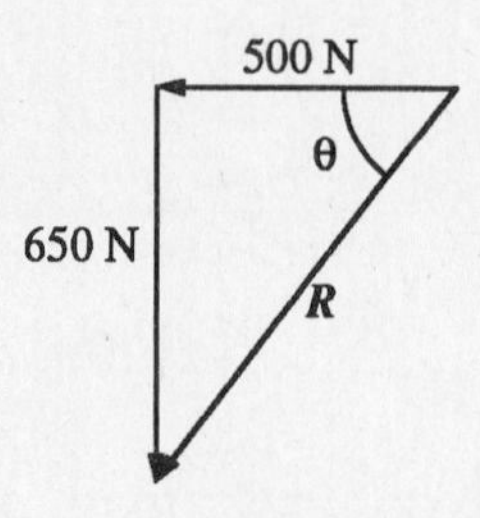

10. A hobo hops a freight car 15 m long and 3.0 m wide. The car is moving east at 2.5 m/s. Exploring the surroundings, the hobo walks from corner *A* to corner *B* in 20.0 s; then from corner *B* to corner *C* in 5.0 s as shown below. With the aid of a vector diagram, compute the hobo's displacement relative to the ground.

$d_{car} = vt = (2.5\text{ m/s})(25.0\text{ s}) = 63\text{ m}$
$d_E = 63\text{ m} - 15\text{ m} = 48\text{ m}$
$R^2 = (48\text{ m})^2 + (3.0\text{ m})^2$
$R = 48.1\text{ m}$
$R = 48.1\text{ m}, 3.6°\text{ N of E}$

$\tan\theta = \frac{3.0\text{ m}}{48} = 0.063$
$\theta = 3.6°$

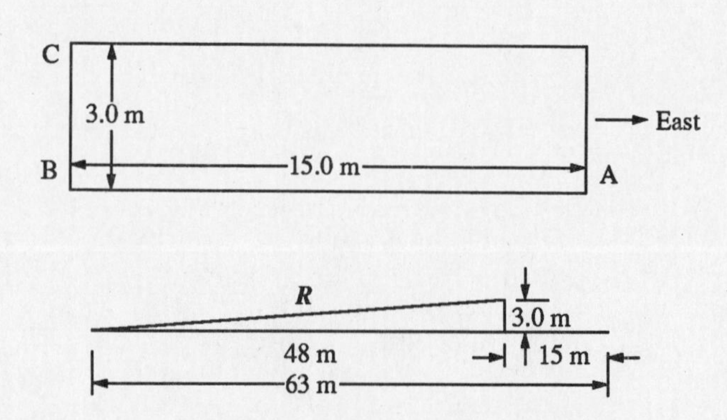

11. A plane travels on a heading of 40.0° for a distance of 3.00×10^2 km. How far north and how far east does the plane travel?

$d_N = d \sin \theta = (3.00 \times 10^2 \text{ km})(\sin 40°)$
$= 1.93 \times 10^2$ km, north
$d_E = d \cos \theta = (3.00 \times 10^2 \text{ km})(\cos 40°)$
$= 2.30 \times 10^2$ km, east

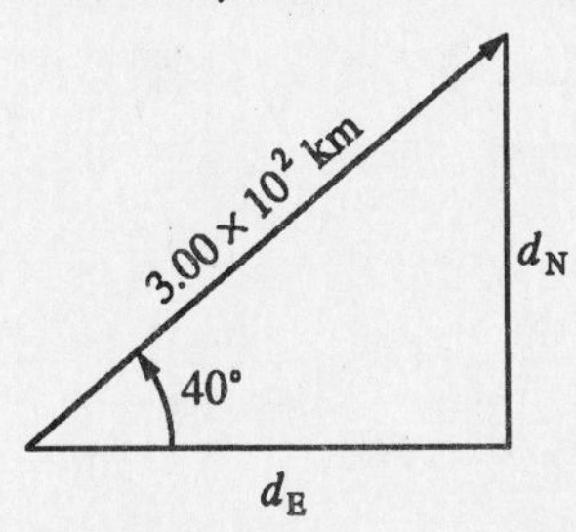

12. A water skier is towed by a speedboat. The skier moves to one side of the boat in such a way that the tow rope forms an angle 55° with the direction of the boat. The tension on the rope is 350 N. What would be the tension on the rope if the skier were directly behind the boat?

$F_T = (350 \text{ N})(\cos 55°) = 200$ N

13. What are the x and y components of a velocity vector of magnitde 100 km/h and direction of 240°.

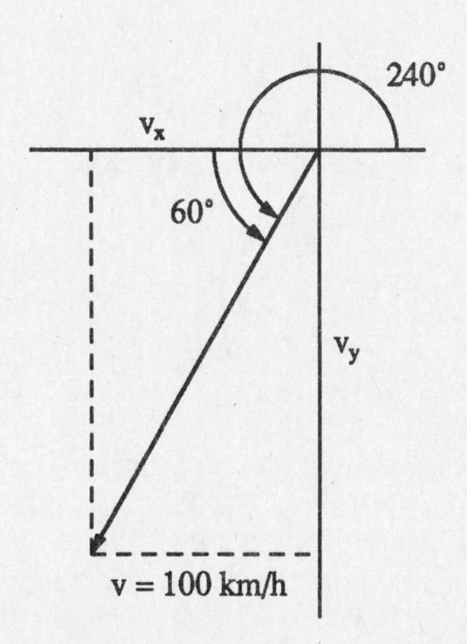

$v_x = v \cos \theta = (100 \text{ km/h}) \cos 240°$
$= -(100 \text{ km/h} \cos 60° = -50.0$ km/h
$v_y = v \sin \theta = (100 \text{ km/h}) \sin 240°$
$= -(100 \text{ km/h}) \sin 60° = -86.6$ km/h
$v_x = -50.0$ km/h, $v_y = -86.6$ km/h

Supplemental Problems

14. Wendy pushes a lawn spreader across a lawn by applying a force of 95 N along the handle that makes an angle of 60.0° with the horizontal.

a. What are the horizontal and vertical components of the force?

$F_h = F \cos \theta = (95 \text{ N})(\cos 60°) = 48$ N
$F_v = F \sin \theta = (95 \text{ N})(\sin 60°) = 82$ N

b. The handle is lowered so it makes an angle of 30.0° with the horizontal. Now what are the horizontal and vertical components of the force?

$F_h = F \cos \theta = (95 \text{ N})(\cos 30°) = 82$ N
$F_v = F \sin \theta = (95 \text{ N})(\sin 30°) = 48$ N

15. A brick layer applies a force of 100 N along each of two handles of a wheelbarrow. Its mass is 20 kg and it is loaded with 30 bricks, each of mass 1.5 kg. The handles of the wheelbarrow are 30° from the horizontal and the coefficient of friction is 0.20. What initial acceleration is given the wheelbarrow?

$F_N = \pm(200 \text{ N}) \sin 30° [20 \text{ kg}$
$+ (1.5 \text{ kg} \times 30)](9.8 \text{ m/s}^2)$
$= 637$ N
$F_f = \mu F_N = (0.20)(637 \text{ N}) = 127$ N
$F_h = 200 \text{ N} \cos 30° = 173$ N
$a = F/m = (173 \text{ N} - 127 \text{ N})/65 \text{ kg}$
$= 0.71 \text{ m/s}^2$

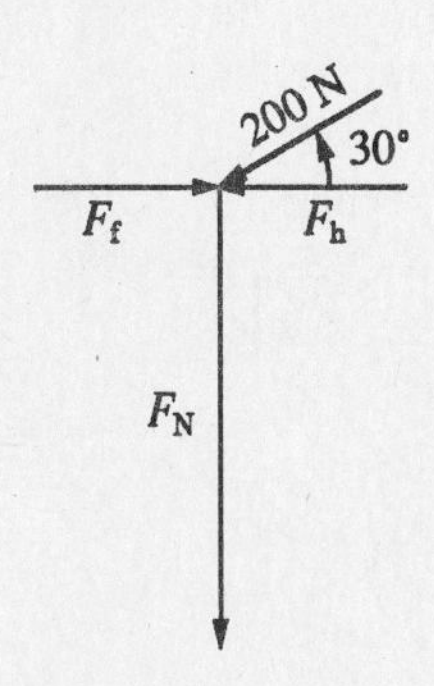

6

16. Two 15–N forces act concurrently on point P. Find the magnitude of their resultant when the angle between them is

See solution to Problem 4 for notation and method of solution using vector addition by components.

a. 0.0°. 30 N

b. 30.0°. 29 N

c. 90.0°. 21 N

d. 120.0°.

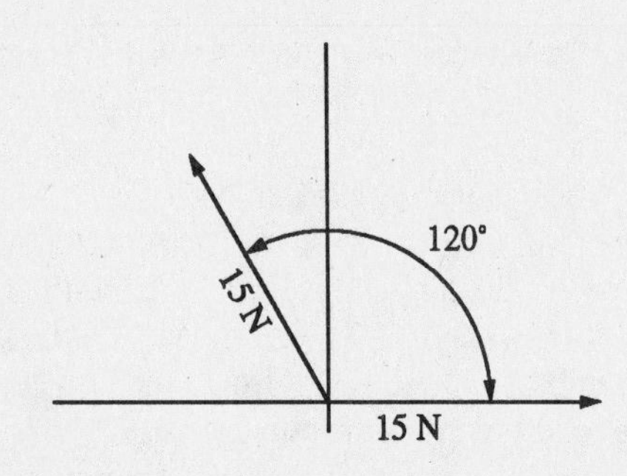

$$F_h = 15\text{ N} + (15\text{ N})\cos 120^\circ$$
$$= 15\text{ N} - 7.5\text{ N} = 7.5\text{ N}$$
$$F_v = (15\text{ N})\sin 120^\circ = 13\text{ N}$$
$$F = \sqrt{(7.5\text{ N})^2 + (13\text{ N})^2} = 15\text{ N}$$

e. 180.0°. 0 N

17. You are a pilot on an aircraft carrier. You must fly to another aircraft carrier, now 1450 km at 45° of your position, moving at 56 km/h due east. The wind is blowing from the south at 72 km/h. Calculate the heading and air speed needed to reach the carrier 2.5 h after you take off. **Hint:** Draw a displacement vector diagram.

Supplemental Problems

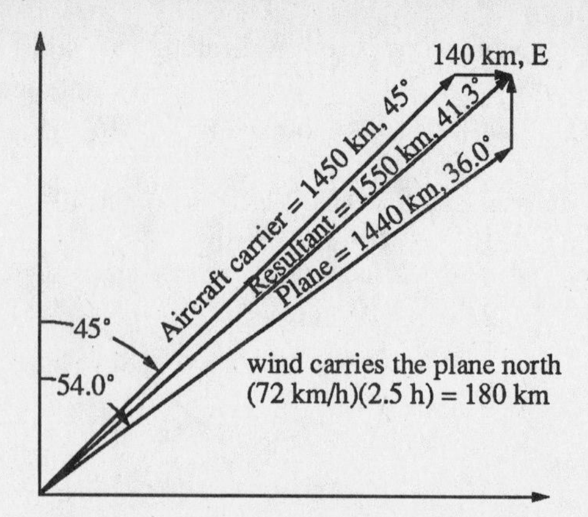

The position of second carrier in 2.5 h

(56 km/h)(2.5 h) = 140 km, E

R^2 = 1450 km, 45° + 140 km, 0°

= 1550 km, 41.3°

The wind will carry the plane 180 km, north during the 2.5 h.

Therefore,

d_1 + 180 km, 90° = R^2 = 1550 km, 41.3°

d_1 = 1440 km, 36.0°

Heading = 90.0° − 36.0° = 54.0° E of N

$$\text{Air speed} = \frac{1440\text{ km}}{2.5\text{ h}} = 580\text{ km/h}$$

580 km/h, 54° E of N

18. A 33–N force acting at 90° and a 44–N force acting at 60° act concurrently on point P. What is the magnitude and direction of a third force that produces equilibrium at point P?

Solution by component method.

$F_{1h} = 0$ N

$F_{1v} = F_1 = 33$ N

$F_{2h} = (44\text{ N})\cos 60^\circ = 22$ N

$F_{2v} = (44\text{ N})\sin 50^\circ = 38$ N

$F_h = 0\text{ N} + 22\text{ N} = 22$ N

$F_v = 33\text{ N} + 38\text{ N} = 71$ N

The resultant of the two given forces is

$$F = \sqrt{(22\text{ N})^2 + (71\text{ N})^2} = 74\text{ N}$$

$$\tan\theta = \frac{71\text{ N}}{22\text{ N}} = 3.23,\ \theta = 73^\circ$$

Equilibrant: 74 N, 253°

19. A person weighs 612 N. If the person sits in the middle of a hammock that is 3.0 m long and sags 1.0 m below the points of support, what force wouldbe exerted by each of the two hammock ropes?

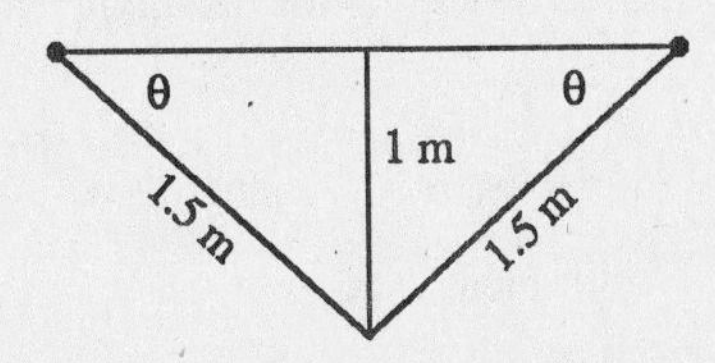

$\sin\theta = \frac{1}{1.5} = 0.667$

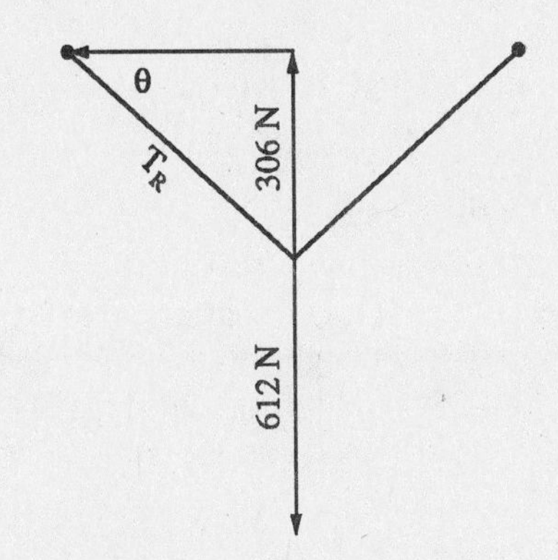

$\sin\theta = \frac{306\text{ N}}{T_R}$

$T_R = \frac{306\text{ N}}{\sin\theta} = \frac{306\text{ N}}{0.667} = 460\text{ N}$

20. A bell ringer decides to use a bowling ball to ring the bell. He hangs the 7.3-kg ball from the end of a 2.0 m long rope. He attaches another rope to the ball, and pulls it horizontally until the ball has moved 0.60 m away from the vertical to pull the ball back. How much force must he apply?

Angle pulled back from vertical given by $\sin\theta = 0.60/2.0 = 0.30$.
In equilibrium forces balance.
Vertical: $T\cos\theta = mg$;
horizontal: $T\sin\theta = F$, where T is the tension in the 2.0 m rope and F is the force on the horizontal rope.
Thus $F/mg = \tan\theta$ so
$F = (7.3\text{ kg})(9.8\text{ m/s}^2)(0.31) = 22\text{ N}$

Supplemental Problems

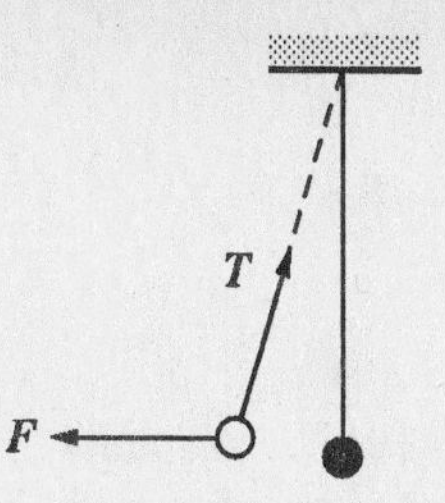

21. A mass, M, starts from rest and slides down the frictionless incline as shown. As it leaves the incline, its speed is 24 m/s. Note: The angle of the incline is 30.0°.

a. What is the acceleration of the mass while on the incline?

$F = W(\sin 30.0°) = 0.5\ W$
$Ma = 0.5\ Mg$
$a = 0.5\ g = 4.9\text{ m/s}^2$

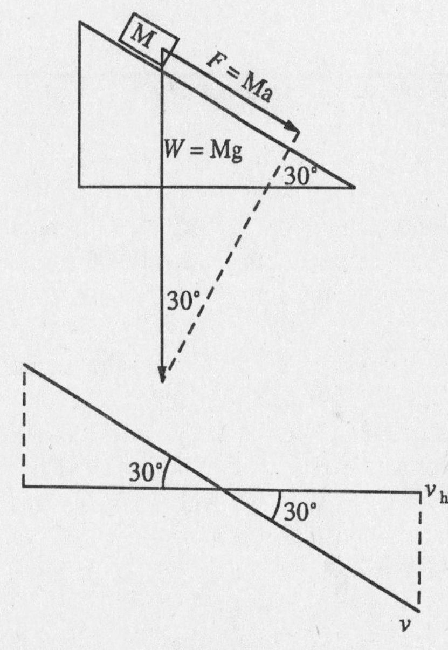

b. What is the length of the incline?

$v_f^2 = v_i^2 + 2ad$

$d = \frac{v_f^2 - v_i^2}{2a} = \frac{(24\text{ m/s})^2 - 0}{(2)(4.9\text{ m/s}^2)}$

$d = \frac{576\text{ m}^2/\text{s}^2}{(2)4.9\text{ m/s}^2} = 59\text{ m}$

c. How long does it take the mass to reach the floor after it leaves the top of the incline?

$a = \frac{\Delta v}{\Delta t}$, or $\Delta t = \frac{\Delta v}{a} = \frac{24\text{ m/s}}{4.9\text{ m/s}^2} = 4.9\text{ s}$

Chapter 7: Motion in Two Dimensions

Practice Problems

page 136

1. A stone is thrown horizontally at a speed of +5.0 m/s from the top of a cliff 78.4 m high.

   a. How long does it take the stone to reach the bottom of the cliff?

   Since $v_y = 0$, $y = v_y t + \frac{1}{2}gt^2$ becomes

   $y = \frac{1}{2}gt^2$, or

   $t^2 = \frac{2y}{g} = \frac{2(-78.4\text{ m})}{-9.80\text{ m/s}^2} = 16.0\text{ s}^2$,

   $t = \sqrt{16.05^2} = 4.00\text{ s}$.

   b. How far from the base of the cliff does the stone strike the ground?

   $x = v_x t = (5.0\text{ m/s})(4.00\text{ s}) = 20\text{ m}$

   c. What are the horizontal and vertical components of the velocity of the stone just before it hits the ground?

   $v_x = 5.0$ m/s. This is the same as the initial horizontal speed because the acceleration of gravity influences only the vertical motion. For the vertical component, use $v_f = v_i + gt$ with $v_f = v_y$ and v_i, the initial vertical component of velocity zero. At $t = 4.00$ s,
   $v_y = gt = (-9.80\text{ m/s}^2)(4.00\text{ s})$
   $= -39.2\text{ m/s}$.

2. How would the three answers to Problem 1 change if

   a. the stone were thrown with twice the horizontal speed?

   (a) no change; 4.00 s

   (b) twice the previous distance; 40 m

   (c) v_x doubles; 10 m/s
   no change in v_y; -39.2 m/s

Practice Problems

   b. the stone were thrown with the same speed but the cliff was twice as high?

   (a) increases by $\sqrt{2}$, since $t = \sqrt{\frac{2y}{g}}$ and y doubles; 5.66 s

   (b) increases by $\sqrt{2}$, since t increases by $\sqrt{2}$; 28 m

   (c) no change in v_x; 5.0 m/s
   v_y increases by $\sqrt{2}$, since t increases by $\sqrt{2}$; -55.4 m/s

3. A steel ball rolls with constant velocity across a tabletop 0.950 m high. It rolls off and hits the ground +0.352 m horizontally from the edge of the table. How fast was the ball rolling?

   Since $v_y = 0$, $y = \frac{1}{2}gt^2$ and the time to reach the ground is

   $t = \sqrt{\frac{2y}{g}} = \sqrt{\frac{2(-0.950\text{ m})}{-9.80\text{ m/s}}} = 0.440\text{ s}$.

   From $x = v_x t$,

   $v_x = \frac{x}{t} = \frac{0.352\text{ m}}{0.440\text{ s}} = 0.800\text{ m/s}$.

page 137

4. An auto, moving too fast on a horizontal stretch of mountain road, slides off the road, falling into deep snow 43.9 m below the road and 87.7 m beyond the edge of the road.

   a. How long did the auto take to fall?

   Following the method of Practice Problem 3,

   $t = \sqrt{\frac{2y}{g}} = \sqrt{\frac{2(-43.9\text{ m})}{-9.80\text{ m/s}^2}} = 2.99\text{ s}$.

b. How fast was it going when it left the road? (in m/s and km/h)

$$v_x = \frac{x}{t} = \frac{87.7\ \text{m}}{2.99\ \text{s}} = 29.3\ \text{m/s}$$

$$= 29.3\ \text{m/s}\left[\frac{1\ \text{km}}{1000\ \text{m}}\right]\left[\frac{3600\ \text{s}}{1\ \text{h}}\right]$$

$$= 105\ \text{km/h.}$$

c. What was its acceleration 10 m below the edge of the road?

$g = -9.80\ \text{m/s}^2$ at at all times.

page 139

5. A player kicks a football from ground level with a velocity of magnitude 27.0 m/s at an angle of 30.0° above the horizontal, Figure 7–6. Find

a. its "hang time," that is, the time the ball is in the air.

$$v_x = v_i \cos\theta = (27.0\ \text{m/s})\cos 30.0^\circ = 23.4\ \text{m/s}$$

$$v_y = v_i \sin\theta = (27.0\ \text{m/s})\sin 30.0^\circ = 13.5\ \text{m/s}$$

When it lands, $y = v_y t + \frac{1}{2}gt^2 = 0$.

Therefore,

$$t = \frac{-2v_y}{g} = \frac{-2(13.5\ \text{m/s})}{-9.8\ \text{m/s}^2} = 2.76\ \text{s.}$$

b. the distance the ball travels before it hits the ground.

$$x = v_x t = (23.4\ \text{m/s})(2.76\ \text{s}) = 64.6\ \text{m}$$

c. its maximum height.

Maximum height occurs at half the "long time," or 1.38 s. Thus,

$$y = v_y t + \frac{1}{2}gt^2$$

$$= (13.5\ \text{m/s})(1.38\ \text{s})$$

$$+ \frac{1}{2}(-9.80\ \text{m/s}^2)(1.38\ \text{s})^2$$

$$= 18.6\ \text{m} - 9.3\ \text{m} = 9.3\ \text{m.}$$

6. The kicker now kicks the ball with the same speed, but at 60.0° from the horizontal or 30.0° from the vertical. Find

a. its "hang time," that is, the time the ball is in the air.

Following the method of Practice Problem 5,

$$v_x = v_i \cos\theta = (27.0\ \text{m/s})\cos 60.0^\circ = 13.5\ \text{m/s}$$

$$v_y = v_i \sin\theta = (27.0\ \text{m/s})\sin 60.0^\circ = 23.4\ \text{m/s}$$

$$t = \frac{-2v_y}{g} = \frac{-2(23.4\ \text{m/s})}{-9.80\ \text{m/s}^2} = 4.78\ \text{s.}$$

b. the distance the ball travels before it hits the ground.

$$x = v_x t = (13.5\ \text{m/s})(4.78\ \text{s}) = 64.5\ \text{m.}$$

c. its maximum height.

at $t = \frac{1}{2}(4.78\ \text{s}) = 2.39\ \text{s}$,

$$y = v_y t + \frac{1}{2}gt^2$$

$$= (23.4\ \text{m/s})(2.39\ \text{s})$$

$$+ \frac{1}{2}(-9.80\ \text{m/s}^2)(2.39\ \text{s})^2 = 27.9\ \text{m.}$$

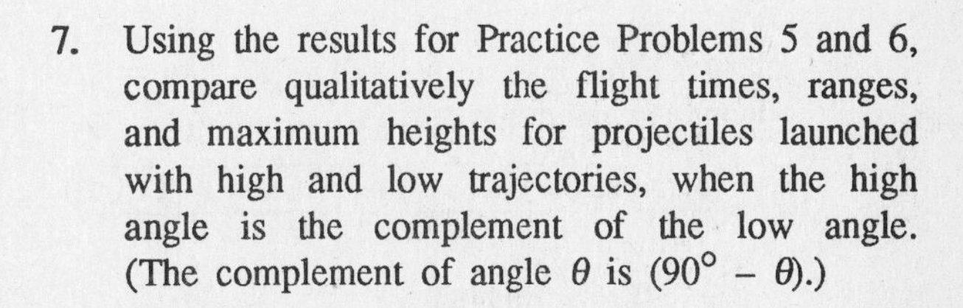
7. Using the results for Practice Problems 5 and 6, compare qualitatively the flight times, ranges, and maximum heights for projectiles launched with high and low trajectories, when the high angle is the complement of the low angle. (The complement of angle θ is $(90^\circ - \theta)$.)

For two projectiles with the same initial velocity and complementary launch angles, the projectile with the higher trajectory has the longeest flight time and the greatest maximum height. The ranges are the same.

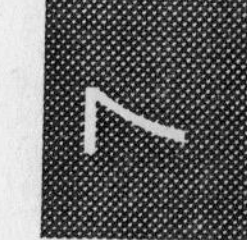

Practice Problems

8. A rude tourist throws a peach pit horizontally with a 7.0 m/s velocity out of an elevator cage.

a. If the elevator is not moving, how long will the pit take to reach the ground, 17.0 m below?

$v_y = 0$ and $y = -17.0$ m = ground level.

Therefore, $y = v_y t = \frac{1}{2}gt^2$ becomes

$$y = \frac{1}{2}gt^2 \text{ or } t = \sqrt{\frac{2y}{g}} = \sqrt{\frac{2(-17.0 \text{ m})}{-9.80 \text{ m/s}^2}}$$

$$= 1.86 \text{ s.}$$

b. How far (horizontally) from the elevator will the pit land?

$v_x = 7.0$ m/s, so

$$x = v_x t = (7.0 \text{ m/s})(1.86 \text{ s})$$
$$= 13 \text{ m}$$

c. He throws the next pit when the elevator is at the same height but moving upward at a constant 8.5 m/s velocity. How long will it take this pit to land?

Now $v_y = 8.5$ m/s and

$y = v_y t + \frac{1}{2}gt^2$ becomes

$$-17.0 \text{ m} = (8.5 \text{ m/s})t + \frac{1}{2}(-9.80 \text{ m/s})t^2,$$

or $(4.90 \text{ m/s}^2)t^2 - (8.5 \text{ m/s})t - 17.0 \text{ m} = 0.$
Using the quadratic formula to solve for t,

$$t = \frac{8.5\text{m/s} \pm \sqrt{(8.5\text{m/s})^2 - 4(4.90\text{m/s}^2)(-17.0\text{m})}}{2(4.90\text{m/s}^2)}$$

$$= \frac{8.50 \text{ m/s} \pm 20.1 \text{ m/s}}{9.80 \text{ m/s}^2}.$$

Choosing the + sign to make flight time position $t = 2.92$ s.

d. How far away will this pit land?

$v_x = 7.0$ m/s, so
$$x = v_x t = (7.0 \text{ m/s})(2.92 \text{ s})$$
$$= 20 \text{ m}$$

Practice Problems

page 145

9. a. Suppose the mass of the rubber stopper in the Example Problem on page 145 is doubled, but all other given quantities remain the same. How would the velocity, acceleration, and force change?

Since r and T remain the same,

$v = \frac{2\pi r}{T}$ and $a = \frac{v^2}{r}$ remain the same. The new value of the mass is $m' = 2m$. The new force is $F' = m'a = 2ma = 2F$, double the original force.

b. If the radius in the Example Problem were twice as large, but all other given quantities remained the same, how would velocity, acceleration, and force change?

The new radius is $r' = 2r$, so the new velocity is $v' = \frac{2\pi r'}{T} = \frac{2\pi(2r)}{T} = 2v$, twice the original velocity. The new acceleration is $a' = \frac{(v')^2}{r'} = \frac{(2v)^2}{2r} = 2a$, twice the original. The new force is $F' = ma' = m(2a) = 2F$, twice the original.

c. Finally, if the stopper were swung in the same circle so it had a period half as large as in the example, how would the answers change?

new velocity, $v' = \frac{2\pi r}{T'} = \frac{2\pi r}{\left(\frac{1}{2}T\right)} = 2v$,

twice
the original;

new acceleration, $a' = \frac{(v')^2}{r} = \frac{(2v)^2}{r} = 4a$,

four times original;
new force, $F' = ma' = m(4a) = 4F$, four times original

Practice Problems

10. A runner moving at a speed of 8.8 m/s rounds a bend with a radius of 25 m.

a. Find the centripetal acceleration of the runner.

$$a_c = \frac{v^2}{r} = \frac{(8.8\ \text{m/s})^2}{25\ \text{m}} = 3.1\ \text{m/s}^2$$

b. What supplies the force needed to give this acceleration to the runner?

The track friction force acting on the runner's shoes

11. Racing on a flat track, a car going 32 m/s rounds a curve 56 m in radius.

a. What is the car's centripetal acceleration?

$$a_c = \frac{v^2}{r} = \frac{(32\ \text{m/s})^2}{56\ \text{m}} = 18\ \text{m/s}^2$$

b. What would be the minimum coefficient of static friction between tires and road that would be needed for the car to round the curve without skidding?

Recall $F_f = \mu F_n$. The friction force must supply the centripetal force so $F_f = ma_c$. The normal force is $F_N = -W = -mg$. The coefficient of friction must be at least

$$\mu = \frac{F_f}{F_N} = \frac{ma_c}{-mg} = \frac{a_c}{-g} = \frac{18\ \text{m/s}^2}{-(-9.80\ \text{m/s}^2)}$$

$= 1.8.$

page 146

12. A racing car rounds a curve that is banked.

a. Sketch the auto tire on the incline, drawing vectors representing all the forces on the tire.

Practice Problems

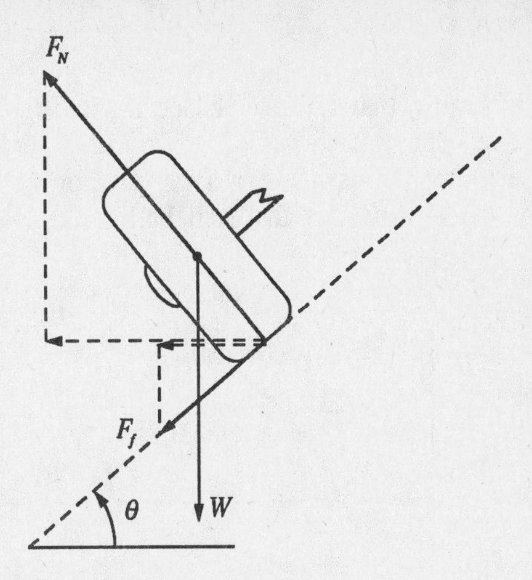

b. Components of what two forces provide the centripetal acceleration for the auto tire, and therefore, the auto?

The horizontal component of the normal force and the horizontal component of the friction force. These component forces, $F_N \sin\theta$ and $F_f \cos\theta$, are shown by dotted lines in the figure.

page 149

13. What is the length of a simple pendulum whose period is 1.00 s? Assume normal g.

From $T = 2\pi\sqrt{\frac{l}{g}}$, we obtain

$$l = \frac{gT^2}{4\pi^2} = \frac{(9.80\ \text{m/s}^2)(1.00\ \text{s})^2}{4\pi^2} = 0.248\ \text{m}.$$

14. A future astronaut lands on a planet with an unknown value of g. She finds that the period of a pendulum 0.65 m long is 2.8 s. What is g for the surface of this planet?

From $T = 2\pi\sqrt{\frac{l}{g}}$, we obtain

$$g = \frac{4\pi^2 l}{T^2} = \frac{4\pi^2(0.65\ \text{m})}{(2.85)^2} = 3.3\ \text{m/s}^2.$$

pages 152–153

1. Assuming that the two baseballs in Figure 7–19 have the same velocity, 25 m/s, draw two separate graphs using y as a function of t and x as a function of t for each ball.

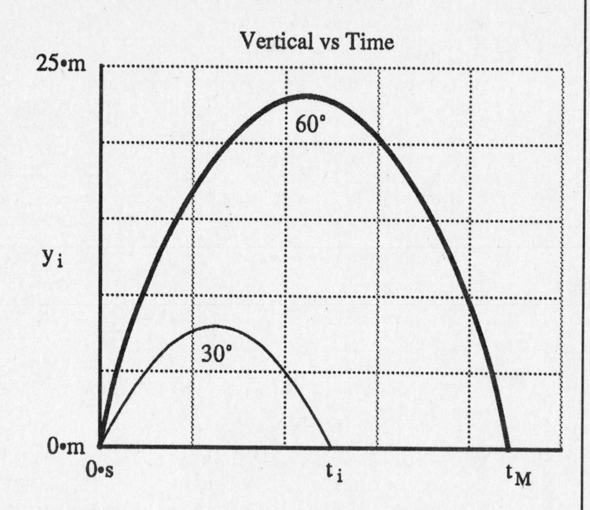

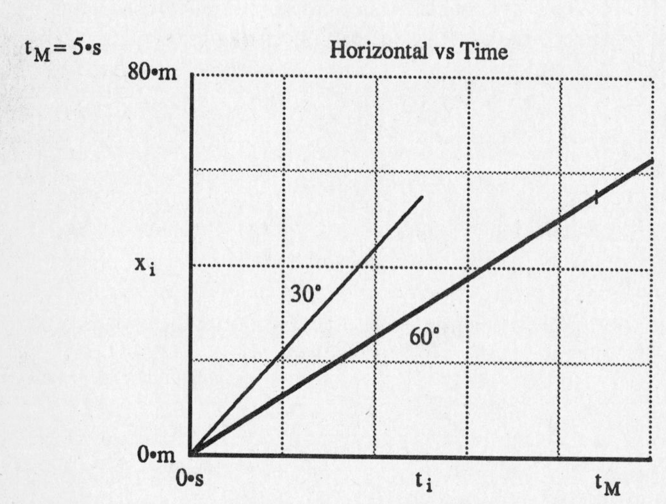

Ignore x_i when $y_i < 0$

2. A stone is thrown horizontally at 8.0 m/s from a cliff 78.4 m high. How far from the base of the cliff does the stone strike the ground?

$$y = v_y t + \frac{1}{2}gt^2$$

Since initial vertical velocity is zero,

$$t = \sqrt{\frac{2d}{g}} = \sqrt{\frac{(2)(-78.4\text{ m})}{-9.8\text{ m/s}^2}} = 4.0\text{ s}$$

$$d = \bar{v}t = (8.0\text{ m/s})(4.0\text{ s}) = 32\text{ m}$$

Chapter Review Problems

3. A toy car runs off the edge of a table that is 1.225 m high. If the car lands 0.400 m from the base of the table,

   a. how long does it take for the car to fall to the floor?

   $y = v_y t + \frac{1}{2}gt^2$, since initial velocity is zero,

   $$t = \sqrt{\frac{2y}{g}} = \sqrt{\frac{(2)(-1.225\text{ m})}{(-9.80\text{ m/s}^2)}} = 0.500\text{ s}$$

   b. what is the horizontal velocity of the car?

   $$v_x = x/t = \frac{0.40\text{ m}}{0.50\text{ s}} = 0.800\text{ m/s}$$

4. Janet jumps off a high diving platform with a horizontal velocity of 2.8 m/s and lands in the water 2.6 s later. How high is the platform, and how far from the base of the platform does she land?

$$y = v_y t = \frac{1}{2}gt^2$$

$$= 0(2.6\text{ m/s}) + \frac{1}{2}(-9.8\text{ m/s}^2)(2.6\text{ s})^2$$

$= -33$ m, so the platform is 33 m high.

$$x = v_x t = (2.8\text{ m/s})(2.6\text{ s}) = 7.3\text{ m}$$

5. An airplane traveling 1001 m above the ocean at 125 km/h is to drop a box of supplies to shipwrecked victims below.

   a. How many seconds before being directly overhead should the box be dropped?

   $$y = v_y t + \frac{1}{2}gt$$

   $$-1001\text{ m} = 0(t) + \frac{1}{2}(-9.8\text{ m/s}^2)t^2,$$

   $$t = 14.3\text{ s}$$

   b. What is the horizontal distance between the plane and victims when the box is dropped?

   $$y_x t = 125\text{ km/h}\left[\frac{1\text{ h}}{3600\text{ s}}\right]\left[\frac{1000\text{ m}}{1\text{ km}}\right]$$

   $$= 34.7\text{ m/s}$$

   $$x = v_x t = (34.7\text{ m/s})(14.3\text{ s}) = 496\text{ m}$$

Chapter Review Problems

6. Divers at Acapulco dive from a cliff that is 61 m high. If the rocks below the cliff extend outward for 23 m, what is the minimum horizontal velocity a diver must have to clear the rocks safely?

$y = v_y t + \frac{1}{2}gt^2$, since intial velocity is zero,

$$t = \sqrt{\frac{2y}{g}} = \sqrt{\frac{(2)(-61\text{ m})}{(-9.8\text{ m/s}^2)}} = \sqrt{12.4\text{ s}^2} = 3.5\text{ s}$$

$$v_x = x/t = \frac{23\text{ m}}{3.5\text{ s}} = 6.6\text{ m/s}$$

7. A dart player throws a dart horizontally at a speed of +12.4 m/s. The dart hits the board 0.32 m below the height from which it was thrown. How far away is the player from the board?

$y = v_y t + \frac{1}{2}gt^2$, since $v_y = 0$

$$t = \sqrt{\frac{2y}{g}} = \sqrt{\frac{2(-0.32\text{ m})}{(-9.80\text{ m/s}^2)}} = 0.26\text{ s}$$

Now $x = v_x t = (12.4\text{ m/s})(0.26\text{ s}) = 3.2\text{ m}$

8. An arrow is shot at a 30.0° angle with the horizontal. It has a velocity of 49 m/s.

The components of the initial velocity are
$v_x = v_i \cos\theta = (49\text{ m/s}) \cos 30.0 = 42\text{ m/s}$
$v_y = v_i \sin\theta = (49\text{ m/s}) \sin 30.0 = 25\text{ m/s}$

a. How high will the arrow go?

At the high point $v_y = 0$, so
$v_{yf}^2 = v_{yi}^2 + 2gd$ therefore

$$d = \frac{-(v_{yi})^2}{2g} = \frac{-(25\text{ m/s})^2}{2(-9.80\text{ m/s}^2)} = 32\text{ m}$$

b. What horizontal distance will the arrow travel?

$y = v_y t + \frac{1}{2}gt^2$,

but the arrow lands at the same height, so

$y = 0$ and $0 = (v_y + \frac{1}{2}gt)t$ so $t = 0$ or

$$t = \frac{-v_y}{\frac{1}{2}(g)} = \frac{-25\text{ m/s}}{\frac{1}{2}(-9.80\text{ m/s}^2)} = 5.1\text{ s}$$

and $x = v_x t = (42\text{ m/s})(5.1\text{ s})$
$= 2.1 \times 10^2\text{ m}$

9. A pitched ball is hit by a batter at a 45° angle. It just clears the outfield fence, 98 m away. Find the velocity of the ball when it left the bat. Assume the fence is the same height as the pitch.

The components of the initial velocity are
$v_x = v_i \cos\theta$ and $v_y = v_i \sin\theta$

Now $x = v_x t = (v_i \cos\theta)t$, so $t = \frac{x}{v_i \cos\theta}$

And $y = v_y t + \frac{1}{2}gt^2$, but $y = 0$, so

$$0 = \left[v_y + \frac{1}{2}gt\right]t \text{ so } t = 0 \text{ or } v_y + \frac{1}{2}gt = 0,$$

from above $v_i \sin\theta + \frac{1}{2}g\left[\frac{x}{v_i \cos\theta}\right] = 0$

Multiply by $v_i \cos\theta$ gives

$v_i^2 \sin\theta \cos\theta + \frac{1}{2}gx = 0$, so

$$v_i^2 = \frac{-gx}{2\sin\theta\cos\theta} = \frac{-(-9.80\text{ m/s}^2)(98\text{ m})}{2(\sin 45)(\cos 45)}$$

$$= 9.6 \times 10^2\text{ m}^2/\text{s}^2$$

$v_i = 31$ m/s at 45°

10. Trailing by two points, and with only 2.0 s remaining in a basketball game, a player makes a jump-shot at an angle of 60° with the horizontal, giving the ball a velocity of 10 m/s. The ball is released at the height of the basket, 3.05 m above the floor. Yes! It's a score!

The components of the initial velocity are
$v_x = v_i \cos\theta = (10\text{ m/s})(\cos 60) = 5.0\text{ m/s}$
$v_y = v_i \sin\theta = (10\text{ m/s})(\sin 60) = 8.7\text{ m/s}$

a. How much time is left in the game when the basket is made?

$y = v_y t + \frac{1}{2}gt^2$, but $y = 0$, so

$0 = (v_y + \frac{1}{2}gt)t$ and $t = 0$ or

$$t = \frac{-v_y}{\frac{1}{2}g} = \frac{-8.7\text{ m/s}}{\frac{1}{2}(-9.80\text{ m/s}^2)} = 1.8\text{ s}$$

Time left = 2.0 s − 1.8 s = 0.2 s

Chapter Review Problems

b. Shots made outside a semicircle of 6.02–m radius from a spot directly beneath the basket are awarded 3 points, while those inside score 2 points. Did the player tie the game or put the team ahead?

$x = v_x t = 5.0\ \text{m/s}(1.8\ \text{s}) = 9.0\ \text{m}$
She got 3 points to win the game.

11. A basketball player tries to make a half–court jump–shot, releasing the ball at the height of the basket. Assuming the ball is launched at 51.0°, 14.0 m from the basket, what velocity must the player give the ball?

The components of the initial velocity are
$v_x = v_i \cos\theta$ and $v_y = v_i \sin\theta$

Now $x = v_x t = (v_i \cos\theta)t$, so $t = \dfrac{x}{v_i \cos\theta}$

And $y = v_y t + \frac{1}{2}gt^2$, but $y = 0$,

so $0 = \left[v_y + \frac{1}{2}gt\right]t$.

Therefore, $t = 0$ or $v_y + \frac{1}{2}gt = 0$ from above

$$v_i \sin\theta + \frac{1}{2}g\left[\frac{x}{v_i \cos\theta}\right] = 0$$

multiply by $v_i \cos\theta$ gives

$$v_i^2 \sin\theta\cos\theta + \frac{1}{2}gx = 0,\ \text{so}$$

$$v_i = \sqrt{\frac{-gx}{2\sin\theta\cos\theta}}$$

$$= \sqrt{\frac{-(-9.80\ \text{m/s}^2)(14.0\ \text{m})}{2(\sin 51)(\cos 51)}}$$

$= 11.8\ \text{m/s},\ 51.0°$

12. A baseball is hit at 30.0 m/s at an angle of 53.0° with the horizontal. Immediately an outfielder runs 4.00 m/s toward the infield and catches the ball bat the same height it was hit. What was the original distance between the batter and the outfielder?

The components of the initial velocity are
$v_x = v_i \cos\theta = 30.0 \cos 53.0° = 18.1\ \text{m/s}$
$v_y = v_i \sin\theta = 30.0 \sin 53.0° = 24.0\ \text{m/s}$

$y = v_y t + \frac{1}{2}gt^2$, but $y = 0$, so

$0 = \left[v_y + \frac{1}{2}gt\right]t$ therefore $t = 0$ or

$$t = \frac{-v_y}{\frac{1}{2}g} = \frac{-24.0\ \text{m/s}}{\frac{1}{2}(-9.80\ \text{m/s}^2)} = 4.90\ \text{s}$$

The horizontal distance the ball travels is
$x = v_x t = (18.1\ \text{m/s})(4.90\ \text{s}) = 88.5\ \text{m}$
The distance the outfielder travels is
$x = v_x t = (4.00\ \text{m/s})(4.90\ \text{s}) = 19.6\ \text{m}$
original separation $= 88.5\ \text{m} + 19.6\ \text{m}$
$= 108.3\ \text{m}$

13. It takes a 615–kg racing car 14.3 s to travel at a uniform speed around a circular racetrack of 50.0 m radius.

a. What is the acceleration of the car?

$v = 2\pi r/T = 2\pi(50.0\ \text{m})/(14.3\ \text{s})$
$= 22.0\ \text{m/s}$ $a_c = v^2/r$
$= (22.0\ \text{m/s})^2/(50.0\ \text{m}) = 9.65\ \text{m/s}^2$

b. What average force must the track exert on the car's tires to produce this acceleration?

$F_c = ma_c = (615\ \text{kg})(9.65\ \text{m/s}^2)$
$= 5.94 \times 10^3\ \text{N}$

14. An athlete whirls a 7.00–kg hammer tied to the end of a 1.3–m chain in a horizontal circle. The hammer moves at the rate of 1.0 rev/s.

a. What is the centripetal acceleration of the hammer?

$$a_c = \frac{4\pi^2 r}{T^2} = \frac{(4\pi^2)(1.3\ \text{m})}{(1.0\ \text{s})^2} = 51\ \text{m/s}^2$$

Chapter Review Problems

b. What is the tension in the chain?

$F_c = ma_c = (7.00\text{ kg})(51\text{ m/s}^2)$
$= 3.6 \times 10^2\text{ N}$

15. Sue whirls a yo–yo in a horizontal circle. The yo–yo has a mass of 0.20 kg and is attached to a string 0.80 m long.

a. If the yo–yo makes 1.0 complete revolution each second, what force does the string exert on it?

$f = 1.0\text{ Hz, so } T = \frac{1}{f} = 1.0\text{ s}$

$F_c = m\frac{4\pi^2 r}{T^2} = \frac{(0.20\text{ kg})(4\pi^2)(0.80\text{ m})}{(1.0\text{ s})^2}$

$= 6.3\text{ N}$

b. If Sue increases the speed of the yo–yo to 2.0 revolutions per second, what force does the string now exert?

$f = 2.0\text{ Hz, so } T = \frac{1}{f} = 0.50\text{ s}$

$F_c = m\frac{4\pi^2 r}{T^2} = \frac{(0.20\text{ kg})(4\pi^2)(0.80\text{ m})}{(0.50\text{ s})^2}$

$= 25\text{ N}$

c. What is the ratio of answer (b) to (a)? Why?

25 N:6.3 N is 4:1 because velocity has doubled, acceleration doubled, squared; or multiplied by four.

16. A coin is placed on a stereo record revolving at 33 1/3 revolutions per minute.

a. In what direction is the acceleration of the coin, if any?

The acceleration is toward the center of the record.

b. Find the acceleration of the coin when it is placed 5, 10, and 15 cm from the center of the record.

$T = \frac{1}{f} = \frac{1}{33\frac{1}{3}} = (0.0300)\left[\frac{60\text{ s}}{1\text{ min}}\right] = 1.80\text{ s}$

for $r = 5.0$; $a_c = \frac{4\pi^2 r}{T^2} = \frac{4\pi^2(0.05\text{ m})}{(1.80\text{ s})^2}$

$= 0.61\text{ m/s}^2$

for $r = 10$; $ac = \frac{4\pi^2 r}{T^2} = \frac{4\pi^2(0.10\text{ m})}{(1.80\text{ s})^2}$

$= 1.2\text{ m/s}^2$

for $r = 15$; $a_c = \frac{4\pi^2 r}{T^2} = \frac{4\pi^2(0.15\text{ m})}{(1.80\text{ s})^2}$

$= 1.8\text{ m/s}^2$

c. What force accelerates the coin?

Frictional force between coin and record.

d. At which of the three radii listed in b would the coin be most likely to fly off? Why?

15 cm
The largest radius because force to hold it is the greatest.

17. According to the *Guinness Book of World Records*, (1990 edition, p 169) the highest rotary speed ever attained was 2010 m/s (4500 mph). The rotating rod was 15.3 cm (6 in.) long. Assume the speed quoted is that of the end of the rod.

a. What is the centripetal acceleration of the end of the rod?

$a_c = \frac{v^2}{r} = \frac{(2010\text{ m/s})^2}{0.153\text{ m}} = 2.64 \times 10^7\text{ m/s}^2$

b. If you were to attach a 1.00–g object to the end of the rod, what force would be needed to hold it on the rod?

$F_c = ma_c = (0.00100\text{ kg})(2.64 \times 10^7\text{ m/s}^2)$
$= 2.64 \times 10^4\text{ N}$

Chapter Review Problems

c. What is the period of rotation of the rod?

$$a_c = \frac{4\pi^2 r}{T^2}, \text{ so}$$

$$T = \sqrt{\frac{4\pi^2 r}{a_c}} = 2\pi\sqrt{\frac{r}{a_c}} = 2\pi\sqrt{\frac{0.153 \text{ m}}{2.64 \times 10^7 \text{ m/s}^2}}$$

$$= 4.78 \times 10^{-4} \text{ s}$$

18. Refer to Figure 7–8. The carnival ride has a 2.0–m radius and rotates 1.1 times per second.

$$T = \frac{1}{f} = \frac{1}{1.1} = 0.91 \text{ s}$$

a. Find the speed of a rider.

$$v = \frac{\Delta d}{\Delta t} = \frac{2\pi r}{T} = \frac{2\pi(2.0 \text{ m})}{(0.91 \text{ s})} = 14 \text{ m/s}$$

b. Find the centripetal acceleration of a rider.

$$a_c = \frac{v^2}{r} = \frac{(14 \text{ m/s})^2}{2.0 \text{ m}} = 98 \text{ m/s}^2$$

c. What produces this acceleration?

Force of the drum walls.

d. When the floor drops down, riders are held up by a friction. What coefficient of friction is needed to keep the riders from slipping?

Downward force of gravity $F = mg$.
Frictional force $F_f = \mu F_N$.
F_N is the force of the drum, ma_c.
To balance $g = \mu a_c$, so we need
$\mu = g/a_c = 0.10$.

19. An early major objection to the idea that Earth is spinning on its axis was that Earth would turn so fast at the equator that people would be thrown off into space. Show the error in this logic by calculating

a. the speed of a 97–kg person at the equator. The radius of Earth is about 6400 km.

$$v = \frac{\Delta d}{\Delta t} = \frac{2\pi r}{T} = \frac{2\pi(6.40 \times 10^6 \text{ m})}{\left[\frac{24 \text{ h}}{1}\right]\left[\frac{3600 \text{ s}}{1 \text{ h}}\right]}$$

$$= 465 \text{ m/s}$$

b. the centripetal force on the person.

$$F_c = ma_c = \frac{mv^2}{r} = \frac{(97 \text{ kg})(465 \text{ m/s})^2}{(6.40 \times 10 \text{ m})}$$

$$= 3.3 \text{ N}$$

c. the weight of the person.

$$F = mg = (97 \text{ kg})(9.80 \text{ m/s}^2) = 950 \text{ N}$$
$$= 9.5 \times 10^2 \text{ N}$$

20. Friction provides the centripetal force necessary for a car to travel around a flat circular race track. What is the maximum speed at which a car can safely travel around a circular track of radius 80.0 m if the coefficient of friction between tire and road is 0.30?

$$F_c = F_f = \mu F_N = \mu mg$$

But $F_c = \frac{mv^2}{r}$, thus $\frac{mv^2}{r} = \mu mg$ and the mass of

the car divides out to give $v^2 = \mu gr$, so

$$v = \sqrt{\mu gr} = \sqrt{(0.30)(9.80 \text{ m/s}^2)(80.0 \text{ m})} = 15 \text{ m/s}$$

21. A pendulum has a length of 0.67 m.

a. Find its period.

$$T = 2\pi\sqrt{(\ell/g)} = 1.6 \text{ s.}$$

b. How long would the pendulum have to be to double the period?

Since the period is proportional to the square root of the length, the pendulum would have to be four times as long, or 2.7 m.

c. Why is your answer to part b not just double the length?

The period is proportional to the *square root* of the length, not the length, so the answer cannot be doubled.

Chapter Review Problems

22. Find the length of a pendulum oscillating on the moon that would have the same period as a 1.0-m pendulum oscillating on Earth. The moon's gravity is one-sixth of Earth's gravity.

$$T = 2\pi\sqrt{\frac{\ell_e}{g_e}} = 2\pi\sqrt{\frac{\ell_m}{g_m}},\ \sqrt{\frac{\ell_e}{g_e}} = \sqrt{\frac{\ell_m}{g_m}} \text{ so}$$

$$\frac{\ell_e}{g_e} = \frac{\ell_m}{g_m},\ \frac{1.0 \text{ m}}{9.8 \text{ m/s}^2} = \frac{\ell_m}{1.6 \text{ m/s}^2} = 0.16 \text{ m}$$

Supplemental Problems (Appendix B)

1. A ball falls from rest from a height of 490 m.

a. How long does it remain in the air?

$y = v_y t + \frac{1}{2}gt^2$, since initial vertical velocity is zero,

$$t = \sqrt{\frac{2y}{g}} = \sqrt{\frac{(2)(-490 \text{ m})}{(-9.80 \text{ m/s}^2)}} = 10.0 \text{ s}$$

b. If the ball has a horizontal velocity of 2.00×10^2 m/s when it begins its fall, what horizontal displacement will it have?

$$x = v_x t = (2.00 \times 10^2 \text{ m/s})(1.00 \times 10^1 \text{ s})$$
$$= 2.00 \times 10^3 \text{ m}$$

2. An archer stands 40.0 m from the target. If the arrow is shot horizontally with a velocity of 90.0 m/s, how far above the bull's-eye must he aim to compensate for gravity pulling his arrow downward?

$$t = \frac{x}{v_x} = \frac{40.0 \text{ m}}{90.0 \text{ m/s}} = 0.444 \text{ s}$$

$$y = v_y t + \frac{1}{2}gt^2$$

$$= 0(0.444 \text{ s}) + \frac{1}{2}(9.80 \text{ m/s}^2)(0.444 \text{ s})^2$$

$$= 0.966 \text{ m}$$

Supplemental Problems (Appendix B)

3. A bridge is 176.4 m above a river. If a lead-weighted fishing line is thrown from the bridge with a horizontal velocity of 22.0 m/s, how far has it moved horizontally when it hits the water?

$$y = v_y t + \frac{1}{2}gt^2$$

Since initial velocity is zero,

$$t = \sqrt{\frac{2y}{g}} = \sqrt{\frac{(2)(-176.4 \text{ m})}{(-9.80 \text{ m/s}^2)}} = 6.00 \text{ s}$$

$$x = v_x t = (22.0 \text{ m/s})(6.00 \text{ s}) = 132 \text{ m}$$

4. A beach ball, moving with a speed of +1.27 m/s, rolls off a pier and hits the water 0.75 m from the end of the pier. How high is the pier above the water?

We need to know how long it takes the ball to hit the water in order to use $y = v_y t + \frac{1}{2}gt^2$, $v_y = 0$, to calculate pier height. This time is determined by the horizontal motion $x = v_x t$.
$t = x/v_x = (0.75 \text{ m})/(1.27 \text{ m/s}) = 0.59$ s.
This gives a vertical displacement

$$y = \frac{1}{2}gt^2 = \left(\frac{1}{2}\right)(-9.80 \text{ m/s}^2)(0.59 \text{ s})^2 = -1.7 \text{ m}$$

and hence a pier height of 1.7 m.

5. Pete has a tendency to drop his bowling ball on his release. Instead of having the ball on the floor at the completion of his swing, Pete lets go with the ball 0.35 m above the floor. If he throws it horizontally with a velocity of 6.3 m/s, what distance does it travel before you hear a "thud?"

$y = v_y t + \frac{1}{2}gt^2$ where $v_y = 0$. Taking downward position, the time to hit floor is

$t = \sqrt{\frac{2y}{g}} = \sqrt{\frac{2(0.35 \text{ m})}{9.8 \text{ m/s}^2}} = 0.275$ so travel distance is $x = v_x t = (6.3 \text{ m/s})(0.275) = 1.7$ m

7

6. A discus is released at an angle of 45° and a velocity of 24.0 m/s.

 a. How long does it stay in the air?

 $v_y = v_i \sin 45° = (24.0 \text{ m/s}) \sin 45°$
 $= 17.0 \text{ m/s}$
 so time to maximum height is

 $t = \frac{v_{top} - v_y}{a} = \frac{0 - 17.0 \text{ m/s}}{-9.80 \text{ m/s}^2} = 1.73$ s and
 by symmetry total time is 3.46 s.

 b. What horizontal distance does it travel?

 $v_x = v_i \cos 45° = (24.0 \text{ m/s}) \cos 45°$
 $= 17.0 \text{ m/s}$
 so $x = v_x t = 17.0 \text{ m/s}(3.46 \text{ s}) = 58.8 \text{ m}$

7. A shot put is released with a velocity of 12 m/s and stays in the air for 2.0 s.

 a. At what angle with the horizontal was it released?

 $v_f = v_i + at$ where $v_f = 0$ at maximum height and $v_i = v_y$.
 Since time to maximum height is 1.0 s,
 $v_y = v_f - at = 0 - (-9.8 \text{ m/s}^2)(1.0 \text{ s})$
 $= 9.8$ m/s where upward is taken positive.

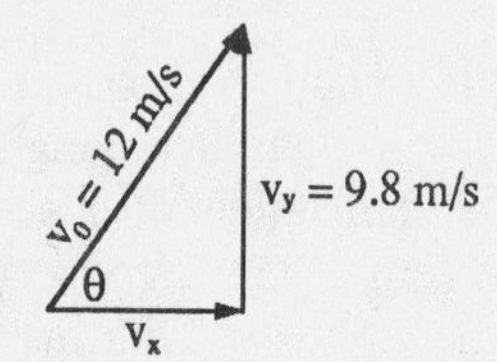

 $\sin \theta = \frac{v_y}{v_o} = \frac{9.8 \text{ m/s}}{12 \text{ m/s}} = 0.817$
 $\theta = 55°$

 b. What horizontal distance did it travel?

 $v_x = v_o \cos 55° = (12 \text{ m/s}) \cos 55°$
 $= 6.9 \text{ m/s}$
 so $x = v_x t = (6.9 \text{ m/s})(2.0 \text{ s}) = 14 \text{ m}$

Supplemental Problems

8. A football is kicked at 45° and travels 82 m before hitting the ground.

 a. What was its initial velocity?

 $x = v_x t$ and $y = v_y t + \frac{1}{2}gt^2$. At end $y = 0$,

 so $0 = v_y t + \frac{1}{2}gt^2 = t(vy + gt/2)$ and

 $t = -2v_y/g$. But $t = x/v_x$,

 so $x/v_x = -2v_y/g$ or $v_x v_y = -\frac{1}{2}xg$.
 Now $v_x = v_o \cos \theta$ and $v_y = v_o \sin \theta$,
 so $v_x v_y = v_o^2 \cos \theta \sin \theta$, or

 $v_o^2 = -\frac{1}{2}xg/\cos \theta \sin \theta$.

 Here $v_o^2 = \frac{-1/2(82 \text{ m})(-9.80 \text{ m/s}^2)}{(0.707)(0.707)}$

 $= 804 \text{ m}^2/\text{s}^2$
 or $v_o = 28$ m/s.

 b. How long was it in the air?

 $v_x = v_o \cos 45° = (28 \text{ m/s}) \cos 45°$
 $= 20 \text{ m/s}$
 so $t = x/v_x = (82 \text{ m})/(20 \text{ m/s}) = 4.1 \text{ s}$.

 c. How high did it go?

 Max height occurs at half the flight time, so since
 $v_y = v_o \sin 45° = (28 \text{ m/s}) \sin 45°$
 $= 20 \text{ m/s}$,

 $y = (20 \text{ m/s})(2.1 \text{ s}) + \frac{1}{2}(-9.8 \text{ m/s}^2)(2.1 \text{ s})^2$

 $= 20 \text{ m}$

9. A golf ball is hit with a velocity of 24.5 m/s at 35.0° above the horizontal. Find

a. the range of the ball.

$v_x = v_i \cos\theta = (24.5 \text{ m/s})(0.819)$
$= 20.1 \text{ m/s}$
$v_y = v_i \sin\theta = (24.5 \text{ m/s})(0.574)$
$= 14.1 \text{ m/s}.$

$$y = v_y t + \frac{1}{2}gt^2 = t(v_y + gt/2)$$

When $y = 0$,
$t = -2v_y/g = -2(14.1 \text{ m/s})/(-9.80 \text{ m/s}^2)$
$= 2.88 \text{ s, so } x = v_x t = 57.9 \text{ m}$

b. the maximum height of the ball.

In half the flight time, $\left[\frac{1}{2}\right](2.88 \text{ s})$, it falls

$$y = \left[\frac{1}{2}\right]gt^2 = \left[\frac{1}{2}\right](-9.80 \text{ m/s}^2)(1.44 \text{ s})^2$$

$= -10.2$ m,
so its maximum height is 10.2 m.

10. A carnival clown rides a motorcycle down a ramp and around a "loop-the-loop." If the loop has a radius of 18 m, what is the slowest speed the rider can have at the top of the loop to avoid falling? **Hint:** At this slowest speed, at the top of the loop, the clown's weight is equal to the centripetal force.

$F = ma$ and $F_c = W$, so
$mv^2/r = mg$;
$v = \sqrt{gr} = \sqrt{(9.80 \text{ m/s}^2)(18 \text{ m})} = 13 \text{ m/s}$

11. A 75-kg pilot flies a plane in a loop. At the top of the loop, where the plane is completely upside-down for an instant, the pilot hangs freely in the seat and does not push against the seat belt. The airspeed indicator reads 120 m/s. What is the radius of the plane's loop?

Since the centripetal force is exactly equal to the weight of the pilot, $\frac{mv^2}{r} = mg$, or

$$r = \frac{v^2}{g} = \frac{(120 \text{ m/s})^2}{9.8 \text{ m/s}^2} = 1.5 \times 10^3 \text{ m}$$

Supplemental Problems

12. A 2.0-kg object is attached to a 1.5 m long string and swung in a vertical circle at a constant speed of 12 m/s.

a. What is the tension in the string when the object is at the bottom of its path?

$F_c = mv^2/r = (2.0 \text{ kg})(12 \text{ m/s}^2)/(1.5 \text{ m})$
$= 1.9 \times 10^2 \text{ N}$

$W = mg = (2.0 \text{ kg})(9.8 \text{ m/s}^2) = 20 \text{ N}$
$T = F_c + W$

$= 1.9 \times 10^2 \text{ N} + 0.20 \times 10^2 \text{ N}$
$= 2.1 \times 10^2 \text{ N}$

b. What is the tension in the string when the object is at the top of its path?

$T = F_c - W = 1.9 \times 10^2 - 0.20 \times 10^2 \text{ N}$
$= 1.7 \times 10^2 \text{ N}$

13. A 60.0-kg speed skater with a velocity of 18.0 m/s comes into a curve of 20.0-m radius. How much friction must be exerted between the skates and the ice to negotiate the curve?

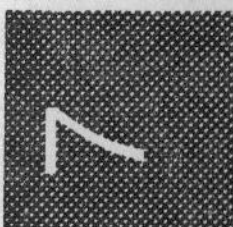

$$F_f = F_c = \frac{mv^2}{r} = \frac{(60.0 \text{ kg})(18.0 \text{ m/s})^2}{20.0 \text{ m}} = 972 \text{ N}$$

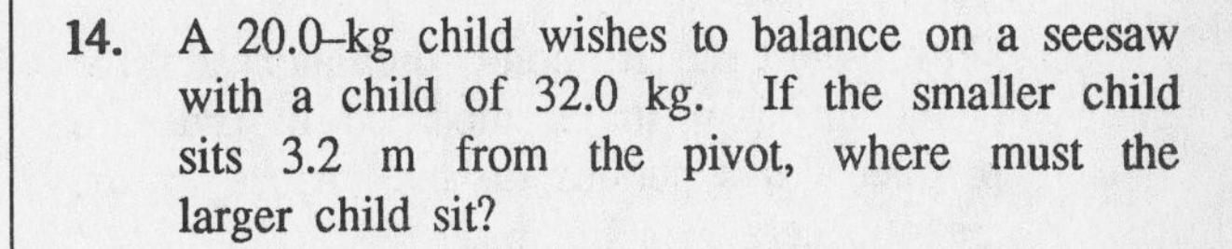

14. A 20.0-kg child wishes to balance on a seesaw with a child of 32.0 kg. If the smaller child sits 3.2 m from the pivot, where must the larger child sit?

$m_1 g d_1 = m_2 g d_2$
Since g is common to both sides,
$(20.0)(3.2) = (32.0)(d_2)$ and $d_2 = 2.0$ m

15. A pendulum has a length of 1.00 m.

$$T = 2\pi\sqrt{\frac{\ell}{g}}$$

a. What is its period on Earth?

$$T = 2\pi\sqrt{\frac{1.00 \text{ m}}{9.80 \text{ m/s}^2}} = 2.01 \text{ s}$$

b. What is its period on the moon where the acceleration due to gravity is 1.67 m/s²?

$$T = 2\pi\sqrt{\frac{1.00 \text{ m}}{1.67 \text{ m/s}^2}} = 4.86 \text{ s}$$

Supplemental Problems

16. The period of an object oscillating on a spring is

$$T = 2\pi\sqrt{\frac{m}{k}},$$

where m is the mass of the object and k is the spring constant which indicates the force necessary to produce a unit elongation of the spring. The period of a simple pendulum is

$$T = 2\pi\sqrt{\frac{l}{g}}.$$

a. What mass will produce a 1.0–s period of oscillation if it is attached to a spring with a spring constant of 4.0 N/m?

$T = 2\pi\sqrt{m/k}$, so
$m = kT^2/4\pi^2 = (4.0\text{ N/m})(1.0\text{ s})^2/(4)(\pi^2)$
$= 0.10\text{ kg}$

b. What length pendulum will produce a period of 1.0 s?

$T = 2\pi\sqrt{l/g}$, so $l = gT^2/4\pi^2$
$l = (9.80\text{ m/s}^2)(1.0\text{ s})^2/(4)(\pi^2)$
$= 0.25\text{ m}$

c. How would the harmonic oscillator and the pendulum have to be modified in order to produce 1.0–s periods on the surface of the moon, where g is 1.6 m/s²?

No change is necessary for the harmonic oscillator. For the pendulum, since l is proportional to g,
$l' = g'l/g = (1.6\text{ m/s}^2)(0.25\text{ m})/(9.8\text{ m/s}^2)$
$= 0.041\text{ m}.$
The pendulum must be shortened to 4.1 cm.

Chapter 8: Universal Gravitation

Practice Problems

page 160

1. An asteroid revolves around the sun with a mean average orbital radius twice that of Earth's. Predict the period of the asteroid in earth years.

$$\left[\frac{T_a}{T_E}\right]^2 = \left[\frac{r_a}{r_E}\right]^3 \text{ with } r_a = 2r_E.$$

$$\text{Thus, } T_a^2 = \left[\frac{r_a}{r_E}\right]^3 T_E^2$$

$$= \left[\frac{2r_E}{r_E}\right]^3 (1\text{ yr})^2 = 8\text{ yr}^2,\ T_a = 2.8\text{ yr}$$

2. From Table 8–1, you can calculate that, on the average, Mars is 1.52 times as far from the sun as is Earth. Predict the time required for Mars to circle the sun in earth days.

$$\left[\frac{T_M}{T_E}\right] = \left[\frac{r_M}{r_E}\right]^3, \text{ with } r_M = 1.52r_E.$$

$$\text{Thus, } T_M^2 = \left[\frac{r_M}{r_E}\right]^3 T_E^2 = \left[\frac{1.52r_E}{r_E}\right]^3 (365\text{ days})^2$$

$$= 4.679 \times 10^5\text{ days}^2,$$

$$T_M = 684\text{ days}$$

3. The moon has a period of 27.3 days and has a mean distance of 3.90×10^5 km from the center of Earth. Find the period of an artificial satellite that is 6.70×10^3 km from the center of Earth.

$$\left[\frac{T_s}{T_m}\right]^2 = \left[\frac{r_s}{r_m}\right]^3,\ T_s^2 = \left[\frac{r_s}{r_m}\right]^3 T_m^2$$

$$= \left[\frac{6.70 \times 10^3\text{ km}}{3.90 \times 10^5\text{ km}}\right]^3 (27.3\text{ days})^2$$

$$= 3.779 \times 10^{-3}\text{ days}^2,$$

$$T_s = 6.15 \times 10^{-2}\text{ days} = 88.5\text{ min}$$

Practice Problems

4. From the data on the period and radius of revolution of the moon in Practice Problem 3, find the mean distance from Earth's center to an artificial satellite that has a period to 1.00 day.

$$\left[\frac{T_s}{T_m}\right]^2 = \left[\frac{r_s}{r_m}\right]^3, \text{ so } r_s^3 = r_m^3\left[\frac{T_s}{T_m}\right]^2$$

$$= (3.90 \times 10^5\text{ km})^3\left[\frac{1.00}{27.3}\right]^2$$

$$= 7.96 \times 10^{13}\text{ km}^3,$$

$$\text{so } r_s = 4.30 \times 10^4\text{ km}$$

page 166

Assume a near–circular orbit for all calculations.

5. **a.** Calculate the velocity that a satellite shot from Newton's cannon must have in order to orbit Earth, 150 km above its surface.

$$v = \sqrt{\frac{GM_E}{r}} = \sqrt{\frac{(6.67 \times 10^{-11})(5.98 \times 10^{24})}{6.52 \times 10^6}}$$

$$= 7.82 \times 10^3\text{ m/s}$$

b. How long would it take for the satellite to return to the cannon in seconds and minutes?

$$T = 2\pi\sqrt{\frac{r^3}{GM_E}}$$

$$= 2\pi\sqrt{\frac{(6.52 \times 10^6\text{ m})^3}{(6.67\times10^{-11}\text{ Nm}^2/\text{kg}^2)(5.98\times10^{24}\text{ kg})}}$$

$$= 5.24 \times 10^3\text{ s} = 87.3\text{ min}$$

6. Use the data in Table 8–1 for Mercury to find

a. the speed of a satellite in orbit 265 km above the surface.

$$v = \sqrt{\frac{GM_m}{r}}, \text{ with } r = r_m + 265\text{ km}$$

$$= 2.43 \times 10^6\text{ m} = 0.265 \times 10^6\text{ m}$$

$$= 2.70 \times 10^6\text{ m}$$

$$v = \sqrt{\frac{(6.67 \times 10^{-11}\text{ Nm}^2/\text{kg}^2)(3.2 \times 10^{23}\text{ kg})}{2.70 \times 10^6\text{ m}}}$$

$$= 2.8 \times 10^3\text{ m/s}$$

Practice Problems

b. the period of the satellite.

$$T = 2\pi\sqrt{\frac{r^3}{GM_m}}$$

$$= 2\pi\sqrt{\frac{(2.70\times10^6\ \text{m})^3}{(6.67\times10^{-11}\ \text{Nm}^2/\text{kg}^2)(3.2\times10^{23}\ \text{kg})}}$$

$$= 6.03\times10^3\ \text{s} = 1.0\times10^2\ \text{min}$$

7. a. Find the velocity with which Mercury moves around the sun.

$v = \sqrt{\frac{GM}{r}}$, where here M is the mass of the sun.

$$v = \sqrt{\frac{(6.67\times10^{-11}\ \text{Nm}^2/\text{kg}^2)(1.991\times10^{30}\ \text{kg})}{(5.80\times10^{10}\ \text{m})}}$$

$$= 4.79\times10^4\ \text{m/s}.$$

b. Also, find the velocity of Saturn. Now, comment on whether or not it makes sense that Mercury is named after a speedy messenger of the gods, while Saturn is named after the father of Jupiter.

$$v = \sqrt{\frac{(6.67\times10^{-11}\ \text{Nm}^2/\text{kg}^2)(1.991\times10^{30}\ \text{kg})}{(1.427\times10^{12}\ \text{m})}}$$

$= 9.65\times10^3$ m/s, about 1/5 as fast as Mercury.

8. We can consider the sun to be a satellite of our galaxy, the Milky Way. The sun revolves around the center of the galaxy with a radius of 2.2×10^{20} m. The period of one rotation is 2.5×10^8 years.

a. Find the mass of the galaxy.

Using $T = 2\pi\sqrt{\frac{r^3}{GM}}$, with

$T = 2.5\times10^8\text{y} = 7.9\times10^{15}$ s

$$M = \frac{4\pi^2 r^3}{GT^2}$$

$$= \frac{4\pi^2(2.2\times10^{20}\ \text{m})^3}{(6.67\times10^{-11}\ \text{Nm}^2/\text{kg}^2)(7.9\times10^{15}\ \text{s})^2}$$

$$= 1.0\times10^{41}\ \text{kg}$$

Practice Problems

b. Assuming the average star in the galaxy has the mass of the sun, find the number of stars.

$$\text{number of stars} = \frac{\text{total galaxy mass}}{\text{mass per star}}$$

$$= \frac{1.0\times10^{41}\ \text{kg}}{2.0\times10^{30}\ \text{kg}}$$

$$= 5.0\times10^{10}$$

c. Find the speed with which the sun moves around the center of the galaxy.

$$v = \sqrt{\frac{GM}{r}}$$

$$= \sqrt{\frac{(6.67\times10^{-11}\ \text{Nm}^2/\text{kg}^2)(1.0\times10^{41}\ \text{kg})}{2.2\times10^{20}\ \text{m}}}$$

$$= 1.7\times10^5\ \text{m/s} = 6.1\ \text{km/h}$$

Chapter Review Problems

Use $G = 6.670\times10^{-11}\ \text{N}\cdot\text{m}^2/\text{kg}^2$

1. Jupiter is 5.2 times farther than Earth is from the sun. Find Jupiter's orbital period in earth years.

$\left[\frac{T_J}{T_E}\right]^2 = \left[\frac{r_J}{r_E}\right]^3$, so

$$T_J^2 = \left[\frac{r_J}{r}\right]^3 T_E^2$$

$$= \left[\frac{5.2}{1.0}\right]^3(1.0\ \text{yr})^2 = 141\ \text{yr}^2$$

So $T_J = 12$ yr.

2. Uranus requires 84 years to circle the sun. Find Uranus's orbital radius as a multiple of Earth's orbital radius.

$\left[\frac{T_U}{T_E}\right]^2 = \left[\frac{r_U}{r_E}\right]^3$, so

$$r_U^3 = \left[\frac{T_U}{T_E}\right]^2 r_E^3$$

$$= \left[\frac{84\ \text{yr}}{1.0\ \text{yr}}\right]^2(1.0\ r_E)^3 = 7.06\times10^3 r_E^3$$

So $r_U = 19\ r_E$

Chapter Review Problems

3. Venus has a period of revolution of 225 earth days. Find the distance between the sun and Venus as a multiple of Earth's orbital radius.

$$\left[\frac{T_V}{T_E}\right]^2 = \left[\frac{r_V}{r_E}\right]^3, \text{ so } r_V^3 = \left[\frac{T_V}{T_E}\right]^2 r_E^3 = \left[\frac{225}{365}\right]^2 r_E^3 = 0.380\ r_E^3. \text{ So } r_v = 0.724\ r_E.$$

4. If a small planet were located 8.0 times as far from the sun as Earth, how many years would it take the planet to orbit the sun?

$$\left[\frac{T_x}{T_E}\right]^2 = \left[\frac{r_x}{r_E}\right]^3, \text{ so } T_x^2 = \left[\frac{r_x}{r_E}\right]^3 T_E^2 = \left[\frac{8.0}{1.0}\right]^3 (1.0 \text{ yr})^2 = 512 \text{ yr}^2. \text{ So } T_x = 23 \text{ yr}.$$

5. A satellite is placed in orbit with a radius that is half the radius of the moon's orbit. Find its period in units of the period of the moon.

$$\left[\frac{T_S}{T_m}\right]^2 = \left[\frac{r_S}{r_m}\right]^3, \text{ so } T_S^2 = \left[\frac{r_S}{r_m}\right]^3 T_m^2 = \left[\frac{0.50\ r_m}{r_m}\right]^3 T_m^2 = \frac{1}{8.0} T_m^2. \text{ So } T_S = 0.35\ T_m.$$

6. An apparatus like the one Cavendish used to find G has a large lead ball that is 5.9 kg in mass and a small one that is 0.047 kg. Their centers are separated by 0.055 m. Find the force of attraction between them.

$$F = \frac{Gm_1m_2}{d^2} = \frac{(6.670 \times 10^{-11} \text{ N}\cdot\text{m}^2/\text{kg}^2)(5.9 \text{ kg})(4.7 \times 10^{-2} \text{ kg})}{(5.5 \times 10^{-2} \text{ m})^2} = 6.1 \times 10^{-9} \text{ N}$$

7. Use the data in Table 8–1 to compute the gravitational force the sun exerts on Jupiter.

$$F = \frac{Gm_sm_j}{d^2} = \frac{(6.67 \times 10^{-11} \text{ N}\cdot\text{m}^2/\text{kg}^2)(1.991 \times 10^{30} \text{ kg})(1.901 \times 10^{27} \text{ kg})}{(7.781 \times 10^{11} \text{ m})^2} = 4.17 \times 10^{23} \text{ N}$$

8. Tom has a mass of 70.0 kg and Sally has a mass of 50.0 kg. Tom and Sally are standing 20.0 m apart on the dance floor. Sally looks up and she sees him. She feels an attraction. If the attraction is gravitation, find its size. Assume that both can be replaced by spherical masses.

$$F = \frac{Gm_Tm_S}{d^2} = \frac{(6.67 \times 10^{-11} \text{ N}\cdot\text{m}^2/\text{kg}^2)(70.0 \text{ kg})(50.0 \text{ kg})}{(20.0 \text{ m})^2} = 5.84 \times 10^{-10} \text{ N}$$

9. Two balls have their centers 2.0 m apart. One has a mass of 8.0 kg. The other has a mass of 6.0 kg. What is the gravitational force between them?

$$F = G\frac{m_1m_2}{r^2} = \frac{(6.67 \times 10^{-11} \text{ N}\cdot\text{m}^2/\text{kg}^2)(8.0 \text{ kg})(6.0 \text{ kg})}{(2.0 \text{ m})^2} = 8.0 \times 10^{-10} \text{ N}$$

10. Two bowling balls each have a mass of 6.8 kg. They are located next to one another with their centers 21.8 cm apart. What gravitational force do they exert on each other?

$$F = G\frac{m_1m_2}{r^2} = \frac{(6.67 \times 10^{-11} \text{ N}\cdot\text{m}^2/\text{kg}^2)(6.8 \text{ kg})(6.8 \text{ kg})}{(0.218 \text{ m})^2} = 6.5 \times 10^{-8} \text{ N}$$

11. Sally has a mass of 50.0 kg and Earth has a mass of 5.98×10^{24} kg. The radius of Earth is 6.371×10^6 m.

a. What is the force of gravitation attraction between Sally and Earth?

$$F = \frac{Gm_Sm_E}{d^2} = \frac{(6.67 \times 10^{-11} \text{ N}\cdot\text{m}^2/\text{kg}^2)(50.0 \text{ kg})(5.98 \times 10^{24} \text{ kg})}{(6.371 \times 10^6 \text{ m})^2} = 491 \text{ N}$$

8

b. What is Sally's weight?

$W = mg = (50.0\ \text{kg})(9.80\ \text{m/s}^2) = 490\ \text{N}$

12. The gravitational force between two electrons 1.00 m apart is 5.42×10^{-71} N. Find the mass of an electron.

$F = \dfrac{Gm_1m_2}{d^2}$, but $m_1 = m_2 = m_e$

So $m_e^2 = \dfrac{Fd^2}{G} = \dfrac{(5.42 \times 10^{-71}\ \text{N})(1.00\ \text{m})^2}{6.67 \times 10^{-11}\ \text{N}\cdot\text{m}^2/\text{kg}^2} = 8.13 \times 10^{-62}\ \text{kg}^2$

So $m_e = 9.01 \times 10^{-31}$ kg

13. Two spherical balls are placed so their centers are 2.6 meters apart. The force between the two balls is 2.75×10^{-12} N. What is the mass of each ball if one ball is twice the mass of the other ball?

$F = \dfrac{Gm_1m_2}{d^2}$, but $m_2 = 2m_1$, so $F = \dfrac{G(m_1)(2m_1)}{d^2}$ and $m_1 = \sqrt{\dfrac{Fd^2}{2G}} = \sqrt{\dfrac{(2.75 \times 10^{-12}\ \text{N})(2.6\ \text{m})^2}{2(6.67 \times 10^{-11}\ \text{N}\cdot\text{m}^2/\text{kg}^2)}}$

$m_1 = 0.37$ kg
$m_2 = 2m_1 = 0.75$ kg

14. Using the fact that a 1.0-kg mass weighs 9.8 N on the surface of Earth and the radius of Earth is roughly 6.4×10^6 m,

a. calculate the mass of Earth.

$F = G\dfrac{m_1m_2}{r^2}$

$m_e = \dfrac{Fr^2}{Gm} = \dfrac{(9.8\ \text{N})(6.4 \times 10^6\ \text{m})^2}{(6.67 \times 10^{-11}\ \text{N}\cdot\text{m}^2/\text{kg})(1.0\ \text{kg})} = 6.0 \times 10^{24}\ \text{kg}$

b. calculate the average density of Earth.

$V = \dfrac{4}{3}\pi r^3 = \dfrac{(4\pi)(6.4 \times 10^6\ \text{m})^3}{3} = 1.1 \times 10^{21}\ \text{m}^3$

$D = \dfrac{M}{V} = \dfrac{6.0 \times 10^{24}\ \text{kg}}{1.1 \times 10^{21}\ \text{m}^3} = 5.5 \times 10^3\ \text{kg/m}^3$

15. The moon is 3.9×10^5 km from Earth's center and 1.5×10^8 km from the sun's center. If the masses of the moon, Earth, and sun are 7.3×10^{22} kg, 6.0×10^{24} kg, and 2.0×10^{30} kg, respectively, find the ratio of the gravitational forces exerted by Earth and the sun on the moon.

$F = G\dfrac{m_1m_2}{d^2}$

Earth on moon: $F_e = \dfrac{G(6.0 \times 10^{24}\ \text{kg})(7.3 \times 10^{22}\ \text{kg})}{(3.9 \times 10^8\ \text{m})^2} = 1.9 \times 10^{20}\ \text{N}$

Sun on moon: $F_s = \dfrac{G(2.0 \times 10^{30}\ \text{kg})(7.3 \times 10^{22}\ \text{kg})}{(1.5 \times 10^{11}\ \text{m})^2} = 4.3 \times 10^{20}\ \text{N}$

Ratio is $\dfrac{F_e}{F_s} = \dfrac{1.9 \times 10^{20}\ \text{N}}{4.3 \times 10^{20}\ \text{N}} = \dfrac{1.0}{2.3}$.

The sun pulls more than twice as hard on the moon as the Earth.

Chapter Review Problems

16. A force of 40.0 N is required to pull a 10.0-kg wooden block at a constant velocity across a smooth glass surface on Earth. What force would be required to pull the same wooden block across the same glass surface on Jupiter? (Jupiter's mass is 1.90×10^{27} kg and its radius is 7.18×10^7 m.)

$\mu = \frac{F_f}{F_N} = \frac{F_f}{m_b g}$ where m_b is the mass of the block.

On Jupiter the normal force is equal to the gravitational attraction between the block and Jupiter, or

$$F_N = \frac{Gm_b m_J}{R_J^2}$$

Now $\mu = \frac{F_f}{F_N}$, so $F_{fJ} = \mu F_N = \mu \frac{Gm_b m_J}{R_J^2}$

But $\mu = \frac{F_f}{m_b g}$ so $F_{fJ} = \frac{F_f G m_b m_J}{m_b g R_J^2} = \frac{(40.0\ \text{N})(6.67 \times 10^{-11}\ \text{N}\cdot\text{m}^2/\text{s}^2)(1.90 \times 10^{27}\ \text{kg})}{(9.80\ \text{m/s}^2)(7.18 \times 10^7\ \text{m})^2}$

$= 100$ N

Note, the mass of the block divided out.

17. Use the information for Earth from Table 8-1 to calculate the mass of the sun using Newton's variations of Kepler's third law.

$$T^2 = \left[\frac{4\pi^2}{Gm}\right] r^3, \text{ so } mT^2 = \left[\frac{4\pi^2}{G}\right] r^3 \text{ and}$$

$$m = \left[\frac{4\pi^2}{G}\right]\frac{r^3}{T^2} = \left[\frac{4\pi^2}{6.670 \times 10^{-11}\ \text{N}\cdot\text{m}^2/\text{s}^2}\right]\frac{(1.4957 \times 10^{11}\ \text{m})^3}{(3.156 \times 10^7\ \text{s})^2} = 1.989 \times 10^{30}\ \text{kg}$$

18. Mimas, a moon of Saturn, has an orbital radius of 1.87×10^8 m and an orbital period of about 23 hours. Use Newton's variation of Kepler's third law and this data to find the mass of Saturn.

$$T^2 = \left[\frac{4\pi^2}{Gm}\right] r^3, \text{ so } m = \frac{4\pi^2 r^3}{GT^2} = \frac{4\pi^2(1.87 \times 10^8\ \text{m})^3}{(6.67 \times 10^{-11}\ \text{N}\cdot\text{m}^2/\text{kg}^2)(82\,800\ \text{s})^2} = 5.6 \times 10^{26}\ \text{kg}$$

19. Use Newton's variation of Kepler's third law to find the mass of Earth. The moon is 3.9×10^8 m away from Earth and the moon has a period of 27.33 days. Compare this mass to the mass found in Problem 14.

$$T^2 = \left[\frac{4\pi^2}{Gm}\right] r^3 \text{ so } m = \left[\frac{4\pi^2}{G}\right]\frac{r^3}{T^2} = \left[\frac{4\pi^2}{6.67 \times 10^{-11}\ \text{N}\cdot\text{m}^2/\text{kg}^2}\right]\frac{(3.9 \times 10^8\ \text{m})^3}{(2.361 \times 10^6\ \text{s})^2} = 6.3 \times 10^{24}\ \text{kg}$$

very close

20. A geosynchronous satellite appears to remain over one spot on Earth. A geosynchronous satellite has an orbital radius of 4.23×10^7 m.

a. Calculate its speed in orbit.

$$v = \sqrt{\frac{Gm_e}{r}} = \sqrt{\frac{(6.67 \times 10^{-11}\ \text{N}\cdot\text{m}^2/\text{kg}^2)(5.979 \times 10^{24}\ \text{kg})}{(4.23 \times 10^7\ \text{m})}} = \sqrt{9.43 \times 10^6\ \text{m}^2/\text{s}^2}$$

$= 3.07 \times 10^3$ m/s or 3.07 km/s

8

b. Calculate its period.

$$T = 2\pi\sqrt{\frac{r^3}{Gm_e}} = 2\pi\sqrt{\frac{(4.23 \times 10^7\ \text{m})^3}{(6.67 \times 10^{-11}\ \text{N}\cdot\text{m}^2/\text{kg}^2)(5.979 \times 10^{24}\ \text{kg})}} = 2\pi\sqrt{1.90 \times 10^8\ \text{s}^2}$$

$$= 8.66 \times 10^4\ \text{s or } 24.0\ \text{h}$$

21. On July 19, 1969, Apollo II's orbit around the moon was adjusted to an average orbit of 111 km. The radius of the moon is 1785 km and the mass of the moon is 7.3×10^{22} kg.

r = 111 km + 1785 km = 1896 km.

a. How many minutes did it take to orbit once?

$$T = 2\pi\sqrt{\frac{r^3}{Gm}} = 2\pi\sqrt{\frac{(1896 \times 10^3\ \text{m})^3}{6.67 \times 10^{-11}\ \text{N}\cdot\text{m}^2/\text{kg}^2)(7.3 \times 10^{22}\ \text{kg})}} = 2\pi\sqrt{1.4 \times 10^6\ \text{s}^2}$$

$$= 7.4 \times 10^3\ \text{s} = 1.2 \times 10^2\ \text{min}$$

b. At what velocity did it orbit the moon?

$$v = \sqrt{\frac{Gm}{r}} = \sqrt{\frac{(6.67 \times 10^{-11}\ \text{N}\cdot\text{m}^2/\text{kg}^2)(7.3 \times 10^{22}\ \text{kg})}{1896 \times 10^3\ \text{m}}} = \sqrt{2.6 \times 10^6\ \text{m}^2/\text{s}^2} = 1.6 \times 10^3\ \text{m/s}$$

22. The asteroid Ceres has a mass 7×10^{20} kg and a radius of 500 km.

a. What is g on the surface?

$$g = \frac{Gm}{d^2} = \frac{(6.67 \times 10^{-11}\ \text{N}\cdot\text{m}^2/\text{kg}^2)(7 \times 10^{20}\ \text{kg})}{(500 \times 10^3\ \text{m})^2} = 0.2\ \text{m/s}^2$$

b. How much would an 85-kg astronaut weigh on Ceres?

$$W = mg = (85\ \text{kg})(0.2\ \text{m/s}^2) = 17 = 2 \times 10^1\ \text{N}$$

23. The radius of Earth is about 6.40×10^3 km. A 7.20×10^3-N spacecraft travels away from Earth. What is the weight of the spacecraft at the following distances from Earth's surface?

$R_E = 6.40 \times 10^3$ km

$$W \propto \frac{1}{d^2}$$

a. 6.40×10^3 km

$d = R_E + R_E = 2R_E$.

Therefore, $W = \frac{1}{4}$ original weight $= \frac{1}{4}(7.20 \times 10^3\ \text{N}) = 1.80 \times 10^3\ \text{N}$

b. 1.28×10^4 km

$d = R_E + 2R_E = 3R_E$;

$W = \frac{1}{9}(7.20 \times 10^3\ \text{N}) = 800\ \text{N}$

Chapter Review Problems

24. How high does a rocket have to go above Earth's surface until its weight is half what it would be on Earth?

Now $W \propto \frac{1}{d^2}$ so $d \propto \sqrt{\frac{1}{W}}$

If the weight is $\frac{1}{2}$ the distance is $\sqrt{2}$ or $d = \sqrt{2}$ $(6.40 \times 10^6 \text{ m}) = 9.05 \times 10^6$ m

$9.05 \times 10^6 \text{ m} - 6.40 \times 10^6 \text{ m} = 2.65 \times 10^6 \text{ m} = 2.65 \times 10^3$ km.

25. The formula for the period of a pendulum, T, is $T = 2\pi\sqrt{l/g}$.

$$g = \frac{Gm}{R^2} = \frac{(6.670 \times 10^{-11} \text{ N}\cdot\text{m}^2/\text{kg}^2)(7.34 \times 10^{22} \text{ kg})}{(1.74 \times 10^6 \text{ m})^2} = 1.62 \text{ m/s}^2$$

a. What would be the period of a 2.0 m long pendulum on the moon's surface? The moon's mass is 7.34×10^{22} kg and its radius is 1.74×10^6 m.

$$T = 2\pi\sqrt{l/g} = 2\pi\sqrt{\frac{(2.0 \text{ m})}{(1.62 \text{ m/s}^2)}} = 7.0 \text{ s}$$

b. What is the period of this pendulum on Earth?

$$T = 2\pi\sqrt{l/g} = 2\pi\sqrt{\frac{(2.0 \text{ m})}{(9.80 \text{ m/s}^2)}} = 2.8 \text{ s}$$

26. A 1.25-kg book in space has a weight of 8.35 N. What is the value of the gravitational field at that location?

$g = F/m = (8.35 \text{ N})/(1.25 \text{ kg}) = 6.68$ N/kg

27. The moon's mass is 7.34×10^{22} kg and it is 3.8×10^8 m away from Earth. Earth's mass can be found in Table 8–1.

a. Calculate the gravitational force of attraction between the two.

$$F = \frac{Gm_e m_m}{d^2} = \frac{(6.67 \times 10^{-11} \text{ N}\cdot\text{m}^2/\text{kg}^2)(5.979 \times 10^{24} \text{ kg})(7.34 \times 10^{22} \text{ kg})}{(3.8 \times 10^8 \text{ m})^2} = 2.0 \times 10^{20} \text{ N}$$

b. Find the Earth's gravitational field at the moon.

$$g = F/m = \frac{2.0 \times 10^{20} \text{ N}}{7.34 \times 10^{22} \text{ kg}} = 0.0028 \text{ N/kg}$$

28. Earth's gravitational field is 7.83 N/kg at the altitude of the space shuttle. What is the size of the force of attraction between a student, mass of 45.0 kg, and Earth?

$g = F/m$, so $F = mg = (45.0)(7.83) = 352$ N

Supplemental Problems (Appendix B)

1. Comet Halley returns every 74 years. Find the average distance of the comet from the sun.

   $(r_a/r_b)^3 = (T_a/T_b)^2$, so
   $r_a^3 = r_b^3(T_a/T_b)^2 = (1.0\text{ AU})^3(74\text{ y}/1.0\text{ y})^2 = 5.48 \times 10^3\text{ AU}^3$,
   so $r_a = 18$ AU or $18(1.5 \times 10^{11}\text{ m}) = 2.7 \times 10^{12}$ m

2. Area is measured in m², so the rate at which area is swept out by a planet or satellite is measured in m²/s.

   The total area for one orbit is πr^2 and the total time is one period T. The rate is $\pi r^2/T$.

   a. How fast is area swept out by Earth in its orbit about the sun. See Table 8–1.

   $r = 1.49 \times 10^{11}$ m and $T = 3.156 \times 10^7$ s, so
   $\pi r^2/T = \pi(1.49 \times 10^{11}\text{ m})^2/\text{s}/(3.156 \times 10^7\text{ s}) = 2.21 \times 10^{15}\text{ m}^2/\text{s}$

   b. How fast is area swept out by the moon in its orbit about Earth? Use 3.9×10^8 m as the average distance between the Earth and the moon, and 27.3 days as the moon's period.

   $\pi(3.9 \times 10^8\text{ m})^2/(2.36 \times 10^7\text{ s}) = 2.0 \times 10^{11}\text{ m}^2/\text{s}$

3. You wish to launch a satellite that will remain above the same spot on Earth's surface. This means the satellite must have a period of exactly one day. Calculate the radius of the circular orbit this satellite must have. **Hint:** The moon also circles Earth and both the moon and satellite will obey Kepler's third law. The moon 3.8×10^8 m from Earth and its period is 27.33 days.

   $$\left[\frac{T_S}{T_m}\right]^2 = \left[\frac{r_S}{r_m}\right]^3, \text{ so } r_S^3 = \left[\frac{T_S}{T_m}\right]^2 r_m^3 = \left[\frac{1000\text{ dy}}{27.33\text{ dy}}\right]^2 (3.8 \times 10^8\text{ m})^3 = 7.35 \times 10^{22}\text{ m}^3$$

   so $r_S = 4.2 \times 10^7$ m

4. The mass of an electron is 9.1×10^{-31} kg. The mass of a proton is 1.7×10^{-27} kg. They are about 1.0×10^{-10} m apart in a hydrogen atom. What gravitational force exists between the proton and the electron of a hydrogen atom?

   $$F = \frac{Gm_em_p}{d^2} = \frac{(6.67 \times 10^{-4}\text{ N}\cdot\text{m}^2/\text{kg}^2)(9.1 \times 10^{-31}\text{ kg})(1.7 \times 10^{-27}\text{ kg})}{(1.0 \times 10^{-10}\text{ m})^2} = 1.0 \times 10^{-47}\text{ N}$$

5. Two 1.00-kg masses have their centers 1.00 m apart. What is the force of attraction between them?

   $$F_g = G\frac{m_1m_2}{d^2} = \frac{(6.67 \times 10^{-11}\text{ N}\cdot\text{m}^2/\text{kg}^2)(1.00\text{ kg})(1.00\text{ kg})}{(1.00\text{ m})^2} = 6.67 \times 10^{-11}\text{ N}$$

6. Two satellites of equal mass are put into orbit 30 m apart. The gravitational force between them is 2.0×10^{-7} N.

   a. What is the mass of each sattelite?

   $$F = G\frac{m_1m_2}{r_2}$$

   $$m = \sqrt{\frac{Fr^2}{G}} = \sqrt{\frac{(2.0 \times 10^{-7}\text{ N})(30\text{ m})^2}{(6.67 \times 10^{-11}\text{ N}\cdot\text{m}^2/\text{kg}^2)}} = \sqrt{2.698 \times 10^6\text{ kg}^2} = 1.6 \times 10^3\text{ kg}$$

b. What is the initial acceleration given to each satellite by the gravitational force?

$F = ma$

$a = \frac{F}{m} = \frac{2.0 \times 10^{-7}\ \text{N}}{1.6 \times 10^{3}\ \text{kg}} = 1.3 \times 10^{-10}\ \text{m/s}^2$

7. Two large spheres are suspended close to each other. Their centers are 4.0 m apart. One sphere weighs 9.8×10^2 N. The other sphere has a weight of 1.96×10^2 N. What is the gravitational force between them?

$m_1 = \frac{W}{g} = \frac{9.8 \times 10^2\ \text{N}}{9.8\ \text{m/s}^2} = 1.0 \times 10^2\ \text{kg}$

$m_2 = \frac{W}{g} = \frac{1.96 \times 10^2\ \text{N}}{9.8\ \text{m/s}^2} = 2.0 \times 10^1\ \text{kg}$

$F = G\frac{m_1 m_2}{d^2} = [(6.67 \times 10^{-11}\ \text{N}\cdot\text{m}^2/\text{kg}^2)(1.0 \times 10^2\ \text{kg})(2.0 \times 10^1\ \text{kg})] \div (4.0\ \text{m})^2$

$= 8.3 \times 10^{-9}\ \text{N}$

8. If the centers of Earth and the Moon are 3.9×10^8 m apart, the gravitational force between them is about 1.9×10^{20} N. What is the approximate mass of the moon?

$F = G\frac{m_1 m_2}{r^2}$

$m_m = \frac{Fr^2}{Gm_e} = \frac{(1.9 \times 10^{20}\ \text{N})(3.9 \times 10^8\ \text{m})^2}{(6.67 \times 10^{-11}\ \text{N}\cdot\text{m}^2/\text{kg}^2)(6.0 \times 10^{24}\ \text{kg})} = 7.2 \times 10^{22}\ \text{kg}$

9. **a.** What is the gravitational force between two 8.00-kg spherical masses that are 5.0 m apart?

$F = G\frac{m_1 m_2}{r^2} = \frac{(6.67 \times 10^{-11}\ \text{N}\cdot\text{m}^2/\text{kg}^2)(8.0\ \text{kg})(8.0\ \text{kg})}{(5.0\ \text{m})^2} = 1.7 \times 10^{-10}\ \text{N}$

b. What is the gravitational force between them when they are 5.0×10^1 m apart?

$F = G\frac{m_1 m_2}{r^2} = \frac{(6.67 \times 10^{-11}\ \text{N}\cdot\text{m}^2/\text{kg}^2)(8.0\ \text{kg})(8.0\ \text{kg})}{(5.0 \times 10^1\ \text{m})^2} = 1.7 \times 10^{-12}\ \text{N}$

10. A satellite is placed in a circular orbit of 1.0×10^7 m radius with a period of 9.9×10^3 s. Calculate the mass of Earth. **Hint:** Gravity supplies the needed centripetal force for such a satellite. Scientists have actually measured the mass of Earth this way.

$F = m_s v^2/r = G m_s m_e/r^2$. Since, $v = 2\pi r/T$, $\left[\frac{m_s}{r}\right]\left[\frac{4\pi^2 r^2}{T^2}\right] = \frac{Gm_s me}{r^2}$

$m_e = 4\pi^2 r^3/GT^2 = (4)(3.14)^2(1.0 \times 10^7\ \text{m})^3/(6.67 \times 10^{-11}\ \text{N}\cdot\text{m}^2/\text{kg}^2)(9.9 \times 10^3\ \text{s})^2$
$m_e = 6.0 \times 10^{24}\ \text{kg}$

11. If you weigh 637 N on Earth's surface, how much would you weigh on the planet Mars? (Mars has a mass of 6.37×10^{23} kg and a radius of 3.43×10^6 m.)

$m = W/g = (637\ \text{N})/(9.80\ \text{m/s}^2) = 65.0\ \text{kg}$
$F = Gm_1m_2/d^2 = (6.67 \times 10^{-11}\ \text{N}\cdot\text{m}^2/\text{kg}^2)(65.0\ \text{kg})(6.37 \times 10^{23}\ \text{kg})/(3.43 \times 10^6\ \text{m}) = 235\ \text{N}$

12. Using Newton's variation of Kepler's third law and information from Table 8–1, calculate the period of Earth's moon if the radius of orbit was twice the actual value of 3.9×10^8 m.

$$(T_p^2) = \left[\frac{4\pi^2}{GME}\right](R^3) = \left[\frac{4\pi^2}{(6.67 \times 10^{-11}\ \text{N}\cdot\text{m}^2/\text{kg}^2)(5.979 \times 10^{24}\ \text{kg})}\right](7.8 \times 10^8\ \text{m})^3$$

$T_p = 6.85 \times 10^6$ s or 79 days

13. Use the data from Table 8–1 to find the speed and period of a satellite that would orbit Mars 175 km above its surface.

$r = Rm + 175\ \text{km} = 3.56 \times 10^6$ m

$$v = \sqrt{\frac{GM_m}{r}} = \sqrt{\frac{(6.67 \times 10^{-11}\ \text{N}\cdot\text{m}^2/\text{kg}^2)(6.42 \times 10^{23}\ \text{kg})}{(3.56 \times 10^6\ \text{m})}}$$

$v = 3.47 \times 10^3$ m/s

$$T = 2\pi\sqrt{\frac{r^3}{GM_m}} = 2\pi\sqrt{\frac{(3.56 \times 10^6\ \text{m})^3}{(6.67 \times 10^{-11}\ \text{N}\cdot\text{m}^2/\text{kg}^2)(6.42 \times 10^{23}\ \text{kg})}}$$

$T = 6.45 \times 10^3$ s or 1.79 h

14. What would be the value of g, accleration of gravity, if Earth's mass was double its actual value, but its radius remained the same? If the radius was doubled, but the mass remained the same? If both the mass and radius were doubled?

$$g = \frac{GM_e}{R_e^2}$$

$2M_e \Rightarrow g = 19.6\ \text{m/s}^2$
$2R_e \Rightarrow g = 2.45\ \text{m/s}^2$
$2M_e$ and $2R_e \Rightarrow g = 4.9\ \text{m/s}^2$

15. What would be the strength of Earth's gravitational field at a point where an 80.0–kg astronaut would experience a 25% reduction in weight?

$W = mg = (80.0\ \text{kg})(9.80\ \text{m/s}^2) = 784$ N
$W_{reduced} = (784\ \text{N})(.75) = 588$ N

$$g_{reduced} = \frac{W_{reduced}}{m} = 588\ \text{N}/80.0\ \text{kg} = 7.35\ \text{m/s}^2$$

16. On the surface of the moon, a 91.0–kg physics teacher weighs only 145.6 N. What is the value of the moon's gravitational field at its surface?

$$W = mg,\ g = \frac{W}{m} = \frac{145.6\ \text{N}}{91.0\ \text{kg}} = 1.60\ \text{m/s}^2$$

Chapter 9: Momentum and its Conservation

9

Practice Problems

page 178

1. A compact car, mass 725 kg, is moving at +100 km/h.

   a. Find its momentum.

   100 km/h = 27.8 m/s,
   $p = mv = (725 \text{ kg})(27.8 \text{ m/s})$
   $= 2.02 \times 10^4 \text{ kg·m/s}$

   b. At what velocity is the momentum of a larger car, mass 2175 kg, equal to that of the smaller car?

   $$v = p/m = \frac{(2.02 \times 10^4 \text{ kg·m/s})}{(2175 \text{ kg})}$$
   $$= 9.29 \text{ m/s} = 33.4 \text{ km/h}$$

page 179

2. A snowmobile has a mass of 2.50×10^2 kg. A constant force is exerted on it for 60.0 s. The snowmobile's initial velocity is 6.00 m/s and its final velocity 28.0 m/s.

   a. What is its change in momentum?

   $\Delta p = m(v_f - v_i)$
   $= (250 \text{ kg})(28.0 \text{ m/s} - 6.0 \text{ m/s})$
   $= 5.50 \times 10^3 \text{ kg·m/s}$

   b. What is the magnitude of the force exerted on it?

   $$F = \Delta p/\Delta t = \frac{(5.50 \times 10^3 \text{ kg·m/s})}{(60.0 \text{ s})} = 91.7 \text{ N}$$

3. The brakes exert a 6.40×10^2 N force on a car weighing 15 680 N and moving at 20.0 m/s. The car finally stops.

   a. What is the car's mass.

   $$m = W/g = \frac{(15\ 680 \text{ N})}{(9.80 \text{ m/s}^2)} = 1.60 \times 10^3 \text{ kg}$$

Practice Problems

   b. What is its initial momentum?

   $p_i = mv_i = (1600 \text{ kg})(20.0 \text{ m/s})$
   $= 3.20 \times 10^4 \text{ kg·m/s}$

   c. What is the change in the car's momentum?

   $\Delta p = p_f - p_i = 0 - 3.20 \times 10^4 \text{ kg·m/s}$
   $= -3.20 \times 10^4 \text{ kg·m/s}$

   d. How long does the braking force act on the car to bring it to a halt?

   $F\Delta t = \Delta p,\ \Delta t = \Delta p/F$
   $$= \frac{(-3.20 \times 10^4 \text{ kg·m/s})}{(-6.40 \times 10^2 \text{ N})}$$
   $$= 50.0 \text{ s}$$

4. Figure 9–1 shows, as a function of time, the force exerted by a ball that collided with a box at rest. The impulse, $F\Delta t$, is the area under the curve.

   a. Find the impulse given to the box by the ball.

   $F\Delta t$ = Area
   = (52.5 squares)(0.100 N·s/square)
   = 5.25 N·s.

   b. If the box has a mass of 2.4 kg, what velocity did it have after the collision?

   $\Delta p = m\Delta V$ with $\Delta p = F\Delta t$, so

   $$\Delta v = \frac{\Delta p}{m} = \frac{F\Delta t}{m} = \frac{(5.25 \text{ N·s})}{(2.4 \text{ ks})} = 2.2 \text{ m/s}$$

Practice Problems

page 185

5. A 0.105-kg hockey puck moving at 48 m/s is caught by a 75-kg goalie at rest. With what speed does the goalie slide on the ice?

$p_h + p_g = p_h' + p_g'$ or $m_h v_h + m_g v_g = m_h v_h' + m_g v_g'$.
Since $v_g = 0$, $m_h v_h = (m_h + m_g)v'$
where $v' = v_h' = v_g'$ is the common final speed of goalie and puck.

$$v' = \frac{m_h v_h}{(m_h + m_g)}$$
$= (0.105 \text{ kg})(48 \text{ m/s})(0.105 \text{ kg} + 75 \text{ kg})$
$= 0.067 \text{ m/s}$

6. A 35.0-g bullet strikes a 5.0-kg stationary wooden block and embeds itself in the block. The block and bullet fly off together at 8.6 m/s. What was the original velocity of the bullet?

$m_b v_b + m_w v_w = (m_b + m_w)v'$ where v' is the common final velocity of bullet and wooden block.
Since $v_w = 0$,
$v_b = (m_b + m_w)v'/m_b$

$$= \frac{(0.035 \text{ kg} + 5.0 \text{ kg})(8.6 \text{ m/s})}{(0.035 \text{ kg})}$$
$= 1.2 \times 10^3 \text{ m/s}$

7. A 35.0-g bullet moving at 475 m/s strikes a 2.5-kg wooden block. The bullet passes through the block, leaving at 275 m/s. The block was at rest when it was hit. How fast is it moving when the bullet leaves?

$m_b v_b + m_w v_w = m_b v_b' + m_w v_w'$ with $v_w = 0$.

$$v_w' = \frac{(m_b v_b - m_b v_b')}{m_w} = \frac{m_b(v_b - v_b')}{m_w}$$
$$= \frac{(0.035 \text{ kg})(475 \text{ m/s} - 275 \text{ m/s})}{(2.5 \text{ kg})}$$
$= 2.8 \text{ m/s}$

Practice Problems

8. A 0.50-kg ball traveling at 6.0 m/s collides head-on with a 1.00-kg ball moving in the opposite direction at a velocity of – 12.0 m/s. The 0.50-kg ball moves away at – 14 m/s after the collision. Find the velocity of the second ball.

$m_A v_A + m_B v_B = m_A v_A' + m_B v_B'$, so v_B'

$$= \frac{(m_A v_A + m_B v_B - m_A v_A')}{m_B}$$
$= [(0.50 \text{ kg})(6.0 \text{ m/s}) + (1.00 \text{ kg})(-12.0 \text{ m/s}) - (0.50 \text{ kg})(-14 \text{ m/s})]/(1.00 \text{ kg})$
$= -2.0 \text{ m/s}$

page 188

9. A 4.00-kg model rocket is launched, shooting 50.0 g of burned fuel from its exhaust at an average velocity of 625 m/s. What is the velocity of the rocket after the fuel has burned? (Ignore effects of gravity and air resistance.)

$p_r + p_f = p_r' + p_f'$ where $p_r + p_f = 0$.
If the initial mass of the rocket (including fuel) is $m_r = 4.00$ kg, then the final mass of the rocket is
$m_r' = 4.00 \text{ kg} - 0.050 \text{ kg} = 3.95 \text{ kg}$.
$0 = m_r' v_r' + m_f v_f'$,

$$v_r' = \frac{-m_f v_f'}{m_r'}$$
$$= \frac{-(0.050 \text{ kg})(-625 \text{ m/s})}{(3.95 \text{ kg})}$$
$= 7.91 \text{ m/s}$

10. A thread holds two carts together on a frictionless surface as in Figure 9-12. A compressed spring acts upon the carts. After the thread is burned, the 1.5-kg cart moves with a velocity of 27 cm/s to the left. What is the velocity of the 4.5-kg cart?

$p_A + p_B = p_A' + p_B'$ with $p_A + p_B = 0$,
$m_B v_B' = -m_A v_A'$,
$$\text{so } v_B = \frac{-m_A v_A'}{m_B} = \frac{-(1.5 \text{ kg})(-27 \text{ cm/s})}{(4.5 \text{ kg})}$$
$= 9.0$ cm/s, or 9.0 cm/s to the right.

Practice Problems

page 189

11. Two campers dock a canoe. One camper steps onto the dock. This camper has a mass of 80.0 kg and moves forward at 4.0 m/s. With what speed and direction do the canoe and the other camper move if their combined mass is 110 kg?

$p_A + p_B = p_A' + p_B'$ with $p_A + p_B = 0$,
$m_A v_A' = -m_B v_B'$, so

$$v_B' = \frac{-m_A v_A'}{m_B}$$

$$= \frac{-(80.0 \text{ kg})(4.0 \text{ m/s})}{(110 \text{ kg})}$$

$= -2.9$ m/s, or 2.9 m/s in the opposite direction.

12. A colonial gunner sets up his 225–kg cannon at the edge of the flat top of a high tower. It shoots a 4.5–kg cannon ball horizontally. The ball hits the ground 215 m from the base of the tower. The cannon also moves, on frictionless wheels, and falls off the back of the tower, landing on the ground.

a. What is the horizontal distance of the cannon's landing, measured from the base of the back of the tower?

Both the cannon and the ball fall to the ground in the same time from the same height. In that fall time, the ball moves 215 m, the cannon an unknown distance we will call x. Now $t = \frac{d}{v}$, so $\frac{(215\,m)}{v_{ball}} = \frac{x}{v_{cannon}}$, so $x = \left[\frac{v_{cannon}}{v_{ball}}\right]$ related by conservation of momentum;
$(4.5 \text{ kg})v_{ball} = -(225 \text{ kg})v_{cannon}$, so

$$\left[\frac{v_{cannon}}{v_{ball}}\right] = \frac{(4.5 \text{ kg})}{(225 \text{ kg})}.$$

Thus $x = \left[\frac{4.5}{225}\right](215 \text{ m}) = 4.3$ m.

b. Why do you not need to know the width of the tower?

While on top, the cannon moves with no friction, and its velocity doesn't change, so it can take any amount of time to reach the back edge.

Practice Problems

page 191

13. A 1325–kg car moving north at 27.0 m/s collides with a 2165–kg car moving east at 17.0 m/s. They stick together. Draw a vector diagram of the collision. In what direction and with what speed do they move after the collision?

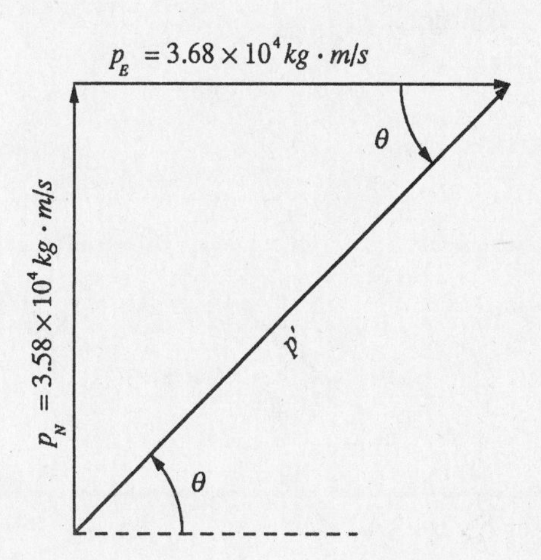

$p_N + p_E = p'$(vector sum)
$p_N = m_N v_N = (1325 \text{ kg})(27.0 \text{ m/s})$
$= 3.58 \times 10^4$ kg·m/s
$p_E = m_E v_E = (2165 \text{ kg})(17.0 \text{ m/s})$
$= 3.68 \times 10^4$ kg·m/s

$$\tan\theta = \frac{p_N}{p_E} = \frac{3.58 \times 10^4 \text{ kg·m/s}}{3.68 \times 10^4 \text{ kg·m/s}} = 0.973,$$

$\theta = 44.2°$, north of east
$(p')^2 = (p_N)^2 + (p_E)^2$
$= (3.58 \times 10^4 \text{ kg·m/s})^2 + (3.68 \times 10^4 \text{ kg·m/s})^2$
$= 2.64 \times 10^9 \text{ kg}^2\text{ m}^2/\text{s}^2$,
$p' = 5.13 \times 10^4$ kg·m/s
$p' = m'v' = (m_N + m_E)v'$,

$$v' = \frac{p'}{(m_N + m_E)}$$

$$= \frac{(5.13 \times 10^4 \text{ kg·m/s})}{(1325 \text{ kg} + 2165 \text{ kg})}$$

$= 14.7$ m/s

Practice Problems

14. A 6.0–kg object, *A*, moving at velocity 3.0 m/s, collides with a 6.0–kg object, *B*, at rest. After the collision, *A* moves off in a direction 40.0° to the left of its original direction. *B* moves off in a direction 50.0° to the right of *A*'s original direction.

a. Draw a vector diagram and determine the momenta of object *A* and object *B* after the collision.

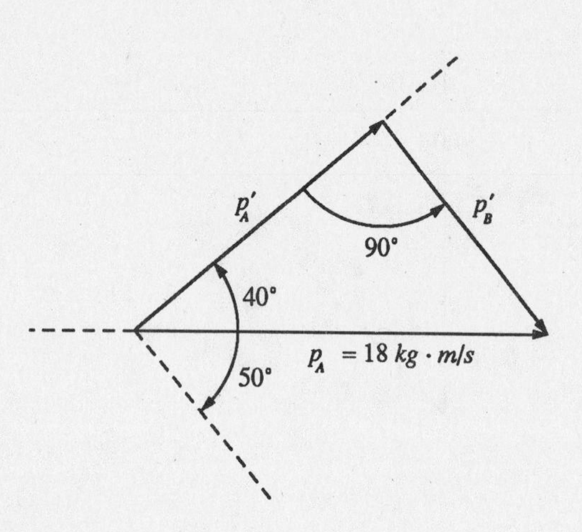

$p_A + p_B = p_A' + p_B'$ (vector sum)
with $p_B = 0$
$p_A = m_A v_A = (6.0 \text{ kg})(3.0 \text{ m/s}) = 18 \text{ kg} \cdot \text{m/s}$
$p_A' = p_A \cos 40° = (18 \text{ kg} \cdot \text{m/s}) \cos 40°$
$p_A' = p_A \sin 40° = (18 \text{ kg} \cdot \text{m/s}) \sin 40°$
$= 14 \text{ kg} \cdot \text{m/s}$
$p_B' = p_A \sin 40° = (18 \text{ kg} \cdot \text{m/s}) \sin 40°$
$= 12 \text{ kg} \cdot \text{m/s}$

b. What is the velocity of each object after the collision?

$p_A' = m_A v'_A,$

$v_A' = \dfrac{p_A'}{m_A} = \dfrac{(14 \text{ kg} \cdot \text{m/s})}{(6.0 \text{ kg})}$

$= 2.3$ m/s, 40° to left

$p_B' = m_B v_B',$

$v_B' = \dfrac{p_B'}{m_B} = \dfrac{(12 \text{ kg} \cdot \text{m/s})}{(6.0 \text{ kg})}$

$= 2.0$ m/s, 50° to right

Practice Problems

15. A stationary billiard ball of mass 0.17 kg is struck by a second, identical ball moving at 4.0 m/s. After the collision, the second ball moves off in a direction 60° to the left of its original direction. The stationary ball moves off in a direction 30° to the right of the second ball's original direction. What is the velocity of each ball after the collision?

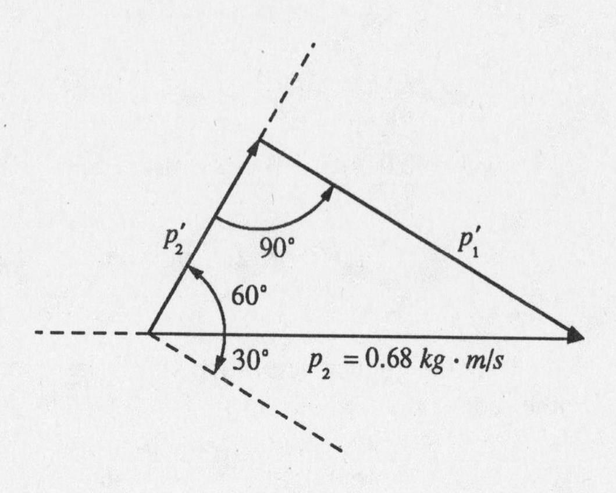

$p_1 + p_2 = p_1' + p_2'$ (vector sum) with $p_1 = 0$
$m_1 = m_2 = m = 0.17$ kg
$p_2 = m_2 v_2 = (0.17 \text{ kg})(4.0 \text{ m/s}) = 0.68 \text{ kg} \cdot \text{m/s}$
$p_1' = p_2 \sin 60°,\ mv'_1 = mv_2 \sin 60°,$
$v_1' = v_2 \sin 60° = (4.0 \text{ m/s}) \sin 60°$
$= 3.5$ m/s, 30° to right
$p_2' = p_2 \cos 60°,\ mv'_2 = mv_2 \cos 60°,$
$v_2' = v_2 \cos 60° = (4.0 \text{ m/s}) \cos 60°$
$= 2.0$ m/s, 60° to left

Chapter Review Problems

1. Jenny has a mass of 35.6 kg and her skateboard has a mass of 1.3 kg. What is Jenny and her skateboard's momentum if they are going 9.50 m/s?

Total mass is 35.6 kg + 1.3 kg = 36.9 kg
$mv = (36.9 \text{ kg})(9.50 \text{ m/s}) = 351$ kg m/s

2. A hockey player makes a slap shot, exerting a force of 30.0 N on the hockey puck for 0.16 s. What impulse is given to the puck?

$F\Delta t = (30.0 \text{ N})(0.16 \text{ s}) = 4.8 \text{ kg} \cdot \text{m/s}$

3. The hockey puck shot in Problem 2 has a mass of 0.115 kg and was at rest before the shot. With what speed does it head toward the goal?

$$F\Delta t = m\Delta v, \text{ so } \Delta v = \frac{F\Delta t}{m} = \frac{4.8 \text{ kg m/s}}{0.115 \text{ kg}}$$

$$= 42 \text{ m/s}$$

4. A force of 6.00 N acts on a 3.00–kg object for 10.0 s.

a. What is the object's change in momentum?

$$m\Delta v = F\Delta t = (6.00 \text{ N})(10.0 \text{ s}) = 60.0 \text{ N}\cdot\text{s}$$

b. What is its change in velocity?

$m\Delta v = F\Delta t$, so

$$\Delta v = \frac{F\Delta t}{m} = \frac{60.0 \text{ N}\cdot\text{s}}{3.00 \text{ kg}} = 20.0 \text{ m/s}$$

5. The velocity of a 600–kg auto is changed from +10.0 m/s to 44.0 m/s in 68.0 s by an applied, constant force.

a. What change in momentum does the force produce?

$$\begin{aligned}\Delta p &= m\Delta v \\ &= (600 \text{ kg})(44.0 \text{ m/s} - 10.0 \text{ m/s}) \\ &= 2.04 \times 10^4 \text{ N}\cdot\text{s}\end{aligned}$$

b. What is the magnitude of the force?

$F\Delta t = m\Delta v$, so

$$F = \frac{m\Delta v}{\Delta t} = \frac{2.04 \times 10^4 \text{ N}\cdot\text{s}}{68.0 \text{ s}} = 300 \text{ N}$$

6. A 845–kg drag race car accelerates from rest to 100 km/h in 0.90 seconds.

a. What is the change in momentum of the car?

$$m\Delta v = (845 \text{ kg})\left[\left[100 \frac{\text{km}}{\text{h}}\right]\left[\frac{1000 \text{ m}}{1 \text{ km}}\right]\left[\frac{1 \text{ h}}{3600 \text{ s}}\right] - 0\right]$$

$$= 2.35 \times 10^4 \text{ kg}\cdot\text{m/s}$$

Chapter Review Problems

b. What average force is exerted on the car?

$F\Delta t = m\Delta v$, so

$$F = \frac{m\Delta v}{\Delta t} = \frac{2.35 \times 10^4 \text{ kg}\cdot\text{m/s}}{0.90 \text{ s}}$$

$$= 2.6 \times 10^4 \text{ N}$$

7. A sprinter with a mass of 76 kg accelerates from 0 to 9.4 m/s in 2.8 s. Find the average force acting on the runner.

$$\begin{aligned}m\Delta v &= (76 \text{ kg})(9.4 \text{ m/s} - 0) \\ &= 7.1 \times 10^2 \text{ kg}\cdot\text{m/s}\end{aligned}$$

$F\Delta t = m\Delta v$, so

$$F = \frac{m\Delta v}{\Delta t} = \frac{7.1 \times 10^2 \text{ kg}\cdot\text{m/s}}{2.8 \text{ s}} = 2.6 \times 10^2 \text{ N}$$

8. A 0.25–kg soccer ball is rolling 6.0 m/s toward a player. The player kicks the ball back in the opposite direction and gives it a velocity of – 14 m/s. What is the average force during the interaction between the player's foot and the ball if the interaction lasts 2.0×10^{-2} s?

$F\Delta t = m\Delta v$, so

$$F = \frac{m\Delta v}{\Delta t} = \frac{(0.25 \text{ kg})[(-14 \text{ m/s}) - (6.0 \text{ m/s})]}{2.0 \times 10^{-2} \text{ s}}$$

$$= -2.5 \times 10^2 \text{ N}$$

9. A force of 1.21×10^3 N is needed to bring a car moving at +22.0 m/s to a halt in 20.0 s? What is the mass of the car?

$m\Delta v = F\Delta t$, so

$$m = \frac{F\Delta t}{\Delta v} = \frac{(-1.21 \times 10^3 \text{ N})(20.0 \text{ s})}{0 - 22.0 \text{ m/s}}$$

$$= 1.10 \times 10^3 \text{ kg}$$

10. Small rockets are used to make small adjustments in the speed of satellites. One such rocket has a thrust of 35 N. If it is fired to change the velocity of a 72 000–kg spacecraft by 63 cm/s, how long should it be fired?

$F\Delta t = m\Delta v$, so

$$\Delta t = \frac{m\Delta v}{F} = \frac{(72\,000 \text{ kg})(0.63 \text{ m/s})}{35 \text{ N}}$$

$$= 1.3 \times 10^3 \text{ s}$$

or about 22 min

Chapter Review Problems

11. A 10 000–kg freight car is rolling along a track at 3.00 m/s. Calculate the time needed for a force of 1000 N to stop the car.

$F\Delta t = m\Delta v$, so $\Delta t = \dfrac{m\Delta v}{F}$

$\Delta v = v_f - v_i = 0 - 3.00$ m/s and
$F = -1000$ N (the negative sign is because it is a retarding force), therefore

$$\Delta t = \frac{(10\,000\text{ kg})(-3.00\text{ m/s})}{(-1000\text{ N})} = 30.0\text{ s}$$

12. A car moving at 10 m/s crashes into a barrier and stops in 0.25 m.

a. Find the time required to stop the car.

$d = \frac{1}{2}(v_f + v_i)t$, so

$$t = \frac{2d}{v_f + v_i} = \frac{2(0.25\text{ m})}{0 + 10\text{ m/s}} = 5.0 \times 10^{-2}\text{ s}$$

b. If a 20–kg child were to be stopped in the same time as the car, what average force must be exerted?

$F\Delta t = m\Delta v$, so

$$F = \frac{m\Delta v}{\Delta t} = \frac{(20\text{ kg})(0 - 10\text{ m/s})}{5.0 \times 10^{-2}\text{ s}}$$

$$= -4.0 \times 10^3\text{ N}$$

c. Approximately what is the mass of an object whose weight equals the force from part **b**? Could you lift such a mass with your arm?

$W = mg$, so

$$m = \frac{W}{g} = \frac{4.0 \times 10^3\text{ N}}{9.80\text{ m/s}^2} = 4.1 \times 10^2\text{ kg}$$

No.

d. What does your answer to part **c** say about holding an infant on your lap instead of using a separate infant restraint?

Holding the child on your lap is dangerous to both the child and yourself.

13. An animal–rescue plane flying due east at 36.0 m/s drops a bale of hay from an altitude of 60.0 m. If the bale of hay weighs 175 N, what is the momentum of the bale the moment it strikes the ground?

First use projectile motion to find the velocity of the bale.

$v_x = 36.0$ m/s

$v_y^2 = v_{oy}^2 + 2dg$, so

$$v_y = \sqrt{2dg} = \sqrt{2(-60.0\text{ m})(-9.80\text{ m/s}^2)}$$

$$= \sqrt{1.18 \times 10^3\text{ m}^2/\text{s}^2} = 34.3\text{ m/s}$$

$$v = \sqrt{v_x^2 + v_y^2} = \sqrt{(36.0\text{ m/s})^2 + (34.3\text{ m/s})^2}$$

$$= 49.7\text{ m/s}$$

Now find the mass from $w = mg$, so

$$m = \frac{W}{g} = \frac{175\text{ N}}{9.80\text{ m/s}^2} = 17.9\text{ kg}$$

$mv = (17.9\text{ kg})(49.7\text{ m/s}) = 888\text{ kg}\cdot\text{m/s}$

Now the angle from the two velocities.

$$\tan\theta = \frac{v_y}{v_x} = \frac{34.3\text{ m/s}}{36.0\text{ m/s}},\ \text{so } \theta = 43.6°$$

The momentum is 888 kg·m/s at 43.6° below horizontal.

14. A 10–kg lead brick falls from a height of 2.0 m.

a. Find its momentum as it reaches the ground.

$v_y^2 = v_{oy}^2 + 2gd$, so

$v_y = \sqrt{2gd} = \sqrt{2(9.80\text{ m/s}^2)(2.0\text{ m})} = 6.3\text{ m/s}$

$mv = (10\text{ kg})(6.3\text{ m/s}) = 63\text{ kg}\cdot\text{m/s}$

b. What impulse is needed to bring the brick to rest?

$F\Delta t = m\Delta v = 63\text{ N}\cdot\text{s}$

c. The brick falls onto a carpet, 1.0 cm thick. Assuming the force stopping it is constant, find the average force the carpet exerts on the brick.

$d = \frac{1}{2}(v_f + v_i)t$, so

$t = \frac{2d}{v_f + v_i} = \frac{2(0.010 \text{ m})}{0 + 6.3 \text{ m/s}} = 3.2 \times 10^{-3}$ s

$F\Delta t = m\Delta v$, so

$F = \frac{m\Delta v}{\Delta t} = \frac{63 \text{ kg}\cdot\text{m/s}}{3.2 \times 10^{-3} \text{ s}} = 2.0 \times 10^4$ N

d. If the brick falls onto a 5.0–cm foam rubber pad, what constant force is needed to bring it to rest?

$t = \frac{2d}{v_f + v_i} = \frac{2(0.050 \text{ m})}{0 + 6.3 \text{ m/s}} = 1.6 \times 10^{-2}$ s

$F = \frac{m\Delta v}{\Delta t} = \frac{63 \text{ kg}\cdot\text{m/s}}{1.6 \times 10^{-2} \text{ s}} = 4.0 \times 10^3$ N

15. A 60–kg dancer leaps 0.32 m high.

a. With what momentum does the dancer reach the ground?

$v_f^2 = v_i^2 + 2gd$, so

$v_f = \sqrt{2gd} = \sqrt{2(9.80 \text{ m/s}^2)(0.32 \text{ m})}$
$= 2.5$ m/s

$mv = (60 \text{ kg})(2.5 \text{ m/s}) = 1.5 \times 10^2$ kg·m/s

b. What impulse is needed to make a stop?

$F\Delta t = m\Delta v = 1.5 \times 10^2$ N·s

c. As the dancer lands, the knees bend, lengthening the time required to stop to 0.050 s. Find the average force exerted on the body.

$F\Delta t = 1.5 \times 10^2$ N·s, so

$F = \frac{1.5 \times 10^2 \text{ N}\cdot\text{s}}{\Delta t} = \frac{1.5 \times 10^2 \text{ N}\cdot\text{s}}{0.050 \text{ s}}$
$= 3.0 \times 10^3$ N

d. Compare the stopping force to the performer's weight.

$W = mg = (60 \text{ kg})(9.80 \text{ m/s}^2)$
$= 5.9 \times 10^2$ N

or the force is about 5 times the weight.

Chapter Review Problems

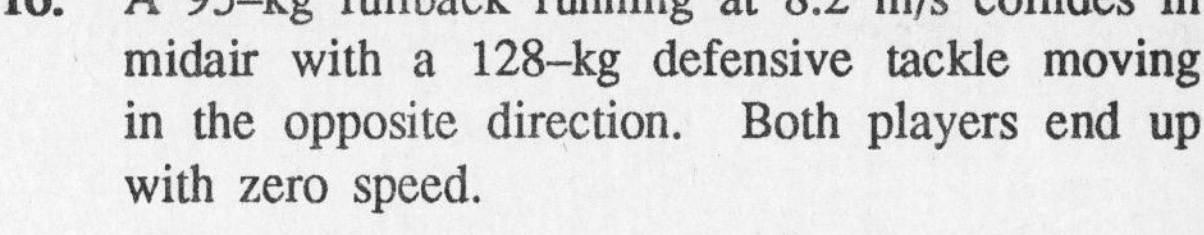

16. A 95–kg fullback running at 8.2 m/s collides in midair with a 128–kg defensive tackle moving in the opposite direction. Both players end up with zero speed.

a. What was the fullback's momentum before the collision?

$mv = (95 \text{ kg})(8.2 \text{ m/s}) = 7.8 \times 10^2$ kg·m/s

b. What was the change in the fullback's momentum?

$0 - 7.8 \times 10^2$ kg·m/s
$= -7.8 \times 10^2$ kg·m/s

c. What was the change in the tackle's momentum?

-7.8×10^2 kg·m/s

d. What was the tackle's original momentum?

7.8×10^2 kg·m/s

e. How fast was the tackle moving originally?

$mv = 7.8 \times 10^2$ kg·m/s, so

$m = \frac{7.8 \times 10^2 \text{ kg}\cdot\text{m/s}}{128 \text{ kg}} = 6.1$ m/s

17. A glass ball, ball *A*, of mass 5.0 g moves at a velocity of 20.0 cm/s. It collides with a second glass ball, ball *B*, of mass 10.0 g moving along the same line with a velocity of 10.0 cm/s. After the collision, ball *A* is still moving but with a velocity of 8.0 cm/s.

a. What was the original momentum of ball *A*?

$m_A v_A = (5.0 \times 10^{-3} \text{ kg})(0.200 \text{ m/s})$
$= 1.0 \times 10^{-3}$ kg·m/s

b. What is the change in momentum of ball *A*?

$m_A \Delta v_A$
$= (5.0 \times 10^{-3} \text{ kg})(0.080 \text{ m/s} - 0.200 \text{ m/s})$
$= -6.0 \times 10^{-4}$ kg·m/s

c. What is the change in momentum of ball *B*?

$+6.0 \times 10^{-4}$ kg·m/s

Chapter Review Problems

d. What is the momentum of ball *B* after the collision?

$$mv_f = mv_i + \Delta mv$$
$$= (10.0 \times 10^{-3}\text{ kg})(0.100\text{ m/s}) + 6.0 \times 10^{-4}\text{ kg}\cdot\text{m/s}$$
$$= 1.60 \times 10^{-3}\text{ kg}\cdot\text{m/s}$$

e. What is ball *B*'s speed after the collision?

$mv = 1.60 \times 10^{-3}\text{ kg}\cdot\text{m/s}$, so

$$v = \frac{1.6 \times 10^{-3}\text{ kg}\cdot\text{m/s}}{10.0 \times 10^{-3}\text{ kg}} = 0.160\text{ m/s}$$
$$= 16.0\text{ cm/s}$$

18. Before a collision, a 25–kg object is moving at +12 m/s. Find the impulse that acted on this object if after the collision it moves at

a. +8.0 m/s.

$$F\Delta t = m\Delta v = (25\text{ kg})(8.0\text{ m/s} - 12\text{ m/s})$$
$$= -1.0 \times 10^2\text{ kg}\cdot\text{m/s}$$

b. –8.0 m/s.

$$F\Delta t = m\Delta v = (25\text{ kg})(-8.0\text{ m/s} - 12\text{ m/s})$$
$$= -5.0 \times 10^2\text{ kg}\cdot\text{m/s}.$$

19. A 2575 kg van runs into the back of an 825–kg compact car at rest. They move off together at 8.5 m/s. Assuming no friction with the ground, find the initial speed of the van.

$$p_A + p_B = p_A' + p_B'$$
$m_A v_A = (m_A + m_B)v'$, so

$$v_A = \frac{(m_A + m_B)}{m_A}v'$$
$$= \frac{(2575\text{ kg} + 825\text{ kg})(8.5\text{ m/s})}{2575\text{ kg}}$$
$$= 11\text{ m/s}$$

20. A 15–g bullet is shot into a 5085 g wooden block standing on a frictionless surface. The block, with the bullet in it, acquires a velocity of 1.0 m/s. Calculate the velocity of the bullet before striking the block.

$m_b v_b + m_w v_w = (m_b + m_w)v_i$ if $v_w = 0$,

$$v_b = \frac{(m_b + m_w)v}{m_b}$$
$$= \frac{(15\text{ g} + 5085\text{ g})(1.0\text{ m/s})}{15\text{ g}}$$
$$= 3.4 \times 10^2\text{ m/s}$$

21. A hockey puck, mass 0.115 kg, moving at 35.0 m/s, slides into an octopus thrown on the ice by a fan. The octopus has a mass of 0.265 kg. The puck and octopus slide off together. Find their velocity.

$m_p v_p + m_o v_o = (m_p + m_o)v'$, so

$$v' = \frac{m_p v_p}{m_p + m_o} = \frac{(0.115\text{ kg})(35\text{ m/s})}{0.115\text{ kg} + 0.265\text{ kg}}$$
$$= 10.6\text{ m/s}$$

22. A 50–kg woman is riding on a 10–kg cart, and is moving east at 5.0 m/s. The woman jumps off the cart and hits the ground at 7.0 m/s eastward, relative to the ground. Calculate the velocity of the cart after she jumps off.

Let east be positive.
$(m_w + m_c)v = m_w v_w' + m_c v_c'$ so

$$v_c' = \frac{[m_w + m_c]\,v - m_w v_w'}{m_c}$$
$$= \frac{[50\text{ kg}+10\text{ kg}](5.0\text{ m/s})-(50\text{ kg})(7.0\text{ m/s})}{10\text{ kg}}$$
$$= -5.0\text{ m/s or } 5.0\text{ m/s, west}$$

23. Two students on roller skates stand face–to–face, then push each other away. One student has a mass of 90 kg, the other 60 kg. Find the ratio of their velocities just after their hands lose contact. Which student has the greater speed?

$P_A + P_B = 0 = P_A' + P_B'$, so $m_A v_A' + m_B v_B' = 0$, and $m_A v_A' = -m_B v_B'$

$$v_A'/v_B' = -m_B/m_A = -90/60 = -1.5$$

The negative sign shows that the velocities are in opposite directions. The student with the smaller mass has the larger velocity.

24. A car with mass 1245 kg moving at 29 m/s, strikes a 2175–kg car at rest. If the two cars stick together, with what speed do they move?

$$p_A + p_B = p_A' + p_B'$$

$$m_A v_A + m_B v_B = m_A v_A' + m_B v_B' = (m_A + m_B)v'$$

$$v' = \frac{m_A v_A}{(m_A + m_B)} = \frac{(1245\ \text{kg})(29\ \text{m/s})}{(1245\ \text{kg} + 2175\ \text{kg})} = 10\ \text{m/s}$$

25. A 92–kg fullback running at 5.0 m/s, attempts to dive across the goal line for a touchdown. Just as he reaches the goal line, he is met head–on in midair by two 75–kg linebackers, one moving at 2.0 m/s and the other at 4.0 m/s. If they all become entangled as one mass, with what velocity do they travel? Does the fullback score?

$$p_A + p_P + p_C = p_A' + p_B' + p_C'$$

$$m_A v_A + m_B v_B + m_C v_C = m_A v_A' + m_B v_B' + m_C v_C' = (m_A + m_B + m_C)v'$$

$$m_A v_A + m_B v_B + m_C v_C = v'(m_A + m_B + m_C)$$

$$v' = \frac{(m_A v_A + m_B v_B + m_C v_C)}{(m_A + m_B + m_C)}$$

$$= \frac{(92\ \text{kg})(5.0\ \text{m/s}) + (75\ \text{kg})(-2.0\ \text{m/s}) + (75\ \text{kg})(-4.0\ \text{m/s})}{(92\ \text{kg} + 75\ \text{kg} + 75\ \text{kg})}$$

$= 0.041$ m/s, over the goal line — touchdown!

26. A 5.00–g bullet is fired with a velocity of 100 m/s toward a 10.00–kg stationary solid block resting on a frictionless surface.

a. What is the change in momentum of the bullet if it becomes embedded in the block?

$$m_b v_b = m_b v' + m_w v' = (m_b + m_w)v', \text{ so } v' = \frac{m_b v_b}{m_b + m_w} = \frac{(5.00 \times 10^{-3}\ \text{kg})(100\ \text{m/s})}{5.00 \times 10^{-3}\ \text{kg} + 10.00\ \text{kg}}$$

$$= 5.0 \times 10^{-2}\ \text{m/s}$$

$$\Delta mv = m_b(v' - v) = (5.00 \times 10^{-3}\ \text{kg})(5.0 \times 10^{-2}\ \text{m/s} - 100\ \text{m/s}) = -0.500\ \text{kg}\cdot\text{m/s}$$

b. What is the change in momentum of the bullet if it ricochets in the opposite direction with a speed of 99 m/s — almost the same speed as it had originally?

$$\Delta mv = m_b(v' - v) = (5.00 \times 10^{-3}\ \text{kg})(-99\ \text{m/s} - 100\ \text{m/s}) = -0.995\ \text{kg}\cdot\text{m/s}$$

Chapter Review Problems

27. A 0.200–kg plastic ball moves with a velocity of 0.30 m/s. It collides with a second plastic ball of mass 0.100 kg moving along the same line at a velocity of 0.10 m/s. After the collision, the velocity of the 0.100–kg ball is 0.26 m/s. What is the new velocity of the first ball?

$m_A v_A + m_B v_B = m_A v_A' + m_B v_B'$, so

$$v_A' = \frac{m_A v_A + m_B v_B - m_B v_B'}{m_A}$$

$$= \frac{(0.200\text{ kg})(0.30\text{ m/s}) + (0.100\text{ kg})(0.10\text{ m/s}) - (0.100\text{ kg})(0.26\text{ m/s})}{0.200\text{ kg}}$$

$= 0.22$ m/s in the original direction.

28. Figure 9–18 shows a brick weighing 24.5 N being released from rest on a 1.00 m, frictionless plane inclined at an angle of 30.0°. The brick slides down the incline and strikes a second brick weighing 36.8 N.

a. Calculate the speed of the brick at the bottom of the incline.

$F_{\parallel} = F_W \sin\theta = (24.5\text{ N})(\sin 30.0°) = 12.3\text{ N}$

$F = ma$, and $m = \frac{W}{g}$, so $a = \frac{F}{m} = \frac{Fg}{W} = \frac{F_{\parallel}g}{F_W} = \frac{(12.3\text{ N})(9.80\text{ m/s}^2)}{24.5\text{ N}} = 4.9\text{ m/s}^2$

$v^2 = 2ad = 2(4.9\text{ m/s}^2)(1.00\text{ m})$, so $v = 3.1$ m/s

b. If the two bricks stick together, with what initial speed will they move along the table?

$m_A v_A = (m_A + m_B)v'$, so $v' = \frac{m_A v_B}{m_A + m_B} = \frac{(2.50\text{ kg})(3.1\text{ m/s})}{2.50\text{ kg} + 3.76\text{ kg}} = 1.24\text{ m/s}$

c. If the force of friction acting on the two bricks is 5.0 N, how much time will elapse before the bricks come to rest?

$F\Delta t = m\Delta v$, so $\Delta t = \frac{m\Delta v}{F} = \frac{(2.50\text{ kg} + 3.76\text{ kg})(1.24\text{ m/s})}{5.0\text{ N}} = 1.6\text{ s}$

d. How far will the two bricks slide before coming to rest?

$d = \frac{1}{2}(v_1 + v)t = \frac{1}{2}(1.24\text{ m/s} + 0)(1.6\text{ s}) = 0.99\text{ m}$

29. Ball A, rolling west at 3.0 m/s, has a mass of 1.0 kg. Ball B has a mass of 2.0 kg and is stationary. After colliding with ball B, ball A moves south at 2.0 m/s. Calculate the momentum and velocity of ball B after the collision.

Before

After

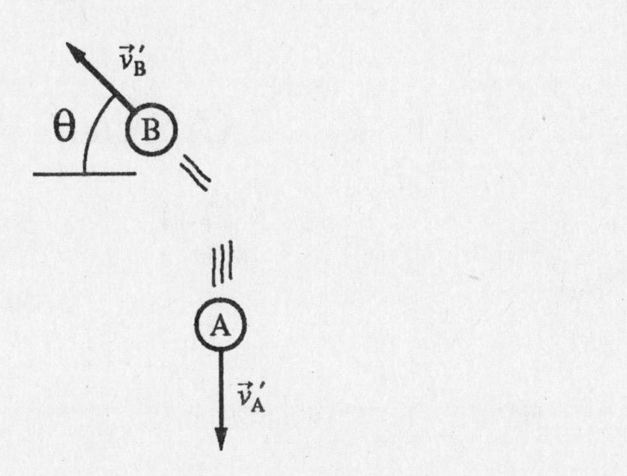

Horizontal: $m_A v_A = m_B v_B$, so
$m_B v_B = (1.0\text{ kg})(3.0\text{ m/s}) = 3.0\text{ kg}\cdot\text{m/s}$
Vertical: $0 = m_A v' + m_B v_B'$, so
$m_B v_B' = -(1.0\text{ kg})(2.0\text{ m/s}) = -2.0\text{ kg}\cdot\text{m/s}$
The vector sum is;

$$mv = \sqrt{(3.0\text{ kg}\cdot\text{m/s})^2 + (-2.0\text{ kg}\cdot\text{m/s})^2} = 3.6\text{ kg}\cdot\text{m/s and}$$

$$\tan\theta = \frac{2.0\text{ kg}\cdot\text{m/s}}{3.0\text{ kg}\cdot\text{m/s}},\ \text{so } \theta = 34^\circ.$$

Therefore, $m_B v_B' = 3.6\text{ kg}\cdot\text{m/s}$ at 34° N of W

$$v = \frac{3.6\text{ kg}\cdot\text{m/s}}{2.0\text{ kg}} = 1.8\text{ m/s at } 34^\circ\text{ N of W}$$

30. A cue ball, moving with 7.0 N·s of momentum strikes the 9–ball at rest. The 9–ball moves off with 2.0 N·s in the original direction of the cue ball and 2.0 N·s perpendicular to that direction. What is the momentum of the cue ball after the collision?

Before

After

Horizontal: $m_C v_C = m_C v_C' + m_9 v_9'$, so
$7.0\text{ N}\cdot\text{s} = m_C v_C' + 2.0\text{ N}\cdot\text{s}$, so
$m_C v_C' = 5.0\text{ N}\cdot\text{s}$
Vertical: $0 = m_C v_C' + m_9 v_9'$, so
$m_C v_C' = -m_9 v_9' = -2.0\text{ N}\cdot\text{s}$
The vector sum is;

$$\sqrt{(5.0\text{ N}\cdot\text{s})^2 + (2.0\text{ N}\cdot\text{s})^2} = 5.4\text{ N}\cdot\text{s and}$$

$$\tan\theta = \frac{2.0\text{ N}\cdot\text{s}}{5.0\text{ N}\cdot\text{s}},\ \text{so } \theta = 22^\circ.$$

Therefore $m_C v_C' = 5.4\text{ N}\cdot\text{s}$ at 22° from original direction.

31. A 7600–kg space probe is traveling through space at 120 m/s. Mission control determines that a change in course of 30.0° is necessary and, by electronic communication, instructs the probe to fire rockets perpendicular to its direction of motion. If the escaping gas leaves the craft's rockets at an average speed of 3200 m/s, what mass of gas should be expelled?

$$\tan 30.0^\circ = \frac{m\Delta v}{m_p \Delta v_p}$$

$$m\Delta v = m_p \Delta v_p \tan 30.0^\circ = (7600\text{ kg})(120\text{ m/s})(\tan 30.0) = 5.3\times10^5\text{ kg}\cdot\text{m/s}$$

$$m_p \Delta v_p = m_g \Delta v_g = m\Delta v$$

$$m_g = \frac{m\Delta v}{\Delta v_g} = \frac{(5.3\times10^5\text{ kg}\cdot\text{m/s})}{(3.2\times10^3\text{ m/s})} = 170\text{ kg}$$

32. Figure 9–19, which is drawn to scale, shows two balls during an elastic collision. The balls enter from the left of the page, collide, and bounce away. The heavier ball at the bottom of the diagram has a mass of 600 g, while the ball on the top has a mass of 400 g. Using a vector diagram, determine if momentum is conserved in this collision. ***Hint:*** *Remember that the two masses are not equal.* Try to account for any discrepancy found in the total momentum before and after the collision.

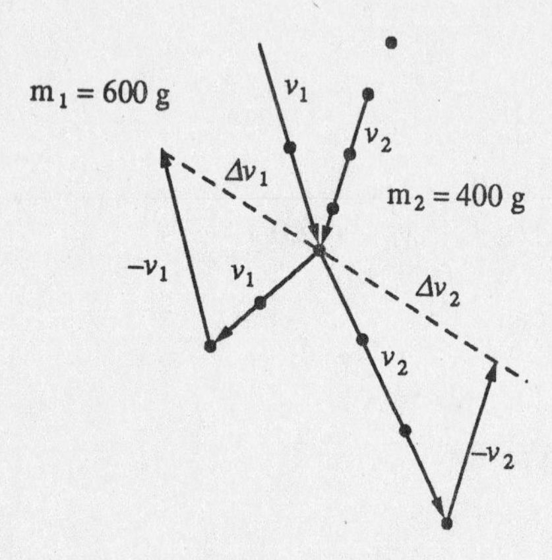

Dotted lines show that the changes of momentum for each ball are equal and opposite: $\Delta(m_1v_1) = \Delta(m_2v_2)$. Since the masses are in a 3:2 ratio, a 2:3 ratio of velocity changes will compensate.

33. The head of a 1.0–kg hammer, moving at 3.6 m/s, strikes a nail and drives it into hardwood.

a. The head stays in contact 2.0 ms and rebounds with negligible velocity. What is the average force exerted on the nail?

The force on the nail is opposite the force on the hammer, so

$$F_n = -F_h = \frac{-m_n\Delta v_n}{\Delta t}$$

$$= -\frac{(1.0\text{ kg})(0 - 3.6\text{ m/s})}{2.0\times 10^{-3}\text{ s}}$$

$$= 1.8\times 10^3\text{ N}$$

b. When the same hammer hits a springy nail, it rebounds with the same speed, 3.6 m/s. The contact time is the same. What force is exerted this time?

$$F_n = -F_n = \frac{-m_n\Delta v_n}{\Delta t}$$

$$= -\frac{(1.0\text{ kg})(-3.6\text{ m/s} - 3.6\text{ m/s})}{2.0\times 10^{-3}\text{ s}}$$

$$= 3.6\times 10^3\text{ N}$$

Supplemental Problems (Appendix B)

1. Jim strikes a 0.058–kg golf ball with a force of 272 N and gives it a velocity of 62.0 m/s. How long was the club in contact with the ball?

$$\Delta t = \frac{m\Delta v}{F} = \frac{(0.058\text{ kg})(62.0\text{ m/s})}{272\text{ N}} = 0.013\text{ s}$$

2. A force of 186 N acts on a 7.3–kg bowling ball for 0.40 s.

a. What is the bowling ball's change in momentum?

$$\Delta p = F\Delta t = (186\text{ N})(0.40\text{ s}) = 74\text{ N}\cdot\text{s}$$

b. What is its change in velocity?

$$\Delta v = \frac{\Delta p}{M} = \frac{74\text{ N}\cdot\text{s}}{7.3\text{ kg}} = 1.0\times 10^1\text{ m/s}$$

3. A 5500–kg freight truck accelerates from 4.2 m/s to 7.8 m/s in 15.0 s by applying a constant force.

a. What change in momentum occurs?

$$\Delta p = m\Delta v = (5500\text{ kg})(7.8\text{ m/s} - 4.2\text{ m/s})$$
$$= 2.0\times 10^4\text{ kg}\cdot\text{m/s}$$

b. How large of a force is exerted?

$$F = \frac{\Delta p}{\Delta t} = \frac{2.0\times 10^4\text{ kg}\cdot\text{m/s}}{15.0\text{ s}}$$

$$= 1.3\times 10^3\text{ N}$$

4. In running a ballistics test at the police department, Officer Spears fires a 6.0–g bullet at 350 m/s into a container that stops it in 0.30 m. What average force stops the bullet?

$$\Delta p = m\Delta v = (0.0060 \text{ kg})(-350 \text{ m/s}) = -2.1 \text{ kg}\cdot\text{m/s}$$

$$t = d\left[\frac{2}{v_f + v_i}\right] = (0.30 \text{ m})\left[\frac{2}{0 \text{ m/s} + 350 \text{ m/s}}\right] = 1.7 \times 10^{-3} \text{ s}$$

$$F = \frac{\Delta p}{\Delta t} = \frac{-2.1 \text{ kg}\cdot\text{m/s}}{1.7 \times 10^{-3} \text{ s}} = -1.2 \times 10^3 \text{ N}$$

5. A 0.24–kg volleyball aproaches Jennifer with a velocity of 3.8 m/s. Jennifer bumps the ball giving it a velocity of -2.4 m/s. What average force did she apply if the interaction time between her hands and the ball is 0.025 s?

$$F = \frac{m\Delta v}{\Delta t} = \frac{(0.24 \text{ kg})(-2.4 \text{ m/s} - 3.8 \text{ m/s})}{0.025 \text{ s}} = -6.0 \times 10^1 \text{ N}$$

6. A 0.145–kg baseball is pitched at 42 m/s. The batter hits it horizontally to the pitcher at 58 m/s.

a. Find the change in momentum of the ball.

Take the direction of the pitch to be positive direction
$\Delta p = mv_f - mv_i = m(v_f - v_i) = (0.145 \text{ kg})(-58 \text{ m/s} - (+42 \text{ m/s})) = -14.5 \text{ kg}\cdot\text{m/s}$

b. If the ball and bat were in contact 4.6×10^{-4} s, what would be the average force while they touched?

$F\Delta t = \Delta p$,
$F = \Delta p/\Delta t = (-14.5 \text{ kg}\cdot\text{m/s})/(4.6 \times 10^{-4} \text{ s}) = -3.2 \times 10^4 \text{ N}$

7. A 550–kg car traveling at 24.0 m/s collides head–on with a 680–kg pick–up truck. Both vehicles come to a complete stop upon impact.

a. What is the momentum of the car before collision?

$P = mv = (550 \text{ kg})(24.0 \text{ m/s}) = 1.32 \times 10^4 \text{ kg}\cdot\text{m/s}$

b. What is the change in the car's momentum?

-1.32×10^4 kg·m/s, since car stops on impact

c. What is the change in the truck's momentum?

$+1.32 \times 10^4$ kg·m/s, by conservation of momentum

d. What is the velocity of the truck before collision?

$$v = \frac{P}{M} = \frac{-1.32 \times 10^4 \text{ kg}\cdot\text{m/s}}{680 \text{ kg}} = -19.4 \text{ m/s}$$

8. A truck weighs four times as much as a car. If the truck coasts into the car at 12 km/h and they stick together, what is their final velocity?

Ans: Momentum before: (4 m)(12 km/h).
Momentum after: (4m + 1m)v, so
v = (4m/5m)(12 km/h) = 9.6 km/h

9. A 50.0–g projectile is launched with a horizontal velocity of 647 m/s from a 4.65–kg launcher moving in the same direction at 2.00 m/s. What is the velocity of the launcher after the projectile is launched?

$p_A + p_B = p_A' + p_B'$,
$m_Av_A + mBv_B = m_Av_A' + m_Bv_B'$,
so $v_B' = (m_Av_A + m_Bv_B - m_Av_A')/m_B$.
Assuming projectile (A) is launched in direction of launcher (B) motion,

$$v_B' = \frac{(0.0500 \text{ kg})(2.00 \text{ m/s}) + (4.65 \text{ kg})(2.00 \text{ m/s}) - (0.0500 \text{ kg})(647 \text{ m/s})}{(4.65 \text{ kg})}$$

v_B' = – 4.94 m/s, or 4.94 m/s backwards

10. Two lab carts are pushed together with a spring mechanism compressed between them. Upon release, the 5.0–kg cart repels one way with a velocity of 0.12 m/s while the 2.0–kg cart goes in the opposite direction. What velocity does it have?

$m_1v_1 = m_2v_2$
(5.0 kg)(0.12 m/s) = (2.0 kg)(v_2)
v_2 = 0.30 m/s

11. A 12.0–kg rubber bullet travels at a velocity of 150 m/s, hits a stationary 8.5–kg concrete block resting on a frictionless surface, and ricochets in the opposite direction with a velocity of – 100 m/s. How fast will the concrete block be moving?

Momentum of bullet before collision: P_B = (0.0120 kg)(150 m/s) = 1.80 kg·m/s
Momentum of bullet and block after collision: P_A = (0.0120 kg)(– 100 m/s) + (8.5 kg)(v)
$P_B = P_A$
1.80 kg·m/s = (0.0120 kg)(– 100 m/s) + (8.5 kg)(v)

$$v = \frac{3.0 \text{ kg}\cdot\text{m/s}}{8.5 \text{ kg}} = 0.35 \text{ m/s}$$

12. A 6500–kg freight car traveling at 2.5 m/s collides with an 8000–kg stationary freight car. If they interlock upon collision, what is their velocity?

$m_1v_1 + m_2v_2 = (m_1 + m_2)v$
(6500 kg)(2.5 m/s) = (6500 kg + 8000 kg)v
v = 1.1 m/s

13. Tim, mass 42.00 kg, is riding a skateboard, mass 2.00 kg, traveling at 1.20 m/s. Tim jumps off and the skateboard stops dead in its tracks. In what direction and with what velocity did he jump?

$(m_1 + m_2)v_B = m_1v_A + m_2v$
(42.00 kg + 2.00 kg)(1.20 m/s) = (42.00 kg)(v_A) + 0
v_A = 1.26 m/s in the same direction as he was riding.

14. A cue ball, mass 0.16 kg, rolling at 4.0 m/s, hits a stationary eight–ball of similar mass. If the cue ball travels 45° above its original path, and the eight–ball at 45° below, what is the velocity of each after collision?

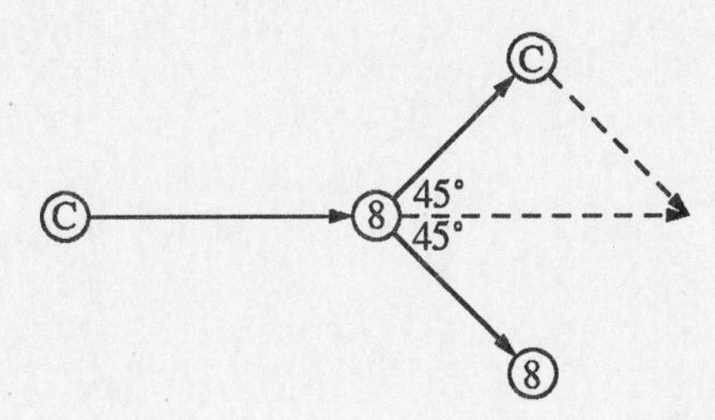

$P_{before} = (0.16\text{ kg})(4.0\text{ m/s}) = 0.64\text{ kg}\cdot\text{m/s}$
$P_8 = P_C$

$$\cos 45° = \frac{P_8}{0.64\text{ kg}\cdot\text{m/s}}$$

$P_8 = 0.45\text{ kg}\cdot\text{m/s}$

$$v = \frac{0.45\text{ kg}\cdot\text{m/s}}{0.16\text{ kg}} = 2.8\text{ m/s}$$

15. Two opposing hockey players, one of mass 82.0 kg skating north at 6.0 m/s and the other of mass 70.0 kg skating east at 3.0 m/s, collide and become tangled.

a. Draw a vector momentum diagram of the collision.

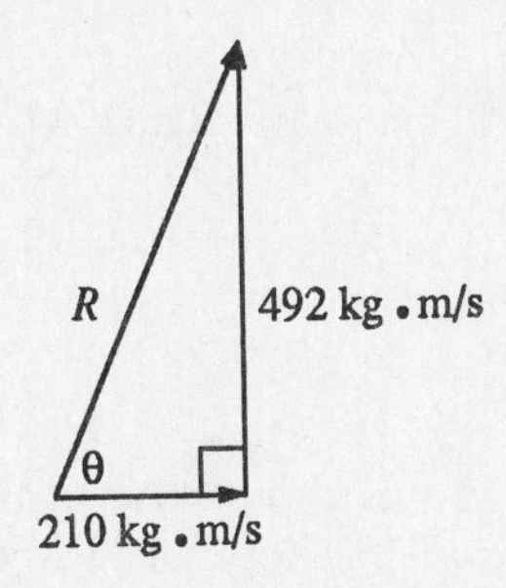

Supplemental Problems

b. In what direction and with what velocity do they move after collision?

$$\tan \theta = \frac{492}{210} = 67°$$

$R^2 = (492^2 + 210^2)\text{kg}^2\cdot\text{m}^2/\text{s}^2$
$R = 535\text{ kg}\cdot\text{m/s}$

$$v = \frac{535\text{ kg}\cdot\text{m/s}}{152\text{ kg}} = 3.5\text{ m/s, } 67°$$

Chapter 10: Work, Energy and Simple Machines

Practice Problems

page 199

1. A force of 825 N is needed to push a car across a lot. Two students push the car 35 m.

   a. How much work is done?

   $W = Fd = (825\ N)(35\ m) = 2.9 \times 10^4\ J$.

   b. After a rainstorm, the force needed to push the car doubled because the ground became soft. By what amount does the work done by the student change?

   The work doubles; when displacement remains the same, work is directly proportional to force.

2. A delivery clerk carries a 34–N package from the ground to the fifth floor of an office building, a total height of 15 m. How much work is done by the clerk?

   $W = Fd = (34\ N)(15\ m) = 510\ J$

3. What work is done by a forklift raising a 583–kg box a distance of 1.2 m?

   $W = Fd = mgd = (583\ kg)(9.80\ m/s^2)(1.2\ m)$
   $= 6.9 \times 10^3\ J$

4. You and a friend each carry identical boxes to a room one floor above you and down the hall. You choose to carry it first up the stairs, then down the hall. Your friend carries it down the hall, then up another stairwell. Who does more work?

   Both do the same amount of work. Only the height lifted and the vertical force exerted count.

page 202

5. How much work does the force of gravity do when a 25–N object falls a distance of 3.5 m?

   Both the force and displacement are in the same direction, so
   $W = Fd = (25\ N)(3.5\ m) = 88\ J$

Practice Problems

6. An airplane passenger carries a 215–N suitcase up stairs, a displacement of 4.20 m vertically and 4.60 m horizontally.

   a. How much work does the passenger do?

   Since gravity acts vertically, only the vertical displacement needs to be considered.
   $W = Fd = (215\ N)(4.20\ m) = 903\ J$

   b. The same passenger carries the same suitcase back down the same stairs. How much work does the passenger do now?

   Force is upward, but vertical displacement is downward, so
   $W = Fd \cos \theta = Fd \cos 180°$
   $= (215\ N)(4.20\ m)(-1) = -903\ J$.

7. A rope is used to pull a metal box 15.0 m across the floor. The rope is held at an angle of 46.0° with the floor and a force of 628 N is used. How much work does the force on the rope do?

   $W = Fd \cos \theta = (628\ N)(15.0\ m)(\cos 46.0°)$
   $= 6.54 \times 10^3\ J$

8. A worker pushes a crate weighing 93 N up an inclined plane, pushing horizontally, parallel to the ground (Figure 10–6).

   a. The worker exerts a force of 85 N. How much work does he do?

   Displacement in direction of force is 4.0 m, so $W = (85\ N)(4.0\ m) = 340\ J$

   b. How much work is done by gravity? (Be careful of signs.)

   Displacement in direction of force is -3.0 m, so $W = (93\ N)(-3.0\ m) = -279\ J$ (work done against gravity).

Practice Problems

c. The coefficient of friction is μ = 0.20. How much work is done by friction? (Be careful of signs.)

$$W = \mu F_N d$$
$$= 0.20\left[85\ \text{N}\cdot\frac{3}{5} + 93\ \text{N}\cdot\frac{4}{5}\right]5.0\ \text{m}$$
$$= 1.3 \times 10^2\ \text{J}$$

page 203

9. A box that weighs 575 N is lifted a distance of 20.0 m straight up by a rope. The job is done in 10.0 s. What power is developed in watts and kilowatts?

$$P = \frac{W}{t} = \frac{Fd}{t} = \frac{(575\ \text{N})(20.0\ \text{m})}{10.0\ \text{m}}$$
$$= 1.15 \times 10^3\ \text{W} = 1.15\ \text{kW}$$

10. A rock climber wears a 7.50-kg knapsack while scaling a cliff. After 30.0 minutes, the climber is 8.2 m above the starting point.

a. How much work does the climber do on the knapsack?

$$W = mgd = (750\ \text{kg})(9.80\ \text{m/s}^2)(8.2\ \text{m})$$
$$= 6.0 \times 10^2\ \text{J}$$

b. If the climber weighs 645 N, how much work does she do lifting herself and the knapsack?

$$W = Fd + 6.0 \times 10^2\ \text{J}$$
$$= (645\ \text{N})(8.2\ \text{m}) + 6.0 \times 10^2\ \text{J}$$
$$= 5.9 \times 10^3\ \text{J}$$

c. What is the average power developed by the climber?

$$P = \frac{W}{t} = \frac{5.9 \times 10^3\ \text{J}}{(30\ \text{min})(60\ \text{s/min})}$$
$$= 3.3\ \text{W}$$

Practice Problems

11. An electric motor develops 65 kW of power as it lifts a loaded elevator 17.5 m in 35.0 s. How much force does the motor exert?

$$P = \frac{W}{t},\ \text{and}\ W = Fd$$
$$\text{so}\ F = \frac{Pt}{d} = \frac{(65 \times 10^3\ \text{W})(35.0\ \text{s})}{17.5\ \text{m}}$$
$$= 1.3 \times 10^3\ \text{N}.$$

12. Two cars travel the same speed, so that they move 105 km in one hour. One car, a sleek sports car, has a motor that delivers only 35 kW of power at this speed. The other car needs its motor to produce 65 kW to move the car this fast. Forces exerted by friction from the air resistance cause the difference.

a. For each car, list the external horizontal forces exerted on it, and give the cause of each force. Compare their magnitudes.

Forward: force of road on cart
Rearward; force of air on car;
These forces are equal in magnitude when the car moves with constant speed.

b. By Newton's third law, the car exerts forces. What are their directions?

Car exerts a rearward force on road and a forward force on air.

c. Calculate the magnitude of the forward frictional force exerted by each car.

$$P = \frac{W}{t}\ \text{and}\ W = Fd,\ \text{so}\ P = \frac{Fd}{t},$$
$$\text{so}\ F = \frac{Pt}{d} = \frac{P}{v}.\ \text{For sports car,}$$
$$F = \frac{35 \times 10^3\ \text{W}}{29.2\ \text{m/s}} = 1.2 \times 10^3\ \text{N};$$

for other,

$$F = \frac{65 \times 10^3\ \text{W}}{29.2\ \text{m/s}} = 2.2 \times 10^3\ \text{N}.$$

d. The car engines did work. Where did the energy they transferred come from?

From the chemical energy in the gasoline.

Practice Problems

page 210

13. A sledge hammer is used to drive a wedge into a log to split it. When the wedge is driven 20 cm into the log, the log is separated a distance of 5.0 cm. A force of 1.9 x 10^4 N is needed to split the log, and the sledge exerts a force of 9.8 × 10^3 N.

 a. What is the *IMA* of the wedge?

$$IMA = \frac{d_e}{d_r} = \frac{20\text{ cm}}{5.0\text{ cm}} = 4.0$$

 b. Find the *MA* of the wedge.

$$MA = \frac{F_r}{F_e} = \frac{1.9 \times 10^4\text{ N}}{9.8 \times 10^3\text{ N}} = 1.9$$

 c. Calculate the efficiency of the wedge as a machine.

$$Efficiency = \left[\frac{MA}{IMA}\right] \times 100\%$$

$$= \left[\frac{1.9}{4.0}\right] \times 100\% = 48\%$$

14. A worker uses a pulley system to raise a 225–N carton 16.5 m. A force of 129 N is exerted and the rope is pulled 33.0 m.

 a. What is the mechanical advantage of the pulley system?

$$MA = \frac{F_r}{F_e} = \frac{225\text{ N}}{129\text{ N}} = 1.74$$

 b. What is the efficiency of the system?

$$Efficiency = \left[\frac{MA}{IMA}\right] \times 100\%, \text{ where}$$

$$IMA = \frac{d_e}{d_r} = \frac{33.0\text{ m}}{16.5\text{ m}} = 2.00, \text{ so}$$

$$efficiency = \frac{1.74}{2.00} \times 100\% = 87\%$$

Practice Problems

15. A boy exerts a force of 225 N on a lever to raise a 1.25 × 10^3–N rock a distance of 0.13 m. If the efficiency of the lever is 88.7%, how far did the boy move his end of the lever?

$$eff = \frac{W_o}{W_i} \times 100\% = \frac{F_r d_r}{F_e d_e} \times 100\%, \text{ so}$$

$$d = \frac{F_r d_r (100\%)}{F_e (eff)}$$

$$= \frac{(125 \times 10^3\text{ N})(0.13\text{ m})(100\%)}{(225\text{ N})(88.7\%)}$$

$$= 0.81\text{ m}$$

16. If the gear radius is doubled in the example above, while the force exerted on the chain and the distance the wheel rim moves remain the same, what quantities change, and by how much?

$$IMA = \frac{8.00\text{ cm}}{35.6\text{ cm}} = 0.224$$

$$MA = (95\%)\frac{0.224}{100\%} = 0.214 \text{ (both doubled)}$$

The force exerted by the distance the chain moved, d_e, would also be doubled to 3.14 cm.

Chapter Review Problems

page 213–215

1. Lee pushes horizontally with an 80–N force on a 20–kg mass 10 m across the floor. Calculate the amount of work Lee did.

 $W = Fd = (80\text{ N})(10\text{ m}) = 800\text{ J}$.
 The mass is not important to this problem.

2. The third floor of a house is 8.0 m above street level. How much work is needed to move a 150–kg refrigerator to the third floor?

 $F = mg$, so
 $W = Fd = mgd = (150\text{ kg})(9.8\text{ m/s}^2)(8.0\text{ m})$

3. Stan does 176 J of work lifting himself 0.300 m. What is Stan's mass?

$F = mg$, so $W = Fd = mgd$; therefore,

$$m = \frac{W}{gd} = \frac{176\ \text{J}}{(9.80\ \text{m/s}^2)(0.300\ \text{m})} = 59.9\ \text{kg}$$

4. A crane lifts a 2.25×10^3–N bucket containing 1.15 m^3 of soil (density = 2.00×10^3 kg/m^3) to a height of 7.50 m. Calculate the work the crane performs.

$W = Fd$, where F is the weight of bucket plus soil. The soil mass is
$(1.15\text{m}^3)(2.00 \times 10^3\ \text{kg/m}^3) = 2.30 \times 10^3$ kg.
The bucket's weight is 2.25×10^4 N, so the total weight is 2.48×10^4 N. Thus,
$W = Fd = (2.48 \times 10^4\ \text{N})(7.50\ \text{m})$
$= 1.86 \times 10^5$ J.

5. The graph in Figure 10–16 shows the force needed to stretch a spring. Find the work needed to stretch it from 0.12 m to 0.28 m.

Add the areas of the triangle and rectangle. The area of the triangle is
(base)(height)/2 = (0.16 m)(4.0 N)/2 = 0.32 J.
The area of the rectangle is
(base)(height) = (0.16 m)(3.0 N) = 0.48 J.
Total work is 0.32 J + 0.48 J = 0.80 J.

6. In Figure 10–10 the magnitude of the force necessary to stretch a spring is plotted against the distance the spring is stretched.

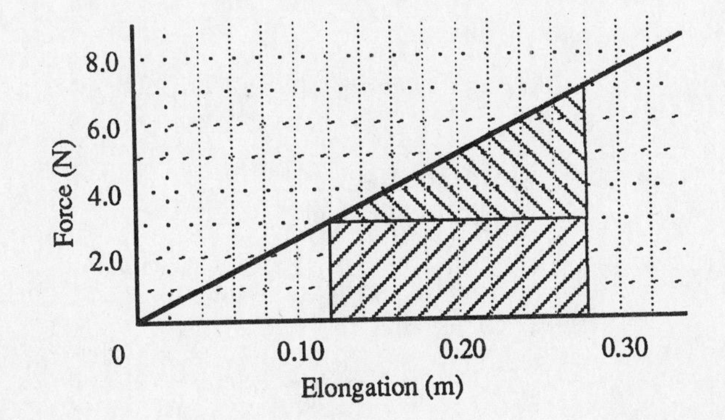

Chapter Review Problems

a. Calculate the slope of the graph and show that

$F = kd$

where k = 25 N/m.

$$m = \frac{\Delta_y}{\Delta_x} = \frac{(5.0\ \text{N} - 0.0\ \text{N})}{(0.20\ \text{m} - 0.00\ \text{m})}$$

$$= \frac{5.0\ \text{N}}{0.20\ \text{m}} = 25\ \text{N/m}$$

$F = kd = (25\ \text{N/m})(0.20\ \text{m}) = 5.0$ N

b. Find the amount of work done in stretching the spring from 0.00 m to 0.20 m by calculating the area under the curve from 0.00 m to 0.20 m in Figure 10–10.

$$A = \frac{1}{2}(\text{base})(\text{height}) = \left[\frac{1}{2}\right](5.0\ \text{N})(0.20\ \text{m})$$

$= 0.50$ J

c. Show that the answer to part b can be calculated using the formula

$$W = \frac{1}{2}kd^2$$

where W is the work, k = 25 N/m (the slope of the graph), and d is the distance the spring is stretched (0.20 m).

$$W = \frac{1}{2}kd^2 = \left[\frac{1}{2}\right](25\ \text{N/m})(0.20\ \text{m})^2 = 0.50\ \text{J}$$

7. John pushes a crate across the floor of a factory with a horizontal force. The roughness of the floor changes, and John must exert a force of 20 N for 5 meters, then 35 N for 12 m, then 10 N for 8 m.

a. Draw a graph of force as a function of distance.

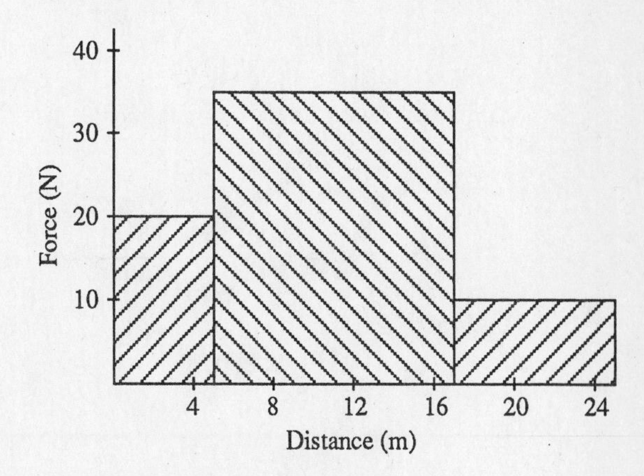

Chapter Review Problems

b. Find the work John does pushing the crate.

Add the areas under the rectangles
(5 m)(20N) + (12 m)(35 N) + (8 m)(10 N)
= 100 J + 420 J + 80 J = 600 J.

8. Sally applies a horizontal force of 462 N with a rope to drag a wooden crate across a floor with a constant speed. The rope tied to the crate is pulled at an angle of 56.0°.

a. How much force is exerted by the rope on the crate?

462 N is the horizontal component, so the force is $\frac{462 \text{ N}}{\cos 56.0°} = 826$ N.

b. What work is done by Sally if the crate is moved 24.5 m?

$W = Fd = (462 \text{ N})(24.5 \text{ m}) = 1.13 \times 10^4$ J

c. What work is done by the floor through force of friction between the floor and the crate?

Force and displacement are in opposite directions, so
$W = -(462 \text{ N})(24.5 \text{ m}) = -1.13 \times 10^4$ J.

9. Mike pulls a sled across level snow with a force of 225 N along a rope that is 35.0° above the horizontal. If the sled moved a distance of 65.3 m, how much work did Mike do?

$W = Fd \cos \theta = (225 \text{ N})(65.3 \text{ m})\cos 35.0°$
$= 1.20 \times 10^4$ J.

10. An 845-N sled is pulled a distance of 185 m. The task requires 1.20×10^4 J of work and is done by pulling on a rope with a force of 125 N. At what angle is the rope held?

$W = Fd \cos \theta$, so

$$\cos \theta = \frac{W}{Fd} = \frac{(1.20 \times 10^4 \text{ J})}{(125 \text{ N})(185 \text{ m})} = 0.519;$$

therefore, $\theta = 58.7°$.

11. Karen has a mass of 57.0 kg and rides the up escalator at Woodley Park Station of the Washington D.C. Metro. Karen rode a distance of 65 m, the longest escalator in the free world. How much work did the escalator do on Karen if it has an inclination of 30°?

$W = Fd$ but $F = mg$, so
$W = mgd$
$= (57.0 \text{ kg})(9.80 \text{ m/s}^2)(65 \text{ m})\sin 30°$
$= 1.8 \times 10^4$ J.

12. Chris carried a carton of milk, weight 10.0 N, along a level hall to the kitchen, a distance of 3.50 m. How much work did Chris do?

No work because the force and the displacement are perpendicular.

13. A student librarian picks up a 22-N book from the floor to a height of 1.25 m. He carries the book 8.0 m to the stacks and places the book on a shelf that is 0.35 m high. How much work does he do on the book?

Only the net vertical displacement counts.
$W = Fd = (22 \text{ N})(0.35 \text{ m}) = 7.7$ J.

14. Pete slides a crate up a ramp at an angle of 30.0° by exerting a 225-N force parallel to the ramp. The crate moves at a constant speed. The coefficient of friction is 0.28. How much work has been done when the crate is raised a vertical distance of 1.15 m?

To find the distance, d, along the plane from h, the vertical distance

$$d = \frac{h}{\sin 30.0°} = \frac{(1.15 \text{ m})}{0.500} = 2.30 \text{ m}.$$

F and d are parallel so
$W = Fd = (225 \text{ N})(2.30 \text{ m}) = 518$ J.

15. A 4200-N piano is to be slid up a 3.5-m frictionless plank that makes an angle of 30.0° with the horizontal. Calculate the work done in sliding the piano up the plank.

The force parallel to the plane is given by $F_{11} = F \sin \theta$, so $W = F_{11}d = Fd \sin \theta$
$W = (4200 \text{ N})(3.5 \text{ m})(\sin 30.0°) = 7.4 \times 10^3$ J

Chapter Review Problems

16. A 60-kg crate is slid up an inclined ramp 2.0 m long onto a platform 1.0 m above floor level. A 400-N force, parallel to the ramp, is needed to slide the crate up the ramp at a constant speed.

a. How much work is done in sliding the crate up the ramp?

$W = Fd = (400\text{ N})(2.0\text{ m}) = 800\text{ J}$

b. How much work would be done if the crate were simply lifted straight up from the floor to the platform?

$W = Fd = mgd = (60\text{ kg})(9.80\text{ m/s}^2)(1.0\text{ m})$
$= 600\text{ J}.$

17. Brutus, a champion weightlifter, raises 240 kg a distance of 2.35 m.

a. How much work is done by Brutus lifting the weights?

$W = Fd = \text{mgd}$
$= (240\text{ kg})(9.80\text{ m/s}^2)(2.35\text{ m})$
$= 5.53 \times 10^3\text{ J}$

b. How much work is done holding the weights above his head?

$d = 0$ so no work.

c. How much work is done lowering them back to the ground?

d is opposite of motion in part a, so W is also the opposite, -5.53×10^3 J.

d. Does Brutus do work if the weights are let go and fall back to the ground?

No. He exerts no force, so he does no work, positive or negative.

e. If Brutus completes the lift in 2.5 seconds, how much power is developed?

$P = \frac{W}{t} = (5.53 \times 10^3\text{ J})/(2.5\text{ s}) = 2.2\text{ kW}.$

18. A force of 300 N is used to push a 145-kg mass 30.0 m horizontally in 3.00 s.

a. Calculate the work done on the mass.

$W = Fd = (300\text{ N})(30.0\text{ m}) = 9.00 \times 10^3\text{ J}$

b. Calculate the power.

$P = \frac{W}{t} = \frac{9.00 \times 10^3\text{ J}}{3.00\text{ s}} = 3.00 \times 10^3\text{ W}$

$= 3.00\text{ kW}$

19. Robin pushes a wheelbarrow by exerting a 145-N force horizontally. Robin moves it 60.0 m at a constant speed for 25.0 s.

a. What power does Robin develop?

$P = \frac{W}{t} = \frac{F \cdot d}{t} = \frac{(145\text{ N})(60.0\text{ m})}{25.0\text{ s}} = 348\text{ W}$

b. If Robin moves the wheelbarrow twice as fast, how much power is developed?

Either d is doubled or t is halved, so P is doubled to 696 W.

20. **a.** Use the graph to calculate the work done to pull the object 7.0 m.

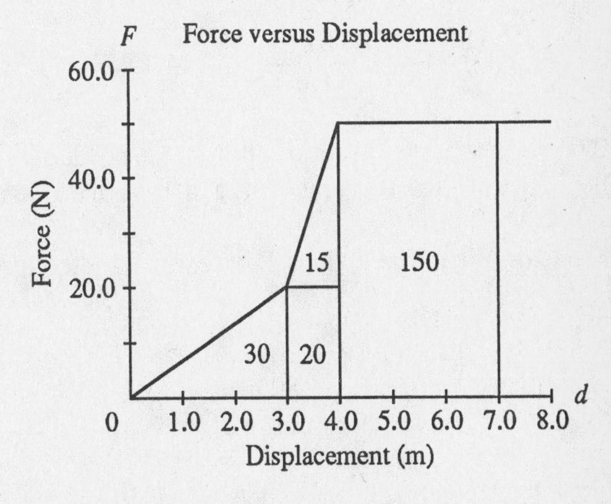

Find the area under the curve (see graph):
0 to 3 m;

$\frac{1}{2}(20.0\ \text{N})(3.0\ \text{m}) = 30\ \text{J}$

3 m to 4 m;

$\frac{1}{2}(30.0\ \text{N})(1.0\ \text{m}) + (20\ \text{N})(1.0\ \text{m}) = 15\ \text{J} + 20\ \text{J} = 35\ \text{J}$

4 m to 7 m;
$(50.0\ \text{N})(3.0\ \text{m}) = 1.5 \times 10^2\ \text{J}$

Total work;
$30\ \text{J} + 35\text{J} + 1.5 \times 10^2\ \text{J} = 2.2 \times 10^2\ \text{J}$

b. Calculate the power if the work were done in 2.0 seconds.

$$P = \frac{W}{t} = \frac{2.2 \times 10^2\ \text{J}}{2.0\ \text{s}} = 1.1 \times 10^2\ \text{W}$$

21. In 35.0 s, a pump delivers 550 dm^3 of oil into barrels on a platform 25.0 m above the pump intake pipe. The density of the oil is 0.820 g/cm^3.

a. Calculate the work done by the pump.

Mass lifted = $(550\ \text{dm}^3)(1000\ \text{cm}^3/\text{dm}^3)(0.820\ \text{g/cm}^3) = 4.51 \times 10^5\ \text{g} = 451\ \text{kg}$

The work done is
$W = F_w d = mg(h) = (451\ \text{kg})(9.80\ \text{m/s}^2)(25.0\ \text{m}) = 1.10 \times 10^5\ \text{J} = 110\ \text{kJ}$

b. Calculate the power produced by the pump.

$$P = \frac{W}{t} = \frac{(110\ \text{kJ})}{(35.0\ \text{s})} = 3.14\ \text{kW}$$

22. A horizontal force of 805 N is needed to drag a crate across a horizontal floor with a constant speed. Pete drags the crate using a rope held at an angle of 32°.

a. What force does Pete exert on the rope?

$F_x = F \cos \theta$, so

$$F = \frac{F_x}{\cos \theta} = \frac{(805\ \text{N})}{\cos 32^\circ} = 949\ \text{N}$$

b. How much work does Pete do on the crate when moving it 22 m?

$W = F_x d = (805\ \text{N})(22\ \text{m}) = 1.8 \times 10^4\ \text{J}$

c. If Pete completes the job in 8.0 s, what power is developed?

$$P = \frac{W}{t} = \frac{1.8 \times 10^4\ \text{J}}{8.0\ \text{s}} = 2.3\ \text{kW}$$

Chapter Review Problems

23. Wayne pulls a 305-N sled along a snowy path using a rope that makes a 45.0° angle with the ground. Wayne pulls with a force of 42.3 N. The sled moves 16 m in 3.0 s. What is Wayne's power?

$$P = \frac{W}{t} = \frac{F_{\parallel}d}{t} = \frac{Fd_1}{t}\cos\theta = (42.3\text{ N})(16\text{ m})(\cos 45.0°)/(3.0\text{ s}) = 1.6 \times 10^2\text{ W}$$

24. A lawn roller is rolled across a lawn by a force of 115 N along the direction of the handle, which is 22.5° above the horizontal. If George develops 64.6 W of power for 90.0 seconds, what distance is the roller pushed?

$$P = \frac{W}{t} = \frac{Fd\cos\theta}{t}$$

$$d = \frac{Pt}{F\cos\theta} = \frac{(64.6\text{ W})(90.0\text{ s})}{(115\text{ N})(\cos 22.5°)} = 54.7\text{ m}$$

25. A 12.0-m long conveyor belt, inclined at 30.0°, is used to transport bundles of newspapers from the mail room up to the cargo bay to be loaded on delivery trucks. Each newspaper has a mass of 1.00 kg and there are 25 newspapers per bundle. Determine the useful power of the conveyor if it delivers 15 bundles per minute.

$$P = \frac{W}{t} = \frac{Fd}{t} = \frac{mgd}{t} = \frac{(25)(15)(1.00\text{ kg})(9.80\text{ m/s}^2)(\sin 30.0°)(12.0\text{ m})}{60.0\text{ s}} = 3.68 \times 10^2\text{ W}$$

26. An engine moves a boat through the water at a constant speed of 15 m/s. The engine must exert a force of 6.0×10^3 N to balance the force that water exerts against the hull. What power does the engine develop?

$$P = \frac{W}{t} = \frac{Fd}{t} = Fv = (6.0 \times 10^3\text{ N})(15\text{ m/s}) = 90\text{ kW}$$

27. A 188-W motor will lift a load at the rate (speed) of 6.50 cm/s. How great a load can the motor lift at this speed?

v = 6.50 cm/s = 0.0650 m/s

$$P = \frac{W}{t} = \frac{Fd}{t} = F\left[\frac{d}{t}\right] = Fv$$

$$P = F_w v$$

$$F_w = \frac{P}{v} = \frac{(188\text{ W})}{(0.0650\text{ m/s})} = 2.89 \times 10^3\text{ N}$$

28. A car is driven at a constant speed of 21 m/s (76/km/h) down a road. The car's engine delivers 48 kW of power. Calculate the average force of friction that is resisting the motion of the car.

$$P = \frac{W}{t} = \frac{Fd}{t} = Fv,\text{ so } F = \frac{P}{v} = \frac{(48{,}000\text{ W})}{(21\text{ m/s})} = 2.3 \times 10^3\text{ N}$$

Chapter Review Problems

29. Stan raises a 1000–N piano a distance of 5.00 m using a set of pulleys. Stan pulls in 20.0 m of rope.

a. How much effort did Stan apply if this was an ideal machine?

$F_e d_e = F_r d_r$, so

$$F_e = \frac{F_r d_r}{d_e} = \frac{(1000 \text{ N})(5.00 \text{ m})}{(20.0 \text{ m})} = 250 \text{ N}$$

b. What force is used to overcome friction if the actual effort is 300 N?

$F = F_f + F_e$,
$F_f = F - F_e = 300\text{N} - 250 \text{ N} = 50 \text{ N}$

c. What is the work output?

$W_o = F_r d_r = (1000 \text{ N})(5.00 \text{ m})$
$= 5.00 \times 10^3 \text{ J}$

d. What is the work input?

300 N

e. What is the mechanical advantage?

$$MA = \frac{d_e}{d_r} = \frac{20.0 \text{ m}}{5.00 \text{ m}} = 4.00$$

30. A mover's dolly is used to deliver a refrigerator up a ramp into a house. The refrigerator has a mass of 115 kg. The ramp is 2.10 m long and rises 0.850 m. The mover pulls the dolly with a force of 496 N up the ramp. The dolly and ramp constitute a machine.

a. What work does the mover do?

$W_i = Fd = (496 \text{ N})(2.10 \text{ m})$
$= 1.04 \times 10^3 \text{ J}$

b. What is the work done on the refrigerator by the machine?

d = height raised = 0.850 m
$W_o = mgd = (115 \text{ kg})(9.80 \text{ m/s}^2)(0.850 \text{ m})$
$= 958 \text{ J}$

c. What is the efficiency of the machine?

$$Efficiency = \frac{W_o}{W_i} \times 100\%$$

$$= \frac{(958 \text{ J})}{(1.04 \times 10^3 \text{ J})} \times 100\%$$

$= 92.1\%$

31. A pulley system lifts a 1345–N weight a distance of 0.975 m. Paul pulls the rope a distance of 3.90 m, exerting a force of 375 N.

a. What is the ideal mechanical advantage of the system?

$$IMA = \frac{d_e}{d_r} = \frac{(3.90 \text{ m})}{(0.975 \text{ m})} = 4.00$$

b. What is the mechanical advantage?

$$MA = \frac{F_r}{F_e} = \frac{(1345 \text{ N})}{(375 \text{ N})} = 3.59$$

c. How efficient is the system?

$$Efficiency = \frac{MA}{IMA} \times 100\%$$

$$= \frac{3.59}{4.00} \times 100\%$$

$= 89.8\%$

32. The ramp in Figure 10–18 is 18 m long and 4.5 m high.

a. What force parallel to the ramp ($F_{\parallel}$) is required to slide a 25 kg box to the top of the ramp if friction is neglected?

$W = F_w h = (25 \text{ kg})(9.8 \text{ m/s}^2)(4.5 \text{ m})$
$= 1.1 \times 10^3 \text{ J}$
$W = F_{\parallel} d$

$$F_{\parallel} = \frac{W}{d} = \frac{(1.1 \times 10^3 \text{ J})}{18 \text{ m}} = 61 \text{ N}$$

b. What is the IMA of the ramp?

$$IMA = \frac{d_e}{d_r} = \frac{(18 \text{ m})}{(4.5 \text{ m})} = 4.0$$

c. What are the real *MA* and the efficiency of the ramp if a parallel force of 75 N is actually required?

$$MA = \frac{F_r}{F_e} = \frac{(25\text{ kg})(9.8\text{ m/s}^2)}{75\text{ N}} = 3.3$$

$$eff = \frac{MA}{IMA} \times 100\% = \frac{(3.3)}{(4.0)} \times 100\%$$

$$= 83\%$$

33. Because there is very little friction, the lever is an extremely efficient simple machine. Using a 90.0% efficient lever, what input work is required to lift an 18.0-kg mass through a distance of 0.50 m?

$$efficient = \frac{W_d}{W_i} \times 100\%$$

$$W_i = \frac{(W_d)(100\%)}{efficient} = \frac{(mgd)(100\%)}{(90.0\%)}$$

$$= \frac{(18.0\text{kg})(9.80\text{ m/s}^2)(0.50\text{m})(100\%)}{90.0\%}$$

$$= 98\text{ J}$$

34. What work is required to lift a 215-kg mass a distance of 5.65 m using a machine that is 72.5% efficient?

$$W_o = F_r d_r = (215\text{ kg})(9.80\text{ m/s}^2)(5.65\text{ m})$$
$$= 1.19 \times 10^4\text{ J}$$

$$\frac{W_o}{W_i} \times 100\% = 72.5\% = 0.725$$

$$W_i = \frac{W_o}{0.725} = \frac{(1.19 \times 10^4\text{ J})}{(0.725)} = 1.64 \times 10^4\text{ J}$$

35. A motor having an efficiency of 88% operates a crane having an efficiency of 42%. With what constant speed does the crane lift a 410-kg crate of machine parts if the power supplied to the motor is 5.5 kW?

Total efficiency = 88% × 42% = 37%
Useful power = 5.5 kW × 37% = 2.0 kW
= 2.0×10^3 W

$$P = \frac{W}{t} = \frac{Fd}{t} = F\left[\frac{d}{t}\right] = Fv$$

$$v = \frac{P}{F_w} = \frac{(2.0 \times 10^3\text{ W})}{(410\text{ kg})(9.8\text{ m/s}^2)} = 0.50\text{ m/s}$$

Chapter Review Problems

36. A complex machine is constructed by attaching the lever to the pulley system. Consider an ideal complex machine consisting of a lever with an *IMA* of 3.0 and a pulley system with an *IMA* of 2.0.

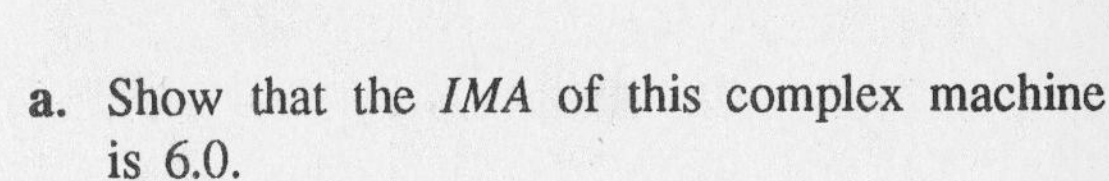

a. Show that the *IMA* of this complex machine is 6.0.

$$W_{ir} = W_o = W_{ir}' = W_o'$$
$$W_i = W_o$$
$$F_e d_e = F_r' d_r'$$

For the complex machine

$$IMA_c = \frac{d_e}{d_r'}$$

$$\frac{d_e}{d_r} = IMA;\ \frac{d_e'}{d_r'} = IMA'$$

$$d_r = d_e'$$

$$\frac{d_e}{IMA} = d_r = d_e' = (IMA')(d_r')$$

$$d_e = (IMA)(IMA')(d_r')$$

$$\frac{d_e}{d_r'} = IMA_c = (IMA)(IMA')$$

$$= (3.0)(2.0) = 6.0$$

b. If the complex machine is 60.0% efficient, how much effort must be applied to the lever to lift a 540-N box?

$$\frac{F_r'}{F_e} = MA_c = \frac{(IMA) \times (eff)}{100\%}$$

$$\frac{F_r'}{F_e} = \frac{(6.0)(60.0\%)}{(100\%)} = 3.6$$

$$F_e = \frac{F_r'}{3.6} = \frac{540\text{ N}}{3.6} = 150\text{ N}$$

c. If you move the effort side of the lever 12.0 cm, how far is the box lifted?

$$\frac{d_e}{d_r'} = IMA_c$$

$$d_r' = \frac{d_e}{IMA} = \frac{12.0\text{ cm}}{6.0} = 2.0\text{ cm}$$

Chapter Review Problems

37. A powerful rifle is one that propels a bullet with a high muzzle velocity. Does this use of the word 'powerful' agree with the Physics definition of power?

    Yes. The higher the muzzle velocity, the larger the kinetic energy and the greater the power for a given time interval. In this case the time interval is really smaller, because of the higher velocity of the bullet and the smaller time interval requires more power.

Supplemental Problems (Appendix B)

1. After scoring a touchdown, an 84.0-kg wide receiver celebrates by leaping 120 cm off the ground. How much work was done in the celebration?

   $W = Fd = mgd$
   $= (84.0 \text{ kg})(9.80 \text{ m/s}^2)(1.20 \text{ m})$
   $= 988 \text{ J}$

2. During a tug-of-war, Team A does 2.20×10^5 J of work in pulling Team B 8.00 m. What force was Team A exerting?

   $$F = \frac{W}{d} = \frac{2.2 \times 10^5 \text{ J}}{8.00 \text{ m}} = 2.75 \times 10^4 \text{ N}$$

3. To keep a car traveling at a constant velocity, 551 N of force is needed to overcome frictional forces. How much work is done against friction by the car in traveling from Columbus to Cincinnati, a distance of 161 km?

   $W = Fd = (551 \text{ N})(1.61 \times 10^5 \text{ m})$
   $= 8.87 \times 10^7 \text{ J}$

4. A weightlifter raises a 180-kg barbell to a height of 1.95 m. How much work was done by the weightlifter in lifting the barbell?

   $PE = mgh = (180 \text{ kg})(9.80 \text{ m/s}^2)(1.95 \text{ m})$
   $= 3.44 \times 10^3 \text{ J}$

Supplemental Problems (Appendix B)

5. A wagon is pulled by a force of 38.0 N on the handle at an angle of 42° with the horizontal. If the wagon is pulled in a circle of radius 25.0 m, how much work is done?

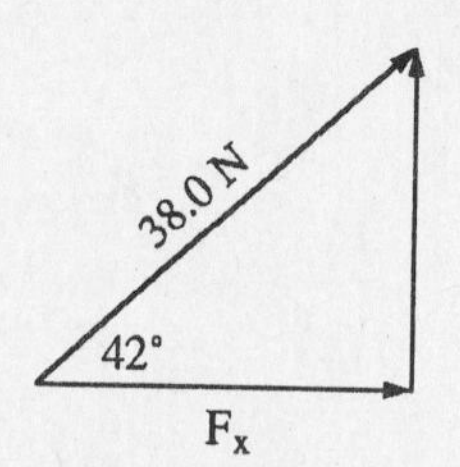

   $F_x = (\cos 42^\circ)(38.0 \text{ N})$
   $F_x = 28 \text{ N}$
   $C = 2\pi r = 2\pi(25.0 \text{ m}) = 157 \text{ m}$
   $W = F_x d = (28 \text{ N})(157 \text{ m}) = 4.4 \times 10^3 \text{ J}$

6. A 185-kg refrigerator is loaded into a moving van by pushing it up a 10.0-m ramp at an angle of inclination of 11°. How much work is done?

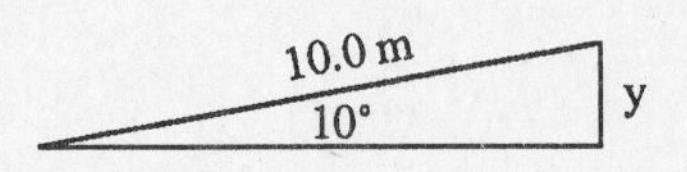

   $y = (10.0 \text{ m})(\sin 11^\circ)$
   $y = 1.9 \text{ m}$
   $W = Fd = (185 \text{ kg})(9.8 \text{ m/s}^2)(1.9 \text{ m})$
   $= 3.4 \times 10^3 \text{ J}$

7. A lawn mower is pushed with a force of 88.0 N along a handle that makes an angle of 41° with the horizontal. How much work is done in pushing the mower 1.2 km in mowing the yard?

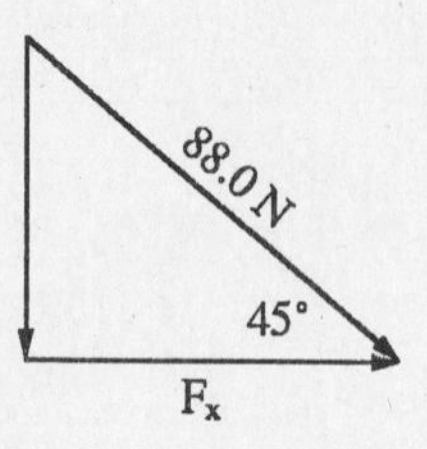

   $F_x = (\cos 41^\circ)(88.0 \text{ N}) = 66.4 \text{ N}$
   $W = F_x d = (66.4 \text{ N})(122 \text{ m}) = 8.0 \times 10^4 \text{ J}$

8. A 17.0-kg crate is to be pulled a distance of 20.0 m requiring 1210 J of work being done. If the job is done by attaching a rope and pulling with a force of 75.0 N, at what angle is the rope held?

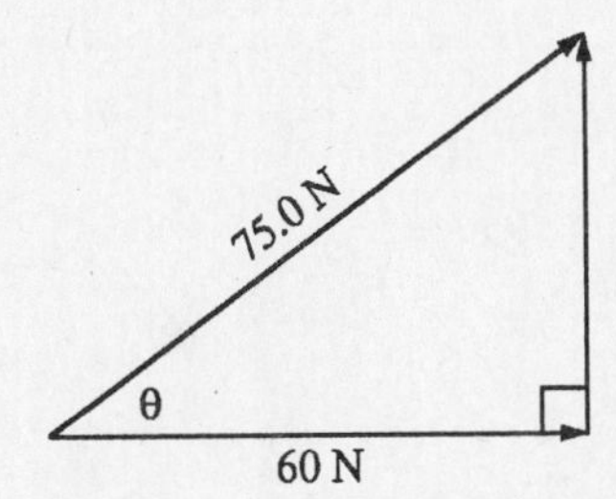

$$F_x = \frac{W}{d} = \frac{1210\text{ J}}{20.0\text{ m}} = 60.5\text{ N}$$

$$\cos\theta = \frac{60.5}{75.0} = 0.807$$

$$\theta = 36.2°$$

9. An elevator lifts a total mass of 1.1 × 10³ kg a distance of 40.0 m in 12.5 s. How much power does the elevator demonstrate?

$$P = \frac{W}{t} = \frac{(1.1\times10^3\text{ kg})(9.8\text{ m/s}^2)(40.0\text{ m})}{12.5\text{ s}}$$

$$= 3.4\times10^4\ W$$

10. A cyclist exerts a force of 15.0 N in riding a bike 251 m in 30.0 s. What is the cyclist's power?

$$P = \frac{W}{t} = \frac{(15.0\text{ N})(251\text{ m})}{30.0\text{ s}} = 126\text{ W}$$

11. A 120-kg lawn tractor goes up a 21° incline of 12.0 m in 2.5 s. What power is shown by the tractor?

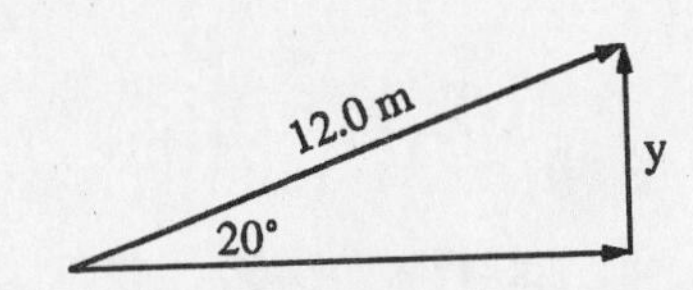

$y = (12.0\text{ m})(\sin 21°) = 4.3\text{ m}$

$W = Fd = (120\text{ kg})(9.8\text{ m/s}^2)(4.3\text{ m})$

$= 5.1\times10^3\text{ J}$

$$P = \frac{W}{t} = \frac{5.1\times10^3\text{ J}}{2.5\text{ s}} = 2.04\times10^3\ W$$

12. What power does a pump develop to lift 35 L of water per minute from a depth of 110 m? (A liter of water has a mass of 1.00 kg.)

$$P = \frac{W}{t} = \frac{mgd}{t}$$

$$\frac{m}{t} = (35\text{ L/min})(1.00\text{ kg/L}) = 35\text{ kg/min}$$

Thus,

$P = (35\text{ kg/min})(1\text{ min}/60\text{ s})(9.80\text{ m/s}^2)(110\text{ m})$

$= 0.63\text{ kW}$

13. A force of 1.4 N is exerted through a distance of 40.0 cm on a rope in a pulley system to lift a 0.50-kg mass 10.0 cm.

a. Calculate the *MA*.

$$MA = \frac{F_r}{F_e} = \frac{(0.50\text{ kg})(9.8\text{ m/s}^2)}{1.4\text{ N}} = \frac{4.9\text{ N}}{1.4\text{ N}}$$

$$= 3.5$$

b. Calculate the *IMA*.

$$IMA = \frac{d_e}{d_r} = \frac{40.0\text{ cm}}{10.0\text{ cm}} = 4.00$$

c. What is the efficiency of the pulley system?

$$EFF = \frac{MA}{IMA}\times 100\% = \frac{3.5}{4.00}\times 100\% = 88\%$$

14. A student exerts a force of 250 N through a distance of 1.6 m on a lever in lifting a 150-kg crate. If the efficiency of the lever is 90%, how far is the crate lifted?

$$F_r = (150\text{ kg})(9.8\text{ m/s}^2) = 1470\text{ N}$$

$$MA = \frac{F_r}{F_e} = \frac{1470\text{ N}}{250\text{ N}} = 5.9$$

$$IMA = \frac{(MA)(100\%)}{EFF} = \frac{(5.9)(100\%)}{90\%} = 6.6$$

$$d_r = \frac{d_e}{IMA} = \frac{1.6\text{ m}}{6.6} = 0.24\text{ m}$$

15. Karen pedals a bicycle with a gear radius of 5.00 cm and a wheel radius of 38.6 cm. What length of chain must be pulled through to make the wheel revolve once?

$$IMA = \frac{GR}{WR} = \frac{5.00\text{ cm}}{38.6\text{ cm}} = 0.130$$

$d_r = 2\pi r = 2\pi(38.6\text{ cm}) = 242.5\text{ cm}$

$d_e = IMA(d_r) = (0.130)(242.5\text{ cm}) = 31.5\text{ cm}$

Chapter 11: Energy

Practice Problems

page 221

1. a. Using the data in Table 11–1, calculate the kinetic energy of a compact car moving at 50 km/h.

50 km/h is 14 m/s, so

$$KE = \frac{1}{2}mv^2 = \frac{1}{2}(750 \text{ kg})(14 \text{ m/s})^2$$

$$= 7.4 \times 10^4 \text{ J}$$

b. How much work must be done on the car to slow it from 100 km/h to 50 km/h?

$$W = \Delta KE = KE_f - KE_i$$
$$= 0.74 \times 10^5 \text{ J} - 2.94 \times 10^5 \text{ J}$$
$$= -2.20 \times 10^5 \text{ J}$$

c. How much work must be done on the car to bring it to rest?

$$W = \Delta KE = 0 - 7.4 \times 10^4 \text{ J}$$
$$= -7.4 \times 10^4 \text{ J}$$

d. The force that does the work slowing the car is constant. Find the ratio of the distance needed to slow the car from 100 km/h to 50 km/h to the distance needed to slow it from 50 km/h to rest. State your conclusion in a sentence.

$W = Fd$, so distance is proportional to work. The ratio is
$(-2.2 \times 10^5 \text{ J})/(-7.4 \times 10^4 \text{ J}) = 3.$
It takes three times the distance to slow the car to half its speed than it does to slow it to a complete stop.

page 222

2. A rifle can shoot a 4.20–g bullet at a speed of 965 m/s.

a. Find the kinetic energy of the bullet.

$$KE = \frac{1}{2}mv^2 = \frac{1}{2}(0.00420 \text{ kg})(965 \text{ m/s})^2$$

$$= 1.96 \times 10^3 \text{ J}$$

Practice Problems

b. What work is done on the bullet if it starts from rest?

$$W = \Delta KE = 1.96 \times 10^3 \text{ J}$$

c. If the work is done over a distance of 0.75 m, what is the average force on the bullet?

$W = Fd$, so

$$F = \frac{W}{d} = (1.96 \times 10^3 \text{ J})/(0.75 \text{ m})$$
$$= 2.6 \times 10^3 \text{ N}$$

d. If the bullet comes to rest by pushing 1.5 cm into metal, what is the average force it exerts?

$$F = \frac{W}{d} = \frac{KE}{d} = (1.96 \times 10^3 \text{ J})/(0.015 \text{ m})$$
$$= 1.3 \times 10^5 \text{ N}$$

3. A comet with mass 7.85×10^{11} kg strikes Earth at a speed, relative to Earth, of 25 km/s.

a. Find the kinetic energy of the comet in joules.

$$KE = \frac{1}{2}mv^2$$

$$= \frac{1}{2}(7.85 \times 10^{11} \text{ kg})(2.5 \times 10^4 \text{ m/s})^2$$

$$= 2.5 \times 10^{20} \text{ J}$$

b. Compare the work done on Earth with the energy released in exploding the largest nuclear weapon ever built, equivalent to 100 million tons of TNT, or 4.2×10^{15} J of energy. Such a comet collision has been suggested as having caused the extinction of the dinosaurs.

The work is that of 60,000 100–megaton bombs.

Practice Problems

4. Table 11–1 shows that 2.2×10^6 J of work are needed to accelerate a 5700–kg trailer truck to 100 km/h.

   a. How fast would it go if just 1/2 as much work were done on it?

   Since $W = \Delta KE = \frac{1}{2}mv^2$, then $v = \sqrt{2W/m}$.

   If $W' = \frac{1}{2}W$,

   $$v' = \sqrt{2W'/m}$$
   $$= \sqrt{2\left[\frac{1}{2}W\right]/m} = \sqrt{\frac{1}{2}}v$$
   $$= (0.707)(100 \text{ km/h}) = 71 \text{ km/h}$$

   b. What if twice as much work was done?

   If $W' = 2W$,

   $$v' = \sqrt{2}(100 \text{ km/h})$$
   $$= 140 \text{ km/h}$$

5. A 90–kg rock climber first climbs 45 m upward to the top edge of a quarry, then, from the top, descends 85 m to the bottom. Find the potential energy of the climber at the edge and at the bottom, using the initial height as reference level.

   $PE = mgh$. At the edge,
   $PE = (90 \text{ kg})(9.8 \text{ m/s}^2)(+45 \text{ m})$
   $= +4.0 \times 10^4$ J.
   At the bottom,
   $PE = (90 \text{ kg})(9.8 \text{ m/s}^2)(+45 \text{ m} - 85 \text{ m})$
   $= -3.5 \times 10^4$ J

6. A 50.0–kg shell is shot from a cannon at Earth's surface to a height of 4.00×10^2 m.

   a. What is the gravitational potential energy with respect to Earth's surface of the Earth–shell system when the shell is at this height?

   $PE = mgh = (50.0 \text{ kg})(9.80 \text{ m/s}^2)(400 \text{ m})$
   $= 1.96 \times 10^5$ J.

   b. What is the change in potential energy of the system when the shell falls to a height of 2.00×10^2 m?

   $\Delta PE = mgh_f - mgh_i = mg(h_f - h_i)$
   $= (50.0 \text{ kg})(9.80 \text{ m/s}^2)(200 \text{ m} - 400 \text{ m})$
   $= -9.80 \times 10^4$ J.

Practice Problems

page 224

7. A person weighing 630 N climbs up a ladder to a height of 5.0 m.

   a. What work does the person do?

   $W = Fd = Fh = (630 \text{ N})(5.0 \text{ m}) = 3200$ J

   b. What is the increase in the gravitational potential energy of the person from the ground to this height?

   $\Delta PE = (mg)h = (630 \text{ N})(5.0 \text{ m}) = 3200$ J. The increase in gravitational potential energy is equal to the work done.

   c. Where does the energy come from to cause this increase in the gravitational potential energy?

   Directly from the work done by the person. Indirectly from the chemical energy stored in the person's body.

8. A pendulum is constructed from a 7.26–kg bowling ball hanging on a 2.5–m long rope. The ball is pulled back until the rope makes a 45° angle with the vertical.

   a. What is the potential energy of the ball?

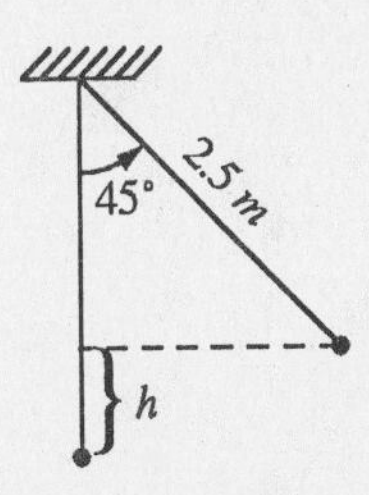

   $h = (2.5 \text{ m})(1 - \cos\theta) = 0.73$ m,
   $PE = mgh = (7.26 \text{ kg})(9.80 \text{ m/s}^2)(0.73 \text{ m})$
   $= 52$ J

   b. What reference level did you use in your calculation?

   the height of the ball when the rope was vertical

Practice Problems

page 230

9. A bike rider approaches a hill with a speed of 8.5 m/s. The total mass of the bike and rider is 85 kg.

   a. Find the kinetic energy of the bike and rider.

   $$KE = \frac{1}{2}mv^2$$

   $$= \frac{1}{2}(85 \text{ kg})(8.5 \text{ m/s})^2 = 3.1 \times 10^3 \text{ J}$$

   b. The rider coasts up the hill. Assuming there is no friction, at what height will the bike come to a stop?

   $$KE_i + PE_i = KE_f + PE_f$$

   $$\frac{1}{2}mv^2 + 0 = 0 + mgh,$$

   $$h = \frac{v^2}{2g} = \frac{(8.5 \text{ m/s})^2}{(2)(9.8 \text{ m/s}^2)} = 3.7 \text{ m}$$

   c. Does your answer depend on the mass of the bike and rider? Explain.

   No. It cancels because both KE and PE are proportional to m.

10. Tarzan, mass 85 kg, swings down from a tree limb on the end of a 20–m vine. His feet touch the ground 4.0 m below the limb.

    a. How fast is Tarzan moving when he reaches the ground?

    $$KE_i + PE_i = KE_f + PE_f$$

    $$0 + mgh = \frac{1}{2}mv^2 + 0,$$

    $$v^2 = 2gh = 2(9.8 \text{ m/s}^2)(4.0 \text{ m}) = 78.4 \text{ m}^2/\text{s}^2,$$
    $$v = 8.9 \text{ m/s}$$

    b. Does your answer depend on Tarzan's mass?

    No

    c. Does your answer depend on the length of the vine?

    No

Practice Problems

11. A skier starts from rest at the top of a 45–m hill, skis down a 30° incline into a valley, and continues up a 40–m hill. Both hill heights are measured from the valley floor. Assume you can neglect friction and the effect of ski poles.

    a. How fast is the skier moving at the bottom of the valley?

    $$KE_i + PE_i = KE_f + PE_f,$$

    $$0 + mgh = \frac{1}{2}mv^2 + 0,$$

    $$v^2 = 2gh = 2(9.8 \text{ m/s}^2)(45 \text{ m}) = 880 \text{ m}^2/\text{s}^2,$$
    $$v = 30 \text{ m/s}$$

    b. What is the skier's speed at the top of the next hill?

    $$KE_i + PE_i = KE_f + PE_f,$$

    $$0 + mgh_i = \frac{1}{2}mv^2 + mgh_f,$$

    $$v^2 = 2g(h_i - h_f)$$
    $$= 2(9.8 \text{ m/s}^2)(45 \text{ m} - 40 \text{ m}) = 98 \text{ m}^2/\text{s}^2,$$
    $$v = 10 \text{ m/s}.$$

12. Suppose, in the case of Practice Problem 9, the bike rider pedaled up the hill and never came to a stop.

    a. How could you define a system in which energy is conserved?

    The system of Earth, bike, and rider remains the same, but now the energy involved is not mechanical energy alone. The rider must be considered as having stored energy, some of which is converted to mechanical energy.

    b. From what form of energy did the bike gain kinetic energy?

    Energy came from the chemical potential energy stored in the rider's body.

Practice Problems

page 234

13. A 2.00-g bullet, moving at 538 m/s, strikes a 0.250-kg piece of wood at rest on a frictionless table. The bullet sticks in the wood, and the combined mass moves slowly down the table.

   a. Find the speed of the combination after the collision.

   From the conservation of momentum,
   $mv = (m + M)V$, so
   $V = mv/(m + M)$
   $= \dfrac{(0.002\text{ kg})(538\text{ m/s})}{0.002\text{ kg} + 0.250\text{ kg}} = 4.27\text{ m/s}$

   b. Find the kinetic energy of the bullet before the collision.

   $KE_i = \frac{1}{2}mv^2 = \frac{1}{2}(0.002\text{ kg})(538\text{ m/s})^2$
   $= 289\text{ J}$

   c. Find the kinetic energy of the combination after the collision.

   $KE_f = \frac{1}{2}(m + M)V^2$
   $= \frac{1}{2}(0.002\text{ kg} + 0.250\text{ kg})(4.27\text{ m/s})^2$
   $= 2.30\text{ J}$

   d. How much kinetic energy did the bullet lose?

   $\Delta KE = KE_i - KE_f = 289\text{ J} - 2\text{ J} = 287\text{ J}$

   e. What per cent of the bullet's original kinetic energy is lost?

   $\%\ KE\text{ lost} = (\Delta KE/KE_i) \times 100$
   $= (287\text{ J}/298\text{ J}) \times 100$
   $= 99.3\%$

page 235

14. An 8.00-g bullet is fired horizontally into a 9.00-kg block of wood on an air table and is embedded in it. After the collision, the block and the bullet slide along a frictionless surface together with a speed of 10 cm/s. What was the initial speed of the bullet?

   Conservation of momentum $mv = (m + M)V$, or
   $v = (m + M)V/m$
   $= \dfrac{(0.008\text{ kg} + 9.00\text{ kg})(0.10\text{ m/s})}{(0.008\text{ kg})}$
   $= 1.1 \times 10^2\text{ m/s}$

Practice Problems

15. As everyone knows, bullets bounce from Superman's chest. Suppose Superman, mass 104 kg, while not moving, is struck by a 4.2-g bullet moving with a speed of 835 m/s. If the collision is elastic, find the speed that Superman has after the collision.

   We have conservation of momentum
   $mv + MV = mv' + MV'$ and conservation of energy $\frac{1}{2}mv^2 + \frac{1}{2}MV^2 = \frac{1}{2}mv'^2 + \frac{1}{2}MV'^2$
   where m, v, v' refer to the bullet, M, V, V' to Superman, and $V = 0$. v' may be eliminated from these equations by solving the momentum equation for $v' = (mv - MV')/m$ and substituting this into the energy equation
   $mv^2 = mv'^2 + MV'^2$. This gives a quadratic equation for V' which, in factored form, is $MV'[(M + m)V' - 2mv] = 0$. We are not interested in the solution $V' = 0$ which corresponds to the case where the bullet does not hit Superman. We want the other,
   $V' = 2mv/(M + m) = \dfrac{2(0.0042\text{ kg})(835\text{ m/s})}{(104\text{ kg} + 0.0042\text{ kg})}$
   $= 6.7 \times 10^{-2}\text{ m/s.}$

16. A 0.73-kg magnetic target is suspended on a long string. A 0.025-kg magnetic dart, shot horizontally, strikes it head on. The dart and the target together swing up 12 cm above the initial level. What was the initial velocity of the dart? (HINT: Since your equation will have two unknowns, you will need an additional equation to solve for v_i. Consider the fact that the target had zero potential energy before the collision, but the dart and target no longer had zero potential energy after the collision.

   Only momentum is conserved in the inelastic dart-target collision, so
   $mv_i + MV_i = (m + M)V_f$ where $V_i = 0$ since the target is initially at rest and V_f is the common velocity just after impact. As the dart-target combination swings upward energy is conserved so $\Delta PE = \Delta KE$ or, at the top of the swing,
   $(m + M)gh = \frac{1}{2}(m + M)V_f^2$. Solving this for V_f and inserting into the momentum equation gives
   $v_i = (m + M)\sqrt{gh'}/m$
   $= \dfrac{(0.025\text{ kg} + 0.73\text{ kg})\sqrt{2(9.8\text{ m/s}^2)(0.12\text{ m})}}{(0.025\text{ kg})}$
   $= 46\text{ m/s.}$

Chapter Review Problems

page 237–239

1. A 1660–kg car travels at a speed of 12.5 m/s. What is its kinetic energy?

$$KE = \frac{1}{2}mv^2 = \left[\frac{1}{2}\right](1600 \text{ kg})(12.5 \text{ m/s})^2$$

$$= 1.25 \times 10^5 \text{ J}$$

2. A racing car has a mass of 1500 kg. What is the kinetic energy if it has a speed of 108 km/h?

$$v = \frac{(108 \text{ km/h})(1000 \text{ m/km})}{(3600 \text{ s/h})} = 30.0 \text{ m/s}$$

$$KE = \frac{1}{2}mv^2 = \left[\frac{1}{2}\right](1500 \text{ kg})(30.0 \text{ m/s})$$

$$= 6.75 \times 10^5 \text{ J}$$

3. Sally has a mass of 45 kg and is moving with a speed of 10.0 m/s.

a. Find Sally's kinetic energy.

$$KE = \frac{1}{2}mv^2 = \left[\frac{1}{2}\right](45 \text{ kg})(10.0 \text{ m/s})^2$$

$$= 2.3 \times 10^3 \text{ J}$$

b. Sally's speed changes to 5.0 m/s. Now what is her kinetic energy?

$$KE = \frac{1}{2}mv^2 = \left[\frac{1}{2}\right](45 \text{ kg})(5.0 \text{ m/s})^2$$

$$= 5.6 \times 10^2 \text{ J}$$

c. What is the ratio of the kinetic energies in a. and b.? Explain the ratio.

$$\frac{1/2(mv_1^2)}{1/2(mv_2^2)} = \frac{v_1^2}{v_2^2} = \frac{(10.0)^2}{(5.0)^2} = \frac{4}{1}$$

Twice the velocity gives four times the kinetic energy.

Chapter Review Problems

4. Shawn and his bike have a total mass of 45.0 kg. Shawn rides his bike 1.80 km in 10.0 min at a constant velocity. What is Shawn's kinetic energy?

$$v = \frac{d}{t} = \frac{(1.80 \text{ km})(1000 \text{ m/km})}{(10.0 \text{ min})(60 \text{ s/min})} = 3.00 \text{ m/s}$$

$$KE = \frac{1}{2}mv^2 = \left[\frac{1}{2}\right](45.0 \text{ kg})(3.00 \text{ m/s})^2$$

$$= 203 \text{ J}$$

5. It is not uncommon during the service of a professional tennis player for the racquet to exert an average force of 150.0 N on the ball. If the ball has a mass of 0.060 kg and is in contact with the strings of the racquet for 0.030 s, what is the kinetic energy of the ball as it leaves the racquet? Assume the ball starts from rest.

$Ft = m\Delta v = mv_f - mv_i$, and $v_i = 0$, so

$$v_f = \frac{Ft}{m} = \frac{(150.0 \text{ N})(3.0 \times 10^2 \text{ s})}{(6.0 \times 10^{-2} \text{ kg})}$$

$$= 75 \text{ m/s}$$

$$KE = \frac{1}{2}mv^2 = \frac{1}{2}(6.0 \times 10^{-2} \text{ kg})(75 \text{ m/s})^2$$

$$= 1.7 \times 10^2 \text{ J}$$

6. Pam has a mass of 40.0 kg and is at rest on smooth, level, frictionless ice. Pam straps on a rocket pack. The rocket supplies a constant force for 22.0 m and Pam acquired a speed of 62.0 m/s.

a. What is the magnitude of the force?

$F = ma$ and $v_f^2 = v_i^2 + 2ad$, so

$$a = \frac{v_f^2 - v_i^2}{2d} \text{ but } v_i = 0, \text{ so } a = \frac{v_f^2}{2d}$$

$$= \frac{(62.0 \text{ m/s})^2}{2(22.0)} = 87.4 \text{ m/s}^2. \text{ Therefore,}$$

$$F = ma = (40.0 \text{ kg})(87.4 \text{ m/s}^2)$$
$$= 3.50 \times 10^3 \text{ N.}$$

b. What is Pam's final kinetic energy?

$$KE = \frac{1}{2}mv^2 = \frac{1}{2}(40.0 \text{ kg})(62.0 \text{ m/s})^2$$

$$= 7.69 \times 10^4 \text{ J}$$

Chapter Review Problems

7. Sally and Lisa have a mass of 45 kg and they are moving together with a speed of 10.0 m/s.

a. What is their combined kinetic energy?

$$KE_e = \frac{1}{2}mv^2 = \frac{1}{2}(m_s + m_l)(v^2)$$

$$= \frac{1}{2}(45\text{ kg} + 45\text{ kg})(10.0\text{ m/s})^2$$

$$= 4.5 \times 10^3\text{ J}$$

b. What is the ratio of their combined mass to Sally's mass?

$$\frac{m_s + m_l}{m_s} = \frac{45\text{ kg} + 45\text{ kg}}{45\text{ kg}} = \frac{90\text{ kg}}{45\text{ kg}} = \frac{2}{1}$$

c. What is the ratio of their combined kinetic energy to Sally's kinetic energy? Explain.

$$KE_s = \frac{1}{2}m_s v^2 = \frac{1}{2}(45\text{ kg})(10.0\text{ m/s})^2$$

$$= 2.25 \times 10^3\text{ J}$$

$$\frac{KE_c}{KE_m} = \frac{4.5 \times 10^3\text{ J}}{2.35 \times 10^3\text{ J}} = \frac{2}{1}$$

The ratio of the kinetic energies is the same as the ratio of their masses

8. In the 1950s an experimental train that had a mass of 2.50×10^4 kg was powered across a level track by a jet engine that produced a thrust of 5.00×10^5 N for a distance of 500 m.

a. Find the work done on the train.

$$w = F \cdot d = (5.00 \times 10^5\text{ N})(500\text{ m})$$
$$= 2.50 \times 10^8\text{ J}$$

b. Find the change in kinetic energy.

$$\Delta KE = w = 2.50 \times 10^8\text{ J}$$

c. Find the final kinetic energy of the train if it started from rest.

$$\Delta KE = KE_f - KE_i,\text{ so } KE_f = \Delta KE + KE_i$$
$$= 2.50 \times 10^8\text{ J} - 0$$
$$= 2.50 \times 10^8\text{ J}$$

d. Find the final speed of the train if there was no friction.

$$KE_f = \frac{1}{2}mv^2,\text{ so}$$

$$v^2 = \frac{KE_f}{1/2\,m}$$

$$= \frac{2.50 \times 10^8\text{ J}}{1/2(2.50 \times 10^4\text{ kg})}\quad\text{so}$$

$$v = \sqrt{2.00 \times 10^4\ m^2/s^2} = 141\text{ m/s}$$

9. A 14 700–N car is traveling at 25 m/s. The brakes are suddenly applied and the car slides to a stop. The average braking force between the tires and the road is 7100 N. How far will the car slide once the brakes are applied?

$$W = F \cdot d = \frac{1}{2}mv^2$$

$$\text{Now } m = \frac{w}{g} = \frac{14{,}700\text{ N}}{9.80\text{ m/s}^2} = 1500\text{ kg.}$$

$$\text{So } d = \frac{\frac{1}{2}mv^2}{F} = \frac{\frac{1}{2}(1500\text{ kg})(25\text{ m/s}^2)}{7100\text{ N}} = 66\text{ m.}$$

10. A 15.0–kg cart is moving with a velocity of 7.50 m/s down a level hallway. A constant force of –10.0 N acts on the cart and its velocity becomes 3.20 m/s.

a. What is the change in kinetic energy of the cart?

$$\Delta KE = KE_f - KE_i = \frac{1}{2}m(v_f^2 - v_i^2)$$

$$= \frac{1}{2}(15.0\text{ kg})[(3.20\text{ m/s})^2 - (7.50\text{ m/s})^2]$$

$$= -345\text{ J}$$

b. How much work was done on the cart?

$$W = \Delta KE = -345\text{ J}$$

c. How far did the cart move while the force acted?

$$W = Fd,\text{ so } d = \frac{W}{F} = \frac{-345\text{ J}}{-10.0\text{ N}} = 34.5\text{ m}$$

11. A 2.00×10^3–kg car has a speed of 12.0 m/s. The car then hits a tree. The tree doesn't move and the car comes to rest.

    a. Find the change in kinetic energy of the car.

    $$\Delta KE = KE_f - KE_i = \frac{1}{2}m(v_f^2 - v_i^2)$$

    $$= \frac{1}{2}(2.00 \times 10^3 \text{ kg})(0^2 - (12.0 \text{ m/s})^2)$$

    $$= -1.44 \times 10^5 \text{ J}$$

    b. Find the amount of work done in pushing in the front of the car.

    $W = \Delta KE = -1.44 \times 10^5$ J

    c. Find the size of the force that pushed the front of the car in 50.0 cm.

    $W = F \cdot d$, so

    $$F = \frac{W}{d} = \frac{-1.44 \times 10^5 \text{ J}}{0.500 \text{ m}}$$

    $$= -2.88 \times 10^5 \text{ N.}$$

    The negative sign implies a retarding force.

12. How much potential energy does Tim, mass of 60.0 kg, gain when he climbs a gymnasium rope a distance of 3.5 m?

    $$PE = mgh = (60.0 \text{ kg})(9.80 \text{ m/s}^2)(3.5 \text{ m}) = 2.1 \times 10^3 \text{ J}$$

13. A 6.4–kg bowling ball is lifted 2.1 m into a storage rack. Calculate the increase in the ball's potential energy.

    $$PE = mgh = (6.4 \text{ kg})(9.80 \text{ m/s}^2)(2.1 \text{ m}) = 1.3 \times 10^2 \text{ J}$$

14. Mary weighs 500 N. She walks down a flight of stairs to a level 5.50 m below her starting point. What is the change in Mary's potential energy?

    $$\Delta PE = mg\Delta h = W\Delta h = (500 \text{ N})(-5.50 \text{ m}) = -2.75 \times 10^3 \text{ J}$$

Chapter Review Problems

15. A weightlifter raises a 180–kg barbell to a height of 1.95 m. What is the increase in the barbell's potential energy?

    $$PE = mgh = (180 \text{ kg})(9.80 \text{ m/s}^2)(1.95 \text{ m}) = 3.44 \times 10^3 \text{ J}$$

16. A 10.0–kg test rocket is fired vertically from Cape Canaveral. Its fuel gives it a kinetic energy of 1960 J by the time the rocket motor burns all of the fuel. What additional height will the rocket rise?

    $PE = mgh = KE$

    $$h = \frac{KE}{mg} = \frac{1960 \text{ J}}{(10.0 \text{ kg})(9.80 \text{ m/s}^2)} = 20.0 \text{ m}$$

17. Ace raised a 12.0–N Physics book from a table, 75 cm above the floor, to a shelf, 2.15 m above the floor. What was the change in potential energy?

    $$PE = mg\Delta h = W\Delta h = W(h_f - h_i) = (12.0 \text{ N})(2.15 \text{ m} - 0.75 \text{ m}) = 16.8 \text{ J}$$

18. A hallway display of energy is constructed. People are told that to do 1.00 J of work, they should pull on a rope that lifts a block 1.00 m. What should be the mass of the block?

    $W = \Delta PE = mgh$, so

    $$m = \frac{W}{gh} = \frac{(1.00 \text{ J})}{(9.80 \text{ m/s}^2)(1.00 \text{ m})} = 0.102 \text{ kg}$$

19. A constant net force of 410 N, up, is applied to a stone that weighs 32 N. The upward force is applied through a distance of 2.0 m, and the stone is then released. To what height, from the point of release, will the stone rise?

    $W = Fd = (410 \text{ N})(2.0 \text{ m}) = 8.20 \times 10^2$ J.
    But $W = \Delta PE = mg\Delta h$, so

    $$\Delta h = \frac{W}{mg} = \frac{8.20 \times 10^2 \text{ J}}{32 \text{ N}} = 26 \text{ m}$$

20. A 98–N sack of grain is hoisted to a storage room 50 m above the ground floor of a grain elevator.

    a. How much work was required?

    $W = Fd = (98 \text{ N})(50 \text{ m}) = 4.9 \times 10^3$ J

b. What is the potential energy of the sack of grain at this height?

$\Delta PE = W = 4.9 \times 10^3$ J

c. The rope being used to lift the sack of grain breaks just as the sack reaches the storage room. What kinetic energy does the sack have just before it strikes the ground floor?

$KE = \Delta PE = 4.9 \times 10^3$ J

21. A 20-kg rock is on the edge of a 100 m cliff.

a. What potential energy does the rock possess relative to the base of the cliff?

$PE = mgh = (20 \text{ kg})(9.80 \text{ m/s}^2)(100 \text{ m})$
$= 2.0 \times 10^4$ J

b. The rock falls from the cliff. What is its kinetic energy just before it strikes the ground?

$KE = \Delta PE = 2.0 \times 10^4$ J

c. What speed does the rock have as it strikes the ground?

$$KE = \frac{1}{2}mv^2$$

$$v = \sqrt{\frac{2KE}{m}} = \sqrt{\frac{(2)(2.0 \times 10^4 \text{ J})}{(20 \text{ kg})}}$$

$= 45$ m/s

22. An archer puts a 0.30-kg arrow to the bowstring. An average force of 201 N is exerted to draw the string back 1.3 m.

a. Assuming no frictional loss, with what speed does the arrow leave the bow?

$W = KE$

$$Fd = \frac{1}{2}mv^2$$

$$v^2 = \frac{2Fd}{m}$$

$$v = \sqrt{\frac{2Fd}{m}} = \sqrt{\frac{(2)(201 \text{ N})(1.3 \text{ m})}{(0.30 \text{ kg})}}$$

$= 42$ m/s

Chapter Review Problems

b. If the arrow is shot straight up, how high does it rise?

$PE = \Delta KE$

$$mgd = \frac{1}{2}mv^2$$

$$d = \frac{v^2}{2g} = \frac{(42 \text{ m/s})^2}{(2)(9.8 \text{ m/s}^2)} = 90 \text{ m}$$

23. A 2.0-kg rock initially at rest loses 400 J of potential energy while falling to the ground.

a. Calculate the kinetic energy that the rock gains while falling.

$PE_i + KE_i = PE_f + KE_f$
$KE_f = PE_i = 400$ J

b. What is the rock's speed just before it strikes the ground?

$$KE = \frac{1}{2}mv^2, \text{ so } v^2 = (2)\frac{KE}{m} = \frac{(2)(400 \text{ J})}{(2.0 \text{ kg})}$$

$= 400 \text{ m}^2/\text{s}^2$, so $v = 20$ m/s.

24. Betty weighs 420 N and is sitting on a playground swing seat that hangs 0.40 m above the ground. Tom pulls the swing back and releases it when the seat is 1.00 m above the ground.

a. How fast is Betty moving when the swing passes through its lowest position?

$\Delta PE = Fd = (420 \text{ N})(0.40 \text{ m} - 1.00 \text{ m})$
$= -250$ J

$$KE = -\Delta PE = \frac{1}{2}mv^2$$

$$v = \sqrt{\frac{2KE}{m}} = \sqrt{\frac{(2)(250 \text{ J})}{(420 \text{ N}/9.8 \text{ m/s}^2)}}$$

$= 3.4$ m/s

b. If Betty moves through the lowest point at 2.0 m/s, how much work was done on the swing by friction?

$$W = PE - KE = 250 \text{ J} - \frac{1}{2}mv^2$$

$$= 250 \text{ J} - \left(\frac{1}{2}\right)\left(\frac{420 \text{ N}}{9.80 \text{ m/s}^2}\right)(2.0 \text{ m/s})^2$$

$= 250 \text{ J} - 86 \text{ J} = 164 \text{ J} = 1.6 \times 10^2$ J

Chapter Review Problems

25. Bill throws a 10.0-g ball straight down from a height of 2.0 m. The ball strikes the floor at a speed of 7.5 m/s. What was the initial speed of the ball?

$KE_f = KE_i + PE_i$

$\frac{1}{2}mv_2^2 = \frac{1}{2}mv_1^2 + mgh$, the mass of the ball dividing out, so $v_1^2 = v_2^2 - 2gh$,

$v_1 = \sqrt{v_2^2 - 2gh}$

$= \sqrt{(7.5 \text{ m/s})^2 - (2)(9.80 \text{ m/s}^2)(2.0 \text{ m})}$

$= 4.1$ m/s

26. Magen's mass is 28 kg. She climbs the 4.8-m ladder of a slide, then reaches a velocity of 3.2 m/s at the bottom of the slide. How much work was done by friction on Magen.

At the top,

$PE = mgh = (28 \text{ kg})(9.80 \text{ m/s}^2)(4.8 \text{ m})$

$= 1.3 \times 10^3$ J.

At the bottom,

$KE = \frac{1}{2}mv^2 = \left[\frac{1}{2}\right](28 \text{ kg})(3.2 \text{ m/s})^2$

$= 1.4 \times 10^2$ J

$W_i = PE - KE = 1.2 \times 10^3$ J

27. A physics book, mass unknown, is dropped 4.50 m. What speed does the book have just before it hits the ground?

$KE = PE$

$\frac{1}{2}mv^2 = mgh$; the mass of the book divides out,

so $\frac{1}{2}v^2 = gh$, or

$\sqrt{2gh} = \sqrt{2(9.80 \text{ m/s}^2)(4.50 \text{ m})}$

$= 9.39$ m/s.

28. A 30.0-kg gun is standing on a frictionless surface. The gun fires a 50.0-g bullet with a muzzle velocity of 310 m/s.

a. Calculate the momenta of the bullet and the gun after the gun was fired.

$P_g = -P_h$ and $P_b = m_b v_b$

$= (0.0500 \text{ kg})(310 \text{ m/s})$

$= 15.5 \frac{\text{kg} \cdot \text{m}}{\text{s}}$

$P_g = -P_b = -15.5 \frac{\text{kg m}}{\text{s}}$

b. Calculate the kinetic energy of both the bullet and the gun just after firing.

$KE_b = \frac{1}{2}mv^2 = \frac{1}{2}(0.0500 \text{ kg})(310 \text{ m/s})^2$

$= 2.40 \times 10^3$ J

$P_g = mv$, so

$v = \frac{P_g}{m} = \frac{-15.5 \frac{\text{kg} \cdot \text{m}}{\text{s}}}{30.0 \text{ kg}}$

$= 0.517$ m/s

$KE_g = \frac{1}{2}mv^2 = \frac{1}{2}(30.0 \text{ kg})(0.517 \text{ m/s})^2$

$= 4.00$ J

29. A railroad car with a mass of 5.0×10^5 kg collides with a stationary railroad car of equal mass. After the collision, the two cars lock together and move off at 4.0 m/s.

a. Before the collision, the first railroad car was moving at 8.0 m/s. What was its momentum?

$mv = (5.0 \times 10^5 \text{ kg})(8.0 \text{ m/s})$

$= 4.0 \times 10^6 \frac{\text{kg} \cdot \text{m}}{\text{s}}$

b. What is the total momentum of the two cars after the collision?

Since momentum is conserved, it must be

$4.0 \times 10^6 \frac{\text{kg} \cdot \text{m}}{\text{s}}$

Chapter Review Problems

c. Find the kinetic energies of the two cars before and after the collision.

Before the collision:

$KE_1 = \frac{1}{2}mv^2$

$= \left[\frac{1}{2}\right](5.0 \times 10^5 \text{ kg})(8.0 \text{ m/s})^2$

$= 1.6 \times 10^7 \text{ J}$

$KE_2 = 0$ since it is at rest.

After the collision:

$KE = \frac{1}{2}mv^2$

$= \left[\frac{1}{2}\right](5.0 \times 10^5 \text{ kg} + 5.0 \times 10^5 \text{ kg})(4.0 \text{ m/s})^2$

$= 8.0 \times 10^6 \text{ J}$

d. Account for the loss of kinetic energy.

While momentum was conserved during the collision, kinetic energy was not. The amount not conserved was turned into heat and sound.

30. From what height would a compact car have to be dropped to have the same kinetic energy that it has when being driven at 100 km/h?

$V = \left[100 \frac{\text{km}}{\text{h}}\right]\left[\frac{1000 \text{ m}}{1 \text{ km}}\right]\left[\frac{1 \text{ h}}{3600 \text{ s}}\right]$

$= 27.8 \text{ m/s}$

$KE = PE$

$\frac{1}{2}mv^2 = mgh$; the mass of the car divides out, so

$\frac{1}{2}v^2 = gh$, so $h = \frac{v^2}{2g} = \frac{(27.8 \text{ m/s})^2}{2(9.80 \text{ m/s}^2)} = 39.4 \text{ m}$

31. A golf ball, mass 0.046 kg, rests on a tee. It is struck by a golf club with an effective mass of 0.220 kg and a speed of 44 m/s. Assuming the collision is elastic, find the speed of the ball when it leaves the tee.

From conservation of momentum, $m_cv_c = m_cv_c' + m_bv_b'$. Solve for v_c',

$v_c' = v_c - \frac{m_bv_b'}{m_c}$.

From conservation of energy,

$\frac{1}{2}m_cv_c = \frac{1}{2}m_c(v_c')^2 + \frac{1}{2}m_b(v_b')^2$. Multiply by two and substitution gives

$m_cv_c^2 = m_c[v_c - \frac{m_bv_b'}{m_c}] + m_b(v_b')^2$, or $m_cv_c^2$

$= m_cv_c^2 - 2m_bv_b'v_c + \frac{m_b(v_b')^2}{m_c} + m_b(v_b')^2$.

Simplify and factor:

$0 = (m_bv_b')[-2v_c + \frac{m_b(v_b')}{m_c} + v_b']$. Either

$m_bv_b' = 0$ or $-2v_c + \left[\frac{m_b}{m_c} + 1\right]v_b' = 0$ so

$v_b' = \frac{2v_c}{\left[\frac{m_b}{m_c} + 1\right]} = \frac{2(44 \text{ m/s})}{\left[\frac{0.046 \text{ kg}}{0.220 \text{ kg}} + 1\right]} = 73 \text{ m/s}$

11

Chapter Review Problems

32. A steel ball has a mass of 4.0 kg and rolls along a smooth, level surface at 62 m/s.

a. Find its kinetic energy.

$$KE = \frac{1}{2}mv^2 = \left[\frac{1}{2}\right](4.0 \text{ kg})(62 \text{ m/s})^2$$

$$= 7.7 \times 10^3 \text{ J}$$

b. At first, the ball was at rest on the surface. A constant force acted on it through a distance of 22 m to give it the speed of 62 m/s. What was the magnitude of the force?

a. $W = Fd$

b. $F = \frac{W}{d} = \frac{7.7 \times 10^3 \text{ J}}{22 \text{ m}} = 3.5 \times 10^2 \text{ N}$

33. Show that $W = KE_f - KE_i$ if an object is not originally at rest. Use the equation relating initial and final velocity with constant acceleration and distance.

$v_f^2 = v_i^2 + 2ad$, or $d = \frac{v_f^2 - v_i^2}{2a}$. But

$$W = mad = ma\left[\frac{v_f^2 - v_i^2}{2a}\right] = \frac{1}{2}m(v_f^2 - v_i^2)$$

$= \frac{1}{2}mv_f^2 - \frac{1}{2}mv_i^2$. Therefore,

$W = KE_f - KE_i$.

Supplemental Problems (Appendix B)

1. Calculate the kinetic energy of a proton, mass of 1.67×10^{-27} kg, traveling at 5.20×10^7 m/s.

$$KE = \frac{1}{2}mv^2$$

$$= \frac{1}{2}(1.67 \times 10^{-27} \text{ kg})(5.20 \times 10^7 \text{ m/s})^2$$

$$= 2.26 \times 10^{-12} \text{ J}$$

Supplemental Problems (Appendix B)

2. What is the kinetic energy of a 3.2-kg pike swimming at 2.7 km/hr?

$$2.7 \text{ km/hr} \cdot \frac{1000 \text{ m}}{\text{km}} \cdot \frac{\text{hr}}{3600 \text{ s}} = 0.75 \text{ m/s}$$

$$KE = \frac{1}{2}mv^2 = \frac{1}{2}(3.2 \text{ kg})(0.75 \text{ m/s})^2 = 0.90 \text{ J}$$

3. A force of 30.0 N pushes a 1.5-kg cart, initially at rest, a distance of 2.8 m along a frictionless surface.

a. Find the work done on the cart.

$$W = Fd = (30.0 \text{ N})(2.8 \text{ m}) = 84 \text{ J}$$

b. What is its change in kinetic energy?

$$W = \Delta KE = 84 \text{ J}$$

c. What is the cart's final velocity?

$$v = \sqrt{\frac{2KE}{m}} = \sqrt{\frac{2(84 \text{ J})}{1.5 \text{ kg}}} = 11 \text{ m/s}$$

4. A bike and rider of 82.0-kg combined mass are traveling at 4.2 m/s. A constant force of −140 N is applied by the brakes in stopping the bike. What braking distance is needed?

$$KE = \frac{1}{2}mv^2$$

$$= \frac{1}{2}(82.0 \text{ kg})(4.2 \text{ m/s})^2$$

$= 723$ J of KE is lost

$(-140 \text{ N})d = -723 \text{ J}$

$d = 5.2 \text{ m}$

5. A 712-kg car is traveling at 5.6 m/s when a force acts on it for 8.4 s, changing its velocity to 10.2 m/s.

a. What is the change in kinetic energy of the car?

$$KE_{\text{final}} = \frac{1}{2}mv_f^2 = \frac{1}{2}(712 \text{ kg})(10.2 \text{ m/s})^2$$

$$= 3.7 \times 10^4 \text{ J}$$

$$KE_{\text{initial}} = \frac{1}{2}mv_i^2 = \frac{1}{2}(712 \text{ kg})(5.6 \text{ m/s})^2$$

$$= 1.1 \times 10^4 \text{ J}$$

$$\Delta KE = KE_{\text{final}} - KE_{\text{initial}} = 2.6 \times 10^4 \text{ J}$$

b. How far did the car move while the force acted?

$$d = \left[\frac{v_f + v_i}{2}\right]t = \left[\frac{10.2\ \text{m/s} + 5.6\ \text{m/s}}{2}\right](8.4\ \text{s})$$
$$= 66\ \text{m}$$

c. How large is the force?

$Fd = \Delta KE$
$F(66.4\ \text{m}) = 2.6 \times 10^4\ \text{J}$
$F = 3.9 \times 10^2\ \text{N}$

6. Five identical 0.85-kg books of 2.50-cm thickness are each lying flat on a table. Calculate the gain in potential energy of the system if they are stacked one on top of the other.

Height raised:
book 1 none
book 2 2.5 cm
book 3 5.0 cm
book 4 7.5 cm
book 5 10.0 cm

25 cm total

$\Delta PE = mg\Delta h = (0.85\ \text{kg})(9.80\ \text{m/s}^2)(0.25\ \text{m})$
$= 2.1\ \text{J}$

7. Each step of a ladder increases one's vertical height 40 cm. If a 90.0-kg painter climbs 8 steps of the ladder, what is the increase in potential energy?

$(40\ \text{cm})(8) = 320\ \text{cm}$
$\Delta PE = mg\Delta h = (90.0\ \text{kg})(9.80\ \text{m/s}^2)(3.2\ \text{m})$
$= 2.8 \times 10^3\ \text{J}$

8. A 0.25-kg ball is dropped from a height of 3.2 m and bounces to a height of 2.4 m. What is its loss in potential energy?

$\Delta h = 2.4\ \text{m} - 3.2\ \text{m} = -0.80\ \text{m}$
$\Delta PE = mg\Delta h = (0.25\ \text{kg})(9.80\ \text{m/s}^2)(-0.80\ \text{m})$
$= -2.0\ \text{J}$

Supplemental Problems

9. A 0.18-kg ball is placed on a compressed spring on the floor. The spring exerts an average force of 2.8 N through a distance of 15 cm as it shoots the ball upward. How high will the ball travel above the release spring?

$W = Fd$
$= (2.8\ \text{N})(0.15\ \text{m}) = 0.42\ \text{J}$
$W = \Delta PE = mg\Delta h$
$0.42\ \text{J} = (0.18\ \text{kg})(9.80\ \text{m/s}^2)(\Delta h)$
$\Delta h = 0.24\ \text{m}$

10. A force of 14.0 N is applied to a 1.5-kg cart as it travels 2.6 m along an inclined plane. What is the angle of inclination of the plane.

$W = Fd = (14.0\ \text{N})(2.6\ \text{m}) = 36.4\ \text{J}$
$W = \Delta PE = mg\Delta h$
$36.4\text{k J} = (1.5\ \text{kg})(9.80\ \text{m/s}^2)(|h)$
$\Delta h = 2.48\ \text{m}$

$\sin\theta = \frac{2.48}{2.6}$
$\theta = 72°$

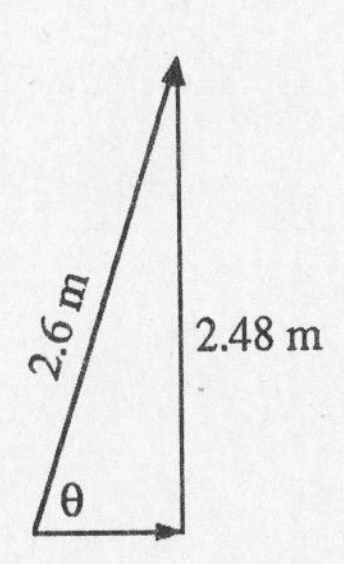

11. A 15.0-kg model plane flies horizontally at a constant speed of 12.5 m/s.

a. Calculate its kinetic energy.

$KE = \frac{1}{2}mv^2 = \left[\frac{1}{2}\right](15.0\ \text{kg})(12.5\ \text{m/s})^2$
$= 1.17 \times 10^3\ \text{J}$

b. The plane goes into a dive and levels off 20.4 m closer to Earth. How much potential energy does it lose during the dive? Assume no additional drag.

$\Delta PE = mgh = (15.0\ \text{kg})(9.80\ \text{m/s}^2)(20.4\ \text{m})$
$= 3.00 \times 10^3\ \text{J}$

c. How much kinetic energy does the plane gain during the dive?

$\Delta KE = \Delta PE = 3.00 \times 10^3$ J

d. What is its new kinetic energy?

$KE = 1.17 \times 10^3 \text{ J} + 3.00 \times 10^3 \text{ J}$
$= 4.17 \times 10^3 \text{ J}$

e. What is its new horizontal velocity?

$$v = \sqrt{\frac{2KE}{m}} = \sqrt{\frac{(2)(4170 \text{ J})}{15.0 \text{ kg}}} = 23.6 \text{ m/s}$$

12. A 1200-kg car starts from rest and accelerates to 72 km/h in 20.0 s. Friction exerts an average force of 450 N on the car during this time.

a. What is the net work done on the car?

$$W = \Delta KE = \frac{1}{2}mv^2$$
$$= \left(\frac{1}{2}\right)(1200 \text{ kg})(20 \text{ m/s})^2$$
$$= 2.4 \times 10^5 \text{ J}$$

b. How far does the car move during its acceleration?

$$d = \frac{(v_f + v_i)t}{2} = \frac{(20 \text{ m/s} + 0)(20.0 \text{ s})}{2}$$
$$= 2.0 \times 10^2 \text{ m}$$

c. What is the net force exerted on the car during this time?

$W = Fd$

$$F = \frac{W}{d} = \frac{(2.4 \times 10^5 \text{ J})}{(2.0 \times 10^2 \text{ m})}$$
$$= 1.2 \times 10^3 \text{ N}$$

d. What is the forward force exerted on the car as a result of the engine, power train, and wheels pushing backward on the road?

$$F_{net} = F_{forward} - F_{friction}$$
$$F_{forward} = F_{net} + F_{friction}$$
$$= (1.2 \times 10^3 \text{ N}) + (450 \text{ N})$$
$$= 1.7 \times 10^3 \text{ N}$$

Supplemental Problems

13. In an electronics factory, small cabinets slide down a 30.0° incline a distance of 16.0 m to reach the next assembly stage. The cabinets have a mass of 10.0 kg each.

a. Calculate the speed each cabinet would acquire if the incline were frictionless.

$$d_v = d \sin \theta = (16.0 \text{ m})(\sin 30.0)$$
$$= 8.00 \text{ m}$$

$$\frac{1}{2}mv^2 = mgh$$

$$v = \sqrt{2gh} = \sqrt{(2)(9.80 \text{ m/s}^2)(8.00 \text{ m})}$$
$$= 12.5 \text{ m/s}$$

b. What kinetic energy would a cabinet have under such circumstances?

$$KE = \frac{1}{2}mv^2 = \left(\frac{1}{2}\right)(10.0 \text{ kg})(12.5 \text{ m/s})^2$$
$$= 781 \text{ J}$$

14. An average force of 8.2 N is used to pull a 0.40-kg rock, stretching a sling shot 43 cm. The rock is shot downward from a bridge 18 m above a stream. What will be the velocity of the rock just before it enters the water?

Initial energy: $W + PE$
$= (8.2 \text{ N})(0.43 \text{ m}) + (0.40 \text{ kg})(9.80 \text{ m/s}^2)(18 \text{ m})$
$= 3.5 \text{ J} + 70.6 \text{ J}$
$= 74.1 \text{ J}$

Energy at water is kinetic energy:
$$KE = \frac{1}{2}mv^2$$

$$v = \sqrt{\frac{2KE}{m}} = \sqrt{\frac{2(74.1 \text{ J})}{0.40 \text{ kg}}} = 19 \text{ m/s}$$

15. A 15-g bullet is fired horizontally into a 3.000-kg block of wood suspended by a long cord. The bullet sticks in the block. Compute the velocity of the bullet if the impact causes the block to swing 10 cm above its initial level.

Consider first the collision of block and bullet. During the collision, momentum is conserved, so momentum just before = momentum just after

$$(0.015 \text{ kg})v_i + 0 = (3.015 \text{ kg})v_f$$

where v_i is the initial speed of the bullet and v_f is the speed of block and bullet after collision.

We have two unknowns in this equation. To find another equation, we can use the fact that the block swings 10 cm high. Therefore, choosing gravitational potential energy = 0 at the initial level of the block,

KE just after collision = final *GPE*

$$\frac{1}{2}(3.015\text{kg})v_f^2 = (3.015 \text{ kg})(9.80 \text{ m/s}^2)(0.10 \text{ m})$$

$$v_f = 1.40 \text{ m/s}$$

$$v_i = \frac{(3.015 \text{ kg})(1.40 \text{ m/s})}{(0.015 \text{ kg})}$$

$$= 2.8 \times 10^2 \text{ m/s}$$

Chapter 12: Thermal Energy

Practice Problems

page 247

1. Make the following conversions.

   a. 0°C to kelvins

   K = °C + 273 = 0 + 273 = 273 K

   b. 0 K to degrees Celsius

   °C = K − 273 = 0 − 273 = −273°C

   c. 273°C to kelvins

   K = °C + 273 = 273 + 273 = 546 K

   d. 273 K to degrees Celsius

   °C = K − 273 = 273 − 273 = 0°C

2. Convert these Celsius temperatures to Kelvin temperatures.

   a. 27°C

   K = 27°C + 273 = 300 K

   b. 560°C

   K = 560°C + 273 = 833 K

   c. −184°C

   K = −184°C + 273 = 89 K

   d. −300°C

   impossible temperature – below absolute zero

Practice Problems

3. Convert these Kelvin temperatures to Celsius temperatures.

   a. 110 K

   °C = 110 − 273 = −163°C

   b. 22 K

   °C = 22 − 273 = −251°C

   c. 402 K

   °C = 402 − 273 = 129°C

   d. 323 K

   °C = 323 − 273 = 50°C

4. Find the Celsius and Kelvin temperatures for the following. Answers will vary.

   a. room temperaure

   68–72°F = 20 to 22°C, 293–295 K

   b. refrigerator temperature

   about 40°F is about 4°C, 277 K

   c. typical hot summer day

   about 86°F is 30°C, 303 K

   d. typical winter night

   about 0°F, −18°C, 255 K

page 248

5. How much heat is absorbed by 60.0 g of copper when it is heated from 20.0°C to 80.0°C?

   $Q = mC\Delta T$
   $= (0.0600 \text{ kg})(385 \text{ J/kg}\cdot\text{K})(80.0°\text{C} - 20.0°\text{C})$
   $= 1.39 \times 10^3 \text{ J}$

Practice Problems

6. A 38-kg block of lead is heated from −26°C to 180°C. How much heat does it absorb during the heating?

   $Q = mC\Delta T = (38\text{ kg})(130\text{ J/kg}\cdot\text{K})(180°\text{C} - (-26°\text{C})) = 1.0 \times 10^6\text{ J}$

7. The cooling system of a car engine contains 20.0 liters of water. (1 L of water has a mass of 1 kg.)

   a. What is the change in the temperature of the water if the engine operates until 836.0 kJ of heat are added?

   $Q = mC\Delta T$,

   $$\Delta T = Q/mC = \frac{(836 \times 10^3\text{ J})}{(20.0\text{ kg})(4180\text{ J/kg}\cdot\text{K})} = 10.0°\text{C}$$

   b. Suppose it is winter and the system is filled with methanol. The density of methanol is 0.80 g/cm³. What would be the increase in temperature of the methanol if it absorbed 836.0 kJ of heat?

   Using 1L = 1000 cm³, the mass of methanol required is
   $DV = (0.80\text{ g/cm}^3)(20\text{ L})(1000\text{ cm}^3\text{/L}) = 16{,}000\text{ g or }16\text{ kg}$.

   $$\Delta T = Q/mC = \frac{(836 \times 10^3\text{ J})}{(16\text{ kg})(2450\text{ J/kg}\cdot\text{K})} = 21°\text{C}$$

   c. Which is the better coolant, water or methanol? Explain.

   Water is the better coolant since its temperature increase is less than half that of methanol when absorbing the same amount of heat.

8. A 565-g cube of iron is cooled from the temperature of boiling water to room temperature (20°C).

   a. How much heat must be absorbed from the cube?

   Iron: $Q = mC\Delta T = (0.565\text{ kg})(450\text{ J/kg}\cdot\text{K})(100°\text{C} - 20°\text{C}) = 2.0 \times 10^4\text{ J}$.

   b. If the iron is cooled by dunking it into water at 0°C that rises in temperature to 20°C, how much water is needed?

   $$\text{Water: } Q = mC\Delta T\text{, so } m = \frac{Q}{C\Delta T} = \frac{(2.0 \times 10^4\text{ J})}{(4180\text{ J/kg}\cdot\text{K})(20°\text{C})} = 0.24\text{ kg}$$

page 252

9. A 2.00×10^2-g sample of water at 80.0°C is mixed with 2.00×10^2 g of water at 10.0°C. Assume no heat loss to the surroundings. What is the final temperature of the mixture?

   $m_A C_A (T_f - T_{Ai}) + m_B C_B (T_f - T_{Bi}) = 0$
   Since $m_A = m_B$ and $C_A = C_B$, there is cancellation in this particular case so that

   $$T_f = \frac{(T_{a,f} + T_{b,i})}{2} = \frac{(80.0°\text{C} + 10.0°\text{C})}{2} = 45.0°\text{C}$$

Practice Problems

10. A 4.00×10^2–g sample of methanol at 16.0°C is mixed with 4.00×10^2 g of water at 85.0°C. Assume no heat loss to the surroundings. What is the final temperature of the mixture?

$m_aC_a(T_f - T_{ai}) + m_wC_w(T_f - T_{wi}) = 0$
Since, in this particular case, $m_a = m_w$, the masses cancel and

$$T_f = \frac{C_aT_{a,i} + C_wT_{w,i}}{C_a + C_w} = \frac{(2450 \text{ J/kg}\cdot\text{C°})(16.0°\text{C}) + (4180 \text{ J/kg}°\text{C°})(85.0°\text{C})}{2450 \text{ J/kg}\cdot\text{C°} + 4180 \text{ J/kg}\cdot\text{C°}} = 59.5°\text{C}$$

11. A 1.00×10^2–g brass block at 90.0°C is placed in a styrofoam cup containing 2.00×10^2 g of water at 20.0°C. No heat is lost to the cup or the surroundings. Find the final temperature of the mixture.

$m_bC_b(T_f - T_{bi}) + m_wC_w(T_f - T_{wi}) = 0$

$$T_f = \frac{m_bC_bT_{bi} + m_wC_wT_{wi}}{m_bC_b + m_wC_w} = \frac{(0.100 \text{ kg})(376 \text{ J/kg}\cdot\text{C°})(90.0°\text{C}) + (0.200 \text{ kg})(4180 \text{ J/kg}\cdot\text{C°})(20.0°\text{C})}{(0.100 \text{ kg})(376 \text{ J/kg}\cdot\text{C°}) + (0.200 \text{ kg})(4180 \text{ J/kg}\cdot\text{C°})}$$

$$= 23.0° \text{ C}$$

12. A 1.0×10^2–g aluminum block at 100.0°C is placed in 1.00×10^2 g of water at 10.0°C. The final temperature of the mixture is 25°C. What is the specific heat of the aluminum?

$m_aC_a(T_f - T_{ai}) + m_wC_w(T_f - T_{wi}) = 0$
Since $m_a = m_w$, the masses cancel and

$$C_a = -C_w(T_f - T_{wi})(T_f - T_{ai}) = \frac{-(4180 \text{ J/kg}\cdot\text{K})(25°\text{C} - 10°\text{C})}{(25°\text{C} - 100°\text{C})} = 8.4 \times 10^2 \text{ J/kg}\cdot\text{K}$$

page 255

13. How much heat is absorbed by 1.00×10^2 g of ice at –20.0°C to become water at 0.0°C?

To warm the ice to 0°C, $Q_w = mC\Delta T$ = (0.100 kg)(2060 J/kg·C°)(0–(–20.0°C)) = 4120 J.
To melt the ice, $Q_m = mH_f$ = (0.100 kg)(3.34×10^5 J/kg) = 3.34×10^4 J.
Total heat required = $Q_w + Q_m$ = $0.41 \times 10^4 + 3.34 \times 10^4$ J = 3.75×10^4 J

14. A 2.00×10^2–g sample of water at 60.0°C is heated to steam at 140.0°C. How much heat is absorbed?

To heat the water from 60°C to 100°C:
$Q = mC\Delta T$ = (0.200 kg)(4180 J/kg·C°)(40°C) = 0.334×10^5 J.

To change the water to steam:
$Q = mH_v$ = (0.200 kg)(2.26×10^6 J/kg) = 4.52×10^5 J.

To heat the steam from 100°C to 140°C:
$Q = mC\Delta T$ = (0.200 kg)(2020 J/kg·C°)(40°C) = 0.162×10^5 J
$Q_{total} = 5.02 \times 10^5$ J

Practice Problems

15. How much heat is needed to change 3.00×10^2 g of ice at –30.0°C to steam at 130.0°C?

Warm ice from –30°C to 0°C:
$Q = mC\Delta T = (0.300 \text{ kg})(2060 \text{ J/kg}\cdot\text{C°})(30.0\text{°C}) = 0.185 \times 10^5 \text{ J}$

Melt ice:
$Q = mH_f = (0.300 \text{ kg})(3.34 \times 10^5 \text{ J/kg}) = 1.00 \times 10^5 \text{ J}$

Heat water 0°C to 100°C:
$Q = mC\Delta T = (0.300 \text{ kg})(4180 \text{ J/kg}\cdot\text{C°})(100\text{°C}) = 1.25 \times 10^5 \text{ J}$

Vaporize water:
$Q = mH_v = (0.300 \text{ kg})(2.26 \times 10^6 \text{ J/kg}) = 6.78 \times 10^5 \text{ J}$

Heat steam 100°C to 130°C:
$Q = mC\Delta T = (0.300 \text{ kg})(2020 \text{ J/kg}\cdot\text{C°})(30\text{°C}) = 0.18 \times 10^5 \text{ J}$
$Q_{total} = 9.40 \times 10^5 \text{ J}$

12

16. A 175-g lump of molten lead at its melting point, 327°C, is dropped into 55 g of water at 20.0°C.

a. What is the temperature of the water when the lead becomes solid?

To freeze, lead must absorb
$Q = -mH_f = -(0.175 \text{ kg})(2.04 \times 10^4 \text{ J/kg}) = -3.57 \times 10^3 \text{ J}$

This will heat the water, $\Delta T = \frac{Q}{mC} = \frac{(3.57 \times 10^3 \text{ J})}{(0.055 \text{ kg})(4180 \text{ J/kg}\cdot\text{K})} = 16\text{°C to } 36\text{°C}$

b. When the lead and water are in thermal equilibrium, what is the temperature?

$$\text{Now, } T_f = \frac{(m_A C_A T_{Ai} + m_B C_B T_{Bi})}{(m_A C_A + m_B C_B)}$$
$$= \frac{(0.175 \text{ kg})(130 \text{ J/kg}\cdot\text{K})(327\text{°C}) + (0.55 \text{ kg})(4180 \text{ J/kg}\cdot\text{K})(35.5\text{°C})}{(0.175 \text{ kg})(130 \text{ J/kg}\cdot\text{K}) + (0.055 \text{ kg})(4180 \text{ J/kg}\cdot\text{K})} = 62\text{°C}$$

Chapter Review Problems

pages 262–263

1. Liquid nitrogen boils at 77°K. Find this temperature in degrees Celsius.

   °C = K – 273 = 77 – 273 = –196°C

2. The melting point of hydrogen is –295.14°C. Find this temperature in kelvin.

   K = °C + 273.15 = –259.14 + 273.15
   = 14.01 K

3. Sadi Carnot showed that no real heat engine can have an efficiency greater than

$$Efficiency = \frac{Work\ output}{Heat\ input} = \frac{T_{hot} - T_{cold}}{T_{hot}}$$

where T_{hot} and T_{cold} are the temperatures of the input and waste thermal energy. Note: kelvin temperatures must be used in this equation.

a. What is the efficiency of an ideal steam engine that uses superheated steam at 685 K to drive the engine and ejects waste steam at 298 K?

$$Efficiency = \frac{T_{hot} - T_{cold}}{T_{hot}} = \frac{685\ \text{K} - 298\ \text{K}}{685\ \text{K}} = 0.565$$

b. If the steam generator produces 1.00×10^8 J each second, how much work can the ideal engine do each second?

$Work\ output = (efficiency)(heat\ input) = 5.65 \times 10^7$ J/s.

4. How much heat is needed to raise the temperature of 50.0 g of water from 4.5°C to 83.0°C?

$Q = mC\Delta T = (0.0500\ \text{kg})(4180\ \text{J/kg}\cdot\text{K})(83.0 - 4.5) = 1.6 \times 10^4\ \text{J}$

5. How much heat must be added to 50.0 g of aluminum at 25°C to raise its temperature to 125°C?

$Q = mC\Delta T = (0.0500\ \text{kg})(903\ \text{J/kg}\cdot\text{K})(125°\text{C} - 25°\text{C}) = 4.5 \times 10^3\ \text{J}$

6. A 5.00×10^2-g block of metal absorbs 5016 J of heat when its temperature changes from 20.0°C to 30.0°C. Calculate the specific heat of the metal.

$$Q = mC\Delta T,\ \text{so}\ C = \frac{Q}{m\Delta T} = \frac{5016\ \text{J}}{(5.00 \times 10^{-1}\ \text{kg})(30.0°\text{C} - 20.0°\text{C})} = 1.00 \times 10^3\ \text{J/kg K}$$

7. A 4.00×10^2-g glass coffee cup is at room temperature, 20.0°C. It is then plunged into hot dishwater, 80.0°C. If the temperature of the cup reaches that of the dishwater, how much heat does the cup absorb? Assume the mass of the dishwater is large enough so its temperature doesn't change appreciably.

$Q = mC\Delta T = (4.00 \times 10^{-1}\ \text{kg})(664\ \text{J/kg}\cdot\text{K})(80.0°\text{C} - 20.0°\text{C}) = 1.59 \times 10^4\ \text{J}$

8. A copper wire has a mass of 165 g. An electric current runs through the wire for a short time and its temperature rises from 21°C to 39°C. What minimum quantity of energy is converted by the electric current?

$Q = mC\Delta T = (0.165\ \text{kg})(385\ \text{J/kg}\cdot\text{K})(39°\text{C} - 21°\text{C}) = 1.1 \times 10^3\ \text{J}$

9. A 1.00×10^2-g mass of tungsten at 100.0°C is placed in 2.00×10^2 g of water at 20.0°C. The mixture reaches equilibrium at 21.6°C. Calculate the specific heat of tungsten.

$\Delta E_t + \Delta E_w = 0$, or $m_t C_t \Delta T_t = -m_w C_w \Delta T_w$, so

$$C_t = \frac{-m_w C_w \Delta T_w}{m_t \Delta T_t} = \frac{-(0.200\ \text{kg})(4180\ \text{J/kg}\cdot\text{K})(21.6°\text{C} - 20.0°\text{C})}{(0.100\ \text{kg})(21.6°\text{C} - 100.0°\text{C})} = 171\ \text{J/kg}\cdot\text{K}$$

Chapter Review Problems

10. A 6.0 × 10²–g sample of water at 90.0°C is mixed with 4.00 × 10² g of water at 22°C. Assume no heat loss to the surroundings. What is the final temperature of the mixture?

$T_f = \dfrac{m_A C_A T_{Ai} + m_B C_B T_{Bi}}{m_A C_A + m_B C_B}$ but $C_A = C_B$, because both liquids are water and C_A's will divide out.

$$T_f = \frac{m_A T_{Ai} + m_B T_{Bi}}{m_A + m_B} = \frac{(6.0 \times 10^2\ g)(90.0^\circ C) + (4.00 \times 10^2\ g)(22^\circ C)}{6.0 \times 10^2\ g + 4.0 \times 10^2\ g} = 63^\circ C$$

11. To get a feeling for the amount of energy needed to heat water, recall from Table 11–1 that the kinetic energy of a compact car moving at 100 km/h is 2.9 × 10⁵ J. What volume of water (in liters) would 2.9 × 10⁵ J of energy warm from room temperature (20°C) to boiling (100°C)?

$$Q = mC\Delta T, \text{ so } m = \frac{Q}{C\Delta T} = \frac{(2.9 \times 10^5\ J)}{(4180\ J/kg \cdot K)(100^\circ C - 20^\circ C)} = 0.87\ kg = 0.87\ L$$

12. A 10.0–kg piece of zinc at 71°C is placed in a container of water. The water has a mass of 20.0 kg and has a temperature of 10.0°C before the zinc is added. What is the final temperature of the water and zinc?

$$T_f = \frac{m_{Zn} C_{Zn} T_{Zni} + m_w C_w T_{wi}}{m_{Zn} C_{Zn} + m_w C_w} = \frac{(10.0\ kg)(388\ J/kg \cdot K)(71^\circ C) + (20.0\ kg)(4180\ J/kg \cdot K)(10.0^\circ C)}{(10.0\ kg)(388\ J/kg \cdot K) + (20.0\ kg)(4180\ J/kg \cdot K)} = 12.7^\circ C$$

13. A 2.00 × 10²–g sample of brass at 100.0°C is placed in a calorimeter cup that contains 261 g of water at 20.0°C. Disregard the absorption of heat by the cup and calculate the final temperature of the brass and water.

$$T_f = \frac{m_w C_w T_{wi} + m_B C_B T_{Bi}}{m_w C_w + m_B C_B} = \frac{(0.261\ g)(4180\ J/kg \cdot K)(20.0^\circ C) + (0.200\ kg)(376\ J/kg \cdot K)(100.0^\circ C)}{(0.261\ g)(4180\ J/kg \cdot K) + (0.200\ kg)(376\ J/kg \cdot K)}$$
$$= 25.1^\circ C$$

14. A 3.00 × 10²–W electric immersion heater is used to heat a cup of water. The cup is made of glass and its mass is 3.00 × 10² g. It contains 250 g of water at 15°C. How much time is needed for the heater to bring the water to the boiling point? Assume the temperature of the cup to be the same as the temperature of the water at all times and no heat is lost to the air.

$Q = m_g C_g \Delta T_g + m_w C_w \Delta T_w$, but $\Delta T_g = \Delta T_w$, so
$Q = [m_g C_g + m_w C_w]\Delta T = [(0.300\ kg)(664\ J/kg \cdot K) + (0.250\ kg)(4180\ J/kg \cdot K)](100^\circ C - 15^\circ C)$
$= 1.1 \times 10^5\ J.$

Now $P = \dfrac{E}{t}$ or $P = \dfrac{Q}{t}$, so $t = \dfrac{Q}{P} = \dfrac{1.1 \times 10^5\ J}{3.00 \times 10^2\ W} = 3.7 \times 10^2\ s$

15. A 2.50 × 10²–kg cast–iron car engine contains water as a coolant. Suppose the engine's temperature is 35°C when it is shut off. The air temperature is 10°C. The heat given off by the engine and water in it as they cool to air temperature is 4.4 × 10⁶ J. What mass of water is used to cool the engine?

$Q = m_w C_w \Delta T + m_i C_i \Delta T$

$$m = \frac{Q - m_i C_i \Delta T}{C_w \Delta T} = \frac{(4.4 \times 10^6\ J) - [(2.50 \times 10^2\ kg)(450\ J/kg \cdot C^\circ)(35^\circ C - 10^\circ C)]}{(4180\ J/kg \cdot C^\circ)(35^\circ C - 10^\circ C)} = 15\ kg$$

16. Years ago, a block of ice with a mass of about 20.0 kg was used daily in a home icebox. The temperature of the ice was 0.0°C when delivered. As it melted, how much heat did a block of ice that size absorb?

$Q = mH_f = (20.0\ kg)(3.34 \times 10^5 J/kg) = 6.68 \times 10^6\ J$

17. A person who eats 2400 food calories each day consumes 1.0×10^7 joules of energy in a day. How much water at 100°C could that much energy vaporize?

$$Q = mH_v, \text{ so } m = \frac{Q}{H_v} = \frac{1.0 \times 10^7 \text{ J}}{2.26 \times 10^6 \text{ J/kg}} = 4.4 \text{ kg}$$

18. A 40.0-g sample of chloroform is condensed from a vapor at 61.6°C to a liquid at 61.6°C. It liberates 9870 joules of heat. What is the heat of vaporization of chloroform?

$$Q = mH_v$$

$$H_v = \frac{Q}{m} = \frac{9870 \text{ J}}{0.0400 \text{ kg}} = 247 \times 10^5 \text{ J/kg}$$

19. How much heat is removed from 60.0 g of steam at 100.0°C to change it to 60.0 g of water at 20.0°C?

The amount of heat liberated when the steam condenses is
$Q = -mH_v$ (negative for condensation) $= -(0.0600 \text{ kg})(2.26 \times 10^6 \text{ J/kg}) = -1.36 \times 10^5$ J.

The amount of heat liberated as the water cools to 20.0°C is
$Q = mC\Delta T = (0.0600 \text{ kg})(4180 \text{ J/kg}\cdot\text{K})(20.0°\text{C} - 100.0°\text{C}) = -2.01 \times 10^4$ J.

The total heat is $(-1.36 \times 10^5 \text{ J}) + (-2.01 \times 10^4 \text{ J}) = 1.56 \times 10^5$ J.

20. A 750-kg car moving at 23 m/s brakes to a stop. The brakes contain about 15 kg of iron that absorb the energy. What is the increase in temperature of the brakes?

During braking, the kinetic energy of the car is converted into heat energy. So $\Delta KE_C + Q_B = 0$ and $\Delta KE_C + m_B C_B \Delta T = 0$ so

$$\Delta T = \frac{-\Delta KE_C}{m_B C_B} = \frac{\frac{1}{2}m_C(v_f^2 - v_i^2)}{m_B C_B} = \frac{-\frac{1}{2}(750 \text{ kg})(0^2 - (23 \text{ m/s})^2)}{(15 \text{ kg})(450 \text{ J/kg}\cdot\text{K})} = 29°\text{C}$$

21. How much heat is added to 10.0 g of ice at −20.0°C to convert it to steam at 120.0°C?

Amount of heat needed to heat ice to 0.0°C,
$Q = mC\Delta T = ((0.0100 \text{ kg})(2060 \text{ J/kg}\cdot°\text{C})(0.0°\text{C} - (-20.0°\text{C}) = 412$ J.

Amount of heat to melt ice,
$Q = mH_f = ((0.0100 \text{ kg})(3.34 \times 10^5 \text{ J/kg}) = 3.34 \times 10^3$ J.

Amount of heat to heat water to 100.0°C,
$Q = mC\Delta T = (0.0100 \text{ kg})(4180 \text{ J/kg}\cdot°\text{C})(100.0°\text{C} - 0.0°\text{C}) = 4.18 \times 10^3$ J.

Amount of heat to boil water,
$Q = mH_v = (0.0100 \text{ kg})(2.26 \times 10^6 \text{ J/kg}) = 2.26 \times 10^4$ J.

Amount of heat to heat steam to 120.0°C,
$Q = mC\Delta T = (0.0100)(2020 \text{ J/kg}\cdot°\text{C})(120.0°\text{C} - 100.0°\text{C}) = 404$ J.

The total heat is $412 \text{ J} + 3.34 \times 10^3 \text{ J} + 4.18 \times 10^3 \text{ J} + 2.26 \times 10^4 \text{ J} + 404 \text{ J} = 3.09 \times 10^4$ J

22. A 50.0–g sample of ice at 0.00°C is placed in a glass beaker containing 4.00×10^2 g of water at 50.0°C. All the ice melts. What is the final temperature of the mixture? Disregard any heat loss to the glass.

$Q_i + Q_w = 0$, so
$[m_i H_f + m_i C\Delta T\ ] + m_w C\Delta T_w$
or $(0.0500\ \text{kg})(3.34 \times 10^5\ \text{J/kg}) + (0.0500\ \text{kg})(4180\ \text{J/kg°C})(T_f - 0.0°\text{C})$
$+ (0.400\ \text{kg})(4180\ \text{J/kg°C})(T_f - 50.0°\text{C}) = 0$ or
$1.67 \times 10^4\ \text{J} + (209\ \text{J})T_f - 0.0 + (1.67 \times 10^3\ \text{J})T_f - 8.36 \times 10^4\ \text{J} = 0$
or $(1.88 \times 10^3\ \text{J})T_f = 6.69 \times 10^4$ J or $T_f = 35.6°\text{C}$.

23. A 4.2–g lead bullet moving at 275 m/s strikes a steel plate and stops. If all its kinetic energy is converted to thermal energy and none leaves the bullet, what is its temperature change?

Because the kinetic energy is converted to thermal energy, $\Delta KE + Q = 0$. So
$\Delta KE + m_B C_B \Delta T$ and

$$\Delta T = \frac{\Delta KE}{m_B C_B} = \frac{\frac{1}{2} m_B (v_f^{\,2} - v_i^2)}{m_B C_B}$$

and the mass of the bullet divides out so

$$\Delta T = \frac{\frac{1}{2}(v_f^2 - v_i^2)}{C_B} = \frac{\frac{1}{2}(0^2 - (275\ \text{m/s})^2)}{130\ \text{J/kg} \cdot °\text{C}}$$

$= 291°\text{C}$.

24. A soft drink from Australia is labeled "Low Joule Cola". The label says "100 mL yields 1.7 kJ". The can contains 375 mL. Sally drinks the cola and then offsets this input of food energy by climbing stairs. How high would she have to climb if Sally has a mass of 65.0 kg?

Sally gained $(3.75)(1.7\ \text{kJ}) = 6.4 \times 10^3$ J of energy from the drink. To conserve energy $E + \Delta PE = 0$ or $6.4 \times 10^3\ \text{J} = -mg\Delta h$ so,

$$\Delta h = \frac{6.4 \times 10^3\ \text{J}}{-mg} = \frac{6.4 \times 10^3\ \text{J}}{-(65.0\ \text{kg})(-9.80\ \text{m/s}^2)} = 10\ \text{m},$$ or about three flights of stairs.

25. When air is compressed in a bicycle pump, an average force of 45 N is exerted as the pump handle moves 0.24 m. During this time 2.0 J of heat leave the cylinder through the walls. What is the net change in thermal energy of the air in the cylinder?

Change in thermal energy = heat added + work done = $-2.0\ \text{J} + (45\ \text{N})(0.24\ \text{m}) = 8.8$ J.

Supplemental Problems (Appendix B)

1. The boiling point of liquid chlorine is –34.60°C. Find this temperature in Kelvin.

   $\text{K} = °\text{C} + 273.15 = -34.60 + 273.15 = 238.55\ \text{K}$

2. Fluorine has a melting point of 50.28 K. Find this temperature in degrees Celsius.

   $°\text{C} = \text{K} - 273.15 = 50.28 - 273.15 = -222.87°\text{C}$

3. Five kilograms of ice cubes are moved from the freezing compartment of a refrigerator into a home freezer. The refrigerator's freezing compartment is kept at –4.0°C. The home freezer is kept at –17°C. How much heat does the freezer's cooling system remove from the ice cubes?

$Q = mC\Delta T = (5.0 \text{ kg})(2060 \text{ J/kg}\cdot\text{K})(-4.0°\text{C} - (-17°\text{C})) = 1.3 \times 10^5 \text{ J removed}$

4. How much heat must be added to 124 g of brass at 12.5°C to raise its temperature to 97.0°C?

$Q = m_C\Delta T = (0.124 \text{ kg})(376 \text{ J/kg}\cdot\text{C°})(84.5°\text{C}) = 3.94 \times 10^3 \text{ J}$

5. 2.8×10^5 J of thermal energy are added to a sample of water and its temperature changes from 293 K to 308 K. What is the mass of water?

$$M = \frac{Q}{C\Delta T} = \frac{2.8 \times 10^5 \text{ J}}{(4180 \text{ J/kg}\cdot\text{C°})(15°\text{C})} = 4.5 \text{ kg}$$

6. 1420 J of thermal energy are added to a 100.0–g block of carbon at –20.0°C. What final temperature will the carbon reach?

$$\Delta T = \frac{Q}{mC} = \frac{1420 \text{ J}}{(710 \text{ J/kg}\cdot\text{C°})(0.100 \text{ kg})} = 20.0°\text{C}.$$

Final temperature is –20°C + 20°C = 0°C

7. A gold brick of mass 10.5 kg requires 2.08×10^4 J of heat to change its temperature from 35.0°C to 50.0°C. What is the specific heat of gold?

$$C = \frac{Q}{m\Delta T} = \frac{2.08 \times 10^4 \text{ J}}{(10.5 \text{ kg})(15.0°\text{C})} = 132 \text{ J/kg}\cdot\text{K}$$

8. An 8.00×10^2–g block of lead is heated in boiling water, 100.0°C, until the block's temperature is the same as the water's. The lead is then removed from the boiling water and dropped into 2.50×10^2 g of cool water at 12.2°C. After a short time, the temperature of both lead and water is 20.0°C.

a. How much heat is gained by the cool water?

$Q = mC\Delta T = (2.50 \times 10^{-1} \text{ kg})(4180 \text{ J/kg}\cdot\text{K})(20.0°\text{C} - 12.2°\text{C}) = 8.2 \times 10^3 \text{ J}$

b. On the basis of these measurements, what is the specific heat of lead?

$$C_{\text{lead}} = \frac{Q}{m\Delta T} = \frac{-8.2 \times 10^3 \text{ J}}{(8.00 \times 10^{-1} \text{ kg})(20.0°\text{C} - 100.0°\text{C})} = 1.3 \times 10^2 \text{ J/kg}\cdot\text{K}$$

9. 250.0 g of copper at 100.0°C are placed in a cup containing 325.0 g of water at 20.0°C. Assume no heat loss to the surroundings. What is the final temperature of the copper and water?

Copper Water

$$Q_{\text{loss}} = Q_{\text{gain}}$$
$$(0.250 \text{ kg})(385 \text{ J/kg}\cdot\text{C°})(100.0°\text{C} - T_f) = (0.325 \text{ kg})(4180 \text{ J/kg}\cdot\text{C°})(T_f - 20.0°\text{C})$$
$$9.63 \times 10^3 - 9.63 \times 10^1\ T_f = 1.36 \times 10^3\ T_f - 2.72 \times 10^4$$
$$1.46 \times 10^3\ T_f = 3.68 \times 10^4$$
$$T_f = 25.2°\text{C}$$

Supplemental Problems

10. A 4.00×10^2 g sample of methanol at 30.0°C is mixed with a 2.00×10^2 g sample of water at 0.0°C. Assume no heat loss to the surroundings. What is the final temperature of the mixture?

Methanol Water

$$Q_{loss} = Q_{gain}$$
$$(4.00 \times 10^{-1}\ kg)(2450\ J/kg \cdot C^\circ)(30.0^\circ C - T_f) = (2.00 \times 10^{-1} kg)(4180\ J/kg \cdot C^\circ)(T_f - 0.0^\circ C)$$
$$2.94 \times 10^4 - 9.80 \times 10^2\ T_f = 8.36 \times 10^2\ T_f$$
$$1.82 \times 10^3\ T_f = 2.94 \times 10^4$$
$$T_f = 16.2^\circ C$$

11. How much heat is needed to change 50.0 g of water at 80.0°C to steam at 110°C?

Step 1: Heat water:
$Q_1 = mC\Delta T = (0.0500\ kg)(4180\ J/kg \cdot C^\circ)(20.0^\circ C) = 4.18 \times 10^3\ J$

Step 2: Boil water:
$Q_2 = mH_v = (0.0500\ kg)(2.26 \times 10^6\ J/kg) = 1.13 \times 10^5\ J$

Step 3: Heat steam:
$Q_3 = mC\Delta T = (0.0500\ kg)(2020\ J/kg \cdot C^\circ)(10.0^\circ C) = 1.01 \times 10^3\ J$

Total:
$Q_1 + Q_2 + Q_3 = 1.18 \times 10^5\ J$

12. The specific heat of mercury is 140 J/kg·C°. Its heat of vaporization is 3.06×10^5 J/kg. How much heat is needed to heat 1.0 kg of mercury metal from 10.0°C to its boiling point and vaporize it completely? The boiling point of mercury is 357°C.

The amount of heat needed to raise mercury to its boiling point is:
$Q = mC\Delta T = (1.0\ kg)(140\ J/kg \cdot K)(357^\circ C - 10^\circ C) = 4.9 \times 10^4\ J.$

The amount of heat needed to vaporize the mercury is:
$Q = mH_v = (1.0\ kg)(3.06 \times 10^5\ J/kg) = 3.1 \times 10^5\ J.$

The total heat needed is
$(4.9 \times 10^4\ J) + (3.1 \times 10^5\ J) = 3.6 \times 10^5\ J.$

13. 30.0 g of −3.0°C ice is placed in a cup containing 104.0 g of water at 62.0°C. All the ice melts. Find the final temperature of the mixture. Assume no heat loss to the surroundings.

$$Q_{loss} = Q_{gain}$$
$$(0.1040\ kg)(4180\ J/kg \cdot C^\circ)(62.0^\circ C - T_f) = (0.0300\ kg)(2060\ J/kg \cdot C^\circ)(3.0^\circ C) + (0.0300\ kg)(3.34 \times 10^5\ J/kg) + (0.0300\ kg)(4180\ J/kg \cdot C^\circ)(T_f - 0.0^\circ C)$$
$$2.70 \times 10^4 - 4.35 \times 10^2\ T_f = 1.85 \times 10^2 + 1.00 \times 10^4 + 1.25 \times 10^2\ T_f$$
$$5.60 \times 10^2\ T_f = 1.68 \times 10^4$$
$$T_f = 30.0^\circ C$$

14. Water flows over a falls 125.0 m high. If the potential energy of the water is all converted to thermal energy, calculate the temperature difference between the water at the top and the bottom of the falls.

$$PE_{loss} = Q_{gain}$$
$$mgh = mC\Delta T$$
$$\Delta T = \frac{gh}{C} = \frac{(9.80\ m/s^2)(125.0\ m)}{4180\ J/kg \cdot C^\circ} = 0.29^\circ C$$

Supplemental Problems

15. During the game, the metabolism of basketball players often increases by as much as 30.0 watts. How much perspiration must a player vaporize per hour to dissipate this extra thermal energy?

$$P = \frac{E}{t}$$

$$E = Pt = (30.0 \text{ W})(3600 \text{ s}) = 108\ 000 \text{ J}$$

$$m = \frac{Q}{H_v} = \frac{108\ 000 \text{ J}}{2260 \text{ J/g}} = 47.8 \text{ g}$$

Chapter 13: States of Matter

Practice Problems

page 268

1. The atmospheric pressure at sea level is about 1.0×10^5 Pa. What is the force exerted on the top of a typical office desk, 152 cm long and 76 cm wide?

$$p = \frac{F}{A} \text{ so}$$

$$F = pA = (1.0 \times 10^5\ Pa)(1.52\ \text{m})(0.76\ \text{m}) = 1.2 \times 10^5\ \text{N}$$

2. A car's tire makes contact with the ground on a rectangular "footprint" 12 cm by 18 cm. The car's mass is 925 kg. What pressure does the car exert on the ground?

$$F = mg = (925\ \text{kg})(9.80\ \text{m/s}^2) = 9.07 \times 10^3\ \text{N}.$$

$$A = 4(0.12\ \text{m})(0.18\ \text{m}) = 0.0864\ \text{m}^2.$$

$$P = \frac{F}{A} = \frac{(9.07 \times 10^3\ \text{N})}{(0.0864\ \text{m}^2)}$$

$$= 1.0 \times 10^5\ \text{Pa}$$

3. A lead brick, $5.0 \times 10 \times 20$ cm, rests on the ground on its smallest face. What pressure does it exert? (Lead has a density 11.8 gm/cm³.)

$$F = (11.8\ \text{gm/cm}^3)(10^{-3}\ \text{kg/g})(5.0\ \text{cm})(10\ \text{cm}) \cdot (20\ \text{cm})(9.80\ \text{m/s}^2) = 116\ \text{N}.$$

$$A = (0.05\ \text{m})(0.10\ \text{m}) = 0.005\ \text{m}^2$$

$$p = \frac{F}{A} = \frac{(116\ \text{N})}{(0.005\ \text{m}^2} = 23\ \text{kPa}$$

4. In a tornado, the pressure can be 15% below normal atmospheric pressure. Further, a tornado can move so quickly that this pressure drop can occur in one second. Suppose a tornado suddenly occurred outside your front door (182 cm high, 91 cm wide). What force would be exerted on the door? In what direction?

$$F_{net} = F_{outside} - F_{inside}$$

$$= (p_{outside} - p_{inside})A$$

$$= (0.85 \times 10^5\ Pa - 1.00 \times 10^5\ Pa) \cdot (1.82\ \text{m})(0.91\ \text{m})$$

$$= -2.5 \times 10^4\ \text{N (toward the outside).}$$

Practice Problems

page 272

5. If the diameter of the larger piston in Figure 13–4 were doubled, what force would be lifted if 20.0 N were applied to the small piston?

$\frac{F_1}{A_1} = \frac{F_2}{A_2}$ with $A_2 = 0.40\ \text{m}^2$, since circular area is proportional to diameter squared and the original diameter has been doubled.

$$F_2 = \frac{A_2F_1}{A_1} = (0.400\ \text{m}^2)(20.0\ \text{N})(0.0500\ \text{m}^2)$$

$$= 160\ \text{N}$$

6. Dentists' chairs are examples of hydraulic lift systems. If the chair weighs 1600 N and rests on a piston with a cross–sectional area of 1400 cm², what force must be applied to the small piston with a cross–sectional area of 72 cm² to lift the chair?

$$\frac{F_1}{A_1} = \frac{F_2}{A_2},$$

$$F_1 = \frac{F_2A_1}{A_2}$$

$$= \frac{(1600\ \text{N})(72\ \text{cm}^2)}{(1440\ \text{cm}^2)} = 80\ \text{N}$$

7. A teenager is floating in a freshwater lake with her head just above the water. If she weighs 600 N, what is the volume of the submerged part of her body?

$$F_{weight} = F_{buoyant} = \rho_{water}Vg$$

$$V = \frac{F_{weight}}{\rho_{water}g}$$

$$= \frac{(600\ \text{N})}{(1000\ \text{kg/m}^3)(9.80\ \text{m/s}^2)}$$

$$= 0.06\ \text{m}^3.$$

This volume does not include that portion of her head that is above the water.

Practice Problems

8. What is the tension in a wire supporting a 1250-N camera submerged in water? The volume of the camera is 8.3×10^{-2} m³.

$T + F_{buoyant} = W$ where W is the air weight of the camera.

$T = W - F_{buoyant} = W - \rho_{water}Vg$
$= 1250$ N
$- (1000 \text{ kg/m}^3)(0.083 \text{ m}^3)(9.80 \text{ m/s}^2)$
$= 4.4 \times 10^2$ N

page 282

9. A piece of aluminum house siding is 3.66 m long on a cold winter day (–28°C). How much longer is it on a very hot summer day (39°C)? $\alpha = 25 \times 10^{-6}$°C⁻¹.

$\Delta L = \alpha L_i \Delta T = (25 \times 10^{-6}°\text{C}^{-1})(3.66 \text{ m})(67°\text{C})$
$= 6.1 \times 10^{-3}$ m, or 6.1 mm

10. A piece of steel is 11.5 m long at 22°C. It is heated to 1221°C, close to its melting temperature. How long is it?

$L_f = L_i + \alpha L_i(T - T_i)$
$= (11.5 \text{ m}) + (11 \times 10^{-6} \text{ °C}^{-1})(11.5 \text{ m})$
$\cdot(1221°\text{C} - 22°\text{C})$
$= 11.7$ m

11. An aluminum soft drink can, 354 mL, is filled to the brim with water in the refrigerator (4.4°C).

a. What will be the volume of the liquid on a warm day (34.5°C)?

For water $\beta = 210 \times 10^{-6}°\text{C}^{-1}$, so
$\Delta V = \beta V \Delta T$
$= (354 \text{ ml})(210 \times 10^{-6}°\text{C}^{-1})(30.1°\text{C})$
$= 2.24$ mL.
$V = 354 \text{ mL} + 2 \text{ mL} = 356 \text{ mL}$

b. What will be the volume of the can? Hint: The can will expand as much as a block of metal the same size.

For Al $\beta = 75 \times 10^{-6}°\text{C}^{-1}$, so
$\Delta V = \beta V \Delta T$
$= (354 \text{ ml})(75 \times 10^{-6}°\text{C}^{-1})(30.1°\text{C})$
$= 0.80$ mL.
$V = 354 \text{ mL} + 1 \text{ mL} = 355 \text{ mL}$

c. How much liquid will spill?

The difference will spill,
2.24 mL – 0.80 mL = 1.44 mL.

Practice Problems

12. A tank truck takes on a load of 45 725 liters of gasoline in Houston at 32.0°C. The coefficient of volume expansion (β) for gasoline is 950×10^{-6}°C⁻¹. The truck delivers its load in Omaha at –18.0°C.

a. How many liters of gasoline does the truck deliver?

$V = V_i + \beta V_i(T - T_i)$
$= 45\,725 \text{ L} + (950 \times 10^{-6}°\text{C}^{-1})(45\,725 \text{ L})$
$\cdot(-18.0°\text{C} - 32.0°\text{C})$
$= 45\,725 \text{ L} - 2170 \text{ L}$
$= 43\,555 \text{ L} = 43\,560 \text{ L}$

b. What happened to the gasoline?

Its volume has decreased because of temperature change.

c. Who pays?

The person who charges by volume rather than mass.

Chapter Review Problems

pages 284–285

1. A hydraulic jack used to lift cars is called a "3–ton jack". The large piston is 22 mm in diameter, the small one 6.3 mm. Assume that a force of three tons is 3.0×10^4 N.

a. What force must be exerted on the small piston to lift the three ton weight?

$\frac{F_1}{A_1} = \frac{F_2}{A_2}$, so

$F_2 = F_1\frac{A_2}{A_1} = F_1\frac{\pi(r_2)^2}{\pi(r_1)^2} = F_1\left[\frac{r_2}{r_1}\right]^2$

$F_2 = (3.0 \times 10^4 \text{ N})\left[\frac{6.3 \text{ mm}}{22 \text{ mm}}\right]^3$

$= 2.5 \times 10^3$ N

Chapter Review Problems

b. Most jacks use a lever to reduce the force needed on the small piston. If the resistance arm is 3.0 cm, how long is the effort arm of an ideal lever to reduce the force to 100 N?

$$MA = \frac{F_r}{F_e} = \frac{(2.5 \times 10^3\ \text{N})}{(1.0 \times 10^2\ \text{N})} = 25, \text{ and}$$

$$IMA = \frac{l_e}{l_r}, \text{ with } MA_1 = IMA$$

$$l_e = (MA)l_r = 25\ (3.0\ \text{cm}) = 75\ \text{cm}$$

2. In a small machine shop, a hydraulic lift is used to raise heavy equipment for repairs. The system has a small piston with a cross–sectional area of 7.0×10^{-2} m² and a large piston with a cross–sectional area of 2.1×10^{-1} m². An engine weighing 2.7×10^3 N is resting on the larger piston.

a. What force must be applied to the small piston in order to lift the engine?

$$\frac{F_1}{A_2} = \frac{F_2}{A_1}$$

$$F_1 = \frac{F_2 A_2}{A_2}$$

$$= \frac{(2.7 \times 10^3\ \text{N})(7.0 \times 10^{-2}\ \text{m}^2)}{(2.1 \times 10^{-1}\ \text{m}^2)}$$

$$= 9.0 \times 10^2\ \text{N}$$

b. If the engine rises 0.20 m, how far does the smaller piston move?

$$V_1 = V_2 \quad \text{and} \quad A_1h_1 = A_2h_2$$

$$h_1 = \frac{A_2 h_2}{A_1}$$

$$= \frac{(2.1 \times 10^{-1}\ \text{m}^2)(0.20\ \text{m})}{(7.0 \times 10^{-2}\ \text{m}^2)}$$

$$= 0.60\ \text{m}$$

3. A 0.75 kg physics book with dimensions of 24 cm by 20 cm is on a table.

a. What force does the book apply to the table?

$$F = mg = (0.75\ \text{kg})(9.80\ \text{m/s}^2) = 7.4\ \text{N}$$

b. What pressure does the book apply?

$$P = \frac{F}{A} = \frac{F}{lw}$$

$$= \frac{7.4\ \text{N}}{(0.24\ \text{m})(0.20\ \text{m})} = 1.5 \times 10^2\ \text{Pa}$$

4. The pressure exerted by the atmosphere is about 1.0×10^5 Pa. Convert this to kPa.

$$\frac{1.0 \times 10^5\ \text{Pa}}{1}\left[\frac{1\ \text{kPa}}{1000\ \text{Pa}}\right] = 1.0 \times 10^2\ \text{kPa}$$

5. A 75–kg solid cylinder 2.5 m long and with an end radius of 5.0 cm stands on one end. How much pressure does it exert?

$$P = \frac{F}{A} = \frac{mg}{\pi r^2} = \frac{(75\ \text{kg})(9.80\ \text{m/s}^2)}{\pi(0.05\ \text{m})^2}$$

$$= 94\ \text{kPa}$$

6. A reservoir behind a dam is 15 m deep. What is the pressure at

a. the base of the dam?

$$P = Phg,\ P_{H_2O} = 1.0\ \text{g/cm}^3 = 1000\ \text{kg/m}^3$$

$$P = (1000\ \text{kg/m}^3)(15\ \text{m})(9.80\ \text{m/s}^2)$$
$$= 1.5 \times 10^5\ \text{Pa} = 1.5 \times 10^2\ \text{kPa}$$

b. 5.0 m from the top of the dam?

$$P = (1000\ \text{kg/m}^3)(5.0\ \text{m})(9.8\ \text{m/s}^2)$$
$$= 49\ \text{kPa}$$

7. A test tube standing vertically in a test tube rack contains 2.5 cm of oil ($\rho = 0.81$ g/cm³) and 6.5 cm of water. What is the pressure on the bottom of the tube?

$$P = P_{oil} + P_{water} = \rho_{oil}hg + \rho_{water}hg$$
$$= (810\ \text{kg/m}^3)(0.025\ \text{m})(9.80\ \text{m/s}^2)$$
$$+ (1000\ \text{kg/m}^3)(0.065\ \text{m})(9.80\ \text{m/s}^2)$$
$$= 198.0\ \text{Pa} + 637\ \text{Pa} = 8.4 \times 10^2\ \text{Pa}$$

8. A metal object is suspended from a spring scale. The scale reads 920 N when the object is suspended in air, and 750 N when the object is completely submerged in water.

a. Draw a diagram showing the three forces acting on the submerged object.

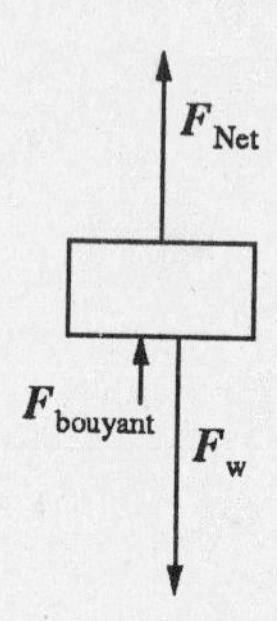

From the force diagram

$F_{net} = F_W - F_{buoyant}$

$F_{buoyant} = F_W - F_{net}$

$= 920\text{ N} - 750\text{ N} = 170\text{ N}$

b. Find the volume of the object.

$F_{buoyant} = V\rho_{water}g$

$V = \dfrac{F_{buoyant}}{\rho_{water}g}$

$= \dfrac{(170\text{ N})}{(1.00 \times 10^3\text{ kg/m}^3)(9.80\text{ m/s}^2)}$

c. Find the density of the metal.

$\rho_{object} = \dfrac{m}{V} = \dfrac{FW}{V_g}$

$= \dfrac{(920\text{ N})}{(1.73 \times 10^{-2}\text{ m}^3)(9.80\text{ m/s}^2)}$

9. During an ecology experiment, an aquarium filled with water is placed on a scale. The scale reads 195 N.

a. A rock weighing 8 N is added to the aquarium. If the rock sinks to the bottom of the aquarium, what will the scale read?

195 N + 8 N = 203 N

Chapter Review Problems

b. The rock is removed from the aquarium, and the amount of water is adjusted until the scale again reads 195 N. A small fish weighing 2 N is added to the aquarium. What is the scale reading while the fish is swimming in the aquarium?

195 N + 2 N = 197 N

In each case the buoyant force is equal to the weight of the water displaced. That is,

$W_{total} = W_{aquarium} + ((W_{rock(fish)} - F_{buoyant}) + W_{water\ displaced})$.

10. What is the size of the buoyant force that acts on a floating ball that normally weighs 5.0 N?

5.0 N

11. What is the apparent weight of a rock submerged in water if the rock weighs 54 N in air and has a volume of $2.3 \times 10^{-3}\text{ m}^3$?

$W_{net} = W - V\rho g$

$= 54\text{ N} - (2.3 \times 10^{-3}\text{ m}^3) \cdot (1.00 \times 10^3\text{ kg/m}^3)(9.80\text{ m/s}^2)$

$= 54\text{ N} - 23\text{ N} = 31\text{ N}$

12. If the rock in the previous problem is submerged in a liquid with a density exactly twice that of water, what will be its new apparent weight reading in the liquid?

The buoyant force will be twice as great as in Exercise 3.

$W_{net} = 54\text{ N} - 2(23\text{ N}) = 8\text{ N}$

13. A 1.0-L container completely filled with mercury has a weight of 133.3 N. If the container is submerged in water, what is the buoyant force acting on it? Explain.

$F_B = V\rho g = (0.0010\text{ m}^3)(1000\ \frac{\text{kg}}{\text{m}^3})(9.80\text{ m/s})$

$= 9.8\text{ N}$

The buoyant force depends only on the volumn of the water displaced about 9.8 N.

14. What is the acceleration of a small metal sphere as it falls through water? The sphere weighs 2.8×10^{-1} N in air and has a volume of 13 cm^3.

$$W_{net} = W - V\rho g$$
$$= (2.8 \times 10^{-1}\ N) - (13\ cm^3) \cdot (10^{-6}\ m^3/cm^3)(1.00 \times 10^3\ kg/m^3) \cdot (9.80\ m/s^2)$$
$$= (2.8 \times 10^{-1}\ N) - (1.3 \times 10^{-1}\ N)$$
$$= 1.5 \times 10^{-1}\ N$$

$$a = \frac{F}{m} = \frac{(1.5 \times 10^{-1}\ N)}{(2.8 \times 10^{-1}\ N/9.80\ m/s^2)} = 5.3\ m/s^2$$

15. What is the maximum weight that a "massless" balloon filled with 1.00 m^3 of helium can lift in air? Assume the density of air is 1.20 kg/m^3 and that of helium is 0.177 kg/m^3.

$$W_{net} = W = F_{buoyant} = V\rho_{He}g - V\rho_{air}g$$
$$= (1.00\ m^3)(0.177\ kg/m^3)(9.80\ m/s^2) - (1.00\ m^3)(1.20\ kg/m^3)(9.80\ m/s^2)$$
$$= -10.0\ N$$

(Net buoyant force is 10.0 N upward.)

$$W_{max} = 10.0\ N$$

16. What is the change in length of a 2.00–m length of copper pipe if its temperature is raised from 23°C to 978°C?

$$\Delta L = L_i \alpha \Delta T$$
$$= (2.00\ m)(1.66 \times 10^{-5}{}^{\circ}C^{-1})(978^{\circ}C - 23^{\circ}C)$$
$$= 3.17 \times 10^{-2}\ m$$

17. Bridge builders often use rivets that are larger than the rivet hole to make the joint tighter. The rivet is cooled before it is put into the hole. A builder drills a hole 1.2230 cm in diameter for a steel rivet 1.2250 cm in diameter. To what temperature must the rivet be cooled if it is to fit into the rivet hole that is at 20°C?

$$\Delta L = \alpha L_i \Delta T$$
$$L_f = L_i + \alpha L_i(T_f - T_i)$$
$$T_f = T_i = \frac{(L_f - L_i)}{\alpha L_i}$$
$$= 20^{\circ}C + \frac{(1.2230\ cm - 1.2250\ cm)}{(12 \times 10^{-6}/^{\circ}C)(1.2250\ cm)}$$
$$= 20^{\circ}C - \frac{(2.0 \times 10^{-3}\ cm)}{(1.5 \times 10^{-5}\ cm/^{\circ}C)}$$
$$= 20^{\circ}C - 130^{\circ}C = -110^{\circ}C$$

Chapter Review Problems

18. A steel tank is built to hold alcohol. The tank is 2.000 m in diameter and 5.000 m high. It is completely filled with alcohol at 10°C. If the temperature rises to 40°C, how much alcohol (in liters) will flow out of the tank? Remember that both the tank and the alcohol expand as the temperature rises.

$$\Delta V = \beta V_i \Delta T = (\beta_{alcohol} - \beta_{steel})V_i \Delta T$$
$$= (1100 \times 10^{-6}/^{\circ}C - 35 \times 10^{-6}/^{\circ}C)(\pi) \cdot (1.000\ m)^2(5.000\ m)(30^{\circ}C)$$
$$= 5.0 \times 10^{-1}\ m^3 = 5.0 \times 10^2\ L$$

19. An aluminum sphere is heated from 11°C to 580°C. If the volume of the sphere was 1.78 cm^3 at 11°C, what is the increase in volume of the sphere at 580°C?

$$\Delta V = \beta V_i \Delta T$$
$$= (75 \times 10^{-6}/^{\circ}C)(1.78\ cm^3)(580^{\circ}C - 11^{\circ}C)$$
$$= 7.6 \times 10^{-2}\ cm^3$$

20. The volume of a copper sphere is 2.56 cm^3 after being heated from 12°C to 984°C. What was the volume of the copper sphere at 12°C?

$$V_f = V_i + V_i \beta \Delta T = V_i(1 + \beta \Delta T)$$
$$V_i = \frac{V_f}{(1 + \beta \Delta T)}$$
$$= \frac{(2.56\ cm^3)}{(1 + (3)(1.66 \times 10^{-5}/^{\circ}C)(984^{\circ}C - 12^{\circ}C))}$$
$$V_i = 2.44\ cm^3$$

Supplemental Problems (Appendix B)

1. How tall must a column of mercury, $\rho = 1.36 \times 10^4\ kg/m^3$, be to exert a pressure equal to the atmosphere?

$$1_{ATM} = 1.013 \times 10^5\ Pa$$
$$P = \rho h g$$
$$h = \frac{P}{\rho g}$$
$$= \frac{1.013 \times 10^5\ Pa}{(1.36 \times 10^4\ kg/m^3)(9.80\ m/s^2)}$$
$$= 0.760\ m$$

13

2. A dog, whose paw has an area of 12.0 cm², has a mass of 8.0 kg. What average pressure does the dog exert while standing?

Total area = $4(0.00120\ m^2) = 0.00480\ m^2$

$$P = \frac{W}{A} = \frac{mg}{A}$$

$$= \frac{(8.0\ kg)(9.80\ m/s^2)}{(0.00480\ m^2)} = 1.6 \times 10^4\ Pa$$

3. A crate, whose bottom surface is 50.4 cm by 28.3 cm, exerts a pressure of 2.50×10^3 Pa on the floor. What is the mass of the crate?

$A = (0.504\ m)(0.283\ m) = 0.143\ m^2$
$W = PA = (2.50 \times 10^3\ Pa)(0.143\ m^2)$
$= 3.58 \times 10^2\ N$

$$m = \frac{W}{g} = \frac{3.58 \times 10^2\ N}{9.80\ m/s^2} = 36.5\ kg$$

4. The dimensions of a waterbed are 2.13 m by 1.52 m by 0.38 m. If the frame has a mass of 91.0 kg and the mattress is filled with water, what pressure does the bed exert on the floor?

$A = (2.13\ m)(1.52\ m) = 3.24\ m^2$
$V = (2.13\ m)(1.52\ m)(0.38\ m) = 1.23\ m^3$
$m = \rho V = (1.00 \times 10^3\ kg/m^3)(1.23\ m^3)$
$= 1.23 \times 10^3\ kg$
Total mass $= 1.23 \times 10^3\ kg + 91.0\ kg$
$= 1.32 \times 10^3\ kg$
$W = mg = (1.32 \times 10^3\ kg)(9.80\ m/s^2)$
$= 1.29 \times 10^4\ N$

$$P = \frac{W}{A} = \frac{1.29 \times 10^4\ N}{3.24\ m^2} = 4.0 \times 10^3\ Pa$$

5. A rectangular block of tin, $\rho = 7.29 \times 10^3\ kg/m^3$, has dimensions of 5.00 cm by 8.50 cm by 2.25 cm. What pressure does it exert on a table top if it is laying on its side of

$V = \ell wh = (0.0500\ m)(0.0850\ m)(0.0225\ m)$
$= 9.56 \times 10^{-5}\ m^3$
$m = \rho V = (7.29 \times 10^3\ kg/m^3)(9.56 \times 10^{-5}\ m^3)$
$= 6.97 \times 10^{-1}\ kg$
$W = mg = (6.97 \times 10^{-1}\ kg)(9.80\ m/s^2)$
$= 6.83\ N$

a. greatest surface area?

$A = (0.0500\ m)(0.0850\ m)$
$= 4.25 \times 10^{-3}\ m^2$

$$P = \frac{W}{A} = \frac{6.83\ N}{4.25 \times 10^{-3}\ m^2}$$

$$= 1.61 \times 10^3\ Pa$$

b. smallest surface are?

$A = (0.0500\ m)(0.0225\ m)$
$= 1.125 \times 10^{-3}\ m^2$

$$P = \frac{W}{A} = \frac{6.83\ N}{1.125 \times 10^{-3}\ m^2}$$

$$= 6.07 \times 10^3\ Pa$$

6. A rowboat of mass 42.0 kg is floating on a lake.

a. What is the size of the buoyant force?

$F_{buoyant} = W = mg = (42.0\ kg)(9.80\ m/s^2)$
$= 412\ N$

b. What is the volume of the submerged part of the boat?

$$V = \frac{F_{buoyant}}{\rho g}$$

$$= \frac{412\ N}{(1.00 \times 10^3 kg/m^3)(9.80\ m/s^2)}$$

$$= 4.20 \times 10^{-2} m^3$$

7. A hydraulic lift consists of a large piston of 20.00–cm diameter and a small piston of 5.00–cm diameter. What is the mechanical advantage of the lift?

$$MA = \frac{F_2}{F_1} = \frac{A_2}{A_1} = \frac{\pi r_2^2}{\pi r_1^2} = \frac{\pi(10.00\ cm)^2}{\pi(2.50\ cm)^2} = 16.0$$

8. A lever on a hydraulic system gives a mechanical advantage of 5.00. The cross–sectional area of the small piston is 0.0400 m², and that of the large piston is 0.280 m². If a force of 25.0 N is exerted on the lever, what is the force given by the larger piston?

$F_1 = (MA)(F_{lever})$
$= (5.00)(25.0\ N) = 125\ N$

$$F_2 = \frac{F_1 A_2}{A_1} = \frac{(125\ N)(0.280\ m^2)}{(0.0400\ m^2)} = 875\ N$$

9. A piece of metal weighs 75.0 N in air and 60.0 N in water. What is the density of the metal?

mass of metal = $\frac{W_m}{g} = \frac{75.0 \text{ N}}{9.80 \text{ m/s}^2} = 7.65 \text{ kg}$

weight of water displaced = 15.0 N

mass of water displaced = $\frac{W_W}{g} = \frac{15.0 \text{ N}}{9.80 \text{ m/s}^2}$

$= 1.53 \text{ kg}$

volume of water displaced

$V_W = \frac{m_m}{\rho_w} = \frac{1.53 \text{ kg}}{1.00 \times 10^3 \text{ kg/m}^3}$

$= 1.53 \times 10^{-3} \text{ m}^3$

volume of metal is also $1.53 \times 10^{-3} \text{ m}^3$

$\rho_m = \frac{m_m}{V_m} = \frac{7.65 \text{ kg}}{1.53 \times 10^{-3} \text{ m}^3} = 5.00 \times 10^3 \text{ kg/m}^3$

10. A river barge with vertical sides is 20.0 m long and 10.0 m wide. It floats 3.00 m out of the water when empty. When loaded with coal the water is only 1.00 m from the top. What is the weight of the load of coal?

Volume of the water displaced

$V_w = \ell wh = (20.0 \text{ m})(10.0 \text{ m})(2.00 \text{ m})$

$= 400 \text{ m}^3$

Mass of the water displaced

$M_w = \rho_w V_w = (1.00 \times 10^3 \text{ kg/m}^3)(400 \text{ m}^3)$

$= 4.00 \times 10^5 \text{ kg}$

Mass of the coal is also 4.00×10^5 kg.

$W = mg = (4.00 \times 10^5 \text{ kg})(9.80 \text{ m/s}^2)$

$= 3.92 \times 10^6 \text{ N}$

11. What is the change in the length of a 15.0–m steel rail as it is cooled from 1535°C to 20°C?

$\Delta L = \alpha L_i \Delta T$

$= (12 \times 10^{-6} \text{°C}^{-1})(15.0 \text{ m})(-1515\text{°C})$

$= -2.7 \times 10^{-1} \text{m}$

or

−27 cm

12. A concrete sidewalk section 8.000 m by 1.000 m by 0.100 m at exactly 0°C will expand to what volume at 35°C?

$V_i = (8.000 \text{ m})(1.000 \text{ m})(0.100 \text{ m})$

$= 0.800 \text{ m}^3$

$\Delta V = \beta V_i \Delta T$

$= (36 \times 10^{-6} \text{°C}^{-1})(0.800 \text{ m}^3)(35\text{°C})$

$\Delta V = 1.0 \times 10^{-3} \text{ m}^3$

$V_{final} = 0.800 \text{ m}^3 + 0.001 \text{ m}^3 = 0.801 \text{ m}^3$

13. An air–filled balloon of 15.0 cm radius at 11°C is heated to 121°C. What change in volume occurs?

$V_i = \frac{4}{3}\pi r^3 = \frac{4}{3}\pi(15.0 \text{ cm})^3 = 1.41 \times 10^4 \text{ cm}^3$

$\Delta V = V_i \beta \Delta T$

$= (1.41 \times 10^4 \text{ cm}^3)(3400 \times 10^{-6} \text{°C}^{-1})(110\text{°C})$

$\Delta V = 5.2 \times 10^3 \text{ cm}^3$

14. A circular pyrex watch glass of 10.0 cm diameter at 21°C is heated to 501°C. What change will be found in the circumference of the glass?

$\Delta d = \alpha d_i \Delta T$

$= (3 \times 10^{-6} \text{°C}^{-1})(10.0 \text{ cm})(480\text{°C})$

$= 1.44 \times 10^{-2} \text{cm}$

$\Delta C = \pi \Delta d$

$= \pi(1.44 \times 10^{-2} \text{ cm}) = 4.5 \times 10^{-2} \text{ cm}$

15. A 200.0–cm copper wire and a 201–cm platinum wire are both at exactly 0°C. At what temperature will they both be of equal length?

Length of Platinum = Length of Copper

$L_P + \Delta L_P \alpha_P \Delta T = L_C + \Delta L_C \alpha_C \Delta T$

$201 \text{ cm} + (201 \text{ cm})(9 \times 10^{-6} \text{°C}^{-1})\Delta T$

$= 200 \text{ cm} + (200 \text{ cm})(16 \times 10^{-6} \text{°C}^{-1})\Delta T$

$1.39 \times 10^{-3}\ \Delta T = 1\text{°C}$

$\Delta T = 719\text{°C}$

Chapter 14: Waves and Energy Transfer

Practice Problems

page 293

1. A sound wave produced by a clock chime 515 m away is heard 1.50 seconds later.

   a. What is the speed of sound in air?

   $$v = \frac{d}{t} = \frac{(515\ \text{m})}{(1.5\ \text{s})} = 343\ \text{m/s}$$

   b. The sound wave has a frequency of 436 Hz. What is its period?

   $$T = \frac{1}{f} = \frac{1}{(436\ \text{Hz})} = 2.29 \times 10^{-3}\ \text{s}$$
   $$= 2.29\ \text{ms}$$

   c. What is its wavelength?

   $$\lambda = \frac{v}{f} = \frac{(343\ \text{m/s})}{(436\ \text{Hz})} = 0.787\ \text{m}$$

2. A hiker shouts toward a vertical cliff 685 m away. The echo is heard 4.00 s later.

   a. What is the speed of sound in air?

   $$v = \frac{d}{t} = \frac{(685\ \text{m})}{(2.0\ \text{s})} = 343\ \text{m/s}$$

   b. The wavelength of the sound is 0.75 m. What is its frequency?

   $$f = \frac{v}{\lambda} = \frac{(342\ \text{m/s})}{(0.750\ \text{m})} = 457\ \text{Hz}$$

   c. What is the period of the wave?

   $$T = \frac{1}{f} = \frac{1}{(456\ \text{Hz})} = 2.19 \times 10^{-3}\ \text{s}$$
   $$= 2.19\ \text{ms}$$

3. A radio wave (a form of electromagnetic wave) has a frequency of 99.5 MHz (99.5×10^6 Hz). What is its wavelength?

   $$\lambda = \frac{v}{f} = \frac{(3.00 \times 10^8\ \text{m/s})}{(99.5 \times 10^6\ \text{Hz})}$$
   $$= 3.02\ \text{m}$$

Practice Problem

4. A typical light wave has a wavelength of 580 nm.

   a. What is the wavelength of the light in meters?

   $$\lambda = (580\ \text{nm})(1 \times 10^{-9}\ \text{m/nm})$$
   $$= 5.8 \times 10^{-7}\ \text{m}$$

   b. What is the frequency of the wave?

   $$f = \frac{v}{\lambda} = \frac{(3.0 \times 10^8\ \text{m/s})}{(5.8 \times 10^{-7}\ \text{m})}$$
   $$= 5.2 \times 10^{14}\ \text{Hz}$$

page 296

5. A pulse is sent along a spring. The spring is attached to a light thread that is tied to the wall, as in Figure 14–12.

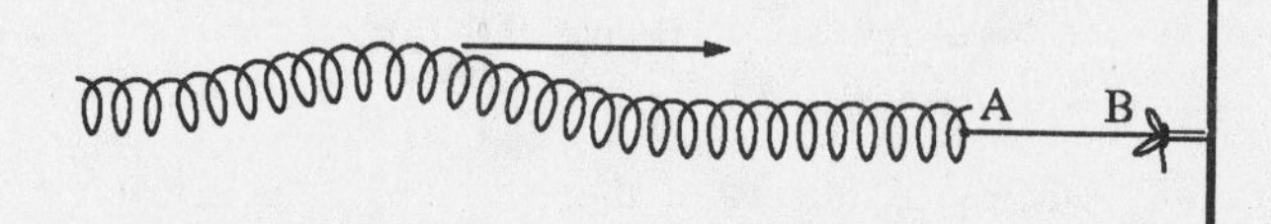

   a. What happens when the pulse reaches point *A*?

   The pulse is partially reflected, partially transmitted.

   b. Is the pulse reflected from *A* erect or inverted?

   Erect, since reflection is from a less dense medium.

   c. What happens when the transmitted pulse reaches *B*?

   It is almost totally reflected from the wall.

   d. Is the pulse reflected from *B* erect or inverted?

   Inverted, since reflection is from a more dense medium.

Practice Problems

page 297

6. A long spring runs across the floor of a room and out the door. A pulse is sent along the spring. After a few seconds, an inverted pulse returns. Is the spring attached to the wall in the next room or is it lying loose on the floor?

   Pulse inversion means rigid boundary; attached to wall.

7. If you want to increase the wavelength of waves in a rope, should you shake it at a higher or lower frequency?

   At a lower frequency because wavelength varies inversely with frequency.

8. A pulse is sent along a thin rope that is attached to a thick rope. The thick rope is itself tied to a wall, as in Figure 14–14.

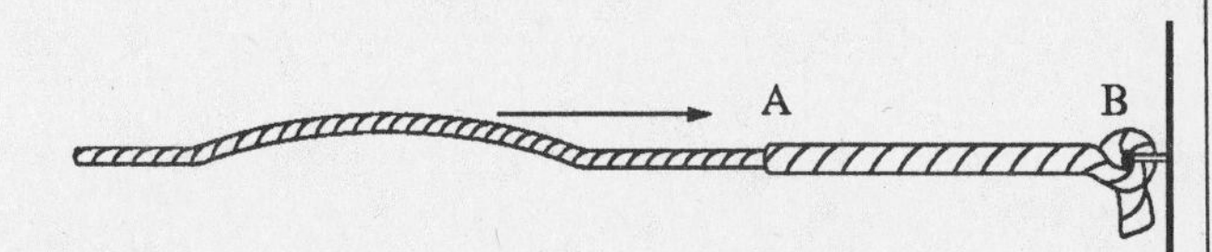

   a. What happens when the pulse reaches point *A*?

   The pulse is partially reflected, partially transmitted.

   b. Is the pulse reflected from *A* erect or inverted?

   Inverted, since reflection is from a more dense medium.

   c. What happens when the transmitted pulse reaches *B*?

   It is almost totally reflected from the wall.

   d. Is the pulse reflected from *B* erect or inverted?

   Inverted, since reflection is from a more dense medium.

Chapter Review Problems

pages 304–305

1. The Sears Building in Chicago sways back and forth with a frequency of about 0.10 Hz. What is its period of vibration?

   $$T = \frac{1}{f} = \frac{1}{(0.10\text{ Hz})} = 10\text{ s}$$

2. An ocean wave has a length of 10.0 m. A wave passes a fixed location every 2.0 s. What is the speed of the wave?

   $$v = f\lambda = \frac{1}{2.0\text{ s}}(10.0\text{ m}) = 5.0\text{ m/s}$$

3. Water waves in a shallow dish are 6.0 cm long. At one point, the water oscillates up and down at a rate of 4.8 oscillations per second.

   a. What is the speed of the water waves?

   $$v = f\lambda = (4.8\text{ Hz})(6.0\text{ cm}) = 29\text{ cm/s}$$

   b. What is the period of the water waves?

   $$T = \frac{1}{f} = \frac{1}{(4.8\text{ Hz})} = 0.21\text{ s}$$

4. Water waves in a lake travels 4.4 m in 1.8 s. The period of oscillation is 1.2 s.

   a. What is the speed of the water waves?

   $$v = \frac{d}{t} = \frac{(4.4\text{ m})}{(1.8\text{ s})} = 2.4\text{ m/s}$$

   b. What is their wavelength?

   $$\lambda = \frac{v}{f} = vT = (2.4\text{ m/s})(1.2\text{ s})$$

   $$= 2.9\text{ m}$$

5. The frequency of yellow light is 5.0×10^{14} Hz. Find its wavelength.

   $$\lambda = \frac{c}{f} = \frac{(3.00 \times 10^{8}\text{ m/s})}{(5.0 \times 10^{14}\text{ Hz})}$$

   $$= 6.0 \times 10^{-7}\text{ m}$$

6. A group of swimmers is resting in the sun on an off–shore raft. They estimate that 3.0 meters separate a trough and an adjacent crest of surface waves on the lake. They count 14 crests that pass by the raft in 20 seconds. How fast are the waves moving?

$\lambda = 2(3.0 \text{ m}) = 6.0 \text{ m},$

$f = \frac{(14 \text{ waves})}{(20 \text{ s})}$

$= 0.70 \text{ Hz}$

$v = f\lambda = (0.70 \text{ Hz})(6.0 \text{ m})$

$= 4.2 \text{ m/s}$

7. AM radio signals are broadcast at frequencies between 550 kHz and 1600 kHz (kilohertz) and travel 3.0×10^8 m/s.

a. What is the range of wavelengths for these signals?

$v = f\lambda$

$\lambda = \frac{v}{f} = \frac{3.0 \times 10^8 \text{ m/s}}{5.5 \times 10^5 \text{ Hz}}$

$= 550 \text{ m}$

$\lambda = \frac{v}{f} = \frac{3.0 \times 10^8 \text{ m/s}}{1.6 \times 10^6 \text{ Hz}}$

$= 190 \text{ m}$

b. FM frequencies range between 88 MHz and 108 MHz (megahertz) and travel at the same speed. What is the range of FM wavelengths?

$\lambda = \frac{v}{f} = \frac{3.0 \times 10^8 \text{ m/s}}{8.8 \times 10^7 \text{ Hz}}$

$= 3.4 \text{ m}$

$\lambda = \frac{v}{f} = \frac{3.0 \times 10^8 \text{ m/s}}{1.08 \times 10^8 \text{ Hz}}$

$= 2.8 \text{ m}$

8. A sonar signal of frequency 1.00×10^6 Hz has a wavelength of 1.50 mm in water.

a. What is the speed of the signal in water?

$v = f\lambda = (1.00 \times 10^6 \text{ Hz})(1.50 \times 10^{-3} \text{ m})$

$= 1.50 \times 10^3 \text{ m/s}$

b. What is its period in water?

$T = \frac{1}{f} = \frac{1}{1.00 \times 10^6 \text{ Hz}} = 1.00 \times 10^{-6} \text{ s}$

Chapter Review Problems

c. What is its period in air?

$T = 1.00 \times 10^{-6}$ s. The period and frequency remain unchanged.

9. A sound wave of wavelength 0.70 m and velocity 330 m/s is produced for 0.50 s.

a. What is the frequency of the wave?

$v = f\lambda, \text{ so } f = \frac{v}{\lambda} = \frac{(330 \text{ m/s})}{(0.70 \text{ m})}$

$= 470 \text{ Hz}$

b. How many complete waves are emitted in this time interval?

$ft = (470 \text{ Hz})(0.50 \text{ s})$

$= 240$ complete waves

c. After 0.50 s, how far is the front wave from the source of the sound?

$d = vt$

$= (330 \text{ m/s})(0.50 \text{ s})$

$= 170 \text{ m}$

10. The speed of sound in water is 1498 m/s. A sonar signal is sent from a ship at a point just below the water surface and 1.80 s later the reflected signal is detected. How deep is the ocean beneath the ship?

The time for the wave to travel down and back up is 1.80 s. The time one way is half 1.80 s or 0.900 s.

$d = vt = (1498 \text{ m/s})(0.900 \text{ s}) = 1350 \text{ m}$

11. The velocity of the transverse waves produced by an earthquake is 8.9 km/s, while that of the longitudinal waves is 5.1 km/s. A seismograph records the arrival of the transverse waves 73 seconds before that of the longitudinal waves. How far away was the earthquake?

$d = vt$. We don't know t, only the difference in time Δt. The transverse distance, $d_T = v_T t$, is the same as the longitudinal distance, $d_L = V_L(t + \Delta t)$. Use $v_T t = v_L(t + \Delta t)$, solving for $t = v_L \Delta t/(v_T - v_L) = 98$ s. Then, $d = v_T t = (8.9 \text{ km/s})(98 \text{ s}) = 8.7 \times 10^2$ km.

Chapter Review Problems

12. The velocity of a wave on a string depends on how hard the string is stretched, and the mass per unit length of the string. If T is the force exerted on the string, and μ is the mass/unit length, then the velocity, v, is

$$v = \sqrt{\frac{T}{\mu}}.$$

A piece of string 5.30 m long has a mass of 15.0 g. What must the tension in the string be to make a wavelength of a 125 Hz wave 120.0 cm?

$v = f\lambda = (125 \text{ Hz})(1.200 \text{ m}) = 150 \text{ m/s}$, and

$\mu = \frac{m}{\ell} = \frac{1.50 \times 10^{-2} \text{ kg}}{5.30 \text{ m}} = 2.83 \times 10^{-3} \text{ kg/m}.$

Now $v = \sqrt{\frac{T}{\mu}}$, so

$T = v^2\mu = (150 \text{ m/s})^2(2.83 \times 10^{-3} \text{ kg/m})$
$= 63.7 \text{ N}$

13. The time needed for a water wave to change from the equilibrium level to the crest is 0.18 s.

a. What fraction of a wave length is this?

$\frac{1}{4}$ wavelength

b. What is the period of the wave?

$T = 4(0.18 \text{ s}) = 0.72 \text{ s}$

c. What is the frequency of the wave?

$f = \frac{1}{T} = \frac{1}{(0.72 \text{ s})} = 1.4 \text{ Hz}$

14. The wave speed in a guitar string is 265 m/s. The length of the string is 63 m. You pluck the center of the string by pulling it up and letting go. Pulses move in both directions and are reflected off the ends of the string.

a. How long does it take for the pulse to move to the string end and return to the center?

$d = 2(63 \text{ cm})/2 = 63 \text{ cm}$, so

$t = \frac{d}{v} = \frac{(0.63 \text{ m})}{(265 \text{ m/s})} = 2.4 \times 10^{-3} \text{ s}.$

b. When the pulses return, is the string above or below its resting location?

Pulses are inverted when reflected, so returning pulse is down (below).

c. If you plucked the string 15 cm from one end of the string, where would the two pulses meet?

15 cm from the other end, where the distances travelled are the same.

15. Sketch what happens, for each of the three cases shown in Figure 14–23, when centers of the two wave pulses lie on the dashed line so the pulses exactly overlap.

a. The amplitude is doubled.

b. The amplitudes cancel each other.

c. If the amplitude of the first pulse is $\frac{1}{2}$ of the second, the resultant pulse is $\frac{1}{2}$ of the second.

16. If you slosh the water back and forth in a bathtub at the correct frequency, the water rises first at one end and then at the other. Suppose you can make a standing wave in a 150–cm long tub with a frequency of 0.30 Hz. What is the velocity of the water wave?

$d = 3.0 \text{ m}, \ t = \frac{1}{(0.30 \text{ Hz})}$

$v = \frac{d}{t} = (3.0 \text{ m})(0.30 \text{ Hz}) = 0.90 \text{ m/s}$

1. A periodic transverse wave that has a frequency of 10.0 Hz travels along a string. The distance between a crest and either adjacent trough is 2.50 m. What is its wavelength?

   The wavelength is the distance between adjacent crests, or twice the distance between a crest and an adjacent trough.
   $\lambda = 2(2.50\ \text{m}) = 5.00\ \text{m}$

2. A wave generator produces 16.0 pulses in 4.00 s.

   a. What is its period?

   $$\frac{(4.00\ \text{s})}{(16.0\ \text{pulses})} = 0.250\ \text{s/pulse, so}$$

   $T = 0.250\ \text{s}$

   b. What is its frequency?

   $$f = \frac{1}{T} = \frac{1}{(0.250\ \text{s})} = 4.00\ \text{Hz}$$

3. A wave generator produces 22.5 pulses in 5.50 s.

   a. What is its period?

   $$\frac{(5.50\ \text{s})}{(22.5\ \text{pulses})} = 0.244\ \text{s/pulse, so}$$

   $T = 0.244\ \text{s}$

   b. What is its frequency?

   $$f = \frac{1}{T} = \frac{1}{(0.244\ \text{s})} = 4.10\ \text{Hz}$$

4. What is the speed of a periodic wave disturbance that has a frequency of 2.50 Hz and a wavelength of 0.600 m?

   $v = \lambda f = (0.600\ \text{m})(2.50\ \text{Hz}) = 1.50\ \text{m/s}$

5. One pulse is generated every 0.100 s in a tank of water. What is the speed of propagation of the wave if the wavelength of the surface wave is 3.30 cm?

   $$v = \frac{\lambda}{T} = \frac{(3.30\ \text{cm})}{(0.100\ \text{s})} = 33.0\ \text{cm/s} = 0.330\ \text{m/s}$$

Supplemental Problems

6. Five pulses are generated every 0.100 s in a tank of water. What is the speed of propagation of the wave if the wavelength of the surface wave is 1.20 cm?

   $$\frac{(0.100\ \text{s})}{(5\ \text{pulses})} = 0.0200\ \text{s/pulse, so } T = 0.0200\ \text{s.}$$

   $$v = \frac{\lambda}{T} = \frac{(1.20\ \text{cm})}{(0.0200\ \text{s})} = 60.0\ \text{cm/s} = 0.600\ \text{m/s}$$

7. A periodic longitudinal wave that has a frequency of 20.0 Hz travels along a coil spring. If the distance between successive compressions is 0.400 m, what is the speed of the wave?

   $v = \lambda f = (0.400\ \text{m})(20.0\ \text{Hz}) = 8.00\ \text{m/s}$

8. What is the wavelength of a water wave that has a frequency of 2.50 Hz and a speed of 4.0 m/s?

   $$\lambda = \frac{v}{f} = \frac{(4.0\ \text{m/s})}{(2.50\ \text{Hz})} = 1.6\ \text{m}$$

9. The speed of a transverse wave in a string is 15.0 m/s. If a source produces a disturbance that has a frequency of 5.00 Hz, what is its wavelength?

   $$\lambda = \frac{v}{f} = \frac{(15.0\ \text{m/s})}{(5.00\ \text{Hz})} = 3.00\ \text{m}$$

10. The speed of a transverse wave in a string is 15.0 m/s. If a source produces a disturbance that has a wavelength of 1.25 m, what is the frequency of the wave?

    $$f = \frac{v}{\lambda} = \frac{(15.0\ \text{m/s})}{(1.25\ \text{m})} = 12.0\ \text{Hz}$$

11. A wave has an angle of incidence of 24°. What is the angle of reflection?

    The angle of incidence is equal to the angle of reflection; thus, both are 24°.

Chapter 15: Sound

Practice Problems

page 309

1. Sound with a frequency of 261.6 Hz travels through water at a speed of 1435 m/s. Find its wavelength in water.

$v = \lambda f$ so $\lambda = \frac{v}{f} = \frac{1435 \text{ m/s}}{261.6 \text{ Hz}} = 5.485$ m

2. Find the frequency of a sound wave moving in air at room temperature with a wavelength of 0.667 m.

$v = \lambda f$ so $f = \frac{v}{\lambda} = \frac{343 \text{ m/s}}{0.667 \text{ m}} = 514$ Hz

3. The human ear can detect sounds with frequencies between 20 Hz and 16 kHz. Find the largest and smallest wavelengths the ear can detect, assuming the sound travels through air with a speed of 343 m/s at 20°C.

From $v = \lambda f$ the largest wavelength is

$\lambda = \frac{v}{f} = \frac{343 \text{ m/s}}{20 \text{ Hz}} = 17$ m; the smallest is

$\lambda = \frac{v}{f} = \frac{343 \text{ m/s}}{16000 \text{ Hz}} = 0.021$ m.

4. **a.** What is the frequency of sound in air at 20°C having a wavelength equal to the diameter of a 15–inch (38 cm) "woofer" loudspeaker?

Woofer diameter 38 cm,

$f = \frac{v}{\lambda} = \frac{(343 \text{ m/s})}{(0.38 \text{ m})} = 0.90$ kHz

b. What is the frequency of sound in air at 20°C having a wavelength equal to the diameter of a 3–inch (7.6 cm) diameter "tweeter"?

Tweeter diameter 7.6 cm

$f = \frac{v}{f} = \frac{(343 \text{ m/s})}{(0.076 \text{ m})} = 4.5$ kHz

Practice Problems

page 318

5. A 440–Hz tuning fork is held above a closed pipe. Find the spacings between the resonances when the air temperature is 20°C.

Resonance spacing is $\frac{\lambda}{2}$ so using $v = \lambda f$ the resonance spacing is

$\frac{\lambda}{2} = \frac{v}{2f} = \frac{343 \text{ m/s}}{2(440 \text{ Hz})} = 0.390$ m.

6. The 440–Hz tuning fork is used with a resonating column to determine the velocity of sound in helium gas. If the spacings between resonances are 110 cm, what is the velocity of sound in He?

Resonance spacing $= \frac{\lambda}{2} = 1.10$ m so

$\lambda = 2.20$ m and
$v = f\lambda = (440 \text{ Hz})(2.20 \text{ m})$
$= 968$ m/s.

7. The frequency of a tuning fork is unknown. A student uses an air column at 27°C and finds resonances spaced by 39.2 cm. What is the frequency of the tuning fork?

From the previous example problem $v = 347$ m/s at 27°C and the resonance spacing gives $\frac{\lambda}{2} = 0.392$ m or $\lambda = 0.784$ m.

Using $v = \lambda f$, $f = \frac{v}{\lambda} = \frac{347 \text{ m/s}}{(0.784 \text{ m})} = 443$ Hz.

8. The auditory canal, leading to the eardrum, is a closed pipe 3.0 cm long. Find the approximate value (ignoring end correction) of the lowest resonant frequency.

$l = \frac{\lambda}{4}$, $v = \lambda f$, so

$f = \frac{v}{4l} = (343 \text{ m/s})(4 \times 0.03 \text{ m}) = 2.9$ kHz

15

9. A bugle can be thought of as an open pipe. If a bugle were straightened out, it would be 2.65 m long.

The lowest resonant frequency of an open pipe corresponds to the wavelength λ_1, where $\frac{\lambda_1}{2} = L$ = length of pipe. Further resonances are spaced $\frac{\lambda}{2}$ apart, giving the series of resonance wavelengths $L = \frac{\lambda_1}{2}, 2\left[\frac{\lambda_2}{2}\right], 3\left[\frac{\lambda_3}{2}\right], \ldots$.

a. If the speed of sound is 343 m/s, find the lowest frequency that is resonant in a bugle.

$\lambda_1 = 2L = 2(2.65\text{ m}) = 5.30\text{ m}$ so that the lowest frequency is

$$f_1 = \frac{v}{\lambda_1} = \frac{343\text{ m/s}}{5.30\text{ m}} = 64.7\text{ Hz}$$

b. Find the next two higher resonant frequencies in the bugle.

$$f_2 = \frac{v}{\lambda_2} = \frac{v}{L} = \frac{343\text{ m/s}}{2.65\text{ m}} = 129\text{ Hz}$$

$$f_3 = \frac{v}{\lambda_3} = \frac{3v}{2L} = \frac{3(343\text{ m/s})}{2(2.65\text{ m})} = 194\text{ Hz}$$

10. A soprano saxophone is an open pipe. If all keys are closed, it is approximately 65 cm long. Using 343 m/s as the speed of sound, find the lowest frequency that can be played on this instrument (ignoring end corrections).

The lowest resonant frequency corresponds to the wavelength given by $\frac{\lambda}{2} = L$, the length of the pipe. $\lambda = 2L = 2(0.65\text{ m}) = 1.30\text{ m}$ so $f = \frac{v}{\lambda} = \frac{343\text{ m/s}}{1.30\text{ m}} = 260\text{ Hz}$. Since the saxophone is an open pipe,

$\lambda_{max} = 2 \times (\text{pipe length}) = 2(0.65\text{ m})$
$= 1.30\text{ m}$

$$f_{min} = \frac{v}{\lambda_{max}} = \frac{343\text{ m/s}}{1.30\text{ m}} = 260\text{ Hz}$$

page 321

11. A 330–Hz and a 333–Hz tuning fork are struck simultaneously. What will the beat frequency be?

Beat frequency $= |f_2 - f_1|$
$= |333\text{ Hz} - 330\text{ Hz}|$
$= 3\text{ Hz}$

12. A student has two tuning forks, one with a frequency of 349 Hz and the other with an unknown frequency. When struck together, the tuning forks produce three beats a second. What are the possible frequencies of the unknown tuning fork?

The frequency of the second fork could be either
$f_2 = f_1 + f_{beat} = 349\text{ Hz} + 3\text{ Hz} = 352\text{ Hz}$ or
$f_2 = f_1 - f_{beat} = 349\text{ Hz} - 3\text{ Hz} = 346\text{ Hz}$.

Chapter Review Problems

pages 326–327

1. Andrew hears the sound of the firing of a distant cannon 6.00 s after seeing the flash. How far from the cannon is Andrew?

$d = v_s t = (343\text{ m/s})(6.00\text{ s}) = 2.06 \times 10^3\text{ m}$

2. A rifle is fired in a valley with parallel vertical walls. The echo from one wall is heard 2.0 s after the rifle was fired. The echo from the other wall is heard 2.0 s after the first echo. How wide is the valley?

The time it takes sound to go to wall 1 and back is 2.0 s. The time it takes to go to the wall is half the total time or 1.0 s,
$d_1 = v_s t_1 = (343\text{ m/s})(1.0\text{ s}) = 3.4 \times 10^2\text{ m}$.
The total time for the sound to go to wall 2 is half of 4.0 s or 2.0 s.
$d_2 = v_s t_2 = (343\text{ m/s})(2.0\text{ s}) = 6.8 \times 10^2\text{ m}$.
The total distance is $d_1 + d_2 = 1.02 \times 10^3\text{ m}$.

Chapter Review Problems

3. If Karen claps her hands and hears the echo from a distant wall 0.20 seconds later, how far away is the wall?

The total distance = vt = (343 m/s)(0.20 s)
= 68.6 m,
so the distance to the wall is half this, or 34 m.

4. If Karen shouts across a canyon and hears an echo 4.00 seconds later, how wide is the canyon?

$d = vt$ = (343 m/s)(4.00 s) = 1372 m is the total distance travelled. The distance to the wall is $\frac{1}{2}(1372) = 686$ m.

5. A certain instant camera determines the distance to the subject by sending out a sound wave and measuring the time needed for the echo to return to the camera. How long would it take the sound wave to return to the camera if the subject were 3.00 m away?

The total distance the sound must travel is 6.00 m.
$d = vt$, so

$$t = \frac{d}{v} = \frac{(6.00 \text{ m})}{(343 \text{ m/s})} = 0.0175 \text{ s.}$$

6. Carol drops a stone into a mine shaft 122.5 m deep. How soon after she drops the stone does she hear it hit the bottom of the shaft?

First find the time it takes the stone to fall down the shaft by $d = \frac{1}{2}gt^2$, so

$$t = \sqrt{\frac{d}{\frac{1}{2}g}} = \sqrt{\frac{-122.5}{\frac{1}{2}(-9.80)}} = 5.00 \text{ s.}$$

The time it takes the sound to come back up is found with $d = v_s t$, so

$$t = \frac{d}{v_s} = \frac{122.5 \text{ m}}{343 \text{ m/s}} = 0.36 \text{ s.}$$

The total time is 5.00 s + 0.36 s = 5.36 s.

7. If the wavelength of a 4.40×10^2 Hz sound in fresh water is 3.30 m, what is the speed of sound in water?

$v = f\lambda = (4.40 \times 10^2 \text{ Hz})(3.30 \text{ m})$
$= 1.45 \times 10^3$ m/s

8. Sound with a frequency of 442 Hz travels through steel. A wavelength of 11.66 m is measured. Find the speed of the sound in steel.

$v = f\lambda = (442 \text{ Hz})(11.66 \text{ m})$
$= 5.15 \times 10^3$ m/s

9. The sound emitted by bats has a wavelength of 3.5 mm. What is its frequency in air?

$$f = \frac{v}{\lambda} = \frac{(343 \text{ m/s})}{(0.0035 \text{ m})} = 9.8 \times 10^4 \text{ Hz}$$

10. Ultrasound with a frequency of 4.25 MHz can be used to produce images of the human body. If the speed of sound in the body is the same as in salt water, 1.50 km/s, what is the wavelength in the body?

$v = \lambda f$, so

$$\lambda = \frac{v}{f} = \frac{(1.50 \text{ km/s})(1000 \text{ m/km})}{(4.25 \times 10^6 \text{ Hz})}$$
$$= 3.53 \times 10^{-4} \text{ m}$$

11. The equation for the Doppler shift of a sound wave of speed v, reaching a moving detector, is $f' = f\left[\frac{v + v_d}{v - v_s}\right]$, where v_d is the speed of the detector and v_s is the speed of the source; f' is the frequency at the detector. If the detector moves toward the source, v_d is positive and if the source moves toward the detector v_s is positive. A train moving toward a detector at 31 m/s blows a 305-Hz horn. What is detected by a

a. stationary train?

$$f = f\left[\frac{v + v_d}{v - v_s}\right]$$
$$= \frac{(305 \text{ Hz})(343 \text{ m/s} + 0)}{(343 \text{ m/s} - 31 \text{ m/s})}$$
$$= 340 \text{ Hz}$$

b. train moving toward the first train at a speed of 21 m/s?

$$f = f\left[\frac{v + v_d}{v - v_s}\right]$$
$$= \frac{(305 \text{ Hz})(343 \text{ m/s} + (21 \text{ m/s}))}{(343 \text{ m/s} - 31 \text{ m/s})}$$
$$= 360 \text{ Hz}$$

12. The train in the previous problem is moving away from the detector. Now what frequency is detected by a

a. stationary train?

$$f = f\left[\frac{v + v_d}{v - v_s}\right]$$
$$= (305\text{ Hz})\left[\frac{343\text{ m/s} + 0}{343\text{ m/s} - (-31\text{ m/s})}\right]$$
$$= 280\text{ Hz}$$

b. train moving away from the first train at 21 m/s?

$$f = f\left[\frac{v + v_d}{v - v_s}\right]$$
$$= (305\text{ Hz})\left[\frac{343\text{ m/s} + (-21\text{ m/s})}{343\text{ m/s} - (-31\text{ m/s})}\right]$$
$$= 263\text{ Hz}$$

13. A slide whistle has a length of 27 cm. If you want to play a note one octave higher, how long should the whistle be?

$\lambda = \frac{4L}{3} = \frac{4(27\text{ cm})}{3} = 36$ cm. A note one octave higher is the first overtone of the fundamental. Resonances are spaced by $\frac{1}{2}$ wavelength. Since the original whistle length of 27 cm $= \frac{3}{4}$ the wavelength of the first overtone (octave), then the shortest whistle length for the first overtone equals

$$\frac{3\lambda}{4} - \frac{\lambda}{2} = \frac{\lambda}{4} = \frac{36\text{ cm}}{4} = 9\text{ cm}$$

14. Adam, an airport worker working near a jet plane taking off, experiences a sound level of 150 dB.

a. If Adam wore ear protectors that reduce the sound level to that of a chain saw, what decrease in dB would be required?

Chain saw is 110 dB, so 40 dB reduction is needed.

b. If Adam now heard something that sounded like a whisper, what would a person not wearing the protectors hear?

A soft whisper is 10 dB, so the actual level would be 50 dB, or that of an average classroom.

Chapter Review Problems

15. A rock band plays at an 80-dB sound level. How many times greater is the sound pressure from another rock band playing at

a. 100 dB?

Each 20 dB increases pressure by a factor of 10, so

10 dB.

b. 120 dB?

100 dB

16. An open vertical tube is filled with water and a tuning fork vibrates over its mouth. As the water level is lowered in the tube, resonance is heard when the water level has dropped 17 cm, and again after 49 cm of distance exists from the water to the top of the tube. What is the frequency of the tuning fork?

49 cm − 17 cm = 32 cm, or 0.32 m. Since the tube is closed at one end, $\frac{1}{2}\lambda$ exists between points of resonance.

$\frac{1}{2}\lambda = 0.32$ m, so $\lambda = 0.64$ m

$$f = \frac{v}{\lambda} = \frac{343\text{ m/s}}{0.64\text{ m}} = 540\text{ Hz}$$

17. If you hold a 1.0-m metal rod in the center and hit one end with a hammer, it will oscillate like an open pipe. Antinodes of air pressure correspond to nodes of molecular motion, so there is a pressure antinode in the center of the bar. The speed of sound in aluminum is 5150 m/s. What would be the lowest frequency of oscillation?

The rod length is $\frac{1}{2}\lambda$, so $\lambda = 2.0$ m,

$$f = \frac{v}{\lambda} = \frac{(5150\text{ m/s})}{(2.0\text{ m})} = 2.6\text{ kHz.}$$

Chapter Review Problems

18. The lowest note on an organ is 16.4 Hz.

a. What is the shortest open organ pipe that will resonate at this frequency?

$$\lambda = \frac{v}{f}$$

$$= \frac{(343 \text{ m/s})}{(16.4 \text{ Hz})} = 20.9 \text{ m}$$

$$l = \frac{\lambda}{2}$$

$$= \frac{(20.9 \text{ m})}{(2)} = 10.5 \text{ m}$$

b. What would be the pitch if the same organ pipe were closed?

$$f_c = \frac{f_o}{2}$$

$$f_c = \frac{(16.4 \text{ Hz})}{2} = 8.20 \text{ Hz}$$

19. During normal conversation the amplitude of the pressure wave is 0.020 N/m^2.

a. If the area of the eardrum is 0.52 cm^2, what is the force on the eardrum?

$$F = pA = (0.020 \text{ N/m}^2)(0.52 \times 10^{-4} \text{ m}^2)$$
$$= 1.0 \times 10^{-6} \text{ N}$$

b. The mechanical advantage of the bones in the inner ear is 1.5. What force is exerted on the oval window?

$$(1.5)(1.0 \times 10^{-6} \text{ N}) = 1.5 \times 10^{-6} \text{ N}$$

c. The area of the oval window is 0.026 cm^2. What is the pressure increase transmitted to the liquid in the cochlea?

$$p = \frac{F}{A} = \frac{(1.5 \times 10^{-6} \text{ N})}{(0.026 \times 10^{-4} \text{ m}^2)} = 0.58 \text{ N/m}^2$$

20. One tuning fork has a 445–Hz pitch. When a second fork is struck, beat notes occur with a frequency of 3 Hz. What are the two possible frequencies of the second fork?

445 Hz − 3 Hz = 442 Hz and
445 Hz + 3 Hz = 448 Hz

21. A flute acts like an open pipe and sounds a note with a 370–Hz pitch. What are the frequencies of the second, third, and fourth harmonics of this pitch?

$2f$ = (2)(370 Hz) = 740 Hz
$3f$ = (3)(370 Hz) = 1100 Hz
$4f$ = (4)(370 Hz) = 1500 Hz

22. A clarinet sounds the same note as the flute in the previous problem, 370 Hz. However, it only produces harmonics that are odd multiples of the fundamental frequency. What are the frequencies of the lowest three harmonics produced by the clarinet?

$3f$ = (3)(370 Hz) = 1100 Hz
$5f$ = (5)(370 Hz) = 1900 Hz
$7f$ = (7)(370 Hz) = 2600 Hz

23. One closed organ pipe has a length of 2.40 m.

a. What is the frequency of the note played by this pipe?

$$\lambda = 4l = (4)(2.40 \text{ m}) = 9.60 \text{ m}$$
$$v = f\lambda$$

$$f = \frac{v}{\lambda} = \frac{343 \text{ m/s}}{9.60 \text{ m}} = 35.7 \text{ Hz}$$

b. When a second pipe is played at the same time, a 1.40 Hz beat note is heard. By how much is the second pipe too long?

$$f = 35.7 \text{ Hz} - 1.40 \text{ Hz} = 34.3 \text{ Hz}$$
$$v = f\lambda$$

$$\lambda = \frac{v}{f} = \frac{343 \text{ m/s}}{34.3 \text{ Hz}} = 10.0 \text{ m}$$

$$\lambda = 4l$$

$$l = \frac{\lambda}{4} = \frac{10.0 \text{ m}}{4} = 2.50 \text{ m}$$

The difference in lengths is 2.50 m − 2.40 m = 0.10 m.

15

24. One organ pipe has a length of 836 mm. A second pipe should have a pitch one major third higher. How long should this pipe be?

$L = \frac{\lambda}{2}$, so $\lambda = 2L$; and $v = f\lambda$, so $f = \frac{v}{2L}$

$= \frac{(343 \text{ m/s})}{(2)(0.836 \text{ m})} = 205$ Hz.

The ratio of a frequency one major third higher is 5:4, so $(205 \text{ Hz})\left[\frac{5}{4}\right] = 256$ Hz.

The length of the second pipe is

$L = \frac{v}{2f} = \frac{(343 \text{ m/s})}{(2)(256 \text{ Hz})} = 670$ mm.

25. The Doppler shift was first tested in 1845 by the French scientist B. Ballot. He had a trumpet player sound an A, 440 Hz, while riding on a flatcar pulled by a locomotive. At the same time, a stationary trumpeter played the same note. Ballot heard 3.0 beats per second. How fast was the train moving toward him?

440 Hz + 3.0 Hz = 443 Hz

$f' = f\left[\frac{(v + v_d)}{(v - v_s)}\right]$ so $(v - v_s)f' = (v + v_d)f$ and

$v_s = v - \frac{(v + v_d)f}{f'}$

$= (343 \text{ m/s}) - \frac{(343 \text{ m/s} - 0)(440 \text{ Hz})}{443 \text{ Hz}}$

$= 2.3$ m/s

26. A student wants to repeat Ballot's experiment. She plans to have a trumpet played in a rapidly moving car. Rather than listening for beat notes, she wants to have the car move fast enough so the moving trumpet sounds a major third above a stationary trumpet.

Chapter Review Problems

a. How fast would the car have to move?

major third ratio = 5:4

$f' = f\left[\frac{(v + v_d)}{(v - v_s)}\right]$ so

$(v - v_s)f' = (v + v_d)f$ and

$v_s = v - \frac{(v + v_d)f}{f'} = v - (v + v_d)\frac{f}{f'}$

$= (343 \text{ m/s}) - (343 \text{ m/s} - 0)\left[\frac{5}{4}\right]$

$= 69$ m/s = 250 km/h

b. Should she try the experiment?

No, do not try the experiment.

Supplemental Problems (Appendix B)

1. The echo of a ship's fog horn, reflected from an iceberg, is heard 5.0 s after the horn is sounded. How far away is the iceberg?

$d = vt$, where $t = \frac{5.0 \text{ s}}{2} = 2.5$ s, since sound must travel to the iceberg and back.
$d = vt = (343 \text{ m/s})(2.5 \text{ s}) = 8.6 \times 10^2$ m

2. What is the speed of sound that has a frequency of 250 Hz and a wavelength of 0.600 m?

$v = \lambda f = (0.600 \text{ m})(250 \text{ Hz}) = 150$ m/s

3. A sound wave has a frequency of 2000 Hz and travels along a steel rod. If the distance between successive compressions is 0.400 m, what is the speed of the wave?

$v = \lambda f = (0.400 \text{ m})(2000 \text{ Hz}) = 800$ m/s

4. What is the wavelength of a sound wave that has a frequency of 250 Hz and a speed of 400 m/s?

$\lambda = \frac{v}{f} = \frac{(400 \text{ m/s})}{(250 \text{ Hz})} = 1.60$ m

5. What is the wavelength of sound that has a frequency of 539.8 Hz?

$$\lambda = \frac{v}{f} = \frac{(343 \text{ m/s})}{(539.8 \text{ Hz})} = 0.635 \text{ m}$$

6. What is the wavelength of sound that has a frequency of 320.0 Hz?

$$\lambda = \frac{v}{f} = \frac{(343 \text{ m/s})}{(320.0 \text{ Hz})} = 1.07 \text{ m}$$

7. A stone is dropped into a mine shaft 250.0 m deep. How many seconds pass before the stone is heard to strike the bottom of the shaft?

First find the time needed for the stone to strike the bottom of the shaft.

$$d = \frac{1}{2}gt_1^2, \text{ or } t_1 = \left[\frac{2d}{g}\right]^{1/2} = \left[\frac{2(250.0 \text{ m})}{(9.80 \text{ m/s}^2)}\right]^{1/2}$$

$$= 7.14 \text{ s}$$

The time needed for the sound to travel to the top of the shaft is

$$t_2 = \frac{d}{v} = \frac{(250.0 \text{ m})}{(343 \text{ m/s})} = 0.729.$$

The total time is thus
$t = t_1 + t_2 = 7.14 \text{ s} + 0.729 \text{ s} = 7.87 \text{ s}$

8. A rifle is shot in a valley formed between two parallel mountains. The echo from one mountain is heard after 2.00 s and from the other mountain 2.00 s later. What is the width of the valley?

Distance to first mountain:
$d_1 = vt_1 = (343 \text{ m/s})(2.00 \text{ s}/2) = 343 \text{ m}$

Distance to second mountain:
$d_2 = vt_2 = (343 \text{ m/s})(4.00 \text{ s}/2) = 686 \text{ m}$

Width of valley:
$w = d_2 + d_1 = 686 \text{ m} + 343 \text{ m} = 1030 \text{ m}$

9. Sam, a train engineer, blows a whistle that has a frequency of 4.0×10^2 Hz as the train approaches a station. If the speed of the train is 25 m/s, what frequency will be heard by a person at the station?

For the Doppler shift, $f = f\left[\frac{v - v_d}{v - v_s}\right]$, where v_d is the speed of the detector and v_s is the speed of the source.

$$f = (400 \text{ Hz})\left[\frac{343 \text{ m/s} - 0 \text{ m/s}}{343 \text{ m/s} - 25 \text{ m/s}}\right] = 430 \text{ Hz}$$

10. Jane is on a train that is traveling at 95 km/h. The train passes a factory whose whistle is blowing at 288 Hz. What frequency does Jane hear as the train approaches the factory?

$$f = f\left[\frac{v - v_d}{v - v_s}\right], \text{ where}$$

$$v_d = (-95 \text{ km/h})\left[\frac{1\text{h}}{3600 \text{ s}}\right]\left[\frac{1000 \text{ m}}{\text{k}}\right] = -26 \text{ m/s}$$

v_d is negative since its direction is opposite to that of the sound wave.

$$f = (288 \text{ Hz})\left[\frac{343 \text{ m/s} - (-26 \text{ m/s})}{343 \text{ m/s} - 0 \text{ m/s}}\right]$$

$$= 310 \text{ Hz}$$

11. What is the sound level of a sound that has a sound pressure one–tenth of 90 dB?

When the sound pressure is multiplied by one–tenth, the sound level decreases by 20 dB, so the sound level = 90 dB − 20 dB = 70 dB.

12. What is the sound level of a sound that has a sound pressure ten times 90 dB?

When the sound pressure is multiplied by ten, the sound level increases by 20 dB, so the sound level = 90 dB + 20 dB = 110 dB.

Supplemental Problems

13. A tuning fork produces a resonance with a closed tube 19.0 cm long. What is the lowest possible frequency of the tuning fork?

 The longest wavelength occurs when the length of the closed pipe is one–fourth wavelength, so $\frac{\lambda}{4} = 19.0$ cm, or $\lambda = 4(19.0 \text{ cm}) = 76.0$ cm.

 The longest wavelength corresponds to the lowest frequency,

 $$f = \frac{v}{\lambda} = \frac{(343 \text{ m/s})}{(0.760 \text{ m})} = 451 \text{ Hz}.$$

14. How do the frequencies of notes that are an octave apart compare?

 The higher note has a frequency twice that of the lower note.

15. Two tuning forks of 320 Hz and 324 Hz are sounded simultaneously. What frequency of sound will the listener hear?

 beat frequency = 324 Hz − 320 Hz = 4 Hz

16. How many beats will be heard each second when a string with a frequency of 288 Hz is plucked simultaneously with another string that has a frequency of 296 Hz?

 beat frequency = 296 Hz − 288 Hz
 = 8 Hz = 8 beats/s

17. A tuning fork has a frequency of 440 Hz. If another tuning fork of slightly lower pitch is sounded at the same time, 5.0 beats per second are produced. What is the frequency of the second tuning fork?

 The second tuning fork has a lower frequency than the first.
 $f_1 - f_2 = 5.0$ Hz, or
 $f_2 = f_1 - 5.0 \text{ Hz} = 440 \text{ Hz} - 5.0 \text{ Hz} = 435 \text{ Hz}$

Chapter 16: Light

16

Practice Problems

page 332

1. What is the frequency of yellow light, λ = 556 nm?

   $c = \lambda f$, so
   $f = c/\lambda = (3.00 \times 10^8 \text{ m/s})/(556 \times 10^{-9} \text{ m})$
   $= 5.40 \times 10^{14}$ Hz

2. One nanosecond (ns) is 10^{-9} s. Laboratory workers often estimate the distance light travels in a certain time by remembering the approximation "light goes one foot in one nanosecond." How far, in meters, does light actually travel in 1.0 ns?

   $d = ct = (3.00 \times 10^8 \text{ m/s})(1.0 \times 10^{-9} \text{ s})$
   $= 0.30$ m

3. Modern lasers can create a pulse of light that lasts only a few femtoseconds (1 fs = 1×10^{-15} s).

   a. What is the length of a pulse of light that lasts 6.0 fs?

   $d = ct = (3.00 \times 10^8 \text{ m/s})(6.0 \times 10^{-15} \text{ s})$
   $= 1.8 \times 10^{-6}$ m

   b. How many wavelengths of violet light (λ = 400 nm) are included in such a pulse?

   $$\text{Number of wavelengths} = \frac{\text{pulse length}}{\lambda_{\text{violet}}} = \frac{1.8 \times 10^{-6}\text{ m}}{4.0 \times 10^{-7}\text{ m}} = 4.5$$

4. The distance to the moon can be found with the help of mirrors left on the moon by astronauts. A pulse of light is sent to the moon and returns to Earth in 2.562 s. Using the defined velocity of light, calculate the distance to the moon.

   $d = ct = (299792458 \text{ m/s})(1/2)(2.562 \text{ s})$
   $= 3.840 \times 10^8$ m

Practice Problems

5. Use the correct time taken for light to cross Earth's orbit, 16 minutes, and the diameter of the orbit, 3.0×10^{11} m, to calculate the velocity of light using Roemer's method.

   $v = d/t = (3.0 \times 10^{11} \text{ m})/(16 \text{ min})(60 \text{ s/m})$
   $= 3.1 \times 10^8$ m/s

page 336

6. A lamp is moved from 30 cm to 90 cm above the pages of a book. Compare the illumination before and after the lamp is moved.

   $$\frac{E_{\text{after}}}{E_{\text{before}}} = \frac{P/4\pi d_{\text{after}}^2}{P/4\pi d_{\text{before}}^2} = \frac{d_{\text{before}}^2}{d_{\text{after}}^2} = \frac{(30\text{ cm})^2}{(90\text{ cm})^2} = \frac{1}{9}$$

7. What is the illumination on a surface 3.0 m below a 150–watt incandescent lamp that emits a luminous flux of 2275 lm?

   $$E = \frac{P}{4\pi d^2} = \frac{2275\ lm}{4\pi(3.0\text{ m})^2} = 20\ lx$$

8. Draw a graph of the illuminance from a 150–watt incandescent lamp between 0.50 m and 5.0 m.

   Illuminance of a 150–watt bulb
   P = 2275, d = 0.5, .75 ... 5

   $$E(d) = \frac{P}{4\pi d^2}$$

Practice Problems

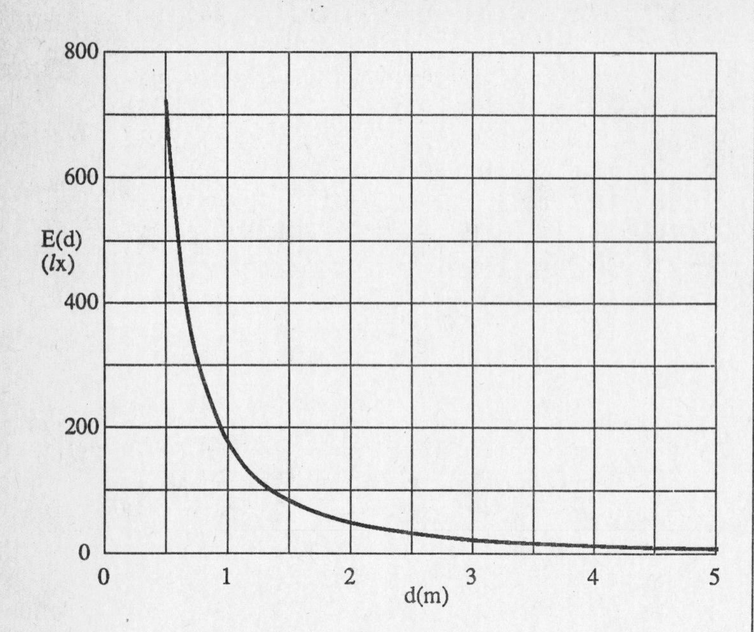

9. A 64-cd point source of light is 3.0 m above the surface of a desk. What is the illumination on the desk's surface in lux?

$P = 4\pi I = 4\pi(64 \text{ cd}) = 256\pi \ lm$

so $E = \dfrac{P}{4\pi d^2} = \dfrac{256\pi \ lm}{4\pi(3.0 \text{ m})^2} = 7.1 \ lx$

10. The illumination on a tabletop is 2.0×10^1 lx. The lamp providing the illumination is 4.0 m above the table. What is the intensity of the lamp?

From $E = \dfrac{P}{4\pi d^2}$,

$P = 4\pi d^2 E = 4\pi(4.0 \text{ m})^2(2.0 \times 10^1 \ lx)$
$= 1280\pi \ lm$

so $I = \dfrac{P}{4\pi} = \dfrac{1280\pi \ lm}{4\pi} = 320 \text{ cd}$

Chapter Review Problems

pages 344–345

1. Convert 700 nm, the wavelength of red light, to meters.

$\dfrac{700 \text{ nm}}{1}\left[\dfrac{1 \times 10^{-9} \text{ m}}{1 \text{ nm}}\right] = 7.00 \times 10^{-7} \text{ m}$

2. Light takes 1.28 s to travel from the moon to Earth. What is the distance between them?

$d = vt = (3.00 \times 10^8 \text{ m/s})(1.28 \text{ s})$
$= 3.84 \times 10^8 \text{ m}$

3. The sun is 1.5×10^8 km from Earth. How long does it take for its light to reach us?

$d = vt$, so

$t = \dfrac{d}{v} = \dfrac{(1.5 \times 10^8 \text{ km})(10^3 \text{ m/km})}{(3.00 \times 10^8 \text{ m/s})}$

$= 5.0 \times 10^2 \text{ s}$

4. Ole Roemer found that the maximum increased delay in the appearance of Io from one orbit to the next was 14 s.

a. How far does light travel in 14 s?

$d = vt = (3.00 \times 10^8 \text{ m/s})(14 \text{ s})$
$= 4.2 \times 10^9 \text{ m}$

b. Each orbit of Io is 42.5 h. Earth traveled the distance calculated above in 42.5 h. Find the speed of Earth in km/s.

$v = \dfrac{d}{t} = \dfrac{(4.2 \times 10^9 \text{ m})}{(42.5 \text{ h})}$

$= 28 \text{ km/s}$

c. See if your answer for part **b** is reasonable. Calculate Earth's speed in orbit using the orbital radius, 1.5×10^8 km, and the period, one year.

$v = \dfrac{d}{t} = \dfrac{2\pi(1.5 \times 10^8 \text{ km})}{(365 \text{ d})}$

$= 30 \text{ km/s}$

Chapter Review Problems

16

5. Radio stations are usually identified by their frequency. One radio station in the middle of the FM band has a frequency of 99.0 MHz. What is its wavelength?

$c = f\lambda$, so

$$\lambda = \frac{c}{f} = \frac{3.00 \times 10^8 \text{ m/s}}{99.0 \text{ MHz}}$$

$$= \frac{3.00 \times 10^8 \text{ m/s}}{99.0 \times 10^6 \ \frac{1}{\text{s}}}$$

$$= 3.03 \text{ m}$$

6. Suppose you wanted to measure the speed of light by putting a mirror on a distant mountain, setting off a camera flash, and measuring the time it takes the flash to reflect off the mirror and return to you. Without instruments, a person can detect a time interval of about 0.1 s. How many kilometers away would the mirror have to be? Compare this size with that of some known objects.

$$d = vt = (3.00 \times 10^8 \text{ m/s})(0.1 \text{ s}) = 3 \times 10^4 \text{ km}$$

The mirror would be half this distance, or 15,000 km away. Earth is 40,000 km in circumference, so this is 3/8 of the way around Earth!

7. What is the frequency of a microwave that has a wavelength of 3.0 cm?

$c = \lambda f$, so

$$f = \frac{c}{\lambda} = \frac{3.00 \times 10^8 \text{ m/s}}{0.030 \text{ m}} = 1.0 \times 10^{10} \text{ Hz}$$

8. Find the illumination 4.0 m below a 405-lm lamp.

$$E = \frac{P}{4\pi d^2} = \frac{(405 \text{ lm})}{4\pi(4.0 \text{ m})^2} = 2.0 \text{ lx}$$

9. A public school law requires a minimum illumination of 160 lx on the surface of each student's desk. An architect's specifications call for classroom lights to be located 2.0 m above the desks. What is the minimum luminous flux the lights must deliver?

$$E = \frac{P}{4\pi d^2}$$

$$P = 4\pi E d^2 = 4\pi(160 \text{ lm/m}^2)(2.0 \text{ m})^2 = 8.0 \times 10^3 \text{ lm}$$

10. A 3-way bulb uses 50-100-150 W of electrical power to deliver 665, 1620, or 2285 lm in its three settings. The bulb is placed 80 cm above a sheet of paper. If an illumination of at least 175 lx is needed on the paper, what is the minimum setting that should be used?

$$E = \frac{P}{4\pi d^2}$$

$$P = 4\pi E d^2 = 4\pi(175 \text{ lx}(0.80 \text{ m})^2) = 1.4 \times 10^3 \text{ lm}$$

Thus, the 100 W (1620 lm) setting is needed.

11. A streetlight contains two identical bulbs 3.3 m above the ground. If the community wants to save electrical energy by removing one bulb, how far from the ground should the streetlight be positioned to have the same illumination on the ground under the lamp?

$$E = \frac{P}{4\pi d^2}$$

If P is reduced by a factor of 2, so must d^2.

Thus, d is reduced by a factor of $\sqrt{2}$, becoming

$$\frac{(3.3 \text{ m})}{\sqrt{2}} = 2.3 \text{ m}$$

12. A student wants to compare the luminous flux from a bulb with that of a 1750–ℓm lamp. The two bulbs equally illuminate a sheet of paper. The 1750–ℓm lamp is 1.25 m away; the unknown bulb is 1.08 m away. What is its luminous flux?

$$E = \frac{P}{4\pi d^2}$$

Since the illumination is equal,
$E_1 = E_2$, so

$$\frac{P_1}{{d_1}^2} = \frac{P_2}{{d_2}^2} \text{ or}$$

$$P_2 = \frac{(P_1)(d_2)^2}{(d_1)^2} = \frac{(1750 \text{ ℓm})(1.08 \text{ m})^2}{(1.25 \text{ m})^2}$$

$$= 1.31 \times 10^3 \text{ ℓm}$$

13. A screen is placed between two lamps so that they illuminate the screen equally. The first lamp emits a luminous flux of 1445 ℓm and is 2.5 m from the screen. What is the distance of the second lamp from the screen if the luminous flux is 2375 ℓm?

Since the illumination is equal,
$E_1 = E_2$, so

$$\frac{P_1}{{d_1}^2} = \frac{P_2}{{d_2}^2}, \text{ or}$$

$$d_2 = d_1\sqrt{(P_2/P_1)} = (2.5 \text{ m})\sqrt{(2375/1445)} = 3.2 \text{ m}$$

14. Two lamps illuminate a screen equally. The first lamp has an intensity of 101 cd and is 5.0 m from the screen. The second lamp is 3.0 m from the screen. What is the intensity of the second lamp?

$$E = \frac{I}{d^2}$$

Since the illumination is equal,

$E_1 = E_2$, so

$$\frac{I_1}{{d_1}^2} = \frac{I_2}{{d_2}^2}, \text{ or}$$

$$I_2 = \frac{(I_1)({d_2}^2)}{({d_1}^2)}$$

$$I_2 = \frac{(101 \text{ cd})(3.0 \text{ m})^2}{(5.0 \text{ m})^2} = 36 \text{ cd}$$

15. A 10–cd point source lamp and a 60–cd point source lamp cast equal intensities on a wall. If the 10–cd lamp is 6.0 m from the wall, how far is the 60–cd lamp?

$E = \frac{I}{d^2}$ since the intensities on the wall are equal, the wall is equally illuminated and

$E_1 = E_2$, so

$$\frac{I_1}{{d_1}^2} = \frac{I_2}{{d_2}^2} \text{ or}$$

$$d_2 = d_1\sqrt{I_2/I_1} = (6.0 \text{ m})\sqrt{\frac{60 \text{ cd}}{10 \text{ cd}}} = 15 \text{ m}$$

Supplemental Problems (Appendix B)

1. The wavelength of blue light is about 4.5×10^{-7} m. Convert this to nm.

$$(4.5 \times 10^{-7} \text{ m})\left[\frac{\text{nm}}{10^{-7} \text{ m}}\right] = 4.5 \times 10^2 \text{ nm}$$

2. As a spacecraft passes directly over Cape Kennedy, radar pulses are transmitted toward the craft and are then reflected back toward the ground. If the total time interval was 3.00×10^{-3} s, how far above the ground was the spacecraft when it passed over Cape Kennedy?

Round trip distance
$d = vt = (3.00 \times 10^8 \text{ m/s})(3.00 \times 10^{-3} \text{ s})$
$= 9.00 \times 10^5$ m,
so distance is 4.50×10^5 m.

3. It takes 4.0 years for light from a star to reach Earth. How far away is this star from Earth?

$$d = vt = (3.00 \times 10^8 \text{ m/s})(4.0 \text{ yr})$$

$$\left[\frac{365 \text{ days}}{\text{yr}}\right]\left[\frac{24 \text{ h}}{\text{day}}\right]\left[\frac{3600 \text{ s}}{\text{h}}\right]$$

$$= 3.8 \times 10^{16} \text{ m}$$

Supplemental Problems

4. The planet Venus is sometimes a very bright object in the night sky. Venus is 4.1×10^{10} m away from Earth when it is closest to Earth. How long would we have to wait for a radar signal to return from Venus and be detected?

   Round trip distance
   $d = 2(4.1 \times 10^{10}\text{ m}) = 8.2 \times 10^{10}\text{ m}$
   $t = d/v = (8.2 \times 10^{10}\text{ m})/(3.00 \times 10^{8}\text{ m/s})$
   $= 2.7 \times 10^{2}\text{ s}$

5. The distance from Earth to the moon is about 3.8×10^{8} m. A beam of light is sent to the moon and, after it reflects, returns to Earth. How long did it take to make the round trip?

   Round trip distance
   $d = 2(3.8 \times 10^{8}\text{ m}) = 7.6 \times 10^{8}\text{ m}$
   $t = d/v = (7.6 \times 10^{8}\text{ m})/(3.00 \times 10^{8}\text{ m/s})$
   $= 2.5\text{ s}$

6. A baseball fan in a ball park is 101 m away from the batter's box when the batter hits the ball. How long after the batter hits the ball does the fan see it occur?

   $t = d/v = (101\text{ m})/(3.00 \times 10^{8}\text{ m/s})$
   $= 3.37 \times 10^{-7}\text{ s}$

7. A radio station on the AM band has an assigned frequency of 825 kHz (kilohertz). What is the wavelength of the station?

   $\lambda = c/f = (3.00 \times 10^{8}\text{ m/s})/(825 \times 10^{3}\text{ Hz})$
   $= 364\text{ m}$

8. A short–wave, HAM, radio operator uses the 5–meter band. On what frequency does the HAM operate?

   $f = c/\lambda = (3.00 \times 10^{8}\text{ m/s})/(5\text{ m})$
   $= 6 \times 10^{7}\text{ Hz} = 60\text{ MHz}$

9. Find the illumination 8.0 m below a 405–ℓm lamp.

   $E = P/4\pi d^2 = (405\text{ ℓm})/4\pi(8.0\text{ m})^2$
   $= 0.50\text{ ℓm/m}^2 = 0.50\text{ ℓx}$

10. Two lamps illuminate a screen equally. The first lamp has an intensity of 12.5 cd and is 3.0 m from the screen. The second lamp is 9.0 m from the screen. What is its intensity?

    Since $P/4\pi = I$, $E = P/4\pi d^2 = I/d^2$
    $E_1 = E_2$, or $I_1/d_1^2 = I_2/d_2^2$, so
    $I_2 = I_1(d_2/d_1)^2 = (12.5\text{ cd})(9.0\text{ m}/3.0\text{ m})^2$
    $= (12.5\text{ cd})(9.0)$
    $= 1.1 \times 10^{2}\text{ cd}$

11. A 15–cd point source lamp and a 45–cd point source lamp cast equal illuminations on a wall. If the 45–cd lamp is 12 m away from the wall, how far from the wall is the 15–cd lamp?

    $E = I/d^2$ and $E_1 = E_2$, so $I_1/d_1^2 = I_2/d_2^2$, or

    $$d_1^2 = \frac{I_1 d_2^2}{I_2} = \frac{(15\text{ cd})(12\text{ m})^2}{45\text{ cd}} = 48\text{ m}^2$$

    $d_1 = 6.9\text{ m}$

12. What is the name given to the electromagnetic radiation that has a wavelength slightly longer than visible light?

    Infrared.

13. What is the name given to the electromagnetic radiation that has a wavelength slightly shorter than visible light?

    Ultraviolet.

14. If a black object absorbs all light ray incident on it, how can we see it?

    The black object stands out from other objects that are not black. It is also illuminated by some diffuse reflection.

15. What is the appearance of a red dress in a closed room illuminated only by green light?

    The dress appears black, since red pigment absorbs green light.

16. A shirt that is the color of a primary color is illuminated with the complement of that primary color. What color do you see?

    Black.

Chapter 17: Reflection and Refraction

Practice Problems

page 354

1. Light in air is incident upon a piece of crown glass at an angle of 45.0° What is the angle of refraction?

   Assume the light is incident from air.
   From $n_i \sin \theta_i = n_r \sin \theta_r$,

   $$\sin \theta_r = \frac{n_i \sin \theta_i}{n_r} = \frac{(1.00) \sin 45.0°}{1.52}$$
   $$= 0.465, \text{ or } \theta_r = 27.7°$$

2. A ray of light passes from air into water at an angle of 30.0°. Find the angle of refraction.

   $n_i \sin \theta_i = n_r \sin \theta_r$ so

   $$\sin \theta_r = \frac{n_i \sin \theta_i}{n_r} = \frac{(1.00) \sin 30.0°}{1.33} = 0.376,$$

   or $\theta_r = 22.1°$

3. A ray of light is incident upon a diamond at 45.0°.

   a. What is the angle of refraction?

   Assume the light is incident from air.
   $n_i \sin \theta_i = n_r \sin \theta_r$ gives

   $$\sin \theta_r = \frac{n_i \sin \theta_i}{n_r} = \frac{(1.00) \sin 45.0°}{2.42} = 0.292,$$

   or $\theta_r = 17.0°$

   b. Compare your answer for part **(a)** to your answer for Practice Problem 1. Does glass or diamond bend light more?

   Diamond bends the light more.

4. A block of unknown material is submerged in water. Light in the water in incident on the block at an angle of 31°. The angle of refraction in the block is 27°. What is the index of refraction of the unknown material?

   $n_1 \sin \theta_1 = n_2 \sin \theta_2$, so
   $n_2 = n_1 \sin \theta_1 / \sin \theta_2 = (1.33)(0.515)/(0.454)$
   $= 1.5$

Practice Problems

page 355

5. Use Table 17–1 to find the speed of light in

   a. ethanol.

   $$v_{\text{ethanol}} = \frac{c}{n_{\text{ethanol}}} = \frac{3.00 \times 10^8 \text{ m/s}}{1.36}$$
   $$= 2.21 \times 10^8 \text{ m/s}$$

   b. quartz.

   $$v_{\text{quartz}} = \frac{c}{n_{\text{quartz}}} = \frac{3.00 \times 10^8 \text{ m/s}}{1.54}$$
   $$= 1.95 \times 10^8 \text{ m/s}$$

   c. flint glass.

   $$v_{\text{flint glass}} = \frac{c}{n_{\text{flint glass}}} = \frac{3.00 \times 10^8 \text{ m/s}}{1.61}$$
   $$= 1.86 \times 10^8 \text{ m/s}$$

6. The speed of light in plastic is 2.00×10^8 m/s. What is the index of refraction of the plastic?

   $$n = \frac{c}{v} = \frac{3.00 \times 10^8 \text{ m/s}}{2.00 \times 10^8 \text{ m/s}} = 1.50$$

7. What is the speed of light for the substance of Practice Problem 4?

   $$n = 1.5 \text{ so } v = \frac{c}{n} = \frac{3.00 \times 10^8 \text{ m/s}}{1.5}$$
   $$= 2.0 \times 10^8 \text{ m/s}$$

8. Suppose you had two pulses of light "racing" each other, one in air, the other in a vacuum. You could tell the winner if the time difference is 10 ns (10×10^{-9} s). How long would the race have to be to determine the winner?

   $t = d/v = dn/c.$
   $\Delta t = d(n_{\text{air}} - n_{\text{vacuum}})/c$
   $= d(1.0003 - 1.0000)/3.00 \times 10^8$ m/s.
   $= d(1 \times 10^{-12}$ s/m).
   Thus, $d = \Delta t/(1 \times 10^{-12}$ s/m)
   $= 1 \times 10^{-8}$ s/1×10^{-12} s/m
   $= 10^4$ m $= 10$ km.

Chapter Review Problems

pages 364–365

1. A ray of light strikes a mirror at an angle of 53° to the normal.

   a. What is the angle of the reflection?

   The angle of reflection is 53°.

   b. What is the angle between the incident ray and the reflected ray?

   The angle between the incident ray and the reflected ray, and *B* in the diagram is 53° + 53° = 106°.

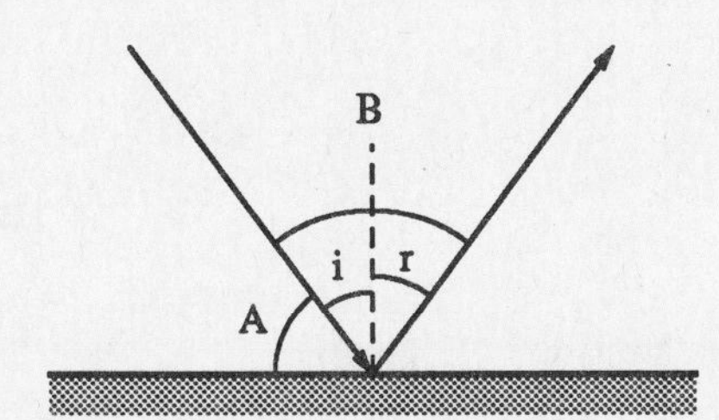

2. A ray of light incident upon a mirror makes an angle of 36.0° with the mirror. What is the angle between the incident ray and the reflected ray?

   Angle *A* in the diagram is 36.0° so the angle of incident is 90 – 36.0 = 54.0° and angle *B* is 54.0° + 54.0° = 108.0°

3. A ray of light has an angle of incidence of 30.0° on a block of quartz and an angle of refraction of 20.0°. What is the index of refraction for this block of quartz?

$$n = \frac{\sin \theta_i}{\sin \theta_r} = \frac{\sin 30.0°}{\sin 20.0°} = 1.46$$

4. A ray of light travels from air into a liquid. The ray is incident upon the liquid at an angle of 30.0°. The angle of refraction is 22.0°.

   a. What is the index of refraction of the liquid?

$$n = \frac{\sin \theta_i}{\sin \theta_r} = \frac{\sin 30.0°}{\sin 22.0°} = 1.34$$

   b. Refer to Table 17–1. What might the liquid be?

   water

Indices of Refraction	
Medium	**n**
vacuum	1.00
air	1.00*
water	1.33
ethanol	1.36
crown glass	1.52
quartz	1.54
flint glass	1.61
diamond	2.42

*Index of refraction of air is 1.0003 which is higher than that of vacuum, 1.0000. However, for practical purposes, they are the same.

5. A ray of light is incident at an angle of 60.0° upon the surface of a piece of crown glass. What is the angle of refraction?

$$n = \frac{\sin \theta_i}{\sin \theta_r}, \text{ so}$$

$$\sin \theta_r = \frac{\sin \theta_i}{n} = \frac{\sin 60.0°}{1.52} = 0.570$$

$$\theta_r = 34.7°$$

6. A light ray strikes the surface of a pond at an angle of incidence of 36.0°. At what angle is the ray refracted?

$$n = \frac{\sin \theta_i}{\sin \theta_r}, \text{ so}$$

$$\sin \theta_r = \frac{\sin \theta_i}{n}$$

$$= \frac{\sin 36.0°}{1.33} = 0.442$$

$$\theta_r = 26.2°$$

Chapter Review Problems

7. Light is incident at an angle of 60.0° on the surface of a diamond. Find the angle of refraction.

$$n = \frac{\sin \theta_i}{\sin \theta_r}, \text{ so}$$

$$\sin \theta_r = \frac{\sin \theta_i}{n}$$

$$= \frac{\sin 60.0°}{2.42} = 0.358$$

$\theta_r = 21.0°$

8. A ray of light has an angle of incidence of 33.0° in crown glass. What is the angle of refraction.

$n_A \sin \theta_A = n_g \sin \theta_g$, so

$$\sin \theta_A = \frac{n_g}{n_A} \sin \theta_g = \frac{1.52}{1.00} \sin 33.0° = 0.828$$

$\theta_A = 55.9°$

9. A ray of light passes from water into crown glass at an angle of 23.2°. Find the angle of refraction.

$n_w \sin \theta_w = n_g \sin \theta_g$, so

$$\sin \theta_g = \frac{n_w \sin \theta_w}{n_g}$$

$$= \frac{(1.33)(\sin 23.2°)}{1.52} = 0.345$$

$\theta_r = 20.2°$

10. Light goes from flint glass into ethanol. The angle of refraction in the ethanol is 25.0°. What is the angle of incidence in the glass?

$n_g \sin \theta_g = n_e \sin \theta_e$, so

$$\sin \theta_g = \frac{n_e \sin \theta_e}{n_g}$$

$$= \frac{(1.36)(\sin 25.0°)}{1.61} = 0.357$$

$\theta_r = 20.9°$

11. A beam of light strikes the flat, glass side of a water-filled aquarium at an angle of 40° to the normal. The index of refraction for glass and water are 1.50 and 1.33, respectively.

a. At what angle does the beam enter the glass?

$n_A \sin \theta_A = ng \sin \theta_g$, so

$$\sin \theta_g = \frac{n_A \sin \theta_A}{n_g} = \frac{1.00 \sin 40°}{1.50} = 0.43$$

$\theta_g = 25°$

b. At what angle does the beam enter the water?

$n_g \sin \theta_g = n_w \sin \theta_w$, so

$$\sin \theta_w = \frac{n_g \sin \theta_g}{n_w} = \frac{1.50 \sin 25°}{1.33} = 0.48$$

$\theta_w = 29°$

c. What would be the entry angle in water if the beam struck the water directly?

$n_A \sin \theta_A = n_w \sin \theta_w$, so

$$\sin \theta_w = \frac{n_A \sin \theta_A}{n_w} = \frac{1.00 \sin 40°}{1.33} = 0.48$$

$\theta_w = 29°$

12. A thick sheet of plastic ($n = 1.500$) is used as the side of an aquarium tank. Light reflected from a fish in the water has an angle of incidence of 35.0°. At what angle does the light enter the air?

$n_w \sin \theta_w = n_p \sin \theta_p$, so

$$\sin \theta_p = \frac{n_w \sin \theta_w}{n_p} = \frac{(1.33)(\sin 35.0°)}{(1.500)}$$

$= 0.509$

The angle of refraction from the water into the plastic is equal to the angle of incidence from the plastic in the air.

$n_A \sin \theta_A = n_p \sin \theta_p$, so

$$\sin \theta_A = \frac{n_p \sin \theta_p}{n_A} = \frac{(1.500)(0.509)}{(1.00)} = 0.764$$

$\theta_r = 49.8°$

13. A light source, S, is located 2.0 m below the surface of a swimming pool and 1.5 m from one edge of the pool. The pool is filled to the top with water.

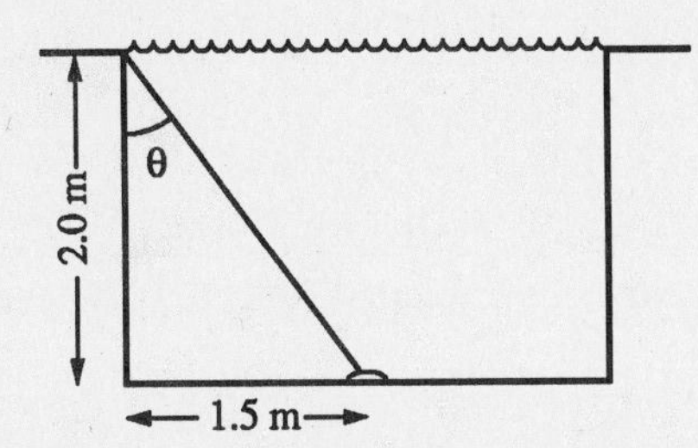

a. At what angle does the light reaching the edge of the pool leave the water?
Find the angle θ as shown in the figure.

$$\tan\theta_i = \frac{1.5\text{ m}}{2.0\text{ m}} = 0.75$$

$\theta_i = 37°$

Then find the angle in air

$n_A \sin\theta_A = n_w \sin\theta_w$, so

$$\sin\theta_A = \frac{n_w \sin\theta_w}{n_A} = \frac{(1.33)(\sin 37°)}{1.00}$$

$= 0.80$

$\theta_r = 53°$

b. Does this cause the light viewed from this angle to appear deeper or shallower than it actually is?

$$\tan 53° = \frac{\text{side opposite}}{\text{side adjacent}}$$

$$\text{side adjacent} = \frac{\text{side opposite}}{\tan 53°} = \frac{1.5\text{ m}}{\tan 53°}$$

$= 1.1$ m, shallower

14. A ray of light is incident upon a 60–60–60 degree glass prism (n = 1.5) as shown in Figure 17–19.

a. Using Snell's law, determine the angle θ_r to the nearest degree.

$n_A \sin\theta_A = n_g \sin\theta_r$, so

$$\sin\theta_r = \frac{n_A \sin\theta_A}{n_g} = \frac{(1.00)\sin 45°}{1.5} = 0.47$$

$\theta_r = 28°$

b. Using elementary geometry, determine the values of angles A, B, and C.

$\theta_A = 90° - 28° = 62°$

$\theta_B = 180° - (62° + 60°) = 58°$

$\theta_C = 90° - 58° = 32°$

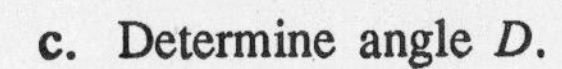

c. Determine angle D.

$n_A \sin\theta_D = n_g \sin\theta_C$, so

$$\sin\theta_D = \frac{n_g \sin\theta_C}{n_A} = \frac{1.5\sin 32°}{1.0}$$

$= 0.795$

$\theta_D = 53°$

15. A sheet of plastic, n = 1.500, 25 mm thick is used in a bank teller's window. A ray of light strikes the sheet at an angle of 45°. The ray leaves the sheet at 45° but at a different location. Use a ray diagram to find the distance between the ray that leaves and the one that would have left if the plastic were not there.

8 mm

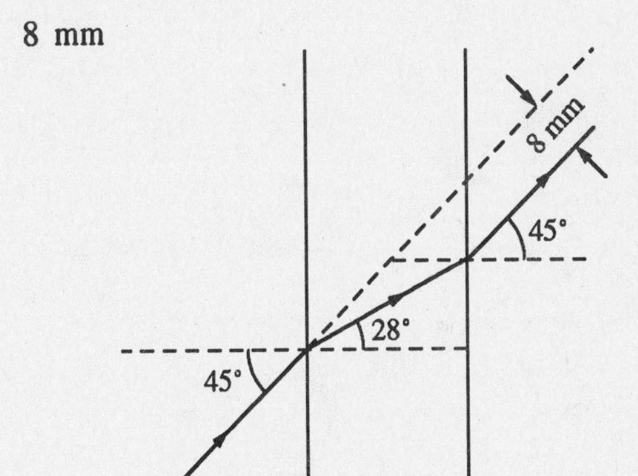

16. What is the speed of light in diamond?

$n_d = \dfrac{c}{v_d}$, so

$$v_d = \frac{c}{n_d} = \frac{3.00 \times 10^8}{2.42}$$

$= 1.24 \times 10^8$ m/s

17. The speed of light in chloroform is 1.99×10^8 m/s. What is its index of refraction?

$$n_c = \frac{c}{v_c} = \frac{3.00 \times 10^8\text{ m/s}}{1.99 \times 10^8\text{ m/s}} = 1.51$$

Chapter Review Problems

18. The speed of light in a clear plastic is 1.90×10^8 m/s. A ray of light enters the plastic at an angle of 22°. At what angle is the ray refracted?

$n_A \sin \theta_A - n_p \sin \theta_p$ and $n_p = \frac{c}{v_p}$, so

$n_A \sin \theta_A = \frac{c}{v} \sin \theta_p$, so

$\sin \theta_p = \frac{v_p n_A \sin \theta_A}{c}$

$= \frac{(1.90 \times 10^8 \text{ m/s})(1.00) \sin 22°}{3.00 \times 10^8 \text{ m/s}}$

$= 0.237$

$\theta_r = 14°$

19. How many more minutes would it take light from the sun to reach Earth if the space between them were filled with water rather than a vacuum? The sun is 1.5×10^8 km from Earth.

Time through vacuum

$t = \frac{d}{v} = \frac{(1.5 \times 10^8 \text{ km})(10^3 \text{ m/km})}{(3.00 \times 10^8 \text{ m/s})} = 500 \text{ s}$

Speed through water

$v = \frac{c}{n} = \frac{(3.00 \times 10^8 \text{ m/s})}{1.33} = 2.26 \times 10^8 \text{ m/s}$

Time through water

$t = \frac{d}{v} = \frac{(1.5 \times 10^8 \text{ km})(10^3 \text{ m/km})}{(2.26 \times 10^8 \text{ m/s})} = 660 \text{ s}$

$\Delta t = 660 \text{ s} - 500 \text{ s} = 160 \text{ s}$
$= (160 \text{ s})(1 \text{ min}/60 \text{ s}) = 2.7 \text{ min}$

20. Find the critical angle for diamond.

$\sin \theta_c = \frac{1}{n} = \frac{1}{2.42} = 0.413$

$\theta_c = 24.4°$

21. A block of glass has a critical angle of 45.0°. What is its index of refraction?

$\sin \theta_c = \frac{1}{n}$, so

$n = \frac{1}{\sin \theta_c} = \frac{1}{\sin 45.0} = 1.41$

22. A ray of light in a tank of water has an angle of incidence of 55°. What is the angle of refraction in air?

$n_w \sin \theta_w = n_A \sin \theta_A$, so

$\sin \theta_A = \frac{n_w \sin \theta_w}{n_A} = \frac{1.33 \sin 55°}{1.00} = 1.1$

There is no angle for which $\sin \theta_r = 1.1$, therefore total internal reflection occurs.

23. A light ray enters a rectangle of crown glass as shown in Figure 17–20. Use a ray diagram to trace the path of the ray until it leaves the glass.

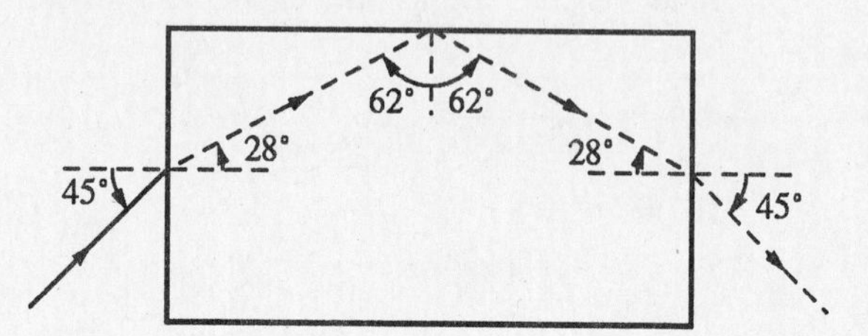

$n_A \sin \theta_A = n_g \sin \theta_g$, so

$\sin \theta_g = \frac{n_A \sin \theta_A}{n_g} = \frac{(1.00) \sin 45°}{1.52} = 0.465$

$\theta_g = 28°$

24. The critical angle for special glass in air is 41°. What is the critical angle if the glass is immersed in water?

$n_g \sin \theta_g = n_w \sin \theta_w = n_w \sin 90° = n_w(1.00)$

and $\sin \theta_c = \frac{1}{n_g}$, so $n_g = \frac{1}{\sin \theta_c}$

therefore $\left[\frac{1}{\sin \theta_c}\right] \sin \theta_g = n_w$, so

$\sin \theta_g = n_w \sin \theta_c = 1.33 \sin 41° = 0.873$
$\theta = 61°$

25. The index of refraction for a diamond for red light, 656 nm, is 2.410, while that for blue light, 434 nm, is 2.450. Suppose white light is incident on the diamond at 30.0°. Find the angles of refraction for these two colors.

$n_A \sin \theta_A = n_d \sin \theta_d$, so $\sin \theta_d = \dfrac{(1.00) \sin \theta_A}{n_d}$

For red light

$\sin \theta_r = \dfrac{(\sin 30.0°)}{2.410} = 0.207$

$\theta_r = 12.0°$

For blue light

$\sin \theta_r = \dfrac{(\sin 30.0°)}{2.450} = 0.204$

$\theta_r = 11.8°$

26. The index of refraction for crown glass for red light is 1.514, while that for blue light is 1.528. White light is incident on the glass at 30.0°.

a. Find the angles of refraction for these two colors.

$n_A \sin \theta_A = n_g \sin \theta_g$, so $\sin \theta_g = \dfrac{n_A \sin \theta_A}{n_g} = \dfrac{1.00 \sin \theta_A}{n_g}$

For red light

$\sin \theta = \dfrac{\sin 30.0°}{1.514} = 0.330$

$\theta = 19.3°$

For blue light

$\sin \theta = \dfrac{\sin 30.0°}{1.528} = 0.327$

$\theta = 19.1°$

b. Compare the difference in angles to that for diamond found in Problem 25.

	Diamond		Crown Glass	
	Red	Blue	Red	Blue
Angle of incidence	30.0°	30.0°	30.0°	30.0°
Angle of refraction	12.0°	11.8°	19.3°	19.1°
Difference	18.0°	18.2°	10.7°	10.9°

c. Use the results to explain why diamonds are said to have "fire."

There is a much larger difference between the angles of incidence and refraction for diamond than for crown glass. This means that diamond has a much smaller critical angle. As a result, less light incident upon a diamond will pass completely through. Instead, more light will be reflected internally until it comes back out of the top of the diamond. Blue light has a smaller critical angle than red light. This means that more red light will emerge from a diamond than blue light. Hence, a diamond appears to have "fire."

Chapter Review Problems

27. The index of refraction of crown glass for violet light is 1.53, while for red light it is 1.51.

$n = \frac{c}{v}$, so $v = \frac{c}{n}$

a. What is the speed of violet light in crown glass?

$$v = \frac{c}{n} = \frac{3.00 \times 10^8 \text{ m/s}}{1.53} = 1.96 \times 10^8 \text{ m/s}$$

b. What is the speed of red light in crown glass.

$$v = \frac{c}{n} = \frac{3.00 \times 10^8 \text{ m/s}}{1.51} = 1.99 \times 10^8 \text{ m/s}$$

28. Just before sunset you see a rainbow in the water from a lawn sprinkler. Carefully draw your location and the locations of the sun and the water from the sprinkler that shows the rainbow.

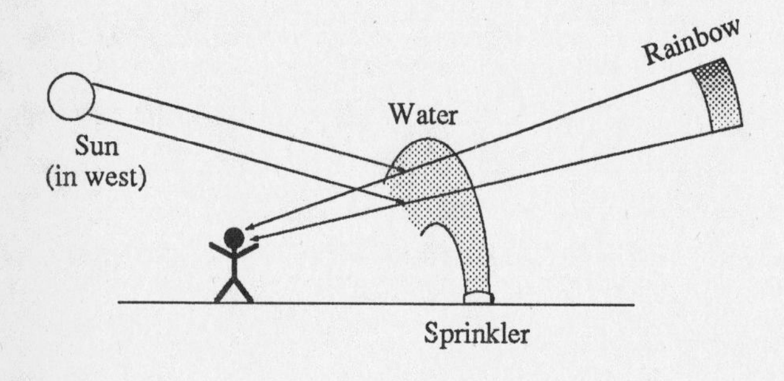

Supplemental Problems (Appendix B)

1. A ray of light strikes a mirror at an angle of incidence of 28°. What is the angle of the reflection?

The angle of reflection is equal to the angle of incidence, or 28°.

Supplemental Problems (Appendix B)

2. A ray of light passes from an unknown substance into air. If the angle of the unknown substance is 35.0° and the angle in air is 52.0°, what is the index of refraction of the unknown substance?

$n_i \sin \theta_i = n_r \sin \theta_r$,
$n_i = n_r \sin \theta_r / \sin \theta_i$
$= (1.00)(\sin 52.0°)/(\sin 35.0°) = 1.37$

3. A ray of light has an angle of incidence of 25.0° upon the surface of a piece of quartz. What is the angle of refraction?

$n_i \sin \theta_i = n_r \sin \theta_r$,
$\sin \theta_r = n_i \sin \theta_i / n_r = (1.00)(\sin 25.0)/(1.54)$
$= 0.274$
$\theta_r = 15.9°$

4. A beam of light passes from water into polyethylene, index of refraction = 1.50. If the angle in water is 57.5°, what is the angle in polyethylene?

$n_i \sin \theta_i = n_r \sin \theta_r$,
$\sin \theta_r = n_i \sin \theta_i / n_r = (1.33)(\sin 57.5°)/(1.50)$
$= 0.748$
$\theta_r = 48.4°$

5. Dave makes some hydrogen sulfide, index of refraction = 1.000 644. If Karen measures an angle of 85.000 000° in the hydrogen sulfide, what angle will Karen measure in air if the index of refraction of air is 1.000 292 6?

$n_i \sin \theta_i = n_r \sin \theta_r$,
$\sin \theta_r = n_i \sin \theta_i / n_r$

$$= \frac{(1.000\ 644)(\sin 85.000\ 000°)}{(1.000\ 292\ 6)}$$

$= 0.996\ 544\ 7$
$\theta_r = 85.\ 235\ 60°$

6. Sue submerged some ice in water and shined a laser beam through the water and into the ice. Sue found the angle in ice was larger than the angle in water. Which material has a larger index of refraction?

$n_i \sin \theta_i = n_r \sin \theta_r$,
$n_i / n_r = \sin \theta_r / \sin \theta_i$
$\theta_r > \theta_i$, so $n_i / n_r = \sin \theta_r / \sin \theta_i > 1$, or $n_i > n_r$ and water (the incident material) has the larger index of refraction.

Supplemental Problems

7. A ray of light enters a triangular crown glass prism perpendicular to one face and it emerges from an adjacent side. If the two adjacent sides meet at a 30.0° angle, what is the angle the light ray has in the air when it comes out?

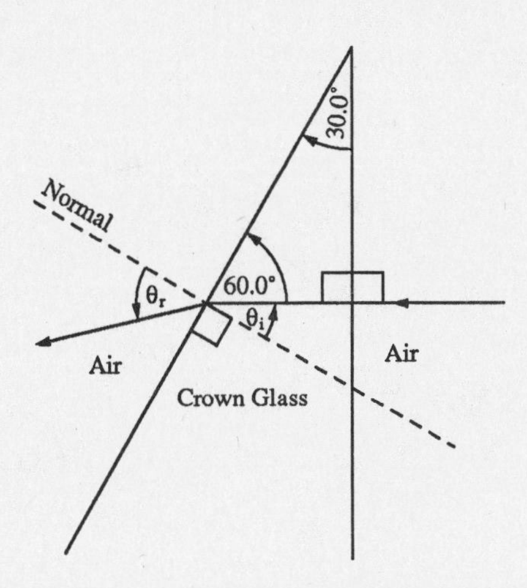

$\theta_i = 180.0° - 60.0° - 90.0° = 30.0°$
$n_i \sin \theta_i = n_r \sin \theta_r$,
$\sin \theta_r = n_i \sin \theta_i / n_r = (1.52)(\sin 30.0°)/(1.00)$
$= 0.760$
$\theta_r = 49.5°$

8. Make a drawing, to scale, of the side of an aquarium in which the water is 12.0 cm deep. From a single point on the bottom, draw two lines upward, one vertical and the other 5.0° from the vertical. Let these two lines represent two light rays that start from the same point on the bottom of the tank. Compute the directions the refracted rays will travel above the surface of the water. Draw in these rays and continue them backward into the tank until they intersect. At what depth does the bottom of the tank appear to be if you look into the water? Divide the apparent depth into the true depth and compare it to the index of refraction.

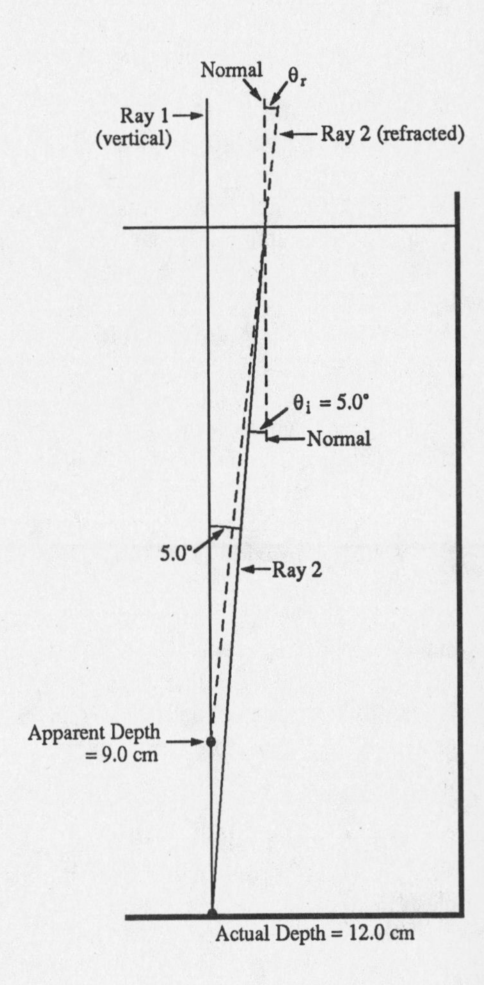

For ray 1, $\theta_r = \theta_i = 0°$.
For ray 2, $n_i \sin \theta_i = n_r \sin \theta_r$,
$\sin \theta_r = n_i \sin \theta_i / n_r = (1.33)(\sin 5.0°)/(1.00)$
$= 0.116$, $\theta_r = 6.7°$
The refracted rays appear to intersect 9.0 cm below the surface; this is the apparent depth.
(apparent depth)/(true depth)
= (9.0 cm)/(12.0 cm) = 0.75
Also, $(n_{air})/(n_{water}) = (1.00)/(1.33) = 0.75$.
Therefore,
(apparent depth)/(true depth) = $(n_{air})/(n_{water})$

9. Find the speed of light in water.

$v_s = c/n_s = (3.00 \times 10^8 \text{ m/s})/(1.33)$
$= 2.26 \times 10^8 \text{ m/s}$

10. Find the speed of light in antimony trioxide, if it has an index of refraction of 2.35.

$v_s = c/n_s = (3.00 \times 10^8 \text{ m/s})/(2.35)$
$= 1.28 \times 10^8 \text{ m/s}$

11. The speed of light in a special piece of glass is 1.75×10^8 m/s. What is its index of refraction?

$n_s = c/v_s = (3.00 \times 10^8 \text{ m/s})/(1.75 \times 10^8 \text{ m/s})$
$= 1.71$

12. Glenn gently pours some acetic acid, index of refraction = 1.37, onto some antimony trioxide, index of refraction = 2.35. What angle will Glenn find in the acetic acid of the angle in the antimony trioxide is 42.0°?

$n_i \sin \theta_i = n_r \sin \theta_r,$
$\sin \theta_r = n_i \sin \theta_i / n_r = (2.35)(\sin 42.0°)/(1.37)$
$= 11.5$
None; this is impossible, since ($\sin \theta_r$) cannot exceed one. Therefore, total internal reflection occurs.

13. Steve finds that a plastic has a critical angle of 40.0°. What is the index of refraction of the plastic?

$\sin \theta_c = 1/n_i,$
$n_i = 1/\sin \theta_c = 1/(\sin 40.0°) = 1.56$

14. Kathy decides to find the critical angle of arsenic trioxide, index of refraction = 2.01, which is very toxic. What angle did Kathy find?

$\sin \theta_c = 1/ni = 1/2.01 = 0.498, \theta_c = 29.8°$

Supplemental Problems

15. A light source is in a cylindrical container of carbon dichloride, index of refraction = 1.500. The light source sends a ray of light parallel to the bottom of the container at a 45.0° angle from the radius, to the circumference as shown. What will the path of the light ray be?

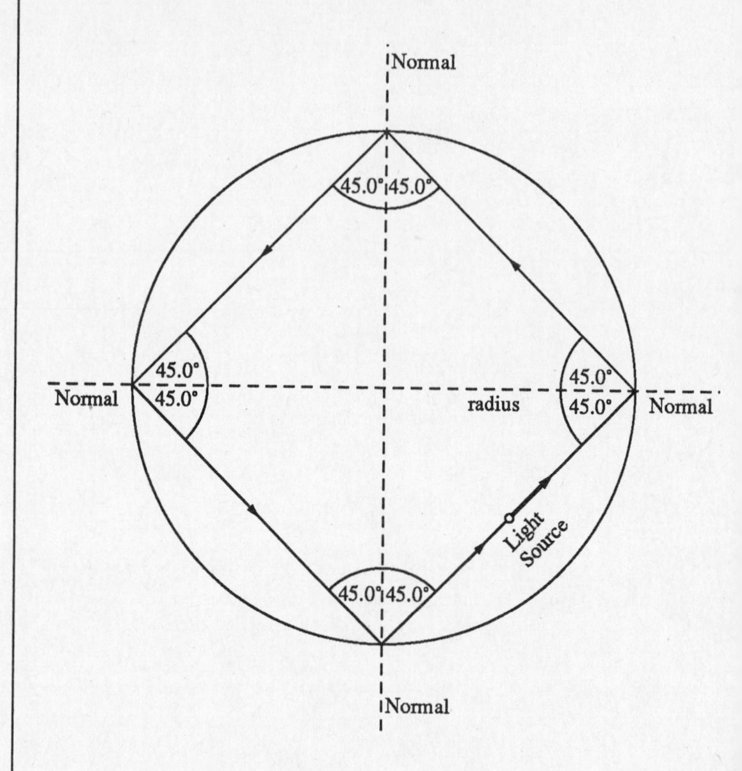

The ray from the light source is incident on the circumference at an angle of 45.0°
$n_i \sin \theta_i = n_r \sin \theta_r,$
$\sin \theta_r = n_i \sin \theta_i / n_r = (1.500)(\sin 45.0°)/(1.00)$
$= 1.06$
This is impossible, since ($\sin \theta_r$) cannot exceed one. Therefore, total internal reflection occurs and the path of the light ray is a diamond, as shown.

16. With a square block of glass, index of refraction = 1.50, it is impossible, when looking into one side, to see out of an adjacent side of the square block of glass. It appears to be a mirror. Use your knowledge of geometry and critical angles to show that this is true.

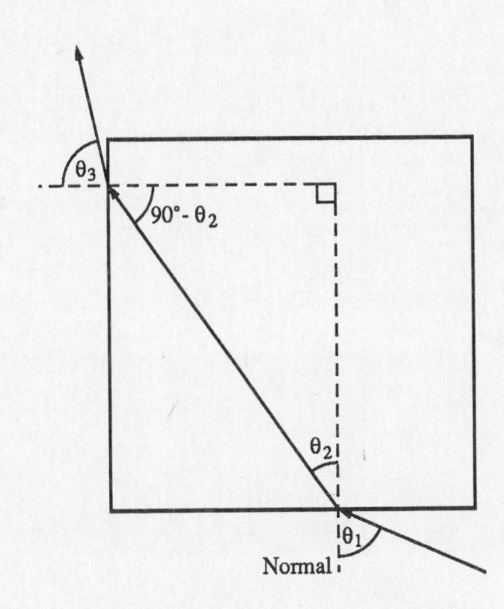

Say the light ray enters the glass at an angle θ_1, and is refracted to an angle θ_2.
$n_{air} \sin \theta_1 = n_{glass} \sin \theta_2$,
$\sin \theta_2 = (n_{air} \sin \theta_1)/(n_{glass}) = (1.0 \sin \theta_1)/(1.5)$
For the light ray to leave an adjacent side, $(90° - \theta_2)$ must be less than the critical angle. The critical angle is found from

$$\sin \theta_c = \frac{1}{n_{glass}} = \frac{1}{1.5} = 0.67, \text{ or } \theta_c = 42°.$$

Therefore, it must be true that
$(90° - \theta_2) < 42°$, or $\theta_2 > 48°$.
Recall that $\sin \theta_2 = (1.0 \sin \theta_1)/(1.5)$, so $\sin \theta_2$ and θ_2 are largest when θ_1 is 90°. In this case, $\sin \theta = 1.0/1.5 = 0.67$, or $\theta_2 = 42°$. But we found above that θ_2 must be greater than 48° for the light ray to leave an adjacent side. Since this is impossible, we conclude that one cannot see out of an adjacent side of a block of glass.

17. The index of refraction for red light in arsenic trioxide is 2.010, while the index of refraction for blue light is 2.023. Find the difference between the angles of refraction if white light is incident at an angle of 65.0°.

$n_i \sin \theta_i = n_r \sin \theta_r$,
$\sin \theta_r = n_i \sin \theta_i / n_r$

For red light,
$\sin \theta_r = (1.00)(\sin 65.0°)/(2.010) = 0.451$
$\theta_r = 26.8°$

For blue light,
$\sin \theta_r = (1.00)(\sin 65.0°)/(2.023) = 0.448$
$\theta_r = 26.6°$

Difference = 26.8° − 26.6° = 0.2°

18. The index of refraction for red light in a diamond is 2.410, while the index of refraction for blue light is 2.450. Find the difference in the speed of light in diamond.

$v_s = c/n_s$

For red light,
$v_s = (2.998 \times 10^8 \text{ m/s})/(2.410)$
$= 1.244 \times 10^8 \text{ m/s}$

For blue light,
$v_s = (2.998 \times 10^8 \text{ m/s})/(2.450)$
$= 1.224 \times 10^8 \text{ m/s}$
Difference $= (1.244 \times 10^8 \text{ m/s}) - (1.224 \times 10^8)$
$= 0.020 \times 10^8 \text{ m/s} = 2.0 \times 10^6 \text{ m/s}$

Chapter 18: Mirrors and Lenses

Practice Problems

page 374

1. Solve the Example Problem above using a ray diagram.

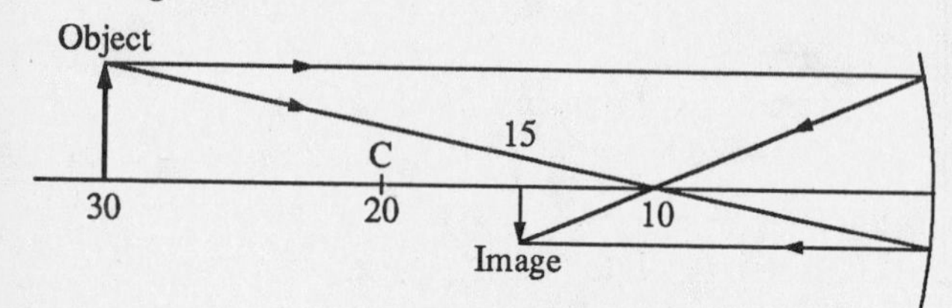

2. An object 3.0 mm high is 10.0 cm in front of a concave mirror having a 6.0–cm focal length. Find the image by means of

a. a ray diagram.

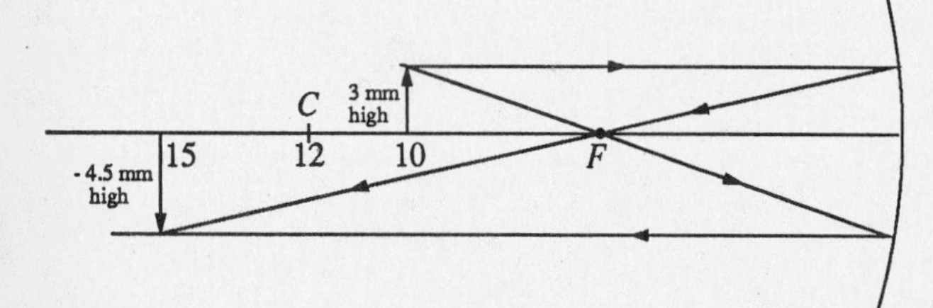

b. the mirror equation.

$$\frac{1}{f} = \frac{1}{d_o} + \frac{1}{d_i}, \text{ so}$$

$d_i = d_o f/(d_o - f)$
$= (10 \text{ cm})(6.0 \text{ cm})/(10 \text{ cm} - 6.0 \text{ cm})$
$= 15 \text{ cm}$

c. Find the magnification of the mirror.

$m = -d_i/d_o = -(15 \text{ cm})/(10.0 \text{ cm}) = -1.5$

d. What is the height of the image?

$m = h_i/h_o$, so
$h_i = mh_o = (-1.5)(3.0 \text{ mm}) = -4.5 \text{ mm}$

3. The image of an object is 30.0 cm from a concave mirror with a 20.0–cm radius of curvature. Locate the object.

$f = r/2 = (20.0 \text{ cm})/2 = 10.0 \text{ cm}$,
$1/d_o + 1/d_i = 1/f$, so
$d_o = fd_i/(d_i - f)$
$= (10.0 \text{ cm})(30.0 \text{ cm})/(30.0 \text{ cm} - 10.0 \text{ cm})$
$= 15.0 \text{ cm}$

Practice Problems

4. An old "magic trick" used a concave mirror to project an image the same size as the object and at the same distance from the mirror. If the object is 25 cm from the mirror, what should be the radius of the curvature of the mirror?

If $d_o = d_i$ then $1/f = 2/d_o$ or $f = \frac{1}{2}d_o$.

Now $r = 2f = d_o = 25$ cm

page 376

5. An object is 4.0 cm in front of a concave mirror having a 12.0–cm radius. Locate the image using the mirror equation and a ray diagram.

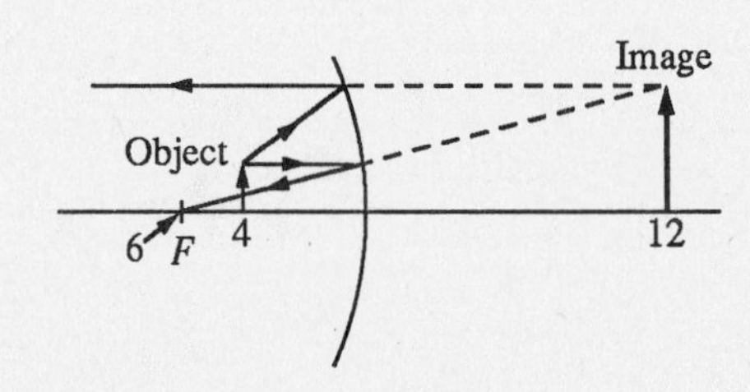

$f = r/2 = (12.0 \text{ cm})/2 = 6.0 \text{ cm}$,
$1/d_o + 1/d_i = 1/f$, so
$d_i = fd_o/(d_o - f)$
$= (6.0 \text{ cm})(4.0 \text{ cm})/(4.0 \text{ cm} - 6.0 \text{ cm})$
$= -12 \text{ cm}$

6. A concave mirror has a focal length of 9.0 cm. A 15–mm high object is placed 6.0 cm from the mirror.

a. Find the image using the mirror equation.

$1/d_o + 1/d_i = 1/f$, so
$d_i = fd_o/(d_o - f)$
$= (9.0 \text{ cm})(6.0 \text{ cm})/(6.0 \text{ cm} - 9.0 \text{ cm})$
$= -18 \text{ cm}$

b. How large is the image?

$m = h_i/h_o = -d_i/d_o = -(-18 \text{ cm})/(6.0 \text{ cm})$
$= +3.0$, so
$h_i = mh_o = (3.0)(15 \text{ mm}) = 45 \text{ mm}$

7. A 4.0–cm high candle is placed 10.0 cm from a concave mirror having a focal length of 16.0 cm.

 a. Where is the image located?

$1/d_o + 1/d_i = 1/f$, so
$d_i = fd_o/(d_o - f)$
$= \frac{(16.0 \text{ cm})(10.0 \text{ cm})}{(10.0 \text{ cm} - 16.0 \text{ cm})}$
$= -27$ cm

 b. What is the height of the candle's image?

$m = h_i/h_o = -d_i/d_o$
$= -(-27 \text{ cm})/(10.0 \text{ cm})$
$= +2.7$, so
$h_i = mh_o = (2.7)(4.0 \text{ cm}) = 11$ cm

8. What should be the radius of curvature of a concave mirror that magnifies an object placed 25 cm from the mirror by a factor of 3.0?

$m = -d_i/d_o = 3$, so
$d_i = -75$ cm
$1/f = 1/d_o + 1/d_i$ so
$f = d_od_i/(d_o + d_i)$
$= (25 \text{ cm})(-75 \text{ cm})/(25 \text{ cm} + (-75 \text{ cm}))$
$= 37.5$ cm and $r = 2f = 75$ cm

page 377

9. An object is 20.0 cm in front of a convex mirror with a – 15.0–cm focal length. Find the location of the image using

 a. a ray diagram.

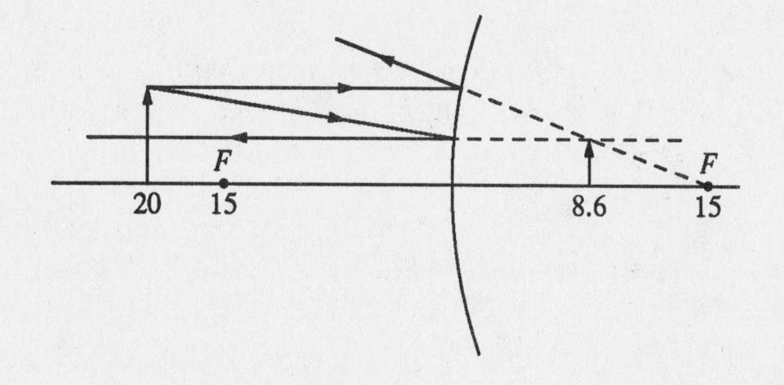

 b. the mirror equation.

$1/d_o + 1/d_i = 1/f$, so
$d_i = fd_o/(d_o - f)$
$= \frac{(-15.0 \text{ cm})(20.0 \text{ cm})}{(20.0 \text{ cm} - (-15.0 \text{ cm}))}$
$= -8.57$ cm

page 378

10. A convex mirror has a focal length of – 12 cm. A light bulb with a diameter of 6.0 cm is placed 60.0 cm in front of the mirror.

 a. Where is the image of the light bulb? Use the mirror equation.

$1/d_o + 1/d_i = 1/f$, so
$d_i = fd_o/(d_o - f)$
$= \frac{(-12 \text{ cm})(60.0 \text{ cm})}{(60.0 \text{ cm} - (-12 \text{ cm}))}$
$= -10$ cm

 b. What is the diameter of the image?

$m = h_i/h_o = -d_i/d_o$
$= -(-10 \text{ cm})/(60.0 \text{ cm}) = +0.17$, so
$h_i = mh_o = (0.17)(6.0 \text{ cm}) = 1.0$ cm

11. In a department store, a mirror used to watch for shoplifters has a focal length of – 40.0 cm. A person stands in an aisle 6.0 m from the mirror. Locate the person's image using the mirror equation. Is it erect or inverted? larger or smaller than the object?

$1/d_o + 1/d_i = 1/f$, so
$d_i = fd_o/(d_o - f)$
$= (-0.40 \text{ m})(6.0 \text{ m})/(6.0 \text{ m} - (-0.40 \text{ m}))$
$= -0.38$ m erect, smaller

Practice Problems

12. A convex mirror is needed to produce an image located 24 cm behind a mirror that is 3/4 the size of the object. What focal length should be specified?

$1/f = 1/d_o + 1/d_i$ so $f = d_o d_i/(d_o + d_i)$ and
$m = -d_i/d_o$ so $d_o = -d_i/m$.
Since $d_i = -24$ cm and $m = 0.75$,

$$d_o = \frac{-(-24 \text{ cm})}{0.75} = 32 \text{ cm and}$$

$$f = \frac{(32 \text{ cm})(-24 \text{ cm})}{32 \text{ cm} + (-24 \text{ cm})} = -96 \text{ cm}$$

page 381

13. Use a ray diagram to find the image position of an object 30 cm to the left of a convex lens with a +10–cm focal length. (Let 1 cm on the drawing represent 20 cm.)

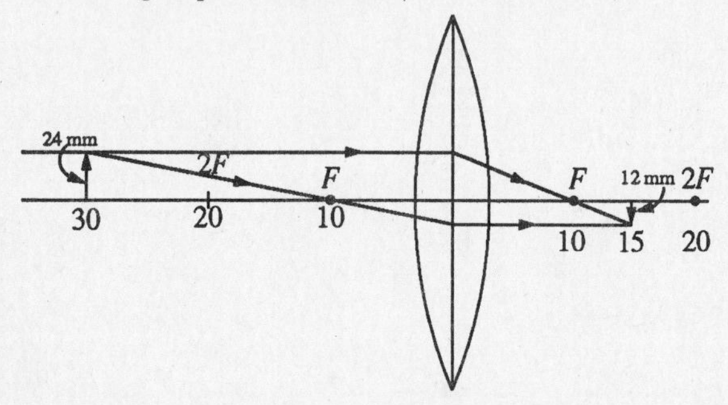

14. An object 2.25 mm high is 8.5 cm to the left of a convex lens of 5.5–cm focal length. Find the image distance and height.

$1/d_o + 1/d_i = 1/f$, so
$d_i = fd_o/(d_o - f)$
$= (5.5 \text{ cm})(8.5 \text{ cm})/(8.5 \text{ cm} - 5.5 \text{ cm})$
$= 16$ cm
$h_i = -d_i h_o/d_o = -(16 \text{ cm})(2.25 \text{ mm})/(8.5 \text{ cm})$
$= -4.2$ mm

15. An object is placed to the left of a 25–mm focal length convex lens so that its image is the same size as the object. What are the image and object distances?

$1/d_o + 1/d_i = 1/f$ with $d_o = d_i$ since
$m = -d_i/d_o$ and $m = -1$. Therefore,
$2/d_o = 1/f$, $d_o = d_i = 2f = 50$ mm

Practice Problems

16. A lens is needed to create an inverted image twice as large as the object when the object is 7.0 cm from the lens. What focal length lens is needed?

$m = -d_i/d_o$
so $d_i = -md_o = -(-2)(7.0 \text{ cm}) = 14$ cm.
$1/f = 1/d_o + 1/d_i$ so
$f = d_o d_i/(d_o + d_i)$
$= (7.0 \text{ cm})(14 \text{ cm})/(7.0 \text{ cm} + 14 \text{ cm})$
$= 4.7$ cm

page 383

17. A newspaper is held 6.0 cm from a convex lens of 20.0–cm focal length. Find the image distance of the newsprint image.

$1/d_o + 1/d_i = 1/f$, so
$d_i = fd_o/(d_o - f)$
$= (20.0 \text{ cm})(6.0 \text{ cm})/(6.0 \text{ cm} - 20.0 \text{ cm})$
$= -8.6$ cm

18. A magnifying glass has a focal length of 12.0 cm. A coin, 2.0 cm in diameter, is placed 3.4 cm from the lens.

a. Locate the image of the coin.

$1/d_o + 1/d_i = 1/f$, so
$d_i = fd_o/(d_o - f)$
$= (12 \text{ cm})(3.4 \text{ cm})/(3.4 \text{ cm} - 12 \text{ cm})$
$= -4.7$ cm

b. What is the diameter of the image?

$h_i = -h_o d_i/d_o$
$= -(2.0 \text{ cm})(-4.7 \text{ cm})/(3.4 \text{ cm})$
$= 2.8$ cm

19. A stamp collector wants to magnify images by 4.0 when the object is 3.5 cm from the lens. What focal length lens is needed?

$m = -d_i/d_o$ so
$d_i = -md_o = -(4.0)(3.5 \text{ cm}) = -14$ cm.
$1/f = 1/d_o + 1/d_i$ so
$f = d_o d_i/(d_o + d_i)$
$= (3.5 \text{ cm})(-14 \text{ cm})/(3.5 \text{ cm} + (-14 \text{ cm}))$
$= 4.7$ cm

Practice Problems

20. Suppose you are looking at a stamp through a magnifying glass and want to increase the size of the image. Should you move the glass closer to the stamp or farther away? Explain and indicate the maximum distance you should move it.

    From Figure (18–17), you can increase image size by making ($d_o - f$) as small as possible. Thus, increase d_o until it is almost f, which is the limit.

Chapter Review Problems

pages 388–389

1. Find the image of the object in Figure 18–25.

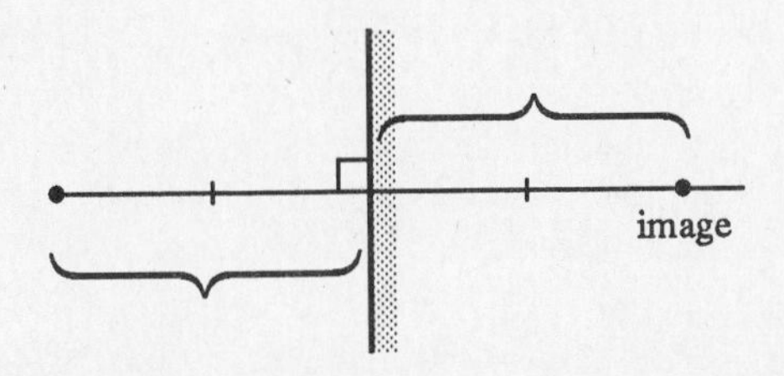

2. Penny wishes to take a picture of her image in a plane mirror. If the camera is 1.2 m in front of the mirror, at what distance should the camera lens be focused?

   The image is 1.2 m behind the mirror, so the camera lens should be set to 2.4 m.

3. Draw a ray diagram of a plane mirror to show that if you want to see yourself from your feet to the top of your head, the mirror must be at least half your height.

   The ray from top of head hits mirror halfway between eyes and top of head. Ray from feet hits mirror halfway between eyes and feet. Distance between the point the two rays hit the mirror is half the total height.

Chapter Review Problems

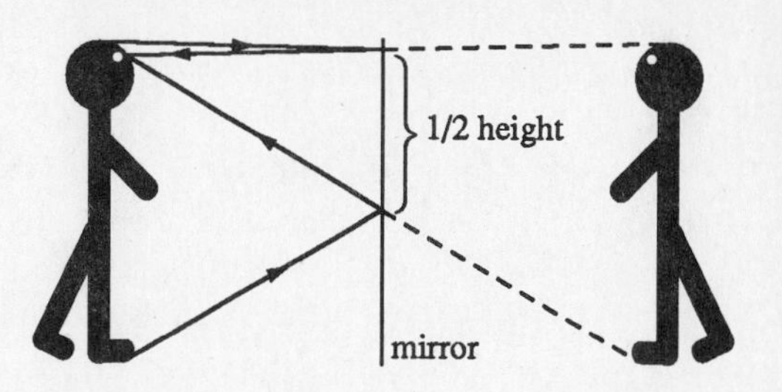

4. A concave mirror has a focal length of 10.0 cm. What is its radius of curvature?

   $c = 2f = 2(10.0 \text{ cm}) = 20.0 \text{ cm}$

5. Light from a distant star is collected by a concave mirror. How far from the mirror is the image of the star if the radius of curvature is 150 cm?

   Stars are far enough away that the light coming into the mirror can be considered to be parallel and parallel light will converge at the focal point. Since $c = 2f$, $f = \frac{c}{2} = \frac{150 \text{ cm}}{2} = 75.0$ cm

6. The sun falls on a concave mirror and forms an image 3.0 cm from the mirror. If an object 24 mm high is placed 12.0 cm from the mirror, where will its image be formed?

   The focal length of the mirror is 3.0 cm since that is the location of the image of the sun.

   a. Use a ray diagram.

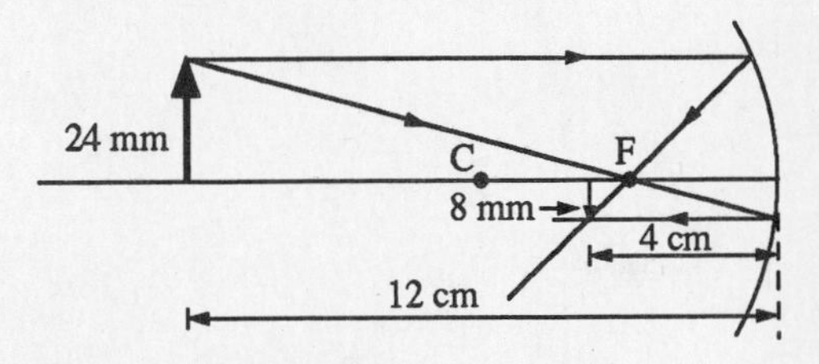

   b. Use the mirror equation.

$$\frac{1}{d_o} + \frac{1}{d_i} = \frac{1}{f}$$

$$d_i = \frac{fd_o}{(d_o - f)} = \frac{(3.0 \text{ cm})(12.0 \text{ cm})}{12.0 \text{ cm} - 3.0 \text{ cm}}$$

$$= 4.0 \text{ cm}$$

18

c. How high is the image?

$$m = \frac{-d_i}{d_o} = \frac{-4.0\text{ cm}}{12.0\text{ cm}} = -0.33$$

$$h_i = mh_o = (-0.33)(24\text{ mm}) = -8.0\text{ mm}$$

7. An object is 30.0 cm from a concave mirror of 15-cm focal length. The object is 1.8 cm high.

a. Locate the image, using the mirror equation.

$$\frac{1}{d_o} + \frac{1}{d_i} = \frac{1}{f}$$

$$d_i = \frac{d_o f}{(d_o - f)} = \frac{(30.0\text{ cm})(15\text{ cm})}{30.0\text{ cm} - 15\text{ cm}}$$

$$= 30\text{ cm}$$

b. How high is the image?

$$\frac{h_i}{h_o} = \frac{-d_i}{d_o}$$

$$h_i = \frac{-d_i h_o}{d_o} = \frac{-(30\text{ cm})(1.8\text{ cm})}{30.0\text{ cm}}$$

$$= -1.8\text{ cm}$$

8. A jeweler inspects a watch, with a diameter of 3.0 cm, by placing it 8.0 cm in front of a concave mirror of 12.0-cm focal length.

a. Where will the image of the watch appear?

$$\frac{1}{d_o} + \frac{1}{d_i} = \frac{1}{f}$$

$$d_i = \frac{d_o f}{(d_o - f)} = \frac{(8.0\text{ cm})(12\text{ cm})}{8.0\text{ cm} - 12.0\text{ cm}}$$

$$= -24\text{ cm}$$

b. What is the diameter of the image?

$$\frac{h_i}{h_o} = \frac{-d_i}{d_o}$$

$$h_i = \frac{-d_i h_o}{d_o} = \frac{-(-24\text{ cm})(3.0\text{ cm})}{8.0\text{ cm}}$$

$$= +9.0\text{ cm}$$

Chapter Review Problems

9. A dentist uses a small mirror of radius 40 mm to locate a cavity in a patient's tooth. If the mirror is concave and held 16 mm from the tooth, what is its magnification of the resulting image?

$$f = \frac{C}{2} = \frac{40\text{ mm}}{2} = 20\text{ mm}$$

$$\frac{1}{d_o} + \frac{1}{d_i} = \frac{1}{f}$$

$$d_i = \frac{d_o f}{(d_o - f)} = \frac{(16\text{ mm})(20\text{ mm})}{16\text{ mm} - 20\text{ mm}}$$

$$= -80\text{ mm}$$

$$m = \frac{-d_i}{d_o} = \frac{-(-80\text{ mm})}{16\text{ mm}} = 5.0$$

10. A production line inspector wants a mirror that produces an upright image with magnification 7.5 when it is located 14.0 mm from a machine part.

a. What kind of mirror would do this job?

An enlarged, upright image only results from a concave mirror, with object inside of the focal length.

b. What is its radius of curvature?

$$m = \frac{-d_i}{d_o}, \text{ so}$$

$$d_i = -md_o = -(7.5)(14.0\text{ mm})$$
$$= -105\text{ mm}$$

$$\frac{1}{d_o} + \frac{1}{d_i} = \frac{1}{f}$$

$$f = \frac{d_o d_i}{(d_i - d_o)} = \frac{(14.0\text{ mm})(-105\text{ mm})}{14.0\text{ mm} - 105\text{ mm}}$$

$$= 16.2\text{ mm}$$

radius of curvature $= 2f = (2)(16.2\text{ mm})$
$= 32.4\text{ mm}$

11. Shiny lawn spheres placed on pedestals are convex mirrors. One such sphere has a diameter of 40 cm. A 12–cm robin sits in a tree 1.5 m from the sphere.

a. Where is the image of the robin?

$r = 20\text{ cm},\ f = -10\text{ cm}$

$$\frac{1}{d_o} + \frac{1}{d_i} = \frac{1}{f}$$

$$d_i = \frac{fd_o}{(d_o - f)} = \frac{(-10.0\text{ cm})(1.5\text{ m})}{1.5\text{ m} - (-10.0\text{ cm})}$$
$$= -9.4\text{ cm}$$

b. How long is the robin's image?

$$m = \frac{h_i}{h_o} = \frac{-d_i}{d_o} = \frac{-(-9.4\text{ cm})}{150\text{ cm}}$$
$$= +0.063$$
$$h_i = mh_o = (0.063)(12\text{ cm}) = 0.75\text{ cm}$$

12. The focal length of a convex lens is 17 cm. A candle is placed 34 cm in front of the lens. Make a ray diagram to find the location of the image.

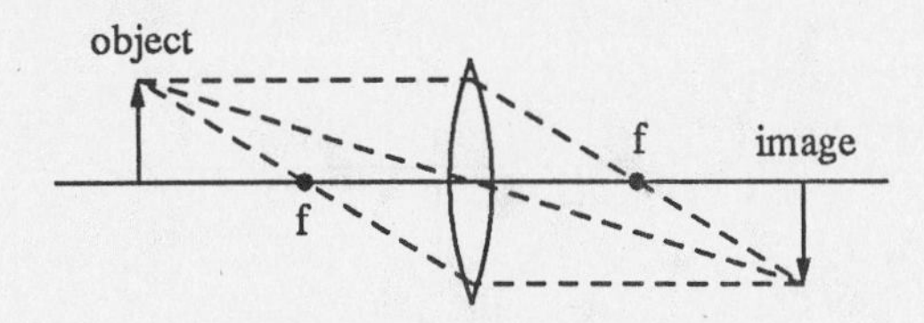

13. The convex lens of a copy machine has a focal length of 25.0 cm. A letter to be copied is placed 40.0 cm from the lens.

a. How far from the lens is the copy paper located?

$$\frac{1}{d_o} + \frac{1}{d_i} = \frac{1}{f}$$

$$d_i = \frac{d_o f}{(d_o - f)} = \frac{(40.0\text{ cm})(25.0\text{ cm})}{40.0\text{ cm} - 25.0\text{ cm}}$$
$$= 66.7\text{ cm}$$

b. The machine was adjusted to give an enlarged copy of the letter. How much larger will the copy be?

$$\frac{h_i}{h_o} = \frac{d_i}{d_o}$$

$$h_i = \frac{d_i h_o}{d_o} = \frac{(66.7\text{ cm})(h_o)}{40.0\text{ cm}} = 1.67\ h_o$$

Chapter Review Problems

14. Camera lenses are described in terms of their focal length. A 50.0 mm lens has a focal length of 50.0 mm.

a. A camera is focused on an object 3.0 m away using a 50.0 mm lens. Locate the position of the image.

$$\frac{1}{d_o} + \frac{1}{d_i} = \frac{1}{f}$$

$$d_i = \frac{d_o f}{(d_o - f)} = \frac{(3.0 \times 10^3\text{ mm})(50.0\text{ mm})}{3.0 \times 10^3\text{ mm} - 50.0\text{ mm}}$$
$$= 51\text{ mm}$$

b. A 1.00×10^3 mm lens is focused on an object 125 m away. Locate the position of the image.

$$\frac{1}{d_o} + \frac{1}{d_i} = \frac{1}{f}$$

$$d_i = \frac{d_o f}{(d_o - f)} = \frac{(125\text{ m})(1.00\text{ m})}{125\text{ m} - 1.00\text{ m}}$$
$$= 1.01\text{ m}$$
$$= 1.01 \times 10^3\text{ mm}$$

15. Solve Problem 10 using a lens rather than a mirror.

An enlarged, upright image requires a convex lens with the object inside the focal length.

$$m = \frac{-d_i}{d_o}$$

$$d_i = -md_o = -(7.5)(14.0\text{ mm}) = -105\text{ mm}$$

$$\frac{1}{d_o} + \frac{1}{d_i} = \frac{1}{f}$$

$$f = \frac{d_o d_i}{(d_i + d_o)} = \frac{(14.0\text{ mm})(-105\text{ mm})}{14.0\text{ mm} - 105\text{ mm}}$$
$$= 16.2\text{ mm}$$

16. A convex lens is needed to produce an image located 24 cm behind the lens that is 0.75 the size of the object. What focal length should be specified?

$$d_i = 0.75 d_o,\ \text{so}\ d_o = \frac{d_i}{0.75} = \frac{24\text{ cm}}{0.75} = 32\text{ cm}$$

$$\frac{1}{f} = \frac{1}{d_i} + \frac{1}{d_o},\ \text{so}$$

$$f = \frac{d_o d_i}{d_o + d_i} = \frac{(32\text{ cm})(24\text{ cm})}{32\text{ cm} + 24\text{ cm}} = 14\text{ cm}$$

Chapter Review Problems

17. A microscope slide with an onion cell is placed 12 mm from the objective lens of a microscope. The focal length of the objective lens is 10.0 mm.

a. How far from the lens is the image formed?

$$\frac{1}{d_o} + \frac{1}{d_i} = \frac{1}{f}$$

$$d_i = \frac{d_o f}{(d_o - f)} = \frac{(12.0 \text{ mm})(10.0 \text{ mm})}{12.0 \text{ mm} - 10.0 \text{ mm}}$$

$$= 60.0 \text{ mm}$$

b. What is the magnification of this image?

$$m_o = \frac{-d_i}{d_o} = \frac{-60.0 \text{ mm}}{12.0 \text{ mm}} = -5.0$$

c. The real image formed is located 10.0 mm beneath the eyepiece lens of the microscope. If the focal length of the eyepiece is 20.0 mm, where does the final image appear?

$$\frac{1}{d_o} + \frac{1}{d_i} = \frac{1}{f}$$

$$d_i = \frac{d_o f}{(d_o - f)} = \frac{(10.0 \text{ mm})(20.0 \text{ mm})}{10.0 \text{ mm} - 20.0 \text{ mm}}$$

$$= -20.0 \text{ mm}$$

d. What is the final magnification of this compound system?

$$m_e = \frac{-d_i}{d_o} = \frac{-(-20.0 \text{ mm})}{10.0 \text{ mm}} = 2.00$$

$$m_{total} = (m_o)(m_e) = (-5.0)(2.00) = -10.0$$

18. In order to clearly read a book at 25 cm away, a farsighted person needs an image distance of −45 cm. What focal length is needed?

$$\frac{1}{f} = \frac{1}{d_o} + \frac{1}{d_i}, \text{ so}$$

$$f = \frac{d_o d_i}{(d_o - d_i)} = \frac{(25 \text{ cm})(-45 \text{ cm})}{25 \text{ cm} + (-45 \text{ cm})}$$

$$= 56 \text{ cm}$$

Supplemental Problems (Appendix B)

1. Sally's face is 75 cm in front of a plane mirror. Where is the image of Sally's face?

75 cm behind the mirror

2. A concave mirror has a focal length of 10.0 cm. What is its radius of curvature?

$r = 2f = 2(10.0 \text{ cm}) = 20.0 \text{ cm}$

3. Light from a distant star is collected by a concave mirror that has a radius of curvature of 150 cm. How far from the mirror is the image of the star?

$$f = \frac{r}{2} = \frac{150 \text{ cm}}{2} = 75.0 \text{ cm}$$

$\frac{1}{f} = \frac{1}{d_i} + \frac{1}{d_o}$, but d_o is extremely large, so

$\frac{1}{f} = \frac{1}{d_i}$, or $d_i f = 75.0 \text{ cm}$

4. An object is placed 25.0 cm away from a concave mirror that has a focal length of 5.00 cm. Where is the image located?

$\frac{1}{f} = \frac{1}{d_i} + \frac{1}{d_o}$, so

$$d_i = \frac{d_o f}{(d_o - f)} = \frac{(25.0 \text{ cm})(5.00 \text{ cm})}{(25.0 \text{ cm} - 5.00 \text{ cm})}$$

$$= 6.25 \text{ cm, or}$$

6.25 cm in front of the mirror

5. An object and its image as seen in a concave mirror are the same height when the object is 48.4 cm from the mirror. What is the focal length of the mirror?

For a concave mirror, an object and its image have the same height when the object is two focal lengths from the mirror. Therefore, 48.4 cm = $2f$, or f = 48.4 cm/2 = 24.2 cm

6. An object placed 50.0 cm from a concave mirror gives a real image 33.3 cm from the mirror. If the image is 28.4 cm high, what is the height of the object?

$$m = \frac{h_i}{h_o} = \frac{-d_i}{d_o} = \frac{-33.3 \text{ cm}}{50.0 \text{ cm}} = -0.666, \text{ so}$$

$$h_o = \frac{h_i}{m} = \frac{-28.4 \text{ cm}}{(-0.666)} = 42.6 \text{ cm}$$

m is negative, so the image is inverted and h_i is negative.

7. An object 15.8 cm high is located 87.6 cm from a concave mirror that has a focal length of 17.0 cm.

a. Where is the image located?

$\frac{1}{f} = \frac{1}{d_i} + \frac{1}{d_o}$, so

$$d_i = \frac{d_o f}{(d_o - f)} = \frac{(87.6 \text{ cm})(17.0 \text{ cm})}{(87.6 \text{ cm} - 17.0 \text{ cm})}$$

$= 21.1$ cm

b. How high is the image?

$$m = \frac{h_i}{h_o} = \frac{-d_i}{d_o} = \frac{(-21.1 \text{ cm})}{(86.7 \text{ cm})} = -0.241, \text{ so}$$

$h_i = mh_o = (-0.241)(15.8 \text{ cm})$
$= -3.81$ cm; inverted

The negative sign indicates an inverted image.

8. The image of the moon is formed by a concave mirror whose radius of curvature is 4.20 m at a time when the moon's distance is 3.80×10^5 km. What is the diameter of the image of the moon if the diameter of the moon is 3480 km?

$$f = \frac{r}{2} = \frac{4.20 \text{ m}}{2} = 2.10 \text{ m}$$

$\frac{1}{f} = \frac{1}{d_i} + \frac{1}{d_o}$, but d_o is extremely large, so

$\frac{1}{f} = \frac{1}{d_i}$, or $d_i = f = 2.10 \text{ m} = 2.10 \times 10^{-3}$ km

$$m = \frac{h_i}{h_o} = \frac{-d_i}{d_o} = \frac{-(2.10 \times 10^{-3} \text{ km})}{(3.80 \times 10^5 \text{ km})}$$

$= -5.53 \times 10^{-9}$, so

$h_i = mh_o = (-5.53 \times 10^{-9})(3480 \text{ km})$
$= -1.92 \times 10^{-5}$ km
$= -1.92$ cm; inverted

The negative sign indicates an inverted image.

9. A shaving mirror has a radius of curvature of 30.0 cm. When a face is 10.0 cm away from the mirror, what is the magnification of the mirror?

A shaving mirror is concave.

$$f = \frac{r}{2} = \frac{30.0 \text{ cm}}{2} = 15.0 \text{ cm}$$

$\frac{1}{f} = \frac{1}{d_i} + \frac{1}{d_o}$, so

$$d_i = \frac{d_o f}{(d_o - f)} = \frac{(10.0 \text{ cm})(15.0 \text{ cm})}{(10.0 \text{ cm} - 15.0 \text{ cm})}$$

$= -30$ cm

$$m = \frac{h_i}{h_o} = \frac{-d_i}{d_o} = \frac{-(-30 \text{ cm})}{(10.0 \text{ cm})} = 3.0$$

m is positive, so the image is erect.

10. A convex mirror has a focal length of -16 cm. How far behind the mirror does the image of a person 3.0 m away appear?

$\frac{1}{f} = \frac{1}{d_i} + \frac{1}{d_o}$, so

$$d_i = \frac{d_o f}{(d_o - f)} = \frac{(3.0 \text{ m})(-0.16 \text{ m})}{(3.0 \text{ m} - (-0.16 \text{ m}))}$$

$= -0.15$ m, or
15 cm behind the mirror.

11. How far behind the surface of a convex mirror, focal length of -6.0 cm, does a car 10.0 m from the mirror appear?

$\frac{1}{f} = \frac{1}{d_i} + \frac{1}{d_o}$, so

$$d_i = \frac{d_o f}{(d_o - f)} = \frac{(10.0 \text{ m})(-0.060 \text{ m})}{(10.0 \text{ m} - (-0.060 \text{ m}))}$$

$= -0.060$ m
or 6.0 cm behind the mirror.

12. A converging lens has a focal length of 25.5 cm. If it is placed 72.5 cm from an object, what distance from the lens will the image be?

$\frac{1}{f} = \frac{1}{d_i} + \frac{1}{d_o}$, so

$$d_i = \frac{d_o f}{(d_o - f)} = \frac{(72.5 \text{ cm})(25.5 \text{ cm})}{(72.5 \text{ cm} - 25.5 \text{ cm})}$$

$= 39.3$ cm

18

13. If an object is 10.0 cm from a converging lens that has a focal length of 5.00 cm, how far from the lens will the image be?

$$\frac{1}{f} = \frac{1}{d_i} + \frac{1}{d_o}, \text{ so}$$

$$d_i = \frac{d_o f}{(d_o - f)} = \frac{(10.0 \text{ cm})(5.00 \text{ cm})}{(10.0 \text{ cm} - 5.00 \text{ cm})}$$

$$= 10 \text{ cm}$$

14. The focal length of a lens in a box camera is 10.0 cm. The fixed distance between the lens and the film is 11.0 cm. If an object is clearly focused on the film, how far must the object be from the lens?

$$\frac{1}{f} = \frac{1}{d_i} + \frac{1}{d_o}, \text{ so}$$

$$d_o = \frac{df}{(d_i - f)} = \frac{(11.0 \text{ cm})(10.0 \text{ cm})}{(11.0 \text{ cm} - 10.0 \text{ cm})}$$

$$= 1.1 \times 10^2 \text{ cm}$$

15. An object 3.0 cm tall is placed 22 cm in front of a converging lens. A real image is formed 11 cm from the lens. What is the size of the image?

$$m = \frac{h_i}{h_o} = \frac{-d_i}{d_o} = \frac{-(11 \text{ cm})}{(22 \text{ cm})} = -0.50, \text{ so}$$

$$h_i = mh_o = (-0.50)(3.0 \text{ cm})$$
$$= -1.5 \text{ cm; inverted}$$

The negative sign indicates an inverted image.

16. An object 3.0 cm tall is placed 20 cm in front of a converging lens. A real image is formed 10 cm from the lens. What is the focal length of the lens?

$$\frac{1}{f} = \frac{1}{d_i} + \frac{1}{d_o} = \frac{1}{(10 \text{ cm})} + \frac{1}{(20 \text{ cm})} = \frac{3}{(20 \text{ cm})},$$

$$\text{so } f = \frac{20 \text{ cm}}{3} = 6.7 \text{ cm}$$

Supplemental Problems

17. What is the focal length of the lens in your eye when you read a book that is 35.0 cm from your eye? The distance from the lens to the retina is 0.19 mm.

$$\frac{1}{f} = \frac{1}{d_i} + \frac{1}{d_o}, \text{ so}$$

$$f = (d_i d_o)/(d_i + d_o) = = \frac{(0.19 \text{ mm})(350 \text{ mm})}{(0.19 \text{ mm} + 350 \text{ mm})}$$

$$= 0.19 \text{ mm}$$

18. When an object 5.0 cm tall is placed 12 cm from a converging lens, an image is formed on the same side of the lens as the object but the image is 61 cm away from the lens.

a. What is the focal length of the lens?

$$f = \frac{d_i d_o}{d_i + d_o} = \frac{(-61 \text{ cm})(12 \text{ cm})}{-61 \text{ cm} + 12 \text{ cm}}$$

$$= 14.9 \text{ cm}$$

b. What is the size of the image?

$$\frac{h_i}{h_o} = \frac{-d_i}{d_o}$$

$$h_i = h_o\left[\frac{-d_i}{d_o}\right] = 5.0 \text{ cm}\left[-\frac{-61}{12}\right] = 25.4 \text{ cm;}$$

image is erect.

Chapter 19: Diffraction and Interference of Light

Practice Problems

page 395

1. Violet light falls on two slits separated by 1.90×10^{-5} m. A first–order line appears 13.2 mm from the central bright line on a screen 0.600 m from the slits. What is the wavelength of the violet light?

$\lambda = xd/L$
$= (13.2 \times 10^{-3}\ \text{m})(1.90 \times 10^{-5}\ \text{m})/(0.600\ \text{m})$
$= 4.18 \times 10^{-7}$ m
$= 418$ nm

2. Yellow–orange light from a sodium lamp of wavelength 596 nm is used instead of the violet light of Practice Problem 1. The slit separation and distance to the screen are not changed. What is the distance from the central line to the first–order yellow line?

$x = \lambda L/d$
$= (5.96 \times 10^{-7}\ \text{m})(0.600\ \text{m})/(1.90 \times 10^{-5}\ \text{m})$
$= 0.0188$ m
$= 18.8$ mm

3. A physics class uses a laser with a known wavelength of 632.8 nm in a double–slit experiment. The slit separation is unknown. A student places a screen 1.000 m from the slits and finds the first–order line 65.5 mm from the central line. What is the slid separation?

$d = \lambda L/x$
$= (6.328 \times 10^{-7}\ \text{m})(1.000\ \text{m})/(65.5 \times 10^{-3}\ \text{m})$
$= 9.66 \times 10^{-6}$ m

4. Using the double–slit apparatus of Practice Problem 3, the student now measures the wavelength of an unknown green light. The first–order line is 55.8 mm from the central line. What is the wavelength of the light?

$\lambda = xd/L$
$= (55.8 \times 10^{-3}\ \text{m})(9.66 \times 10^{-6}\ \text{m})/(1.000\ \text{m})$
$= 5.39 \times 10^{-7}$ m
$= 539$ nm

Practice Problems

page 398

5. Monochromatic green light of wavelength 546 nm falls on a single slit of width 0.095 mm. The slit is located 75 cm from a screen. How far from the center of the central band is the first dark band?

$x = \lambda L/w$
$= (5.46 \times 10^{-7}\ \text{m})(0.75\ \text{m})/(9.5 \times 10^{-5}\ \text{m})$
$= 4.3 \times 10^{-3}$ m
$= 4.3$ mm

6. Light from a He–Ne laser ($\lambda = 632.8$ nm) falls on a slit of unknown width. A pattern is formed on a screen 1.15 m away where the first dark band is 7.5 mm from the center of the central bright band. How wide is the slit?

$$w = \frac{\lambda L}{x}$$

$= (6.328 \times 10^{-7}\ \text{m})(1.15\ \text{m})/(7.5 \times 10^{-3}\ \text{m})$
$= 9.7 \times 10^{-5}$ m

7. Yellow light falls on a single slit 0.0295 mm wide. On a screen 60.0 cm away, there is a dark band 12.0 mm from the center of the bright central band. What is the wavelength of the light?

$$\lambda = \frac{wx}{L}$$

$= (2.95 \times 10^{-5}\ \text{m})(1.20 \times 10^{-2}\ \text{m})/(0.600\ \text{m})$
$= 5.90 \times 10^{-7}$ m
$= 590$ nm

Practice Problems

8. White light falls on a single slit 0.050 mm wide. A screen is placed 1.00 m away. A student first puts a blue–violet filter (λ = 441 nm) over the slit, then a red filter (λ = 622 nm). The student measures the width of the central peak, that is, the distance between the two dark bands.

a. Will the band be wider with the blue or the red filter?

Red, because central peak width is proportional to wavelength.

b. Find the width for the two filters.

Width = $2x = 2\lambda L/w$.

For blue,

$$2x = \frac{2(4.41 \times 10^{-7}\ \text{m})(1.00\ \text{m})}{(5.0 \times 10^{-5}\ \text{m})}$$

$= 18$ mm

For red,

$$2x = \frac{2(6.22 \times 10^{-7}\ \text{m})(1.00\ \text{m})}{(5.0 \times 10^{-5}\ \text{m})}$$

$= 25$ mm.

Chapter Review Problems

pages 404–405

1. Using a compass and ruler, construct a scale diagram of the interference pattern that results when waves 1 cm in length fall on two slits 2 cm apart. The slits may be represented by two dots spaced 2 cm apart and kept to one side of the paper. Draw a line through all lines of reinforcement. Draw dotted lines through all nodal lines.

Chapter Review Problems

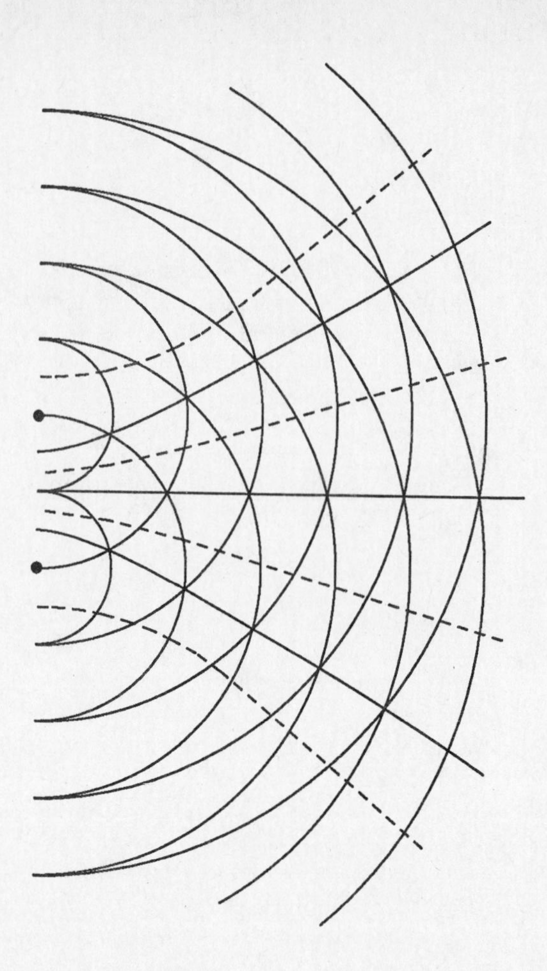

2. A radio station uses two antennas and broadcasts at 600 kHz. Radio waves travel at the speed of light. The waves from the two antennas are kept in step.

a. What is the wavelength of the signals emitted by the station?

$v = f\nu$, so

$$\lambda = \frac{v}{f} = \frac{(3.00 \times 10^{8}\ \text{m/s})}{(600 \times 10^{3}\ \text{Hz})} = 500\ \text{m}$$

b. The occupants of a home that is located 17 500 m from one antenna and 19 500 m from the other antenna have their receiver tuned to the station. Is the reception good or poor? Explain?

The path difference is
19 500 m − 17 500 m = 2000 m.
The reception should be good since it is a multiple of the wavelength, and constructive interference will take place.

Chapter Review Problems

3. Light falls on a pair of slits 1.90×10^{-3} cm apart. The slits are 80.0 cm from the screen. The first–order bright line is 1.90 cm from the central bright line. What is the wavelength of the light?

$$\lambda = \frac{xd}{L} = \frac{(1.90 \text{ cm})(1.90 \times 10^{-3} \text{ cm})}{80.0 \text{ cm}}$$

$$= 4.51 \times 10^{-5} \text{ cm} = 451 \text{ nm}$$

4. Light of wavelength 542 nm falls on a double slit. First–order bright bands appear 4.00 cm from the central bright line. The screen is 1.20 m from the slits. How far apart are the slits?

$$\lambda = \frac{xd}{L}, \text{ so}$$

$$d = \frac{\lambda L}{x} = \frac{(5.42 \times 10^{-7} \text{ m})(1.20 \text{ m})}{4.00 \times 10^{-2} \text{ m}}$$

$$= 1.63 \times 10^{-5} \text{ m}$$

5. A lecturer is demonstrating two–slit interference with sound waves. Two speakers are used, 4.0 m apart. The sound frequency is 325 Hz. (The speed of sound is 343 m/s.) Students sit in seats 4.5 m away. What is the spacing between the locations where no sound is heard because of destructive interference?

$$v = f\lambda, \text{ so}$$

$$\lambda = \frac{v}{f} = \frac{343 \text{ m/s}}{325 \text{ Hz}} = 1.06 \text{ m}$$

$$x = \frac{\lambda L}{d} = \frac{(1.06 \text{ m})(4.5 \text{ m})}{4.0 \text{ m}} = 1.2 \text{ m}$$

6. Monochromatic light passes through a single slit with a width of 0.010 cm and falls on a screen 100 cm away. If the distance from the center of the pattern to the first band is 0.60 cm, what is the wavelength of the light?

$$y = \frac{\lambda L}{w}, \text{ so}$$

$$\lambda = \frac{yw}{L} = \frac{(0.60 \text{ cm})(0.010 \text{ cm})}{100 \text{ cm}}$$

$$= 6.00 \times 10^{-5} \text{ cm}$$

Chapter Review Problems

7. Light with a wavelength of 4.5×10^{-5} cm passes through a single slit and falls on a screen 100 cm away. If the slit is 0.015 cm wide, what is the distance from the center of the pattern to the first dark band?

$$y = \frac{\lambda L}{w} = \frac{(4.5 \times 10^{-5} \text{ cm})(100 \text{ cm})}{0.015 \text{ cm}} = 0.30 \text{ cm}$$

8. Monochromatic light with a wavelength of 400 nm passes through a single slit and falls on a screen 90 cm away. If the distance of the first–order dark band is 0.30 cm from the center of the pattern, what is the width of the slit?

$$y = \frac{\lambda L}{w}, \text{ so}$$

$$w = \frac{\lambda L}{y} = \frac{(4.00 \times 10^{-5} \text{ cm})(90 \text{ cm})}{0.30 \text{ cm}}$$

$$= 1.2 \times 10^{-2} \text{ cm}$$

9. Sound waves of frequency 550 Hz enter a window 1.2 m wide. The window is in the exact center of one wall of a theater 24 m × 12 m. The window is 12 m from the opposite wall, along which is a row of seats occupied by people. The theater is acoustically prepared to prevent the reflection of sound waves, and the speed of sound is 330 m/s. Two people in the row along the wall hear no sound. Where are they sitting?

$$v = f\lambda, \text{ so}$$

$$\lambda = \frac{v}{f} = \frac{330 \text{ m/s}}{550 \text{ Hz}} = 0.60 \text{ m}$$

$$y = \frac{\lambda L}{w} = \frac{(0.60 \text{ m})(12 \text{ m})}{1.2 \text{ m}} = 6.0 \text{ m}$$ to either side of center of the wall

10. A good diffraction grating has 2.50×10^{3} lines/cm. What is the distance between two lines in the grating?

$$d = 1/(2.50 \times 10^{3} \text{ lines/cm})$$
$$= 4.00 \times 10^{-4} \text{ cm}$$

19

Chapter Review Problems

11. Using a grating with spacing of 4.00×10^{-4} cm, a red line appears 16.5 cm from the central line on a screen. The screen is 1.00 m from the grating. What is the wavelength of the red light?

$$\lambda = \frac{xd}{L} = \frac{(16.5\text{ cm})(4.00 \times 10^{-4}\text{ cm})}{100\text{ cm}}$$

$$= 6.60 \times 10^{-5}\text{ cm} = 660\text{ nm}$$

12. A spectrometer uses a grating with 12 000 lines/cm. Find the angles at which red light 632 nm and blue light 421 nm have the first–order bright bands.

$$d = \frac{1}{12\,000\text{ lines/cm}} = 8.33 \times 10^{-5}\text{ cm}$$

$\lambda = d \sin \theta$, so $\sin \theta = \frac{\lambda}{d}$

For red light,

$$\sin \theta = \frac{6.32 \times 10^{-5}\text{ cm}}{8.33 \times 10^{-5}\text{ cm}} = 0.759, \text{ so } \theta = 49.4°$$

For blue light,

$$\sin \theta = \frac{4.21 \times 10^{-5}\text{ cm}}{8.33 \times 10^{-5}\text{ cm}} = 0.505, \text{ so } \theta = 30.4°$$

13. The ridges in the *Morpho* butterfly wing in the chapter opening photograph are spaced about 2.2×10^{-7} m apart. Explain how they could cause the wing to appear iridescent blue.

The ridges act as a diffraction grating. Any blue light of wavelength approximately 4.40×10^{-7} m is reflected strongly from this grating.

14. Janet uses a 33–1/3 rpm record as a diffraction grating. She shines a laser, $\lambda = 632.8$ nm, on the grating. On a screen 4.0 m from the record, a series of red dots 21 mm apart are seen.

a. How many ridges are there in a centimeter on the record?

$\lambda = \frac{xd}{L}$, so

$$d = \frac{\lambda L}{x} = \frac{(6.328 \times 10^{-7}\text{ m})(4.0\text{ m})}{0.021\text{ m}}$$

$$= 1.2 \times 10^{-4}\text{ m} = 1.2 \times 10^{-2}\text{ cm}$$

$$\frac{1}{d} = \frac{1}{1.2 \times 10^{-2}\text{ cm}} = 83\text{ ridges/cm}$$

b. She checks her results by noting that the ridges came from a song that lasted 4.01 minutes and took up 16 mm on the record. How many ridges should there be in a centimeter?

Number of ridges is
(4.01 min)(33.333 rev/min) = 134 ridges.
(134 ridges)/(1.6 cm) = 84 ridges/cm.

15. A camera with a 50 mm lens set at *f*/8 aperture has an opening 6.25 mm in diameter. Suppose this lens acts like a slit 6.25 mm wide. For light with $\lambda = 550$ nm, what is the resolution of the lens, the distance from the middle of the central bright band to the first–order dark band? The film is 50 mm from the lens.

$$y = \frac{\lambda L}{w} = \frac{(5.5 \times 10^{-4}\text{ mm})(50\text{ mm})}{6.25\text{ mm}}$$

$$= 4.4 \times 10^{-3}\text{ mm}$$

16. The owner of the camera in the previous problem tries to decide which film to buy for it. The expensive one, called fine–grain film, has 200 grains/mm. The less costly coarse–grain film has only 50 grains/mm. If the owner wants a grain to be no smaller than the width of the central bright band calculated above, which film should be purchased?

Band width is 4.4×10^{-3} mm.
Coarse grains are 1/50 mm = 2.0×10^{-2} mm, fine grains are 1/2000 mm = 5×10^{-3} mm.
Coarse grain is good enough.

17. Suppose the Hubble Space Telescope, 2.4 m in diameter, is in orbit 100 km above Earth and is turned to look at Earth. If you ignore the effect of the atmosphere, what is the resolution of this telescope? Use λ = 500 nm.

$$y = \frac{\lambda L}{w} = \frac{(5.00 \times 10^{-7}\ \text{m})(100\ 000\ \text{m})}{2.4\ \text{m}}$$

$$= 2.1 \times 10^{-2}\ \text{m} = 2.1\ \text{cm}$$

18. The image formed on the retina of the eye shows the effect of diffraction. The diameter of the iris opening in bright light is 3.0 mm. For green light, 545 nm wavelength, find the resolution of the eye. That is, find the distance from the center of the central band to the dark band. Assume the distance from iris to retina is 2.5 cm.

$$y = \frac{\lambda L}{w} = \frac{(5.45 \times 10^{-5}\ \text{cm})(2.5\ \text{cm})}{0.30\ \text{cm}}$$

$$= 4.5 \times 10^{-4}\ \text{cm}$$

19. Cone cells in the retina are about 1.5 μm apart. On how many cone cells does the image found in the previous problem fall? Would the eye's resolution be better if the iris were much larger, like the 10 mm diameter of the eagle's eye? Explain.

$(4.6 \times 10^{-6}\ \text{m})/(1.5 \times 10^{-6}\ \text{m/cell}) = 3$ cells. You need about 3 cells to tell light and dark edges. It would do no good to increase the resolution of the eye by using a larger iris because resolution is limited by cone separation in the retina.

Supplemental Problems (Appendix B)

1. Monochromatic light passes through two slits that are 0.0300 cm apart and it falls on a screen 120 cm away. The first-order image is 0.160 cm from the middle of the center band. What is the wavelength of the light used?

$\lambda = xd/L$
$= (1.60 \times 10^{-3}\ \text{m})(3.00 \times 10^{-4}\ \text{m})/(1.20\ \text{m})$
$= 4.00 \times 10^{-7}\ \text{m} = 4.00 \times 10^{2}\ \text{nm}$

2. Green light passes through a double slit for which d = 0.20 mm and it falls on a screen 2.00 m away. The first-order image is at 0.50 cm. What is the wavelength of the light?

$\lambda = xd/L$
$= (5.0 \times 10^{-3}\ \text{m})(2.0 \times 10^{-4}\ \text{m})/(2.00\ \text{m})$
$= 5.0 \times 10^{-7}\ \text{m} = 5.0 \times 10^{2}\ \text{nm}$

3. Yellow light that has a wavelength of 6.00×10^{2} nm passes through two narrow slits that are 0.200 mm apart. An interference pattern is produced on a screen 180 cm away. What is the location of the first-order image?

$x = \lambda L/d$
$= (6.00 \times 10^{-7}\ \text{m})(1.80\ \text{m})/(2.00 \times 10^{-4}\ \text{m})$
$= 5.40 \times 10^{-3}\ \text{m} = 5.40\ \text{mm}$

4. Violet light that has a wavelength of 4.00×10^{2} nm passes through two slits that are 0.0100 cm apart. How far away must the screen be so the first-order image is at 0.300 cm?

$L = xd/\lambda$

$$= \frac{(3.00 \times 10^{-3}\ \text{m})(1.00 \times 10^{-4}\ \text{m})}{(4.00 \times 10^{-7}\ \text{m})}$$

$= 0.750\ \text{m}$

5. Two radio transmitters are 25.0 m apart and each one sends out a radio wave with a wavelength of 10.0 m. The two radio towers act exactly like a double-slit source for light. How far from the central band is the first-order image if you are 15.0 km away? (Yes, this really happens, radio stations can and do fade in and out as you cross the nodals and the anti-nodals.)

$x = \lambda L/d = (10.0\ \text{m})(15.0 \times 10^{3}\ \text{m})/(25.0\ \text{m})$
$= 6.00 \times 10^{3}\ \text{m} = 6.00\ \text{km}$

6. Monochromatic light passes through a single slit, 0.500 mm wide, and falls on a screen 1.0 m away. If the distance from the center of the pattern to the first band is 2.6 mm, what is the wavelength of the light?

$\lambda = xw/L$
$= (2.6 \times 10^{-3}\ \text{m})(5.00 \times 10^{-4}\ \text{m})/(1.0\ \text{m})$
$= 1.3 \times 10^{-6}\ \text{m}$

7. Red light that has a wavelength of 7.50×10^2 nm passes through a single slit that is 0.1350 mm wide. How far away from the screen must the slit be if the first dark band is 0.9000 cm away from the central bright band?

$L = xw/\lambda$

$= \frac{(9.000 \times 10^{-3}\text{ m})(1.350 \times 10^{-4}\text{ m})}{(7.50 \times 10^{-7}\text{ m})}$

$= 1.62$ m

8. Microwaves with a wavelength of 3.5 cm pass through a single slit 0.85 cm wide and fall on a screen 91 cm away. What is the distance to the first-order band?

$x = \lambda L/w$
$= (3.5 \times 10^{-2}\text{ m})(0.91\text{ m})/(8.5 \times 10^{-3}\text{ m})$
$= 3.7$ m

9. Radio waves that are emitted by two adjacent radio transmitters behave like light waves coming from a double slit. If two transmitters, 1500 m apart each, send out radio waves with a wavelength of 150 m, what is the diffraction angle?

$\lambda = d \sin \theta$, so
$\sin \theta = \lambda/d = (150\text{ m})/(1500\text{ m}) = 0.101$,
$\theta = 5.71°$

10. What is the average distance between the lines of a diffraction grating if the number of lines per millimeter is 425?

average distance = mm/(425 lines)
$= 2.35 \times 10^{-3}$ mm/line

11. A transmission grating with 5.85×10^3 lines/cm illuminated by monochromatic light that has a wavelength of 492 nm. What is the diffraction angle for the first-order image?

$\lambda = d \sin \theta$, $\sin \theta = \lambda/d$
$d =$ cm/(5.85×10^3 lines)
$= 1.71 \times 10^{-4}$ cm per line
$\sin \theta = \lambda/d = (4.92 \times 10^{-7}\text{ m})/(1.71 \times 10^{-6}\text{ m})$
$= 0.288$,
$\theta = 16.7°$

Supplemental Problems

12. Monochromatic light illuminates a transmission grating having 5900 lines/cm. The diffraction angle for a first-order image is 18.0°. What is the wavelength of the light in nanometers?

$\lambda = d \sin \theta$
$d =$ cm/(5900 lines) $= 1.695 \times 10^{-4}$ cm per line
$\lambda = (1.659 \times 10^{-4}\text{ cm})(\sin 18.0°)$
$= 5.24 \times 10^{-5}$ cm $= 524$ nm

13. A transmission grating, 5.80×10^3 lines/cm, is illuminated by a monochromatic light source that has a wavelength of 495 nm. How far from the center line is the first-order image if the distance to the grating is 1.25 m?

$x = \lambda L/d$
$d =$ cm/(5.80×10^3 lines)
$= 1.72 \times 10^{-4}$ cm per line
$x = (4.95 \times 10^{-7}\text{ m})(1.25\text{ m})/(1.72 \times 10^{-6}\text{ m})$
$= 0.360$ m

14. A pinhole camera uses a 1.5-mm hole instead of a lens to form an image. What is the resolution of this camera for green light, 545-nm wavelength, if the film is 6.0 cm behind the pinhole?

Use single-slit equation, $x = \lambda L/w$

$x = \frac{(5.45 \times 10^{-7}\text{ m})(6.0 \times 10^{-2}\text{ m})}{(1.5 \times 10^{-3}\text{ m})}$

$= 2.18 \times 10^{-5}$ m,
so the resolution is 2.18×10^{-5} m.

Chapter 20: Static Electricity

Practice Problems

page 420

1. Two positive charges of 6.0×10^{-6} C are separated by 0.50 m. What force exists between the charges?

$$F = \frac{Kqq'}{d^2}$$

$$= \frac{(9.0\times10^{9}\ \text{N}\cdot\text{m}^2/\text{C}^2)(6.0\times10^{-6}\ \text{C})(6.0\times10^{-6}\ \text{C})}{(0.5\text{m})^2}$$

$$= 1.3\ \text{N}$$

2. A negative charge of -2.0×10^{-4} C and a positive charge of 8.0×10^{-4} C are separated by 0.30 m. What is the force between the two charges?

$$F = \frac{Kqq'}{d^2}$$

$$= \frac{(9.0\times10^{9}\text{N}\cdot\text{m}^2/\text{C}^2)(-2.0\times10^{-4}\text{C})(8.0\times10^{-4}\text{C})}{(0.30\text{m})^2}$$

$$= -1.6 \times 10^{4}\ \text{N}$$

3. A negative charge of -6.0×10^{-6} C exerts an attractive force 65 N on a second charge 0.050 m away. What is the magnitude of the second charge?

$$F = \frac{Kqq'}{d^2}$$

$$q' = \frac{Fd^2}{Kq}$$

$$= \frac{(65\ \text{N})(0.05\ \text{m})^2}{(9.0\times10^{9}\ \text{N}\cdot\text{m}^2/\text{C}^2)(6.0\times10^{-6}\ \text{C})}$$

$$= 3.0 \times 10^{-6}\ \text{C}$$

Practice Problems

4. An object with charge $+7.5 \times 10^{-7}$ C is placed at the origin. The position of a second object, charge $+1.5 \times 10^{-7}$ C is varied from 1.0 cm to 5.0 cm. Draw a graph of the force on the object at the origin.

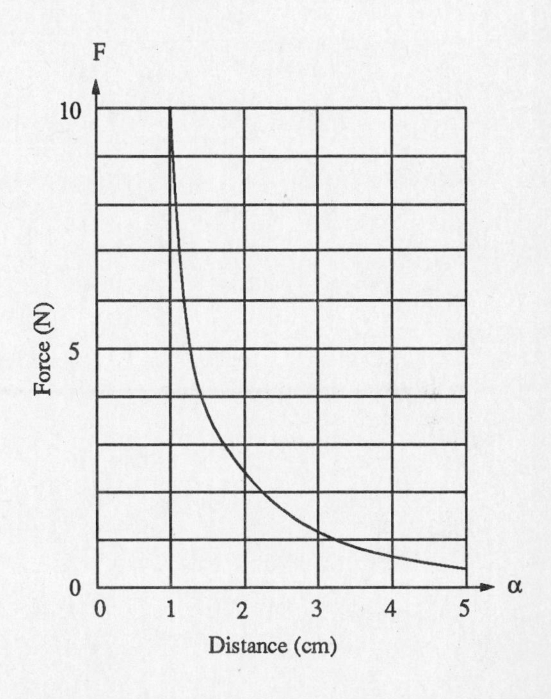

5. The charge on B in the example problem is replaced by $+3.00 \times 10^{-6}$ C. Use graphical methods to find the net force on A.

Magnitudes of all forces remain the same. The direction changes to 42° above the $-x$ axis, or 138°.

20

Chapter Review Problems

pages 422–423

1. Two charges, q_1 and q_2, are separated by a distance, d, and exert a force, f, on each other.

$$F = \frac{Kq_1q_2}{d^2}$$

What new force will exist if

a. q_1 is doubled?

$2q_1$, then new force $= 2f$

b. q_1 and q_2 are cut in half?

$\frac{1}{2}q_1$ and $\frac{1}{2}q_2$, then new force $= \left[\frac{1}{2}\right]\left[\frac{1}{2}\right]f = \frac{1}{4}f$

c. d is tripled?

$3d$, then new force $= \frac{f}{(3)^2} = \frac{1}{9}f$

d. d is cut in half?

$\frac{1}{2}d$, then new force $= \frac{f}{\left[\frac{1}{2}\right]^2} = \left[\frac{2}{1}\right]^2 f = 4f$

e. q_1 is tripled and d is doubled?

$3q_1$ and $2d$, then new force $= \frac{(3)f}{(2)^2} = \frac{3}{4}f$

2. How many excess electrons are on a ball with a charge of -4.0×10^{-17} C?

$$\frac{(-4.0 \times 10^{-17}\text{ C})}{1}\left[\frac{1\text{ electron}}{-1.60 \times 10^{-19}\text{ C}}\right] = 250\text{ electrons}$$

3. How many coulombs of electrical charge are on the electrons in a nickel coin? Follow this method to find the answer.

a. Find the number of atoms in a nickel coin. A nickel coin has a mass of about 5 g. Each mole (6.02×10^{23} atoms) has a mass of about 58 g.

A coin is (5 g)/(58 g) = 0.09 of a mole. Thus it has $(0.09)(6.02 \times 10^{23}) = 5 \times 10^{22}$ atoms.

b. Find the number of electrons in the coin. Each nickel atom has 28 electrons.

$(5 \times 10^{22}$ atoms)(28 electrons/atom) $= 1 \times 10^{24}$ electrons

c. Find how many coulombs of charge are on the electrons.

$(1.6 \times 10^{-19}$ coulombs/electron)$(1 \times 10^{24}$ electrons) $= -2 \times 10^{5}$ coulombs

4. A strong lightning bolt transfers about 25 C to Earth.

   a. How many electrons are transferred?

$$\frac{-25\ \text{C}}{1}\left[\frac{1\ \text{electron}}{-1.60\times10^{-19}\ \text{C}}\right] = 1.6\times10^{20}\ \text{electrons}$$

   b. If each water molecule donates one electron, what mass of water lost an electron to the lightning? One mole of water has a mass of 18 g.

$$\frac{1.6\times10^{20}\ \text{electrons}}{1}\left[\frac{1\ \text{molecule}}{1\ \text{electron}}\right]\left[\frac{1\ \text{mole}}{6.02\times10^{23}\ \text{molecule}}\right]\left[\frac{18\ \text{g}}{\text{mole}}\right] = 4.8\times10^{-3}\ \text{g}$$

5. What is the total charge on all of the electrons in one liter, 1.0 kg, of water? One mole of water has a mass of 18 g and each molecule of water contains 10 electrons.

$$\frac{1.0\ \text{kg}}{1}\left[\frac{1000\ \text{g}}{\text{kg}}\right]\left[\frac{1\ \text{mole}}{18\ \text{g}}\right]\left[\frac{6.02\times10^{23}\ \text{molecules}}{1\ \text{mole}}\right]\left[\frac{10\ \text{electrons}}{\text{molecule}}\right]\left[\frac{-1.6\times10^{-19}\ \text{C}}{\text{electron}}\right] = -5.4\times10^{7}\ \text{C}$$

6. Two electrons in an atom are separated by 1.5×10^{-10} m, the typical size of an atom. What is the force between them?

$$F = \frac{Kqq'}{d^2} = \frac{(9.0\times10^{9}\ \text{N}\cdot\text{m}^2/\text{C}^2)(-1.6\times10^{-19}\ \text{C})(-1.6\times10^{-19}\ \text{C})}{(1.5\times10^{-10}\ \text{m})^2} = 1.0\times10^{-8}\ \text{N}.$$

7. Object A has a charge $+1.8\times10^{-6}$ C. Object B has a charge -1.0×10^{-6} C. They are 0.014 m apart. What is the force on A? on B?

   The magnitudes are equal:
   $F_A = F_B = Kqq'/d^2 = (9.00\times10^{9}\ \text{Nm}^2/\text{C}^2)(+1.8\times10^{-6}\ \text{C})(-1.0\times10^{-6}\ \text{C})/(0.014\ \text{m})^2 = -83\ \text{N}.$
   The directions are opposite ... (or) each toward the other object.

8. A positive and a negative charge, each of magnitude 1.5×10^{-5} C, are separated by a distance of 15 cm. Find the force on each of the particles.

$$F = \frac{Kqq'}{d^2} = \frac{(9.0\times10^{9}\ \text{N}\cdot\text{m}^2/\text{C}^2)(1.5\times10^{-5}\ \text{C})(-1.5\times10^{-19}\ \text{C})}{(1.5\times10^{-2}\ \text{m})^2} = -90\ \text{N}$$

   The force on each charge is 90 N, toward the other charge.

9. Two negatively–charged bodies with -5.0×10^{-5} C are 0.20 m from each other. What force acts on each particle?

$$F = \frac{Kq_1q_2}{d^2} = \frac{(9.0 \times 10^9\ \text{N}\cdot\text{m}^2/\text{C})(-5.0 \times 10^{-5}\ \text{C})^2}{(0.20\ \text{m})^2} = 5.6 \times 10^2\ \text{N}.$$

10. Two negative charges of -3.0×10^{-6} C exert a repulsive force of 2.0 N on each other. By what distance are they separated?

$$F = \frac{Kq^2}{d^2}, \text{ so } d = \sqrt{Kq^2/F}$$

$$d = \sqrt{\frac{(9.0 \times 10^9\ \text{N}\cdot\text{m}^2/\text{C})(-3.0 \times 10^{-6}\ \text{C})^2}{(20.0\ \text{N})}} = 0.20\ \text{m}.$$

11. How far apart are two electrons if they exert a force of repulsion of 1.0 N on each other?

$$F = \frac{Kq_1q_2}{d^2}, \text{ so } d = \sqrt{\frac{Kq_1q_2}{F}} = \sqrt{\frac{(9.0 \times 10^9\ \text{N}\cdot\text{m}^2/\text{C}^2)(-1.60 \times 10^{-19}\ \text{C})^2}{1.0\ \text{N}}} = 1.5 \times 10^{-14}\ \text{m}$$

12. A force of -4.4×10^3 N exists between a positive charge of 8.0×10^{-4} C and a negative charge of -3.0×10^{-4} C. What distance separates the charges?

$$F = \frac{Kq_1q_2}{d^2}, \text{ so } d = \sqrt{\frac{Kq_1q_2}{F}} = \sqrt{\frac{(9.0 \times 10^9\ \text{N}\cdot\text{m}^2/\text{C}^2)(8.0 \times 10^{-4}\ \text{C})(-3.0 \times 10^{-4}\ \text{C})}{-4.4 \times 10^3\ \text{N}}} = 0.70\ \text{m}$$

13. Two identical positive charges exert a repulsive force of 6.4×10^{-9} N when separated by a distance of 3.8×10^{-10} m. Calculate the charge of each.

$$F = \frac{Kq_1q_2}{d^2} = \frac{Kq^2}{d^2}, \text{ so } q = \sqrt{\frac{Fd^2}{K}} = \sqrt{\frac{(6.4 \times 10^{-9}\ \text{N})(3.8 \times 10^{-10}\ \text{m})^2}{9.0 \times 10^9\ \text{N}\cdot\text{m}^2/\text{C}^2}} = 3.2 \times 10^{-19}\ \text{C}$$

14. The hydrogen atom contains a proton, mass 1.67×10^{-27} kg, and an electron, mass 9.11×10^{-31} kg. The average distance between them is 5.3×10^{-11} m. The charge of the proton is the same size, opposite sign of an electron.

a. What is the magnitude of the average electrostatic attraction between them?

$$F_C = \frac{Kq_1q_2}{d^2} = \frac{(9.0 \times 10^9\ \text{N}\cdot\text{m}^2/\text{C}^2)(1.6 \times 10^{-19}\ \text{C})^2}{(5.3 \times 10^{-11}\ \text{m})^2} = 8.2 \times 10^{-8}\ \text{N}.$$

b. What is the magnitude of the average gravitational attraction between them?

$$F_g = \frac{Gm_1m_2}{d^2} = \frac{(6.7 \times 10^{-11}\ \text{N}\cdot\text{m}^2/\text{kg}^2)(9.11 \times 10^{-31}\ \text{kg})(1.67 \times 10^{-27}\ \text{kg})}{(5.3 \times 10^{-11}\ \text{m})^2} = 3.6 \times 10^{-47}\ \text{N}.$$

c. How do the magnitudes of the two forces compare?

Gravitational force is weaker by a huge factor.

Chapter Review Problems

15. A positive charge of 3.0×10^{-6} C is pulled on by two negative charges. One, -2.0×10^{-6} C, is 0.050 m north and the other, -4.0×10^{-6} C, is 0.030 m to the south. What total force is exerted on the positive charge?

$$F_1 = \frac{(9.0 \times 10^9\ \text{N}\cdot\text{m}^2/\text{C}^2)(3.0 \times 10^{-6}\ \text{C})(-2.0 \times 10^{-6}\ \text{C})}{(0.050\ \text{m})^2} = -2.2 \times 10^1\ \text{N, north.}$$

$$F_2 = \frac{(9.0 \times 10^9\ \text{N}\cdot\text{m}^2/\text{C}^2)(3.0 \times 10^{-6}\ \text{C})(-4.0 \times 10^{-6}\ \text{C})}{(0.030\ \text{m})^2} = -1.2 \times 10^2\ \text{N, south.}$$

$$F = F_2 - F_1 = (-1.2 \times 10^2\ \text{N}) - (-2.2 \times 10^1\ \text{N}) = -98\ \text{N, south.}$$

16. Three particles are placed in a line. The left particle has a charge of -67×10^{-6} C, the middle $+45 \times 10^{-6}$ C, and the right -83×10^{-6} C. The middle particle is 72 cm from each of the others.

Let force to the right be positive.

a. Find the net force on the middle particle.

$$F_{\text{net}} = F_\ell + (-F_r) = \frac{Kq_m q_\ell}{d^2} - \frac{Kq_m q_r}{d^2}$$

$$= \frac{(9.0 \times 10^9\ \text{N}\cdot\text{m}^2/\text{C}^2)(45 \times 10^{-6}\ \text{C})(67 \times 10^{-6}\ \text{C})}{(0.72\ \text{m})^2}$$

$$- \frac{(9.0 \times 10^9\ \text{N}\cdot\text{m}^2/\text{C}^2)(45 \times 10^{-6}\ \text{C})(83 \times 10^{-6}\ \text{C})}{(0.72\ \text{m})^2}$$

$$= 13\ \text{N, right}$$

b. Find the net force on the right particle.

$$F_{\text{net}} = (-F_\ell) + (F_m) = -\frac{Kq_\ell q_r}{(2d)^2} + \frac{Kq_m q_r}{d^2}$$

$$= \frac{-(9.0 \times 10^9\ \text{N}\cdot\text{m}^2/\text{C}^2)(67 \times 10^{-6}\ \text{C})(83 \times 10^{-6}\ \text{C})}{[2(0.72\ \text{m})]^2}$$

$$+ \frac{(9.0 \times 10^9\ \text{N}\cdot\text{m}^2/\text{C}^2)(45 \times 10^{-6}\ \text{C})(83 \times 10^{-6}\ \text{C})}{(0.72\ \text{m})^2}$$

$$= 41\ \text{N, left}$$

20

Chapter Review Problems

17. Charges of 4.5×10^{-6} C exist on the three spheres in Figure 20–12. Find the magnitude of the total force on the top sphere (sphere B).

$$F_1 = \frac{Kqq}{d^2} = \frac{(9.0 \times 10^9\ \text{N}\cdot\text{m}^2/\text{C}^2)(4.5 \times 10^{-6}\ \text{C})^2}{(0.040\ \text{m})^2} = 114\ \text{N, to left}$$

The distance between the other two charges is $\sqrt{(0.040\ \text{m})^2 + (0.030\ \text{m})^2} = 0.050$ m, and

$\tan\theta = \dfrac{0.030\ \text{N}}{0.040\ \text{N}}$, so $\theta = 37°$ down from horizontal.

$$F = \frac{Kqq}{d^2} = \frac{(9.0 \times 10^9\ \text{N}\cdot\text{m}^2/\text{C}^2)(4.5 \times 10^{-6}\ \text{C})^2}{(0.050\ \text{m})^2} = 72.9\ \text{N at } 37°.$$

The components of F are:
$F_x = F\cos\theta = 72.9\cos 37° = 58$ N
$F_y = F\sin\theta = 72.9\sin 37° = 44$ N

The components of resultant force are
$F_x = 114$ N + 58 N = 172 N, to left. $F_y = 44$ N, down.

$F = \sqrt{(44\ \text{N})^2 + (172\ \text{N})^2} = 177$ N and $\tan\theta = \dfrac{44\ \text{N}}{172\ \text{N}}$, so $\theta = 14°$

$F = 1.8 \times 10^2$ N at 14° down from horizontal.

18. Two charges, q_1 and q_2, are at rest near a positive test charge, q, of 7.2×10^{-6} C. The first charge, q_1, is a positive charge of 3.6×10^{-6} C, located 0.025 m away from q at 35°; q_2 is a negative charge of -6.6×10^{-6} C, located 0.068 m away at 125°.

a. Determine the magnitude of each of the forces acting on q.

$$F_1 = \frac{Kqq_1}{d^2} = \frac{(9.0 \times 10^9\ \text{N}\cdot\text{m}^2/\text{C}^2)(7.2 \times 10^{-6}\ \text{C})(3.6 \times 10^{-6}\ \text{C})}{(0.025\ \text{m})^2} = 3.7 \times 10^2\ \text{N, away}$$

$$F_2 = \frac{Kqq_2}{d^2} = \frac{(9.0 \times 10^9\ \text{N}\cdot\text{m}^2/\text{C}^2)(7.2 \times 10^{-6}\ \text{C})(-6.6 \times 10^{-6}\ \text{C})}{(0.068\ \text{m})^2} = 92\ \text{N, toward}$$

b. Sketch a force diagram.

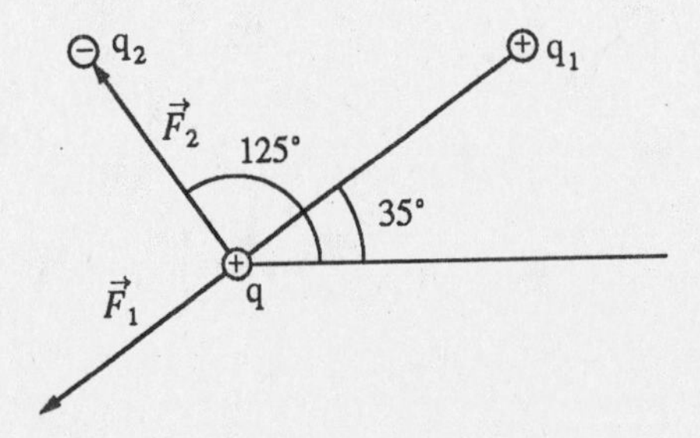

c. Graphically determine the resultant force acting on q.

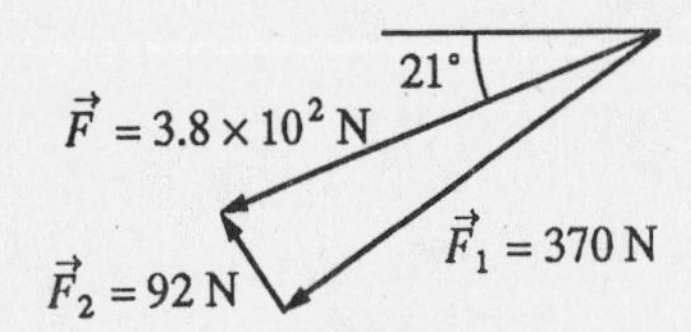

Chapter Review Problems

19. Two pith balls shown in Figure 20–14 each have a mass of 1.0 g and equal charges. One pith ball is suspended by an insulating thread. The other is brought to 3.0 cm from the suspended ball. The suspended ball is now hanging with the thread forming an angle of 30.0° with the vertical. The ball is in equilibrium with F_E, mg and T adding vectorially to yield zero.

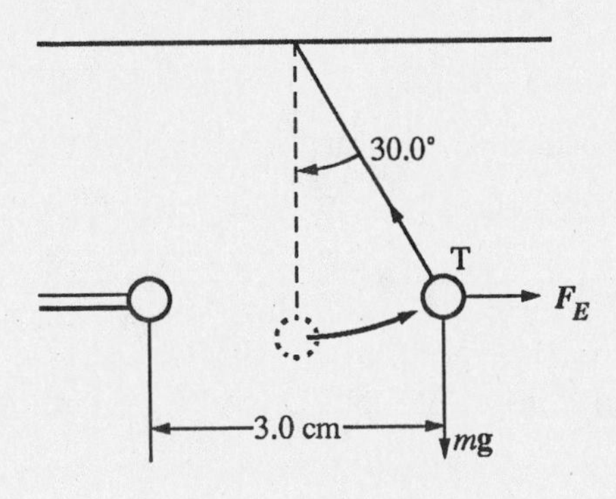

Calculate

a. mg.

$mg = (1.0 \times 10^{-3}\text{ kg})(9.8\text{ m/s}^2) = 9.8 \times 10^{-3}\text{ N}.$

b. F_E.

$$\tan 30.0° = \frac{F}{mg}$$

$$F = mg \tan 30.0° = (1.0 \times 10^{-3}\text{ kg})(9.8\text{ m/s}^2)(\tan 30.0°) = 5.7 \times 10^{-3}\text{ N}$$

c. the charge on the balls.

$$F = \frac{Kqq'}{d^2}$$

$$F = \frac{Kq^2}{d^2}$$

$$q = \sqrt{\frac{Fd^2}{K}} = \sqrt{\frac{(5.7 \times 10^{-3}\text{ N})(3.0 \times 10^{-2}\text{ m})^2}{(9.0 \times 10^9\text{ N}\cdot\text{m}^2/\text{C}^2)}} = 2.4 \times 10^{-8}\text{ C}.$$

Supplemental Problems (Appendix B)

1. Two charges, q_1 and q_2, are separated by a distance, d, and exert a force, f, on each other. What new force, f, will exist if d is doubled?

$$f = \frac{Kq_1q_2}{d^2}$$

$$f' = \frac{Kq_1q_2}{(2d)^2} = \frac{Kq_1q_2}{4d^2} = \frac{f}{4}$$

2. Two charges, q_1 and q_2, are separated by a distance, d, and exert a force, f, on each other. What new force, f, will exist if q_1 and q_2 are both doubled?

$$f = \frac{Kq_1q_2}{d^2}$$

$$f' = \frac{K(2q_1)(2q_2)}{d^2} = \frac{4Kq_1q_2}{d^2} = 4f$$

3. Two identical point charges are separated by a distance of 3.0 cm and they repel each other with a force of 4.0×10^{-5} N. What is the new force if the distance between the point charges is doubled?

$F \propto \frac{1}{d^2}$, so $\frac{F_2}{F_1} = \frac{d_1^2}{d_2^2}$, or

$$F_2 = \left[\frac{d_1}{d_2}\right]^2 F_1 = \left[\frac{1}{2}\right]^2 (4.0 \times 10^{-5}\ \text{N}) = 1.0 \times 10^{-5}\ \text{N}$$

4. An electric force of 2.5×10^{-4} N acts between two small equally–charged spheres which are 2.0 cm apart. Calculate the force acting between the spheres if the charge on one of the spheres is doubled and the spheres move to a 5.0–cm separation.

$F = \frac{Kqq'}{d^2}$, so $F_1 = \frac{Kq_1q_1'}{d_1^2}$, and $F_2 = \frac{Kq_2q_2'}{d_2^2}$, or $\frac{F_2}{F_1} = \left[\frac{q_2q_2'}{q_1q_1'}\right]\left[\frac{d_1}{d_2}\right]^2$

From the problem statement, $q_2 = q_1$, $q_2' = 2q_1'$, and $\frac{d_1}{d_2} = \frac{2.0\ \text{cm}}{5.0\ \text{cm}} = 0.40$.

Therefore, $\frac{F_2}{F_1} = (2)(0.40)^2 = 0.32$, or

$$F_2 = 0.32F_1 = 0.32(2.5 \times 10^{-4}\ \text{N}) = 8.0 \times 10^{-5}\ \text{N}$$

5. How many electrons would be required to have a total charge of 1.00 C on a sphere?

$$(1.00\ \text{C})\left[\frac{\text{electron}}{1.60 \times 10^{-19}\ \text{C}}\right] = 6.25 \times 10^{18}\ \text{electrons}$$

6. If two identical charges, of 1.000 C each, are separated by a distance of 1.00 km, what is the force between them?

$$F = \frac{Kqq'}{d^2} = \frac{(9.0 \times 10^9\ \text{N·m}^2/\text{C}^2)(1.000\ \text{C})^2}{(1.00 \times 10^3\ \text{m})^2} = +9.0 \times 10^3\ \text{N}$$

The positive charge indicates a repulsive force.

7. Two point charges are separated by 10.0 cm. If one charge is $+20.00\ \mu$C and the other is $-6.00\ \mu$C, what is the force between them?

$$F = \frac{Kqq'}{d^2} = \frac{(9.0 \times 10^9\ \text{N·m}^2/\text{C}^2)(20.00 \times 10^{-6}\ \text{C})(-6.0 \times 10^{-6}\ \text{C})}{(0.100\ \text{m})^2}$$

$= -1.1 \times 10^2$ N; the force is attractive.

Supplemental Problems

8. The two point charges in the previous problem are allowed to touch each other and are again separated by 10.0 cm. Now what is the force between them?

   If the charges touch, the two charges become equal and one half of the total charge:
   $q = q' = (+20.00\ \mu C + (-6.00\ \mu C))/2 = +7.00\ \mu C$

   $$F = \frac{Kqq'}{d^2} = \frac{(9.0 \times 10^9\ N \cdot m^2/C^2)(7.00 \times 10^{-6}\ C)^2}{(0.100\ m)^2} = +44\ N \text{ away}$$

   The force is repulsive.

9. Determine the electrostatic force of attraction between a proton and an electron that are separated by 5.00×10^2 nm.

   $$F = \frac{Kqq'}{d^2} = \frac{(9.00 \times 10^9\ N \cdot m^2/C^2)(1.60 \times 10^{-19}\ c)(1.60 \times 10^{-19}\ C)}{(5.00 \times 10^{-7}\ m)^2} = -9.2 \times 10^{-16}\ N$$

10. Find the force between two charged spheres that are 1.25 cm apart if the charge on one sphere is 2.50 μC and the charge on the other sphere is 1.75×10^{-8} C.

    $$F = \frac{Kqq'}{d^2} = \frac{(9.0 \times 10^9\ N \cdot m^2/C^2)(2.50 \times 10^{-6}\ C)(1.75 \times 10^{-8}\ C)}{(1.25 \times 10^{-2}\ m)^2} = +2.5\ N$$

    The force is repulsive.

20

11. Two identical point charges are 3.00 cm apart. Find the charge on each of them, if the force of repulsion is 4.00×10^{-7} N.

    $$F = \frac{Kqq'}{d^2} = \frac{Kq^2}{d^2} \text{ for identical charges.}$$

    $$q^2 = \frac{Fd^2}{K} = \frac{(+4.00 \times 10^{-7}\ N)(0.0300\ m)^2}{(9.0 \times 10^9\ N \cdot m^2/C^2)} = +4.0 \times 10^{-20}\ C$$

    $q = \pm 2.0 \times 10^{-10}$ C
    Either both of the charges are positive, or both are negative.

12. A charge of 4.0×10^{-5} C is attracted by a second charge with a force of 350 N when the separation is 10.0 cm. Calculate the size of the second charge.

    $$F = \frac{Kqq'}{d^2}, \text{ so } q' = \frac{Fd^2}{Kq} = \frac{(-350\ N)(0.100\ m)^2}{(9.0 \times 10^9\ N \cdot m^2/C^2)(4.0 \times 10^{-5}\ C)} = -9.7 \times 10^{-6}\ C$$

13. Three particles are placed on a straight line. The left particle has a charge of $+4.6 \times 10^{-6}$ C, the middle particle has a charge of -2.3×10^{-6} C, and the right particle has a charge of -2.3×10^{-6} C. The left particle is 12 cm from the middle particle and the right particle is 24 cm from the middle particle. Find the total force on the middle particle.

    First find the force that the right particle exerts on the middle particle.

    $F_r = \dfrac{Kq_m q_r}{d_{mr}^{\ 2}} = \dfrac{(9.0 \times 10^9\ \text{N}\cdot\text{m}^2/\text{C}^2)(-2.3 \times 10^{-6}\ \text{C})(-2.3 \times 10^{-6}\ \text{C})}{(0.24\ \text{m})^2} = 0.83\ \text{N}$; the force is repulsive, or leftward.

    Now find the force that the left particle exerts on the middle particle.

    $F_\ell = \dfrac{Kq_m q_\ell}{d_{m\ell}^{\ 2}} = \dfrac{(9.0 \times 10^9\ \text{N}\cdot\text{m}^2/\text{C}^2)(-2.3 \times 10^{-6}\ \text{C})(4.6 \times 10^{-6}\ \text{C})}{(0.12\ \text{m})^2} = -6.6\ \text{N}$; the force is attractive, or leftward.

    The total force is the sum of the two forces:
    $F_{total} = 0.83$ N (leftward) + 6.6 N (leftward) = 7.4 N, leftward

14. The left particle in the problem above is moved directly above the middle particle, still 12 cm away. Find the force on the middle particle.

    The force exerted by the right particle is unchanged; it is 0.83 N leftward.
    The force exerted by the particle above the middle particle is still 6.6 N, now directed upward.

    The resultant force (F_R) has a magnitude of $F_R = ((6.6\ \text{N})^2 + (0.83\ \text{N})^2)^{\frac{1}{2}} = 6.7$ N; its direction is

    $\tan\theta = \dfrac{0.83\ \text{N}}{6.6\ \text{N}}$, $\theta = 7.2°$ to the left of vertical

Chapter 21: Electric Fields

Practice Problems

page 427

1. A negative charge of 2.0×10^{-8} C experiences a force of 0.060 N to the right in an electric field. What is the field magnitude and direction?

$$E = \frac{F}{q'} = \frac{0.060 \text{ N}}{2.0 \times 10^{-8} \text{ C}}$$

$= 3.0 \times 10^{6}$ N/C directed to the left

2. A positive test charge of 5.0×10^{-4} C is in an electric field that exerts a force of 2.5×10^{-4} N on it. What is the magnitude of the electric field at the location of the test charge?

$$E = \frac{F}{q'} = \frac{2.5 \times 10^{-4} \text{ N}}{5.0 \times 10^{-4} \text{ C}} = 0.50 \text{ N/C}$$

3. Suppose the electric field in Practice Problem 2 were caused by a point charge. The test charge is moved to a distance twice as far from the charge. What is the magnitude of the force that the field exerts on the test charge now?

$F_2/F_1 = (Kqq'/d_2^2)/(Kqq'/d_1^2)$
$= (d_1/d_2)^2$ with $d_2 = 2d_1$

$F_2 = (d_1/d_2)^2 F_1 = (d_1/2d_1)^2(2.5 \times 10^{-4} \text{ N})$
$= 6.3 \times 10^{-5}$ N

4. You are probing the field of a charge of unknown magnitude and sign. You first map the field with a 1.0×10^{-6} C test charge, then repeat your work with a 2.0×10^{-6} C charge.

   a. Would you measure the same forces with the two test charges? Explain.

   No. The force on the 2.0 μC charge would be twice that on the 1.0 μC charge.

   b. Would you find the same fields? Explain.

   Yes. You would divide the force by the strength of the test charge, so the results would be the same.

Practice Problems

page 434

5. The electric field intensity between two large, charged, parallel metal plates is 8000 N/C. The plates are 0.05 m apart. What is the potential difference between them?

$V = Ed = (8000 \text{ N/C})(0.05 \text{ m}) = 400 \text{ J/C}$
$= 4 \times 10^{2}$V

6. A voltmeter reads 500 V when placed across two charged parallel plates. The plates are 0.020 m apart. What is the electric field between them?

$V = Ed$

$$E = \frac{V}{d} = \frac{500 \text{ V}}{0.020 \text{ m}} = 2.5 \times 10^{4} \text{ N/C}$$

7. What potential difference is applied to two metal plates 0.500 m apart if the electric field between them is 2.50×10^{3} N/C?

$V = Ed = (2.50 \times 10^{3} \text{ N/C})(0.500 \text{ m})$
$= 1.25 \times 10^{3}$ V

8. What work is done when 5.0 C is raised in potential by 1.5 V?

$W = qV = (5.0 \text{ C})(1.5 \text{ V}) = 7.5$ J

page 437

9. A drop is falling in a Millikan oil drop apparatus when the electric field is off.

   a. What are the forces on it, regardless of its acceleration?

   Gravitational force (weight) downward, frictional force of air upward.

   b. If it is falling at constant velocity, what can be said of the forces on it?

   The two are equal in magnitude.

21

Practice Problems

10. An oil drop weighs 1.9×10^{-15} N. It is suspended in an electric field of 6.0×10^{3} N/C.

   a. What is the charge on the drop?

   $F = Eq$

   $$q = \frac{F}{E} = \frac{1.9 \times 10^{-15}\ \text{N}}{6.0 \times 10^{3}\ \text{N/C}} = 3.2 \times 10^{-19}\ \text{C}$$

   b. How many excess electrons does it carry?

   $$\#\ \text{electrons} = \frac{q}{q_e} = \frac{3.2 \times 10^{-19}\ \text{C}}{1.6 \times 10^{-19}\ \text{C/electron}}$$

   $$= 2\ \text{electrons}$$

page 438

11. A positively–charged oil drop weighs 6.4×10^{-13} N. An electric field of 4.0×10^{6} N/C suspends the drop.

   a. What is the charge on the drop?

   $F = Eq$

   $$q = \frac{F}{E} = \frac{6.4 \times 10^{-13}\ \text{N}}{4.0 \times 10^{6}\ \text{N/C}} = 1.6 \times 10^{-19}\ \text{C}$$

   b. How many electrons is the drop missing?

   $$\#\ \text{electrons} = \frac{q}{1.6 \times 10^{-19}\ \text{C/electron}}$$

   $$= 1\ \text{electron}$$

12. If three more electrons were removed from the drop in Practice Problem 11, what field would be needed to balance the drop?

   $$E = \frac{F}{q} = \frac{6.4 \times 10^{-13}\ \text{N}}{(4)(1.6 \times 10^{-19}\ \text{C})} = 1.0 \times 10^{6}\ \text{N/C}$$

page 442

13. 1 27–μF capacitor has a potential difference of 25 V across it. What is the charge on the capacitor?

   $q = CV = 27\ \mu F(25\ \text{V}) = 6.8 \times 10^{-4}$ C

Practice Problems

14. Both a 3.3–μF and a 6.8–μF capacitor are connected across a 15–V potential difference. Which capacitor has a greater charge? What is it?

   $q = CV$, so the larger capacitor has a greater charge.
   $q = 1.0 \times 10^{-4}$ C

15. The same two capacitors are each charged to 2.5×10^{-4} C. Across which is the potential difference larger? What is it?

   $V = q/C$, so the smaller capacitor has the larger potential difference.
   $V = (2.5 \times 10^{-4}\ \text{C})/(3.3 \times 10^{-6}\ \text{F}) = 76$ V

16. A 2.2–μF capacitor is first charged so that the potential difference is 6.0 V. How much *additional* charge is needed to increase the potential difference to 15.0 V?

   $q = CV$ so $\Delta q = C\Delta V$;
   $\Delta q = (2.2\mu\text{F})(15.0\ \text{V} - 6.0\ \text{V}) = 2.0 \times 10^{-5}$ C

Chapter Review Problems

pages 444–445

The charge on an electron is -1.60×10^{-19} C.

1. A positive charge of 1.0×10^{-5} C experiences a force of 0.20 N when located at a certain point. What is the electric field intensity at that point?

   $$E = \frac{F}{q} = \frac{0.20\ \text{N}}{1.0 \times 10^{-5}\ \text{C}} = 2.0 \times 10^{4}\ \text{N/C}$$

2. What charge exists on a test charge that experiences a force of 1.4×10^{-8} N at a point where the electric field intensity is 2.0×10^{-4} N/C?

   $E = \frac{F}{q}$, so $Eq = F$, and

   $$q = \frac{F}{E} = \frac{1.4 \times 10^{-8}\ \text{N}}{2.0 \times 10^{-4}\ \text{N/C}} = 7.0 \times 10^{-5}\ \text{C}$$

3. A test charge has a force of 0.20 N on it when it is placed in an electric field intensity of 4.5×10^5 N/C. What is the magnitude of the charge?

$$E = \frac{F}{q}, \text{ so}$$

$$q = \frac{F}{E} = \frac{0.20 \text{ N}}{4.5 \times 10^5 \text{ N/C}} = 4.4 \times 10^{-7} \text{ C}$$

4. The electric field in the atmosphere is about 150 N/C (downward).

   a. What is the direction of force on a positively–charged particle?

   Downward.

   b. Find the electric force on a proton with charge $+1.6 \times 10^{-19}$ C.

$$E = \frac{F}{q}, \text{ so}$$

$$F = qE = (1.6 \times 10^{-19} \text{ C})(150 \text{ N/C}) = 2.4 \times 10^{-17} \text{ N}$$

   c. Compare the force in **b** with the force of gravity on the same proton that has a mass of 1.7×10^{-27} kg.

$$F = mg = (1.7 \times 10^{-27} \text{ kg})(9.8 \text{ m/s}^2) = 1.7 \times 10^{-26} \text{ N (downward)},$$ more than one billion times smaller.

5. Electrons are accelerated by the electric field (Table 21–1) in a television picture tube.

   a. Find the force on an electron.

$$E = \frac{F}{q}, \text{ so}$$

$$F = qE = (-1.6 \times 10^{-19} \text{ C})(10^5 \text{ N/C}) = -1.6 \times 10^{-14} \text{ N}$$ opposite the field.

   b. If the field is constant, find the acceleration of the electron, mass = 9.11×10^{-31} kg.

$$F = ma, \text{ so}$$

$$a = \frac{F}{m} = \frac{-1.6 \times 10^{-14} \text{ N}}{9.11 \times 10^{-31} \text{ kg}} = -1.8 \times 10^{16} \text{ m/s}^2$$

Chapter Review Problems

6. A lead nucleus carries the charge of 82 protons.

   a. What is the direction and magnitude of the electric field at 1.0×10^{-10} m from the nucleus?

$$Q = (82 \text{ protons})(1.6 \times 10^{-19} \text{ C/proton}) = 1.3 \times 10^{-17} \text{ C}$$

$$E = \frac{F}{q}, \text{ so}$$

$$F = Eq \text{ and } F = \frac{KqQ}{d^2}, \text{ so}$$

$$E = \frac{KQ}{d^2} = \frac{(9.0 \times 10^9 \text{ N}\cdot\text{m}^2/\text{C}^2)(1.3 \times 10^{-17} \text{ C})}{(10^{-10} \text{ m})^2} = 1.2 \times 10^{13} \text{ N/C, outward}$$

   b. Use Coulomb's law to find the direction and magnitude of the force exerted on an electron located at this distance.

$$F = Eq = (1.2 \times 10^{13} \text{ N/C})(-1.6 \times 10^{-19} \text{ C}) = -1.9 \times 10^{-6} \text{ N, toward the nucleus}$$

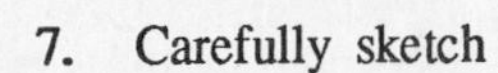

7. Carefully sketch

   a. the electric field produced by a +1.0–μC charge.

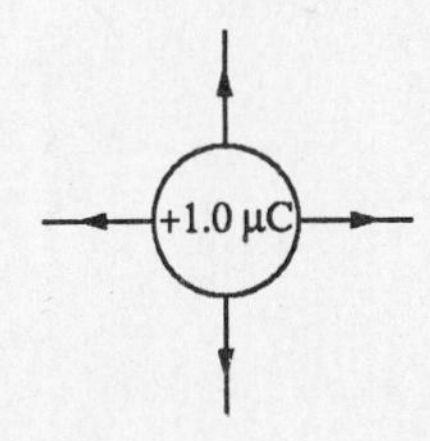

   b. the electric field due to a +2.0–μC charge. Make the number of field lines proportional to the change in charge.

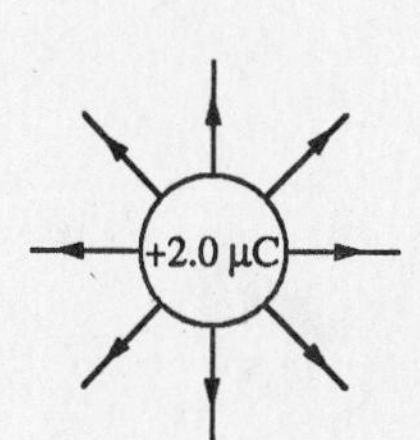

8. Charges x, y and z are all equidistant from each other. x has a +1.0–μC charge, y a +2.0–μC charge, and z a small negative charge.

   a. Draw an arrow showing the force on charge z.

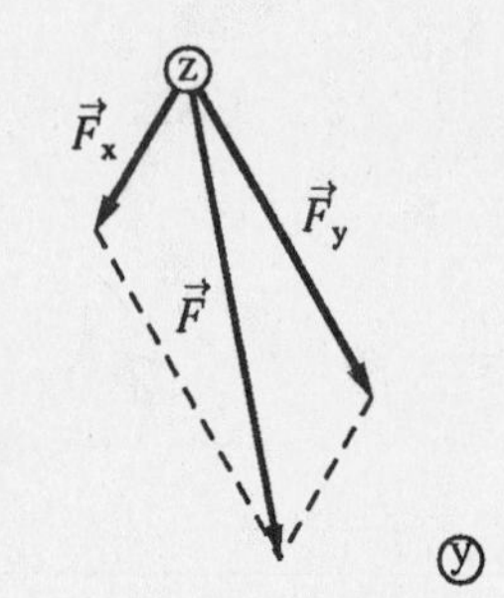

   b. Charge z now has a small positive charge on it. Draw an arrow showing the force on it.

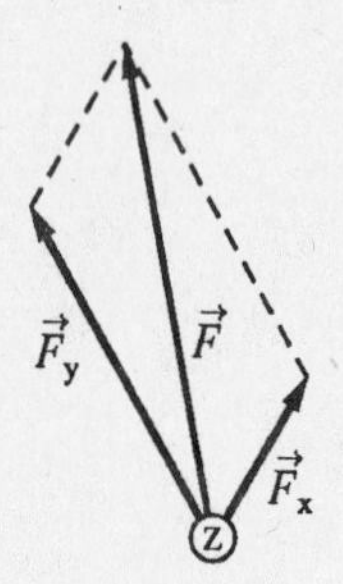

9. A positive test charge of 8.0×10^{-5} C is placed in an electric field of 50.0 N/C intensity. What is the strength of the force exerted on the test charge?

$E = \frac{F}{q}$, so

$F = Eq = (8.0 \times 10^{-5}\ \text{C})(50.0\ \text{N/C}) = 4.0 \times 10^{-3}\ \text{N}$

Chapter Review Problems

10. If 120 J of work are done to move one coulomb of charge from a positive plate to a negative plate, what voltage difference exists between the plates?

$V = \frac{w}{q} = \frac{120\ \text{J}}{1.0\ \text{C}} = 120\ \text{V}$

11. How much work is done to transfer 0.15 C of charge through a potential difference of 9.0 V?

$V = \frac{w}{q}$, so

$w = qV = (0.15\ \text{C})(9.0\ \text{V}) = 1.4\ \text{J}$

12. An electron is moved through a potential difference of 500 V. How much work is done on the electron?

$V = \frac{w}{q}$, so

$w = qV = (-1.60 \times 10^{-19}\ \text{C})(500\ \text{V}) = -8.00 \times 10^{-17}\ \text{J}$

13. A 12–V battery does 1200 J of work transferring charge. How much charge is transferred?

$V = \frac{w}{q}$, so $W = qV$, and

$q = \frac{W}{V} = \frac{1200\ \text{J}}{12\ \text{V}} = 1.0 \times 10^2\ \text{C}$

14. A force of 0.053 N is required to move a charge of 37 μC a distance of 25 cm in an electric field. What is the size of the potential difference between the two points?

$W = F \cdot d$ and

$V = \frac{W}{q} = \frac{F \cdot d}{q} = \frac{(0.053\ \text{N})(0.25\ \text{m})}{37 \times 10^{-6}\ \text{C}} = 3.6 \times 10^2\ \text{V}$

15. The electric field intensity between two charged plates is 1.5×10^3 N/C. The plates are 0.080 m apart. What is the potential difference, in volts, between the plates?

$V = Ed = (1.5 \times 10^3\ \text{N/C})(0.080\ \text{m}) = 1.2 \times 10^2\ \text{V}$

Chapter Review Problems

16. A voltmeter indicates that the difference in potential between two plates is 50.0 V. The plates are 0.020 m apart. What electric field intensity exists between them?

$V = Ed$, so

$$E = \frac{V}{d} = \frac{50.0\ \text{V}}{0.020\ \text{m}} = 2500\ \text{V/m}$$

$$= 2.5 \times 10^3\ \text{N/C}$$

17. A negatively–charged oil drop weighs 8.5×10^{-15} N. The drop is suspended in an electric field intensity of 5.3×10^3 N/C.

a. What is the charge on the drop?

$E = \frac{F}{q}$, so

$$q = \frac{F}{E} = \frac{8.5 \times 10^{-15}\ \text{N}}{5.3 \times 10^3\ \text{N/C}} = 1.6 \times 10^{-18}\ \text{C}$$

b. How many electrons does it carry?

$$\frac{1.6 \times 10^{-18}\ \text{C}}{1}\left[\frac{\text{electron}}{1.6 \times 10^{-19}\ \text{C}}\right] = 10\ \text{electrons}$$

18. In an early set of experiments, (1911), Millikan observed that the following measured charges, among others, appeared at different times on a single oil drop.

What value of elementary charge can be deduced from these data?

a. 6.563×10^{-19} C

b. 8.204×10^{-19} C

c. 11.50×10^{-19} C

d. 13.13×10^{-19} C

e. 16.48×10^{-19} C

f. 18.08×10^{-19} C

g. 19.71×10^{-19} C

h. 22.89×10^{-19} C

i. 26.13×10^{-19} C

1.63×10^{-19} C. Subtracting adjacent values, *b–a*, *c–d*, *d–c*, etc. yields 1.641×10^{-19} C, 3.30×10^{-19} C, 1.63×10^{-19} C, 3.35×10^{-19} C, 1.60×10^{-19} C, 1.63×10^{-19} C, 3.18×10^{-19} C, 3.24×10^{-19} C.
There are two numbers, approximately 1.63×10^{-19} C and 3.2×10^{-19} C, which are common. Averaging each similar group produces one charge of 1.63×10^{-19} C and one charge of 3.27×10^{-19} C (which is two times 1.63×10^{-19} C).
Dividing 1.63×10^{-19} C into each piece of data yields nearly whole number quotients indicating it is the value of an elementary charge.

19. A capacitor that is connected to a 45.0–V source contains 90.0 μC of charge. What is the capacitor's capacitance?

$$C = \frac{q}{V} = \frac{90.0 \times 10^{-6}\ \text{C}}{45.0\ \text{V}} = 2.00\ \mu\text{F}$$

20. A 5.4–μF capacitor is charged with 2.7×10^{-3} C. What potential difference exists across it?

$C = \frac{q}{V}$, so

$$V = \frac{q}{C} = \frac{2.7 \times 10^{-3}\ \text{C}}{5.4 \times 10^{-6}\ \text{F}} = 5.0 \times 10^2\ \text{V}$$

21. What is the charge in a 15.0–pf capacitor when it is connected across a 75.0–V source?

$C = \frac{q}{V}$, so

$$q = CV = (15.0 \times 10^{-12}\ \text{F})(75.0\ \text{V}) = 1.13 \times 10^{-9}\ \text{C}$$

22. The energy stored in a capacitor with capacitance C having a potential difference V is given by $W = \frac{1}{2}CV^2$. One application is in the electronic photoflash or strobe light. In such a unit, a capacitor of 10.0 μF is charged to 3.00×10^2 V. Find the energy stored.

$$W = \frac{1}{2}CV^2 = \frac{1}{2}(10.0 \times 10^{-6}\ \text{F})(3.00 \times 10^2\ \text{V})^2$$

$$= 0.450\ \text{J}$$

21

Chapter Review Problems

23. Suppose it took 30 s to charge the capacitor in the previous problem.

    a. Find the power required to charge it in this time.

    $$P = \frac{W}{t} = \frac{0.450 \text{ J}}{30 \text{ s}} = 2 \times 10^{-2} \text{ W}$$

    b. When this capacitor is discharged through the strobe lamp, it transfers all its energy in 1.0×10^{-4} s. Find the power delivered to the lamp.

    $$P = \frac{W}{t} = \frac{0.450 \text{ J}}{1.0 \times 10^{-4} \text{ s}} = 4.5 \times 10^{3} \text{ W}$$

    $$= 4.5 \text{ kW}$$

    c. How is such a large amount of power possible?

    Power is inversely proportional to the time. The shorter the time for a given amount of energy to be expended, the greater the power.

24. Lasers are used to try to produce controlled fusion reactions that might supply large amounts of electrical energy. The lasers require brief pulses of energy that are stored in large rooms filled with capacitors. One such room has a capacitance of 61×10^{-3} F charged to a potential difference of 10 kV.

    a. Find the energy stored in the capacitors, given $W = \frac{1}{2}CV^2$.

    $$W = 1/2CV^2 = (1/2)(61 \times 10^{-3} \text{ F})(10^4 \text{ V})^2$$
    $$= 3.1 \times 10^6 \text{ J}$$

    b. The capacitors are discharged in 10 ns (1.0×10^{-8} s). What power is produced?

    $$P = W/t = (3.1 \times 10^6 \text{ J})/(1.0 \times 10^{-8} \text{ s})$$
    $$= 3.1 \times 10^{14} \text{ W}$$

    c. If the capacitors are charged by a generator with a power capacity of 1.0 kW, how many seconds will be required to charge the capacitors?

    $$t = W/P = (3.1 \times 10^6 \text{ J})/(1.0 \times 10^3 \text{ W})$$
    $$= 3.1 \times 10^3 \text{ s}$$

Supplemental Problems (Appendix B)

1. How strong would an electric field have to be to produce a force of 1.00 N if the charge were 1.000×10^3 μC.

    $$E = \frac{F}{q} = \frac{1.00 \text{ N}}{1.000 \times 10^{-3}} = 1.00 \times 10^3 \text{ N/C}$$

2. A positive charge of 7.0 mC experiences a 5.6×10^{-2} N force when placed in an electric field. What is the size of the electric field intensity?

    $$E = \frac{F}{q} = \frac{5.6 \times 10^{-2} \text{ N}}{7.0 \times 10^{-3} \text{ C}} = 8.0 \text{ N/C}$$

3. A positive test charge of 6.5×10^{-6} C experiences a force of 4.5×10^{-5} N. What is the magnitude of the electric field intensity?

    $$E = \frac{F}{q} = \frac{4.5 \times 10^{-5} \text{ N}}{6.5 \times 10^{-6} \text{ C}} = 6.9 \text{ N/C}$$

4. A charge experiences a force of 3.0×10^{-3} N in an electric field of intensity 2.0 N/C. What is the magnitude of the charge?

    $$E = \frac{F}{q}, \text{ so}$$

    $$q = \frac{F}{E} = \frac{3.0 \times 10^{-3} \text{ N}}{2.0 \text{ N/C}} = 1.5 \times 10^{-3} \text{ C}$$

    $$= 1.5 \text{ mC}$$

5. What is the size of the force on an electron when the electron is in a uniform electric field that has an intensity of 1.000×10^3 N/C.

    $$E = \frac{F}{q}, \text{ so}$$

    $$F = qE = (-1.60 \times 10^{-19} \text{ C})(1000 \text{ N/C})$$
    $$= -1.60 \times 10^{-16} \text{ N}$$

6. Sketch the electric field lines around a -1.0 μC charge.

    −1.0 μC

Supplemental Problems

7. It takes 8.00 mJ to move a charge of 4.00 μC from point A to point C in an electric field. What is the potential difference between the two points?

$$\Delta V = \frac{\Delta PE}{q} = \frac{8.00 \times 10^{-3}\ \text{J}}{4.00 \times 10^{-6}\ \text{C}} = 2.00 \times 10^{3}\ \text{V}$$

8. How much work is required to move a positive charge of 2.5 μC between two points that have a potential difference of 60 V?

$$\Delta V = \frac{\Delta PE}{q}, \text{ so}$$

$$w = \Delta PE = q\Delta V = (2.5 \times 10^{-6}\ \text{C})(60\ \text{V}) = 1.5 \times 10^{-4}\ \text{J} = 0.15\ \text{mJ}$$

9. A cloud has a potential difference relative to a tree of 9.00×10^{2} MV. During a lightning storm, a charge of 1.00×10^{2} C travels through this potential difference. How much work is done on this charge?

$$\Delta V = \frac{\Delta PE}{q}, \text{ so}$$

$$w = \Delta PE = q\Delta V = (1.00 \times 10^{2}\ \text{C})(9.00 \times 10^{8}\ \text{V}) = 9.00 \times 10^{10}\ \text{J}$$

10. A constant electric field of 750 N/C is between a set of parallel plates. What is the potential difference between the parallel plates if they are 1.5 cm apart?

$$V = Ed = (750\ \text{N/C})(0.015\ \text{m}) = 11\ \text{V}$$

11. A spark will jump between two people if the electric field exceeds 4.0×10^{6} V/m. You shuffle across a rug and a spark jumps when you put your finger 0.15 cm from another person's arm. Calculate the potential difference between your body and the other person's arm.

$$V = Ed = (4.0 \times 10^{6}\ \text{V/m})(0.0015\ \text{m}) = 6.0 \times 10^{3}\ \text{V}$$

12. A potential difference of 0.90 V exists from one side to the other side of a cell membrane that is 5.0 nm thick. What is the electric field across the membrane?

$$V = Ed, \text{ so}$$

$$E = \frac{V}{d} = \frac{0.90\ \text{V}}{5.0 \times 10^{-9}\ \text{m}} = 1.8 \times 10^{8}\ \text{V/m}$$

Supplemental Problems

13. An oil drop having a charge of 8.0×10^{-19} C is suspended between two charged parallel plates. The plates are separated by a distance of 8.0 mm, and there is a potential difference of 1200 V between the plates. What is the weight of the suspended oil drop?

$$mg = Eq, \text{ and } V = Ed, \text{ so } E = \frac{V}{d}, \text{ so}$$

$$mg = \left[\frac{V}{d}\right]q = \left[\frac{1200\ \text{V}}{8.0 \times 10^{-3}\ \text{m}}\right](8.0 \times 10^{-19}\ \text{C}) = 1.2 \times 10^{-13}\ \text{N}$$

14. A capacitor accumulates 4.0 mC on each plate when the potential difference between the plates is 100 V. What is the capacitance of the capacitor?

$$C = \frac{q}{V} = \frac{4.00 \times 10^{-3}\ \text{C}}{100\ \text{V}} = 4.0 \times 10^{-5}\ \text{F} = 40\ \mu F.$$

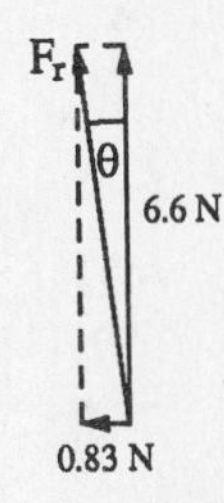

15. What is the voltage across a capacitor with a charge of 6.0 μC and a capacitance 7.0 pF?

$$C = \frac{q}{V}, \text{ so}$$

$$V = \frac{q}{C} = \frac{6.0 \times 10^{-6}\ \text{C}}{7.0 \times 10^{-12}\ \text{F}} = 8.6 \times 10^{5}\ \text{V}$$

16. How large is the charge accumulated on one of the plates of a 30 μF capacitor when the potential difference between the plates is 120 V?

$$C = \frac{q}{V}, \text{ so}$$

$$q = CV = (30 \times 10^{-6}\ \text{F})(120\ \text{V}) = 3.6 \times 10^{-3}\ \text{C} = 3.6\ \text{mC}$$

Chapter 22: Current Electricity

Practice Problems

page 451

1. The current through a light bulb connected across the terminals of a 120–V outlet is 0.5 A. At what rate does the bulb convert electric energy to light?

$P = VI = (120\ \text{V})(0.5\ \text{A}) = 60\ \text{J/s} = 60\ \text{W}$

2. A car battery causes a current of 2.0 A to flow through a lamp while 12 V is across it.. What is the power used by the lamp?

$P = VI = (12\ \text{V})(2.0\ \text{A}) = 24\ \text{W}$

3. What current flows through a 75–W light bulb connected to a 120–V outlet?

$P = VI,\ I = \frac{P}{V} = \frac{75\ \text{W}}{120\ \text{V}} = 0.63\ \text{A}$

4. The current through the starter motor of a car is 210 A. If the battery keeps 12 V across the motor, what electric energy is delivered to the starter in 10.0 s?

$P = VI = (12\ \text{V})(210\ \text{A}) = 2500\ \text{W}$
In 10 s, $E = Pt = (2500\ \text{J/s})(10\ \text{s})$
$= 25000\ \text{J} = 2.5 \times 10^4\ \text{J}$

page 454

5. An automobile headlight with a resistance of 30 Ω is placed across a 12–V battery. What is the current through the circuit?

$I = \frac{V}{R} = \frac{12\ \text{V}}{30\ \Omega} = 0.40\ \text{A}$

6. A motor with an operating resistance of 32 Ω is connected to a voltage source. The current in the circuit is 3.8 A. What is the voltage of the source?

$V = IR = (3.8\ \text{A})(32\ \Omega) = 120\ \text{V}$

Practice Problems

7. A transistor radio uses 2×10^{-4} A of current when it is operated by a 3–V battery. What is the resistance of the radio circuit?

$R = \frac{V}{I} = \frac{3\ \text{V}}{2 \times 10^{-4}\ \text{A}} = 1.5 \times 10^4\ \Omega$
$= 2 \times 10^4\ \Omega$

8. A lamp draws a current of 0.5 A when it is connected to a 120–V source.

a. What is the resistance of the lamp?

$R = \frac{V}{I} = \frac{120\ \text{V}}{0.5\ \text{A}} = 240\ \Omega = 200\ \Omega$

b. What is the power consumption of the lamp?

$P = VI = (120\ \text{V})(0.5\ \text{A}) = 60\ \text{W}$

9. A 75–W lamp is connected to 120 V.

a. How much current flows through the lamp?

$I = P/V = (75\ \text{W})(120\ \text{V}) = 0.63\ \text{A}$

b. What is the resistance of the lamp?

$R = V/I = 120\ \text{V}/0.63\ \text{A} = 190\ \Omega$

10. A resistor is now added in series with the lamp to reduce the current to half of its original value.

a. What is the potential difference across the lamp? Assume the lamp resistance is constant.

The new value of the current is
$0.63\ \text{A}/2 = 0.315\ \text{A}$, so
$V = IR = (0.315\ \text{A})(190\ \Omega) = 60\ \text{V}$

b. How much resistance was added to the circuit?

The total resistance of the circuit is now
$R_{total} = V/I = (120\text{ V})/(0.315\text{ A}) = 380\ \Omega.$
Therefore, $R_{res} = R_{total} - R_{lamp}$
$= 380\ \Omega - 190\ \Omega = 190\ \Omega.$

c. How much power is now dissipated in the lamp?

$P = VI = (60\text{ V})(0.315\text{ A}) = 19\text{ W}$

page 457

11. Draw a circuit diagram to include a 60–V battery, an ammeter, and a resistance of 12.5 Ω in series. Indicate the ammeter reading and the direction of current flow.

$$I = \frac{V}{R} = \frac{60\text{ V}}{12.5\ \Omega} = 4.8\text{ A}$$

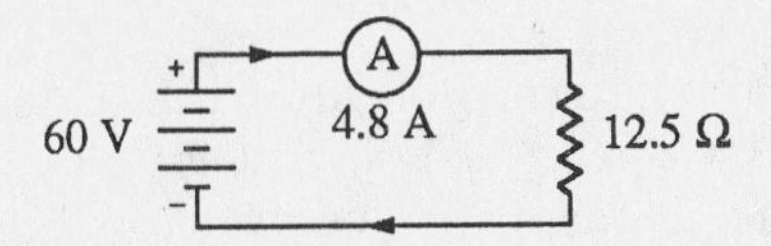

12. Draw a series circuit diagram showing a 4.5–V battery, a resistor, and an ammeter reading 90 mA. Label the size of the resistor. Choose a direction for the conventional current and indicate the positive terminal of the battery.

$R = V/I = (4.5\text{ V})(0.090\text{ A}) = 50\ \Omega$

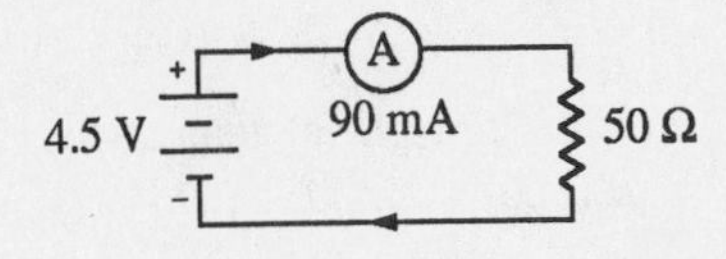

13. Add a voltmeter that measures the potential difference across the resistors in each of the Practice Problems above.

Both circuits will take the form

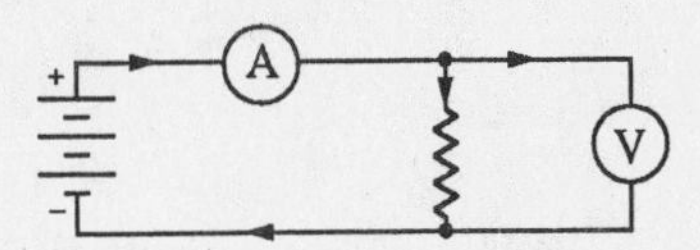

Since the ammeter resistance is assumed zero the voltmeter readings will be
practice problem 11 60 V
practice problem 12 4.5 V.

page 459

14. A 15–Ω electric heater operates on a 120–V outlet.

a. What is the current through the heater?

$I = V/R = (120\text{ V})(15\ \Omega) = 8.0\text{ A}$

b. How much energy is used by the heater in 30.0 s?

$E = I^2Rt = (8.0\text{ A})^2(15\ \Omega)(30.0\text{ s})$
$= 2.9 \times 10^4\text{ J}$

c. How much thermal energy is liberated by the heater in this time?

2.9×10^4 J since all electrical energy is converted to thermal energy

15. A 30–Ω resistor is connected to a 60–V battery.

a. What is the current in the circuit?

$I = V/R = (60\text{ V})/(30\ \Omega) = 2.0\text{ A}$

b. How much energy is used by the resistor in 5 min?

$E = I^2Rt = (2.0\text{ A})^2(30\ \Omega)(5\text{ min})(60\text{ s/min})$
$= 3.6 \times 10^4\text{ J}$

Practice Problems

page 460

16. A 100.0–W lightbulb is 20.0% efficient. That means 20.0% of the electric energy is converted to light energy.

a. How many joules does the light bulb convert into light each minute it is in operation?

$$E = (0.200)(100.0 \text{ J/s})(60.0 \text{ s}) = 1.20 \times 10^3 \text{ J}$$

b. How many joules of thermal energy does the light bulb produce each minute?

$$E = (0.800)(100.0 \text{ J/s})(60.0 \text{ s}) = 4.80 \times 10^3 \text{ J}$$

17. The resistance of an electric stove element at operating temperature is 11 Ω.

a. 220 V are applied across it. What is the current through the stove element?

$$I = V/R = (220 \text{ V})/(11\ \Omega) = 20 \text{ A}$$

b. How much energy does the element convert to thermal energy in 30.0 s?

$$E = I^2Rt = (20\ A)^2(11\ \Omega)(30.0 \text{ s}) = 1.3 \times 10^5 \text{ J}$$

c. The element is being used to heat a kettle containing 1.20 kg of water. Assume that 70% of the heat is absorbed by the water. What is its increase in temperature during the 30.0 s?

$Q = mC\Delta T$ with $Q = 0.70\ E$

$\Delta T = 0.70\ E/mC$

$$= \frac{(0.70)(1.3 \times 10^5 \text{ J})}{(1.20 \text{ kg})(4180 \text{ J/kg}\cdot\text{C}^\circ)} = 18^\circ\text{C}$$

page 463

18. An electric space heater draws 15.0 A from a 120–V source. It is operated, on the average, for 5.0 h each day.

a. How much power does the heater use?

$$P = IV = (15.0 \text{ A})(120 \text{ V}) = 1800 \text{ W} = 1.80 \text{ kW}$$

Practice Problems

b. How much energy in kWh does it consume in 30 days?

$$E = Pt = (1.8 \text{ kW})(5 \text{ h/day})(30 \text{ days}) = 270 \text{ kWh}$$

c. At $0.11 per kWh, what does it cost to operate it for 30 days?

Cost = (0.11 $/kWh)(270 kWh) = $29.70

19. A digital clock has an operating resistance of 12 000 Ω and is plugged into a 115–V outlet. Assume the clock obeys Ohm's law.

a. How much current does it draw?

$$I = \frac{V}{R} = \frac{(115 \text{ V})}{(12{,}000\ \Omega)} = 9.6 \times 10^{-3} \text{ A}$$

b. How much power does it use?

$$P = VI = (115 \text{ V})(9.6 \times 10^{-3} \text{ A}) = 1.10 \text{ W}$$

c. If the owner of the clock pays $0.09 per kWh, what does it cost to operate the clock for 30 days?

$$\text{Cost} = (1.10 \times 10^{-3} \text{ kW})(\$0.09/\text{kWh}) \cdot (30 \text{ days})(24 \text{ h/day}) = \$0.07$$

Chapter Review Problems

pages 465–467

1. The current through a toaster connected to a 120–V source is 8.0 A. What power is dissipated by the toaster?

$$P = VI = (120 \text{ V})(8.0 \text{ A}) = 9.6 \times 10^2 \text{ W}$$

2. A current of 1.2 A flows through a light bulb when it is connected across a 120–V source. What power is dissipated by the bulb?

$$P = VI = (120 \text{ V})(1.2 \text{ A}) = 1.4 \times 10^2 \text{ W}$$

3. A lamp draws 0.50 A from a 120–V generator.

   a. How much power does the generator deliver?

   $P = VI = (120\ \text{V})(0.50\ \text{A}) = 60\ \text{W}$

   b. How much energy does the lamp convert in 5.0 min?

   The definition of power is $P = \frac{E}{t}$, so

   $$E = Pt = 60\ \text{W}\left[\frac{5.0\ \text{min}}{1}\right]\left[\frac{60\ \text{s}}{\text{min}}\right]$$

   $$= 18\ 000\ \text{J} = 1.8 \times 10^4\ \text{J}$$

4. A 12–V automobile battery is connected to an electric starter motor. The current through the motor is 210 A.

   a. How many joules of energy does the battery deliver to the motor each second?

   $P = IV = (210\ \text{A})(12\ \text{V}) = 2500\ \text{J/s}$,
   so $2.5 \times 10^3\ \text{J/s}$

   b. What power in watts does the motor use?

   $P = 2.5 \times 10^3\ \text{W}$

5. A 4000–W clothes dryer is connected to a 220–V circuit. How much current does the dryer draw?

   $P = VI$, so $I = \frac{P}{V} = \frac{4000\ \text{W}}{220\ \text{V}} = 18.2\ \text{A}$

6. A flashlight bulb is connected across a 3.0–V difference in potential. The current through the lamp is 1.5 A.

   a. What is the power rating of the lamp?

   $P = VI = (3.0\ \text{V})(1.5\ \text{A}) = 4.5\ \text{W}$

   b. How much electric energy does the lamp convert in 11 min?

   The definition for power is $P = \frac{E}{t}$, so

   $$E = Pt = 4.5\ \text{W}\left[\frac{10\ \text{min}}{1}\right]\left[\frac{60\ \text{s}}{\text{min}}\right]$$

   $$= 3.0 \times 10^3\ \text{J}$$

Chapter Review Problems

7. How much energy does a 60.0–W light bulb use in half an hour? If the light bulb is 12% efficient, how much thermal energy does it generate during the half hour?

   $P = \frac{E}{t}$, so

   $$E = Pt = (60.0\ \text{W})(30\ \text{min})\left[\frac{60\ \text{s}}{\text{min}}\right]$$

   $$= 1.08 \times 10^5\ \text{J}$$

   If the bulb is 12% efficient, 88% of the energy is lost to heat, so
   $Q = 0.88(1.08 \times 10^5\ \text{J}) = 9.5 \times 10^4\ \text{J}$

8. A resistance of 60 Ω has a current of 0.40 A through it when it is connected to the terminals of a battery. What is the voltage of the battery?

   $V = IR = (0.40\ \text{A})(60\ \Omega) = 24\ \text{V}$

9. What voltage is applied to a 4.0–Ω resistor if the current is 1.5 A?

   $V = IR = (1.5\ \text{A})(4.0\ \Omega) = 6.0\ \text{V}$

10. What voltage is placed across a motor of 15 Ω operating resistance if the current is 8.0 A?

    $V = IR = (8.0\ \text{A})(15\ \Omega) = 1.2 \times 10^2\ \text{V}$

11. A voltage of 75 V is placed across a 15–Ω resistor. What is the current through the resistor?

    $V = IR$, so $I = V/R = (75\ \text{V})/(15\ \Omega) = 5.0\ \text{A}$

12. A 20.0–Ω resistor is connected to a 30.0–V battery. What is the current in the resistor?

    $V = IR$, so $I = \frac{V}{R} = \frac{30.0\ \text{V}}{20.0\ \Omega} = 1.50\ \text{A}$

13. A 12–V battery is connected to a device and 24 mA, 24×10^{-3} A, of current flows through it. If the device obeys Ohm's law, how much current will flow when a 24–V battery is used?

    I is proportional to V, so doubling V doubles I to 48 mA.

14. The damage caused by electric shock depends on the current flowing through the body. 1 mA can be felt. 5 mA are painful. Above 15 mA, a person loses muscle control, and 70 mA can be fatal. A person with dry skin has a resistance from one arm to the other of about $1 \times 10^5\ \Omega$. When skin is wet, the resistance drops to about $5 \times 10^3\ \Omega$.

   a. What is the minimum voltage placed across the arms that would produce a current that could be felt by a person with dry skin?

   $V = IR = (1 \times 10^{-3}\ \text{A})(1 \times 10^5\ \Omega)$
   $= 1 \times 10^2\ \text{V}$

   b. What effect would the same voltage have if the person had wet skin?

   $V = IR$, so

   $$I = \frac{V}{R} = \frac{1 \times 10^2\ \text{V}}{5 \times 10^3\ \Omega} = 2 \times 10^{-2}\ \text{A}$$

   = 20 mA, loss of muscle control

   c. What would be the minimum voltage that would produce a current that could be felt when the skin is wet?

   $V = IR = (1 \times 10^{-3}\ \text{A})(5 \times 10^3\ \Omega) = 5\ \text{V}$

15. A lamp draws a 66–mA current when connected to a 6.0–V battery. When a 9.0–V battery is used, the lamp draws 75 mA.

   a. Does the lamp obey Ohm's law?

   No. The voltage is increased by a factor of (9.0)/(6.0) = 1.5, but the current is increased by a factor of (75)/(66) = 1.1

   b. How much power does the lamp dissipate at 6.0 V?

   $P = IV = (66 \times 10^{-3}\ \text{A})(6.0\ \text{V}) = 0.40\ \text{W}$

   c. How much power does it dissipate at 9.0 V?

   $P = IV = (75 \times 10^{-3}\ \text{A})(9.0\ \text{V}) = 0.68\ \text{W}$

Chapter Review Problems

16. Table 22–1 shows data taken by students. They connected a length of nichrome wire to a variable power supply that could produce a voltage variable from 0 V to 10 V across the wire. They then measured the current through the wire for several voltages. The data table shows the voltages used and currents measured.

Voltage and Current Measurements for Nichrome Wire

Voltage V (volts)	Current I (amps)	Resistance R (ohms)
2.00	0.014	
4.00	0.027	
6.00	0.040	
8.00	0.052	
10.00	0.065	
– 2.00	– 0.014	
– 4.00	– 0.028	
– 6.00	– 0.039	
– 8.00	– 0.051	
– 10.00	– 0.064	

   a. For each measurement, calculate the resistance.

   R = 143 Ω, 148 Ω, 150 Ω, 154 Ω, 154 Ω, 143 Ω, 143 Ω, 154 Ω, 157 Ω, 156 Ω.

   b. Graph I versus V.

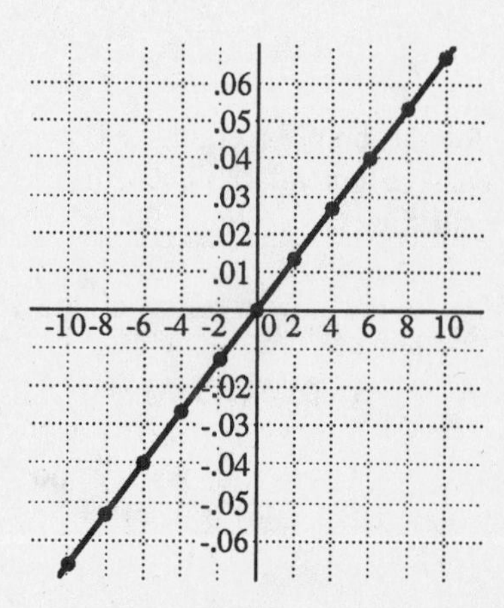

Chapter Review Problems

c. Does the nichrome wire obey Ohm's law? If not, for all the voltages, specify the voltage range for which Ohm's law holds.

Nichrome wire does not obey Ohm's law for all voltages. It obeys for voltages of +8.00 V to +10.00 V and in the −2.00 V to −4.00 V range.

17. The current through a lamp connected across 120 V is 0.40 A when the lamp is on.

a. What is its resistance when it is on?

$V = IR$, so

$$R = \frac{V}{I} = \frac{120\ \text{V}}{0.40\ \text{A}} = 3.0 \times 10^2\ \Omega$$

b. When the lamp is cold, its resistance is one fifth as large as when the lamp is hot. What is its cold resistance?

$$\frac{1}{5}(3.0 \times 10^2\ \Omega) = 60\ \Omega$$

c. What is the current through the lamp as it is turned on if it is connected to a potential difference of 120 V?

$V = IR$, so

$$I = \frac{V}{R} = \frac{120\ \text{V}}{60\ \Omega} = 2.0\ \text{A}$$

18. The graph in Figure 22–17 shows the current that flows through a device called a silicon diode.

a. A potential difference of +0.70 V is placed across the diode. What resistance would be calculated?

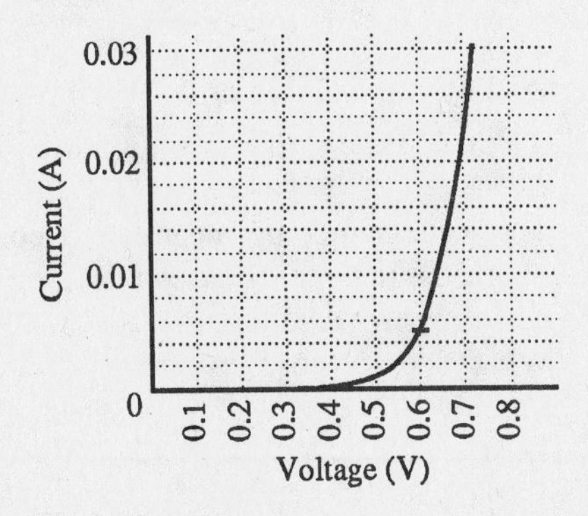

From the graph, $I = 22$ mA, and $V = IR$, so $R = V/I = (0.70\ \text{V})/(2.2 \times 10^{-2}\ \text{A}) = 32\ \Omega$

b. What resistance would be calculated if a +0.60 V potential difference was used?

From the graph, $I = 5.2$ mA and
$R = V/I = (0.60\ \text{V})/(5.2 \times 10^{-3}\ \text{A})$
$= 1.2 \times 10^2\ \text{A}$

c. Does the diode obey Ohm's law?

No. Resistance depends on voltage.

19. Draw a schematic diagram to show a circuit that includes a 90–V battery, an ammeter, and a resistance of 45 Ω connected in series. What is the ammeter reading? Draw arrows showing the direction of conventional current flow.

$V = IR$, so

$$I = \frac{V}{R} = \frac{90\ \text{V}}{45\ \Omega} = 2.0\ \text{A}$$

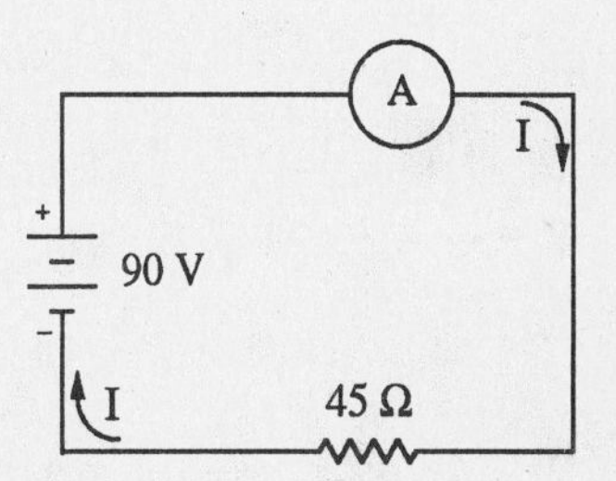

20. Draw a series circuit diagram to include a 16 Ω resistor, a battery, and an ammeter that reads 1.75 A. Current flows through the meter from left to right. Indicate the positive terminal and the voltage of the battery.

$V = IR = (1.75\ \text{A})(16\ \Omega) = 28\ \text{V}$

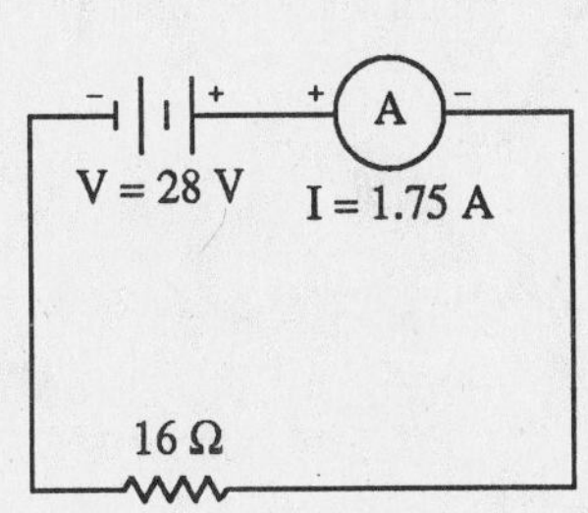

Chapter Review Problems

21. What is the maximum current that should be allowed in a 5.0–W, 220–Ω resistor?

$P = I^2R$, so $I = \sqrt{\frac{P}{R}} = \sqrt{\frac{5.0\text{ W}}{220\ \Omega}} = 0.15$ A

22. The wire in a house circuit is rated at 15.0 A that has a resistance of 0.15 Ω.

a. What is its power rating?

$P = I^2R = (15.0\text{ A})^2(0.15\ \Omega) = 34$ W

b. How much heat does the wire give off in 10.0 min?

$Q = E = I^2Rt$

$= (15.0\text{ A})^2(0.15\ \Omega)(10\text{ min})\left[\frac{60\text{ s}}{\text{min}}\right]$

$= 2.0 \times 10^4$ J

23. A current of 1.2 A flows through a 50–Ω resistor for 5.0 min. How much heat was generated by the resistor?

$Q = E = I^2Rt$

$= (1.2\text{ A})^2(50\ \Omega)(5.0\text{ min})\left[\frac{60\text{ s}}{\text{min}}\right]$

$= 2.2 \times 10^4$ J

24. A 6.0–Ω resistor is connected to a 15 V battery.

a. What is the current in the circuit?

$V = IR$, so

$I = \frac{V}{R} = \frac{15\text{ V}}{6.0\ \Omega} = 2.5$ A

b. How much thermal energy is produced in 10 min.?

$Q = E = I^2Rt$

$= (2.5\text{ A})^2(6.0\ \Omega)(10\text{ min})\left[\frac{60\text{ s}}{\text{min}}\right]$

$= 2.3 \times 10^4$ J

Chapter Review Problems

25. A 110–V electric iron draws 3.0 A of current. How much heat is developed per hour?

$V = IR$, so $R = \frac{V}{I} = \frac{110\text{ V}}{3.0\text{ A}} = 37\ \Omega$ and

$Q = E = I^2Rt = (3.0\text{ A})^2(37\ \Omega)(1\text{ h})\left[\frac{3600\text{ s}}{\text{h}}\right]$

$= 1.2 \times 10^6$ J

26. An electric motor operates a pump that irrigates a farmer's crop by pumping 10 000 L of water a vertical distance of 8.0 m into a field each hour. The motor has an operating resistance of 22.0 Ω and is connected across a 110–V source.

a. What current does it draw?

$V = IR$, so $I = \frac{V}{R} = \frac{110\text{ V}}{22.0\ \Omega} = 5.0$ A

b. How efficient is the motor?

$E_W = mgd$
$= (1.0 \times 10^4\text{ kg})(9.8\text{ m/s}^2)(8.0\text{ m})$
$= 7.8 \times 10^5$ J

$E_m = IVt = (5.0\text{ A})(110\text{ V})(3600\text{ s})$
$= 2.0 \times 10^6$ J

$Eff = \frac{E_W}{E_m} \times 100\% = \frac{7.8 \times 10^5\text{ J}}{2.0 \times 10^6\text{ J}} \times 100\%$

$= 39\%$

27. A transistor radio operates by means of a 9.0–V battery that supplies it with a 50–mA current.

a. If the cost of the battery is \$0.90 and it lasts for 300 h, what is the cost per kWh to operate the radio in this manner?

$P = IV = (0.050\text{ A})(9.0\text{ V}) = 0.45$ W
$= 4.5 \times 10^{-4}$ k

$\frac{Cost}{\text{kWh}} = \frac{\$0.90}{(4.5 \times 10^{-4}\text{ kW})(300\text{ h})} = \$6.70$

b. The same radio, by means of a converter, is plugged into a household circuit by a homeowner who pays \$0.08 per kWh. What does it now cost to operate the radio for 300 h?

$Cost = \frac{\$0.08}{\text{kWh}}(0.1\text{ kWh}) = 1$ cent

28. A heating coil has a resistance of 4.0 Ω and operates on 120 V.

a. What is the current in the coil while it is operating?

$V = IR$, so $I = \frac{V}{R} = \frac{120\ \text{V}}{4.0\ \Omega} = 30\ \text{A}$

b. What energy is supplied to the coil in 5.0 min?

$E = I^2Rt = (30\ \text{A})^2(4.0\ \Omega)(5.0\ \text{min})\left[\frac{60\ \text{s}}{\text{min}}\right]$

$= 1.1 \times 10^6\ \text{J}$

c. If the coil is immersed in an insulated container holding 20.0 kg of water, what will be the increase in the temperature of the water? Assume that 100% of the heat is absorbed by the water.

$Q = mc\Delta T$, so

$\Delta T = \frac{Q}{mc} = \frac{(1.1 \times 10^6\ \text{J})}{(20.0\ \text{kg})(4180\ \text{J/kg}\cdot\text{C}^\circ)}$

$= 13^\circ\text{C}$

d. At \$0.08 per kWh, what does it cost to operate the heating coil 30 min per day for 30 days?

$Cost = \left[\frac{1.1 \times 10^6\ \text{J}}{5\ \text{min}}\right]\left[\frac{30\ \text{min}}{\text{dy}}\right](30\ \text{dy})$

$\left[\frac{1\ \text{kWh}}{3.6 \times 10^6\ \text{J}}\right]\left[\frac{\$0.08}{\text{kWh}}\right]$

$= \$4.40$

29. An electric heater is rated at 500 W.

a. How much energy is delivered to the heater in half an hour?

$E = Pt = (5.00 \times 10^2\ \text{W})(30\ \text{min})\left[\frac{60\ \text{s}}{\text{min}}\right]$

$= 9.00 \times 10^5\ \text{J}$

Chapter Review Problems

b. The heater is being used to heat a room containing 50.0 kg of air. If the specific heat of air is 1.10 kJ/kg·C°, 1100 J/kg·C°, and 50% of the thermal energy heats the air in the room, what is the change in air temperature?

$Q = mc\Delta T$, so

$\Delta T = \frac{Q}{mc} = \frac{(0.5)(9 \times 10^5\ \text{J})}{(50.0\ \text{kg})(1100\ \text{J/kg}\cdot\text{C}^\circ)} = 8^\circ\text{C}$

c. At \$0.08 per kWh, what does it cost to run the heater 6.0 hours per day for 30 days?

$Cost = \left[\frac{500\ \text{J}}{\text{s}}\right]\left[\frac{6.0\ \text{h}}{\text{dy}}\right]\left[\frac{3600\ \text{s}}{\text{h}}\right](30\ \text{dy})$

$\left[\frac{1\ \text{kWh}}{3.6 \times 10^6\ \text{J}}\right]\left[\frac{\$0.08}{\text{kWh}}\right] = \$7.20$

Supplemental Problems (Appendix B)

1. How many amperes of current flow in a wire through which 1.00×10^{18} electrons pass per second?

$(1.00 \times 10^{18}\ e/\text{s})\left[\frac{1.60 \times 10^{-19}\ \text{C}}{e}\right] = 0.160\ \text{c/s}$

$= 0.160\ \text{A}$

2. A current of 5.00 A flowed in a copper wire for 20.0 s. How many coulombs of charge passed through the wire in this time?

$I = \frac{q}{t}$, so

$q = It = (5.00\ \text{A})(20.0\ \text{s}) = 1.00 \times 10^2\ \text{C}$

3. What power is supplied to a motor that operates on a 120–V line and draws 1.50 A of current?

$P = IV = (1.5\ \text{A})(120\ \text{V}) = 180\ \text{W}$

4. An electric lamp is connected to a 110–V source. If the current through the lamp is 0.75 A, what is the power consumption of the lamp?

$P = IV = (0.75\ \text{A})(110\ \text{V}) = 83\ \text{W}$

5. A lamp is labeled 6.0 V and 12 W.

a. What current flows through the lamp when it is operating?

$$P = IV, \text{ so } I = \frac{P}{V} = \frac{120 \text{ W}}{6.0 \text{ V}} = 2.0 \text{ A}$$

b. How much energy is supplied to the lamp in 1.000×10^3 s?

$$P = \frac{E}{t}, \text{ so}$$

$$E = Pt = (12 \text{ W})(1000 \text{ s}) = 1.2 \times 10^4 \text{ J} = 12 \text{ kJ}$$

6. A current of 3.00 A flows through a resistor when it is connected to a 12.0–V battery. What is the resistance of the resistor?

$$R = \frac{V}{I} = \frac{12.0 \text{ V}}{3.00 \text{ A}} = 4.00 \ \Omega$$

7. A small lamp is designed to draw a current of 3.00×10^2 mA in a 6.00–V circuit. What is the resistance of the lamp?

$$R = \frac{V}{I} = \frac{6.00 \text{ V}}{3.00 \times 10^{-1}} = 20.0 \ \Omega$$

8. What potential difference is required if you want a current of 8.00 mA in a load having a resistance of 50.0 Ω?

$$R = \frac{V}{I}, \text{ so}$$

$$V = IR = (8.00 \times 10^{-3} \text{ A})(50.0 \ \Omega) = 0.400 \text{ V}$$

9. In common metals, resistance increases as the temperature increases. An electric toaster has a resistance of 12.0 Ω when hot.

a. What current will flow through it when it is connected to 125 V?

$$R = \frac{V}{I}, \text{ so I} = \frac{V}{R} = \frac{125 \text{ V}}{12.0 \ \Omega} = 10.4 \text{ A}$$

b. When the toaster is first turned on, will the current be more or less than during operation?

When the toaster is first turned on, its temperature is low and its resistance is low, so the current is greater.

10. The resistance of a lamp is 230 Ω. The voltage is 115 V when the lamp is turned on.

a. What is the current in the lamp?

$$R = \frac{V}{I}, \text{ so } I = \frac{V}{R} = \frac{115 \text{ V}}{230 \ \Omega} = 0.500 \text{ A}$$

b. If the voltage rises to 120 V, what is the current?

$$I = \frac{V}{R} = \frac{120 \text{ V}}{230 \ \Omega} = 0.522 \text{ A}$$

11. What should be the resistance of the lamp in part **a** of the previous problem if the lamp is to draw the same current, but in a 230–V circuit?

$$R = \frac{V}{I} = \frac{230 \text{ V}}{0.500 \text{ A}} = 460 \ \Omega$$

12. A 110–W lamp draws 0.909 A. What is the lamp's resistance?

$$P = I^2R, \text{ so } R = \frac{P}{I^2} = \frac{110 \text{ W}}{(0.909 \text{ A})^2} = 133 \ \Omega$$

13. Each coil in a resistance box is capable of dissipating heat at the rate of 4.00 W.

$$P = I^2R, \text{ so } I^2 = \frac{P}{R}, \text{ and } I = \sqrt{\frac{P}{R}}.$$

What is the maximum current that should be allowed across a coil to avoid overheating if the coil has a resistance of

a. 2.00 Ω

$$I = \sqrt{\frac{P}{R}} = \sqrt{\frac{4.00 \text{ W}}{2.00 \ \Omega}} = 1.41 \text{ A}$$

b. 20.0 Ω

$$I = \sqrt{\frac{P}{R}} = \sqrt{\frac{4.00 \text{ W}}{20.0 \ \Omega}} = 0.447 \text{ A}$$

Supplemental Problems

14. What is the power supplied to a lamp that is operated by a battery having a 12 V potential difference across its terminals when the resistance lamp is 6.0 Ω?

$P = I^2R$ and $R = \frac{V}{I}$, so $I = \frac{V}{R}$. Therefore,

$$P = \left[\frac{V}{R}\right]^2 R = \frac{V^2}{R} = \frac{(12\ \text{V})^2}{6.0\ \Omega} = 24\ \text{W}$$

15. How much does it cost to run a 2.00 W clock for one year (365.25 days) if it costs 3.53 cents/kWh?

$$Cost = \frac{3.53\ ¢}{\text{kWh}}(2.00\ \text{W})\left[\frac{\text{kw}}{1000\ \text{W}}\right]\left[\frac{365.25\ \text{dy}}{1\ \text{yr}}\right]\left[\frac{24\ \text{h}}{1\ \text{dy}}\right] = 62\ ¢/\text{yr}$$

16. A small electric furnace that expends 2.00 kW of power is connected across a potential difference of 120 Volts.

a. What is the current in the circuit?

$P = IV$, so

$$I = \frac{P}{V} = \frac{2.00 \times 10^3\ \text{W}}{120\ \text{V}} = 16.7\ \text{A}$$

b. What is the resistance of the furnace?

$$R = \frac{V}{I} = \frac{120\ \text{V}}{16.7\ \text{A}} = 7.19\ \Omega$$

c. What is the cost of operating the furnace for 24.0 h at 7.00 cents/kWh?

$$Cost = \frac{7.00\ ¢}{\text{kWh}}(2.00\ \text{kW})(24\ \text{h}) = \$3.36$$

Chapter 23: Series and Parallel Circuits

Practice Problems

page 471

1. There are three 20–Ω resistors connected in series across a 120–V generator.

   a. What is the effective resistance of the circuit?

   $R = R_1 + R_2 + R_3$
   $= 20\ \Omega + 20\ \Omega + 20\ \Omega$
   $= 60\ \Omega$

   b. What is the current in the circuit?

   $I = V/R = (120\ \text{V})/(60\ \Omega) = 2.0\ \text{A}$

2. A 10–Ω resistor, a 15–Ω resistor, and a 5–Ω resistor are connected in series across a 90–V battery.

   a. What is the effective resistance of the circuit?

   $R = 10\ \Omega + 15\ \Omega + 5\ \Omega = 30\ \Omega$

   b. What is the current in the circuit?

   $I = V/R = (90\ \text{V})/(30\ \Omega) = 3.0\ \text{A}$

page 472

3. Consider a 9–V battery in a circuit with three resistors connected in series.

   a. If the resistance of one of the devices increases, how will the series resistance change?

   It will increase.

   b. What will happen to the current?

   $I = V/R$, so it will decrease.

   c. Will there be any change in the battery voltage?

   No. It does not depend on the resistance.

Practice Problems

4. Ten Christmas tree bulbs connected in series have equal resistances. When connected to 120–V outlet, the current through the bulbs is 0.06 A.

   a. What is the effective resistance of the circuit?

   $R = V/I = (120\ \text{V})/(0.06\ \text{A}) = 2000\ \Omega$

   b. What is the resistance of each bulb?

   $2000\ \Omega/10 = 200\ \Omega$

page 474

5. A 20.0–Ω resistor and a 30.0–Ω resistor are connected in series and placed across a 120–V potential difference.

   a. What is the effective resistance of the circuit?

   $R = 20.0\ \Omega + 30.0\ \Omega = 50.0\ \Omega$

   b. What is the current in the circuit?

   $I = V/R = (120\ \text{V})/(50.0\ \Omega) = 2.40\ \text{A}$

   c. What is the voltage drop across each resistor?

   $V = IR$. Across 20.0 Ω–resistor,
   $V = (2.40\ \text{A})(20.0\ \Omega) = 48.0\ \text{V}$.
   Across 30.0 Ω–resistor,
   $V = (2.40\ \text{A})(30.0\ \Omega) = 72.0\ \text{V}$

   d. What is the voltage drop across the two resistors together?

   $V = 48.0\ \text{V} + 72.0\ \text{V} = 120\ \text{V}$

6. Three resistors of 3.0 kΩ ($3.0 \times 10^3\ \Omega$), 5.0 kΩ, and 4.0 kΩ are connected in series across a 12–V battery.

   a. What is the effective resistance?

   $R = 3.0\ \text{k}\Omega + 5.0\ \text{k}\Omega + 4.0\ \text{k}\Omega = 12.0\ \text{k}\Omega$

Practice Problems

b. What is the current through the resistors?

$I = V/R = (12\text{ V})/(12.0\text{ k}\Omega)$
$= 1.0\text{ mA} = 1.0 \times 10^{-3}\text{ A}$

c. What is the voltage drop across each resistor?

$V = IR$,
so $V = 3.0\text{ V}, 5.0\text{ V}$, and 4.0 V

d. Find the total voltage drop across the three resistors.

$V = 3.0\text{ V} + 5.0\text{ V} + 4.0\text{ V}$
$= 12.0\text{ V}$

7. A student makes a voltage divider from a 45–V battery, a 475–kΩ ($475 \times 10^3\ \Omega$) resistor, and a 235–kΩ resistor. The output voltage is measured across the smaller resistor. What is the voltage?

$V_2 = VR_2/(R_1 + R_2)$
$= (45\text{ V})(235\text{ k}\Omega)/(475\text{ k}\Omega + 235\text{ k}\Omega)$
$= 15\text{ V}$

page 475

8. A photoresistor is used in a voltage divider as R_2. $V = 9.0$ V and $R_1 = 500\ \Omega$.

a. What is the output voltage, V_2 across R_2, when a bright light strikes the photoresistor and $R_2 = 475\ \Omega$?

$V_2 = VR_2/(R_1 + R_2)$
$= (9.0\text{ V})(475\ \Omega)/(500\ \Omega + 475\ \Omega)$
$= 4.4\text{ V}$

b. When the light is dim, $R_2 = 4.0$ kΩ. What is V_2?

$V_2 = VR_2/(R_1 + R_2)$
$= (9.0\text{ V})(4.0\text{ k}\Omega)/(0.50\text{ k}\Omega + 4.0\text{ k}\Omega)$
$= 8.0\text{ V}$

c. When the photoresistor is in total darkness, $R_2 = 0.40$ MΩ ($0.40 \times 10^6\ \Omega$). What is V_2?

$V_2 = VR_2/(R_1 + R_2)$
$$= \frac{(9.0\text{ V})(4.0 \times 10^5\ \Omega)}{(0.005 \times 10^5\ \Omega + 4.0 \times 10^5\ \Omega)}$$
$= 9.0\text{ V}$

Practice Problems

page 477

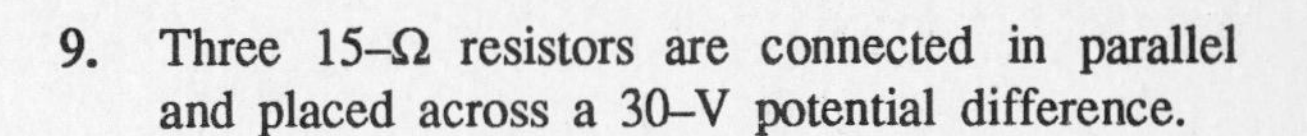

9. Three 15–Ω resistors are connected in parallel and placed across a 30–V potential difference.

a. What is the equivalent resistance of the parallel circuit?

$1/R = 1/R_1 + 1/R_2 + 1/R_3$
$= 3/15\ \Omega,\ R = 5.0\ \Omega$

b. What is the current through the entire circuit?

$I = V/R = (30\text{ V})/(5.0\ \Omega) = 6.0\text{ A}$

c. What is the current through each branch of the parallel circuit?

$I = V/R = (30\text{ V})/(15.0\ \Omega) = 2.0\text{ A}$

10. A 12.0–Ω resistor and a 15.0–Ω resistor are connected in parallel and placed across the terminals of a 15.0–V battery.

a. What is the equivalent resistance of the parallel circuit?

$1/R = 1/15.0\ \Omega + 1/12.0\ \Omega$, so
$R = 6.67\ \Omega$

b. What is the current through the entire circuit?

$I = V/R = (15.0\text{ V})/(6.67\ \Omega) = 2.25\text{ A}$

c. What is the current through each branch of the parallel circuit?

$I = V/R = (15.0\text{ V})/(15.0\ \Omega)$
$= 1.00\text{ A},\ (15.0\text{ V})/(12.0\ \Omega)$
$= 1.25\text{ A}$

page 478

11. A 120.0–Ω resistor, a 60.0–Ω resistor, and a 40.0–Ω resistor are connected in parallel and placed across a potential difference of 12.0 V.

a. What is the equivalent resistance of the parallel circuit?

$1/R = 1/120.0\ \Omega + 1/60.0\ \Omega + 1/40.0\ \Omega$,
$R = 20.0\ \Omega$

Practice Problems

b. What is the current through the entire circuit?

$I = V/R$
$= (12.0\ \text{V})/(20.0\ \Omega)$
$= 0.600\ \text{A}$

c. What is the current through each branch of the parallel circuit?

$I = V/R = (12.0\ \text{V})/(120.0\ \Omega)$
$= 0.100\ \text{A},\ (12.0\ \text{V})/(60.0\ \Omega)$
$= 0.200\ \text{A},\ (12.0\ \text{V})/(40.0\ \Omega)$
$= 0.300\ \text{A}$

12. Suppose the 12.0–Ω resistor in Practice Problem 10 is replaced by a 10.0–Ω resistor.

a. Does the equivalent resistance become smaller, larger, or remain the same?

Smaller.

b. Does the amount of current through the entire circuit change? in what way?

Gets larger.

c. Does the amount of current through the 15.0–Ω resistor change? in what way?

No. It remains the same. Currents are independent.

page 484

13. Two 60–Ω resistors are connected in parallel. This parallel arrangement is connected in series with a 30–Ω resistor. The combination is then placed across a 120–V potential difference.

a. Draw a diagram of the circuit.

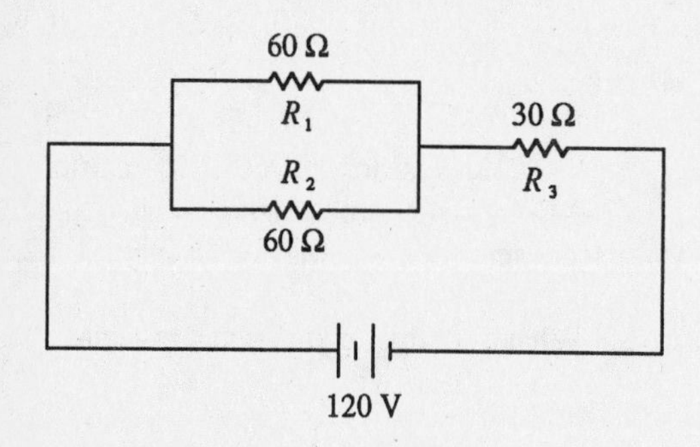

Practice Problems

b. What is the equivalent resistance of the parallel portion of the circuit?

$$\frac{1}{R} = \frac{1}{60\ \Omega} + \frac{1}{60\ \Omega} = \frac{2}{60\ \Omega}$$

$$R = \frac{60\ \Omega}{2} = 30\ \Omega$$

c. What single resistance could replace the three original resistors?

$R_{eff} = 30\ \Omega + 30\ \Omega = 60\ \Omega$

d. What is the current in the circuit?

$$I = \frac{V}{R} = \frac{120\ \text{V}}{60\ \Omega} = 2.0\ \text{A}$$

e. What is the voltage drop across the 30–Ω resistor?

$V_3 = IR_3 = (2.0)(30\ \Omega) = 60\ \text{V}$

f. What is the voltage drop across the parallel portion of the circuit?

$V = IR = (2.0\ \text{A})(30\ \Omega) = 60\ \text{V}$

g. What is the current in each branch of the parallel portion of the circuit?

$$I = \frac{V}{R_1} = \frac{V}{R_2} = \frac{60\ \text{V}}{60\ \Omega} = 1.0\ \text{A}$$

14. Three 15–Ω resistors are connected in parallel. This arrangement is connected in series with a 10–Ω resistor. The entire combination is then placed across a 45–V difference in potential.

a. Draw a diagram of the circuit.

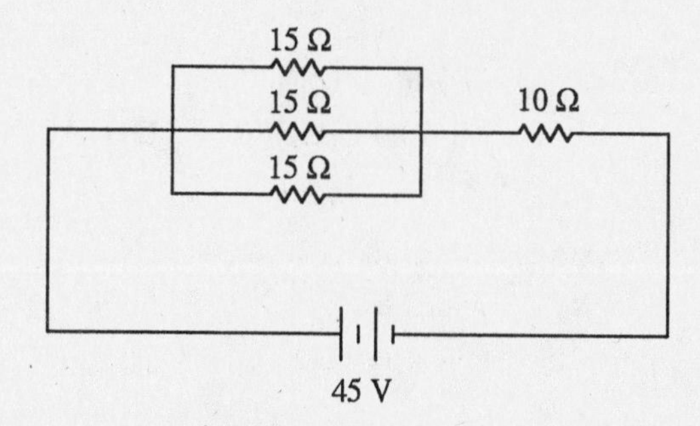

b. What is the equivalent resistance of the parallel portion of the circuit?

$$\frac{1}{R} = \frac{1}{15\ \Omega} + \frac{1}{15\ \Omega} + \frac{1}{15\ \Omega} = \frac{3}{15\ \Omega}$$

$$R = \frac{15\ \Omega}{3} = 5.0\ \Omega$$

c. What is the equivalent resistance of the entire circuit?

$$R_{eff} = 5\ \Omega + 10\ \Omega = 15\ \Omega$$

d. What is the current in the entire circuit?

$$I = \frac{V}{R_{eff}} = \frac{45\ \text{V}}{15\ \Omega} = 3.0\ \text{A}$$

e. What is the voltage drop across the 10–Ω resistor?

$$V = IR = (3.0\ \text{A})(10\ \Omega) = 30\ \text{V}$$

15. Suppose you are given three 68–Ω resistors. You can use them in a series, parallel, or series–parallel circuit. Find the three different resistances you can produce in the circuit.

Series: 68 Ω + 68 Ω + 68 Ω = 204 Ω,
Parallel: 68 Ω/3 = 23 Ω,
Series Parallel: 68 Ω + 68 Ω/2 = 102 Ω

Chapter Review Problems

page 488–489

1. A 20.0–Ω lamp and a 5.0–Ω lamp are connected in series and placed across a difference in potential of 50 V.

a. What is the effective resistance of the circuit?

20.0 Ω + 5.0 Ω = 25.0 Ω

b. What is the current in the circuit?

$$I = \frac{V}{R} = \frac{50\ \text{V}}{25.0\ \Omega} = 2.0\ \text{A}$$

c. What is the voltage drop across each lamp?

$$V = IR = (2.0\ \text{A})(20.0\ \Omega) = 40\ \text{V}$$
$$V = IR = (2.0\ \text{A})(5.0\ \Omega) = 10\ \text{V}$$

d. What is the power dissipated in each lamp?

$$P = IV = (2.0\ \text{A})(40\ \text{V}) = 80\ \text{W}$$
$$P = IV = (2.0\ \text{A})(10\ \text{V}) = 20\ \text{W}$$

2. Three identical lamps are connected in series to a 6.0–V battery. What is the voltage drop across each lamp?

Since each lamp is identical to the others, they will each have the same voltage drop of

$$\frac{6.0\ \text{V}}{3} = 2.0\ \text{V}.$$

3. The load across a 12–V battery consists of a series combination of three resistors of 15 Ω, 21 Ω, and 24 Ω.

a. What is the total resistance of the load?

$$R = R_1 + R_2 + R_3 = 15\ \Omega + 21\ \Omega + 24\ \Omega = 60\ \Omega$$

b. What is the current in the circuit?

$$I = \frac{V}{R} = \frac{12\ \text{V}}{60\ \Omega} = 0.20\ \text{A}$$

4. The load across a battery consists of two resistors connected in series with values of 15 Ω and 45 Ω.

a. What is the total resistance of the load?

$$R = R_1 + R_2 = 15\ \Omega + 45\ \Omega = 60\ \Omega$$

b. What is the voltage of the battery if the current in the circuit is 0.10 A?

$$V = IR = (60\ \Omega)(0.10\ \text{A}) = 6.0\ \text{V}$$

5. A lamp having a resistance of 10 Ω is connected across a 15–V battery.

a. What is the current through the lamp?

$$V = IR,\ \text{so}\ I = \frac{V}{R} = \frac{15\ \text{V}}{10\ \Omega} = 1.5\ \text{A}$$

Chapter Review Problems

b. What resistance must be connected in series with the lamp to reduce the current to 0.50 A?

The total resistance is given by $V = IR$, so
$R = \frac{V}{I} = \frac{15\ \text{V}}{0.50\ \text{A}} = 30\ \Omega$

And $R = R_1 + R_2$, so
$R_2 = R - R_1 = 30\ \Omega - 10\ \Omega = 20\ \Omega$

6. A string of eighteen identical Christmas tree lights are connected in series to a 120–V source. The string dissipates 64 W.

a. What is the equivalent resistance of the light string?

$P = IV$, so $I = \frac{P}{V} = \frac{64\ \text{W}}{120\ \text{V}} = 0.53\ \text{A}$ and

$V = IR$, so $R = \frac{V}{I} = \frac{120\ \text{V}}{0.53\ \text{A}} = 2.3 \times 10^2\ \Omega$

b. What is the resistance of a single light?

R is sum of resistances of 18 lamps, so each resistance is $(230\ \Omega)/18 = 13\ \Omega$.

c. What power is dissipated by each lamp?

$(64\ \text{W})/18 = 3.6\ \text{W}$

7. One of the bulbs in the previous problem burns out. The lamp has a wire that shorts out the lamp filament when it burns out. This drops the resistance of the lamp to zero.

a. What is the resistance of the light string now?

There are now 17 lamps in series instead of 18 lamps. The resistance is
$\frac{17}{18}(2.3 \times 10^2\ \Omega) = 2.2 \times 10^2\ \Omega$

b. Find the power dissipated by the string.

$I = \frac{V}{R} = \frac{120\ \text{V}}{2.2 \times 10^2\ \Omega} = 0.55\ \text{A}$ and

$P = IV = (0.55\ \text{A})(120\ \text{V}) = 66\ \text{W}$

c. Did the power go up or down when a bulb burned out?

It increased!

8. A 75.0–W bulb is connected to a 120–V source.

a. What is the current through the bulb?

$P = IV$, so $I = \frac{P}{V} = \frac{75.0\ \text{W}}{120\ \text{V}} = 0.625\ \text{A}$

b. What is the resistance of the bulb?

$V = IR$, so $R = \frac{V}{I} = \frac{120\ \text{V}}{0.625\ \text{A}} = 192\ \Omega$

c. A lamp dimmer puts a resistance in series with the bulb. What resistance would be needed to reduce the current to 0.300 A?

$V = IR$, so $R = \frac{V}{I} = \frac{120\ \text{V}}{0.300\ \text{A}} = 400\ \Omega$ and
$R = R_1 + R_2$, so
$R_2 = R - R_1 = 400\ \Omega - 192\ \Omega = 208\ \Omega$

9. In the previous problem, you found the resistance of a lamp and a dimmer resistor.

a. Assuming the resistances are constant, find the voltage drops across the lamp and the resistor.

$V = IR = (0.300\ \text{A})(192\ \text{V}) = 57.6\ \text{V}$
$V = IR = (0.300\ \text{A})(208\ \text{V}) = 62.4\ \text{V}$

b. Find the power dissipated by the lamp.

$P = IV = (0.300\ \text{A})(57.6\ \text{V}) = 17.3\ \text{W}$

c. Find the power dissipated by the dimmer resistor.

$P = IV = (0.300\ \text{A})(62.4\ \text{V}) = 18.7\ \text{W}$

10. Amy needs 5.0 V for some integrated circuit experiments. She uses a 6.0–V battery and two resistors to make a voltage divider. One resistor is 330 Ω. She decides to make the other resistor smaller. What value should it have?

$V_2 = \frac{VR_2}{R_1 + R_2}$. Since V_2 is more than half V, the voltage across R_2 is larger than that across R_1, so $R_2 > R_1$.

$R_1 = \frac{VR_2}{V_2} - R_2 = \frac{(6.0\ \text{V})(330\ \Omega)}{5.0\ \text{V}} - 330\ \Omega$
$= 66\ \Omega$

Chapter Review Problems

11. Pete is designing a voltage divider using a 12.0–V battery and a 100–Ω resistor as R_2. What resistor should be used as R_1 if the output voltage across R_2 is to be 4.00 V?

$$V_2 = \frac{VR_2}{R_1 + R_2}, \text{ or } R_1 + R_2 = \frac{VR_2}{R_2}, \text{ so}$$

$$R_1 = \frac{VR_2}{V_2} - R_2 = \frac{(12.0 \text{ V})(100 \text{ } \Omega)}{4.00 \text{ V}} - 100 \text{ } \Omega$$

$$= 200 \text{ } \Omega$$

12. A typical television dissipates 275 W when connected to a 120–V outlet.

a. Find the resistance of the television.

$$P = IV \text{ and } I = \frac{V}{R}, \text{ so } P = \frac{V^2}{R}, \text{ or}$$

$$R = \frac{V^2}{P} = \frac{(120 \text{ V})^2}{275 \text{ W}} = 52.4 \text{ } \Omega$$

b. The television and connecting wires, with a resistance of 2.5 Ω, form a series circuit that works like a voltage divider. Find the voltage drop across the television.

$$V_1 = \frac{VR_1}{R_1 + R_2} = \frac{(120 \text{ V})(52.4 \text{ } \Omega)}{52.4 \text{ } \Omega + 2.5 \text{ } \Omega}$$

$$= 115 \text{ V}$$

c. A 12–Ω hair dryer is now plugged into the same outlet. Find the equivalent resistance of the two appliances.

$$\frac{1}{R} = \frac{1}{R_1} + \frac{1}{R_2} = \frac{1}{52.4 \text{ } \Omega} + \frac{1}{12 \text{ } \Omega} = 9.8 \text{ } \Omega$$

d. Find the voltage drop across the television and hair dryer combination. The lower voltage explains why the television picture sometimes shrinks when another appliance is turned on.

$$V_1 = \frac{VR_1}{R_1 + R_2} = \frac{(120 \text{ V})(9.8 \text{ } \Omega)}{9.8 \text{ } \Omega + 2.5 \text{ } \Omega} = 96 \text{ V}$$

13. Three identical lamps are connected in parallel to each other and then connected to a 6.0–V battery. What is the voltage drop across each lamp?

In parallel circuits, the voltage drop across each branch are the same, in this case 6.0 V.

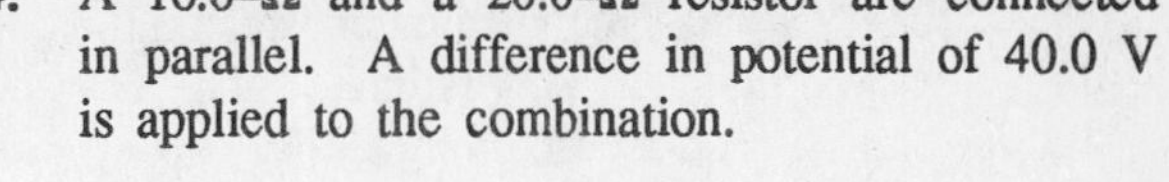

14. A 16.0–Ω and a 20.0–Ω resistor are connected in parallel. A difference in potential of 40.0 V is applied to the combination.

a. Compute the equivalent resistance of the parallel circuit.

$$\frac{1}{R} = \frac{1}{R_1} + \frac{1}{R_2} = \frac{1}{16.0 \text{ } \Omega} + \frac{1}{20.0 \text{ } \Omega}$$

$$R = \frac{1}{0.1125 \text{ } \Omega} = 8.89 \text{ } \Omega$$

b. What is the current in the circuit?

$$I = \frac{V}{R} = \frac{40.0 \text{ V}}{8.89 \text{ } \Omega} = 4.50 \text{ A}$$

c. How large is the current through the 16.0–Ω resistor?

$$I_1 = \frac{V}{R_1} = \frac{40.0 \text{ V}}{16.0 \text{ } \Omega} = 2.50 \text{ A}$$

15. During a laboratory exercise, you are supplied with the following apparatus: a battery of potential difference V, two heating elements of low resistance that can be placed in water, an ammeter of negligible resistance, a voltmeter of extremely high resistance, wires of negligible resistance, a beaker that is well–insulated and has negligible heat capacity, 100.0 g of water at 25°C.

a. By means of a diagram using standard symbols, show how these components should be connected to heat the water as rapidly as possible.

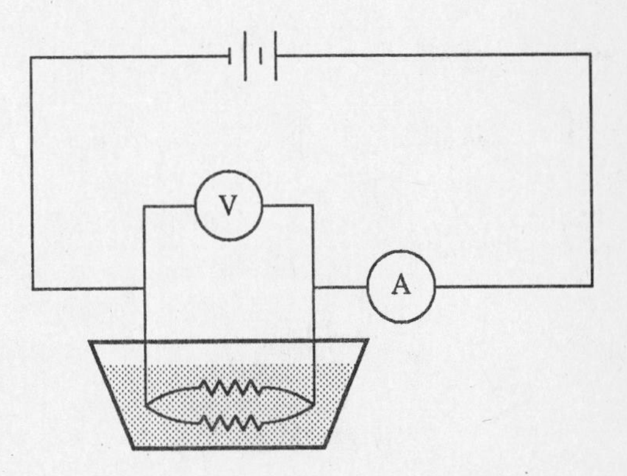

b. If the voltmeter reading holds steady at 50.0 V and the ammeter reading holds steady at 5.0 A, estimate the time in seconds required to completely vaporize the water in the beaker. Use 4200 J/kg·C° as the specific heat of water and 2.30×10^6 J/kg as the heat of vaporization of water.

$$\Delta Q = mc\Delta T = (100.0 \text{ g})(4.2 \text{ J/g}\cdot\text{C}^\circ)(75 \text{ C}^\circ) = 32\,000 \text{ J}$$

$$\Delta Q = mL_v = (100.0 \text{ g})(2300 \text{ J/g}) = 230\,000 \text{ J}$$

$$\Delta Q_{total} = 32\,000 \text{ J} + 230\,000 \text{ J} = 260\,000 \text{ J}$$

Energy is provided at the rate of
$P = IV = (5.0 \text{ A})(50.0 \text{ V}) = 250 \text{ J/s}$

The time required is $t = \dfrac{260\,000 \text{ J}}{250 \text{ J/s}} = 1.0 \times 10^3 \text{ s}$

16. A circuit contains six 240–Ω lamps, 60–W bulbs, and a 10.0–Ω heater connected in parallel. The voltage across the circuit is 120 V. What is the current in the circuit

a. when four lamps are turned on?

$$\frac{1}{R} = \frac{1}{R_1} + \frac{1}{R_2} + \frac{1}{R_3} + \frac{1}{R_4}$$

$$= \frac{1}{240\ \Omega} + \frac{1}{240\ \Omega} + \frac{1}{240\ \Omega} + \frac{1}{240\ \Omega}$$

$$= \frac{4}{240\ \Omega}, \text{ so}$$

$$R = \frac{240\ \Omega}{4} = 60\ \Omega$$

$$I = \frac{V}{R} = \frac{120 \text{ V}}{60\ \Omega} = 2.0 \text{ A}$$

b. when all six lamps are turned on?

$$\frac{1}{R} = \frac{6}{240\ \Omega}$$

$$R = \frac{240\ \Omega}{6} = 40\ \Omega$$

$$I = \frac{V}{R} = \frac{120 \text{ V}}{40\ \Omega} = 3.0 \text{ A}$$

Chapter Review Problems

c. if all six lamps and the heater are operating?

$$\frac{1}{R} = \frac{1}{40\ \Omega} + \frac{1}{10.0\ \Omega} = \frac{5}{40\ \Omega}$$

$$R = \frac{40\ \Omega}{5} = 8.0\ \Omega$$

$$I = \frac{V}{R} = \frac{120 \text{ V}}{8.0\ \Omega} = 15 \text{ A}$$

d. If the circuit has a fuse rated at 12 A, will it melt if everything is on?

Yes. The 15–A current will melt the 12–A fuse.

17. Determine the reading of each ammeter and each voltmeter in Figure 23–18.

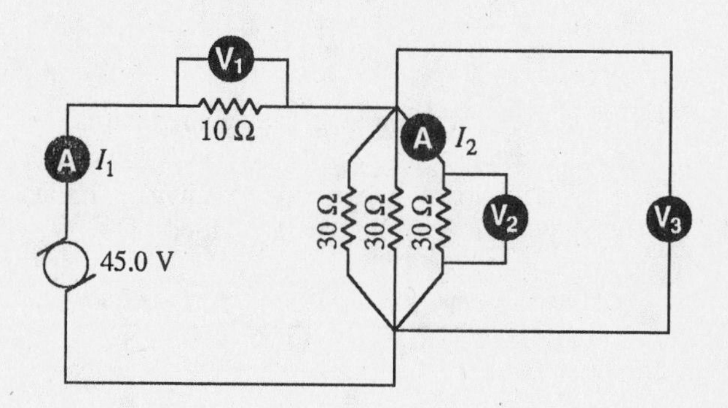

The three resistors in parallel have a total resistance of

$$\frac{1}{R_E} = \frac{1}{R_2} + \frac{1}{R_3} + \frac{1}{R_4}$$

$$= \frac{1}{30.0\ \Omega} + \frac{1}{30.0\ \Omega} + \frac{1}{30.0\ \Omega}, \text{ so}$$

$R_E = 10.0\ \Omega$.
The total resistance of the circuit is
$R_T = R_1 + R_E = 10.0\ \Omega + 10.0\ \Omega = 20.0\ \Omega$

$$I_1 = \frac{V}{R_T} = \frac{45.0 \text{ V}}{20.0\ \Omega} = 2.25 \text{ A}$$

$V_1 = IR_1 = (2.25 \text{ A})(10.0\ \Omega) = 22.5 \text{ V}$
Because the ammeter has an internal resistance of almost zero,
$V_2 = V_3 = 45.0 \text{ V} - V_1 = 45.0 \text{ V} - 22.5 \text{ V} = 22.5 \text{ V}$

$$I_2 = \frac{V_2}{R_2} = \frac{22.5 \text{ V}}{30.0\ \Omega} = 0.750 \text{ A}$$

18. Determine the power used by each resistance shown in Figure 23–18.

Some information is from the previous problem. See figure from Problem 17.

In the 10-Ω resistor,
$P_1 = I_1V_1 = (2.25\ A)(22.5\ V) = 50.6\ W$
In each of the 30-Ω resistors the power will be equal to
$P = IV = (0.750\ A)(22.5\ V) = 16.9\ W.$

19. A typical home circuit is diagrammed in Figure 23–19. Note that the lead lines to the kitchen lamp each have very low resistances of 0.25 Ω. The lamp has a resistance of 240.0 Ω. Although the circuit is a parallel circuit, the lead lines are in series with each of the components of the circuit.

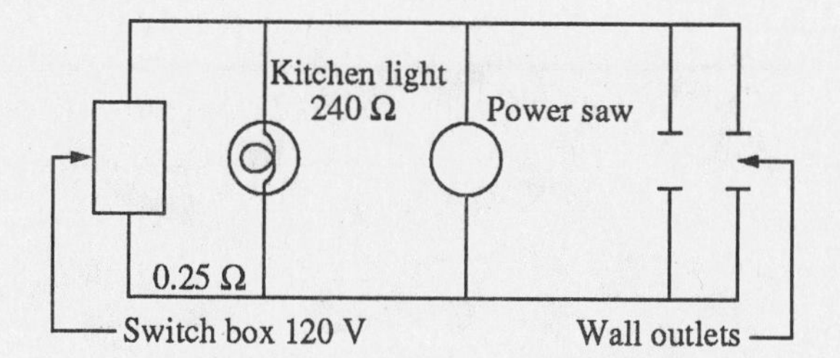

a. Compute the effective resistance of the circuit consisting of just the light and the lead lines to and from the light.

$R = 0.25\ \Omega + 0.25\ \Omega + 240\ \Omega = 240\ \Omega$

b. Find the current to the bulb.

$$I = \frac{V}{R} = \frac{120\ V}{240\ \Omega} = 0.50\ A$$

c. Find the power rating of the bulb.

$P = IV = (0.50\ A)(120\ V) = 60\ W$

d. Since the current in the bulb is 0.50 A, the current in the lead lines must also be 0.50 A. Calculate the voltage drop due to the two leads.

$V = IR = (0.50\ A)(0.50\ \Omega) = 0.25\ V$

Chapter Review Problems

20. A power saw is operated by an electric motor. When the electric motor is first turned on, it has a very low resistance. Suppose that the kitchen light discussed in the previous problem is on and a power saw is suddenly turned on. The saw plus the lead lines have an initial total resistance of 6.0 Ω.

a. Compute the effective resistance of the light–saw parallel circuit.

$$\frac{1}{R} = \frac{1}{240\ \Omega} + \frac{1}{6.0\ \Omega}$$

$R = 5.9\ \Omega$
$R_{eff} = 5.9\ \Omega + 0.25\ \Omega + 0.25\ \Omega = 6.4\ \Omega$

b. What current flows to the light?

$$I = \frac{V}{R} = \frac{120\ V}{6.4\ \Omega} = 19\ A$$

c. What is the total voltage drop across the two leads to the light?

$V = IR = (19\ A)(0.50\ \Omega) = 9.5\ V$

d. What voltage remains to operate the light? Will this voltage cause the light to dim temporarily?

$V = 120\ V - 9.5\ V = 110\ V$
Yes, this will cause a momentary dimming.

Supplementary Problems (Appendix B)

1. The load across a 50.0-V battery consists of a series combination of two lamps with resistances of 125 Ω and 225 Ω.

a. Find the total resistance of the circuit.

$R_T = R_1 + R_2 = 125\ \Omega + 225\ \Omega = 350\ \Omega$

b. Find the current in the circuit.

$$V = IR, \text{ so } I = \frac{V}{R} = \frac{50.0\ V}{350\ \Omega} = 0.143\ A$$

c. Find the potential difference across the 125–Ω lamp.

$V = IR = (0.143\ \text{A})(125\ \Omega) = 17.9\ \text{V}$

2. The load across a 12–V battery consists of a series combination of three resistances that are 15 Ω, 21 Ω, and 24 Ω respectively.

a. Draw the circuit diagram.

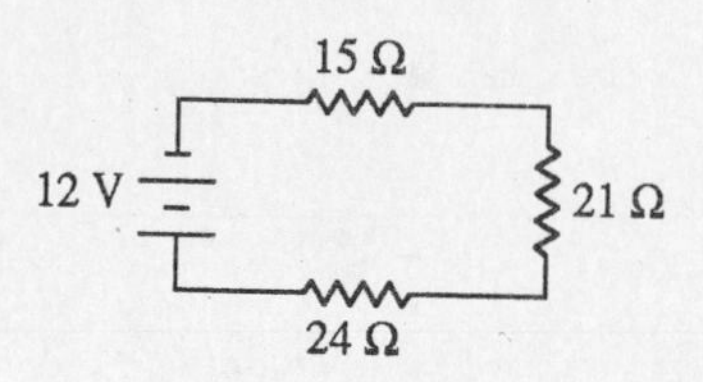

b. What is the total resistance of the load?

$R_T = R_1 + R_2 + R_3 = 15\ \Omega + 21\ \Omega + 24\ \Omega$
$= 60\ \Omega$

c. What is the magnitude of the circuit current?

$V = IR$, so $I = \dfrac{V}{R} = \dfrac{12\ \text{V}}{60\ \Omega} = 0.20\ \text{A}$

3. The load across a 12–V battery consists of a series combination of three resistances R_1, R_2, and R_3. R_1 is 210 Ω, R_2 is 350 Ω and R_3 is 120 Ω.

a. Find the equivalent resistance of the circuit.

$R_T = R_1 + R_2 + R_3$
$= 210\ \Omega + 350\ \Omega + 120\ \Omega$
$= 680\ \Omega$

b. Find the current in the circuit.

$V = IR$, so

$I = \dfrac{V}{R} = \dfrac{12\ \text{V}}{680\ \Omega} = 1.8 \times 10^{-2}\ \text{A} = 18\ \text{mA}$

c. Find the potential difference across R_3.

$V = IR = (1.8 \times 10^{-2}\ \text{A})(120\ \Omega) = 2.2\ \text{V}$

4. The load across a 40–V battery consists of a series combination of three resistances, R_1, R_2, and R_3. R_1 is 240 Ω, and R_3 is 120 Ω. The potential difference across R_1 is 24 V.

a. Find the current in the circuit.

$V = IR$, so $I = \dfrac{V_1}{R_1} = \dfrac{24\ \text{V}}{240\ \Omega} = 0.10\ \text{A}$

b. Find the equivalent resistance of the circuit.

$V = IR$, so $R = \dfrac{V}{I} = \dfrac{40\ \text{V}}{0.10\ \text{A}} = 400\ \Omega$

c. Find the resistance of R_2.

$R_T = R_1 + R_2 + R_3$, so
$R_2 = R_T - R_1 - R_3$
$= 400\ \Omega - 240\ \Omega - 120\ \Omega$
$= 40\ \Omega$

5. Pete is designing a voltage divider using a 12.0–V battery and a 100–Ω resistor as R_2. What resistor should be used as R_1 if the output voltage is 4.75 V?

$V_2 = \dfrac{VR_2}{R_1 + R_2}$, so $(R_1 + R_2)V_2 = VR_2$ and

$R_1V_2 = VR_2 - V_2R_2$, so

$R_1 = \left[\dfrac{V - V_2}{V_2}\right]R_2 = \left[\dfrac{12.0 - 4.75}{4.75}\right]100\ \Omega$

$= 153\ \Omega$

6. Two resistances, one 12 Ω and the other 18 Ω, are connected in parallel. What is the equivalent resistance of the parallel combination?

$\dfrac{1}{R} = \dfrac{1}{R_1} + \dfrac{1}{R_2} = \dfrac{1}{12\ \Omega} + \dfrac{1}{18\ \Omega}$, so $R = 7.2\ \Omega$

7. Three resistances of 12 Ω each are connected in parallel. What is the equivalent resistance?

$\dfrac{1}{R} = \dfrac{1}{R_1} + \dfrac{1}{R_2} + \dfrac{1}{R_3} = \dfrac{1}{12\ \Omega} + \dfrac{1}{12\ \Omega} + \dfrac{1}{12\ \Omega}$

$= \dfrac{3}{12\ \Omega} = \dfrac{1}{4.0\ \Omega}$, so $R = 4.0\ \Omega$

8. Two resistances, one 62 Ω and the other 88 Ω, are connected in parallel. The resistors are then connected to a 12 V battery.

a. What is the equivalent resistance of the parallel combination?

$$\frac{1}{R} = \frac{1}{R_1} + \frac{1}{R_2} = \frac{1}{62\ \Omega} + \frac{1}{88\ \Omega},$$

so $R = 36\ \Omega$

b. What is the current through each resistor?

$$V = IR, \text{ so } I = \frac{V}{R} = \frac{12\text{ V}}{62\ \Omega} = 0.19\text{ A}$$

$$I = \frac{V}{R} = \frac{12\text{ V}}{88\ \Omega} = 0.14\text{ A}$$

9. A 35 Ω, 55 Ω and 85 Ω resistor are connected in parallel. The resistors are then connected to a 35 V battery.

a. What is the equivalent resistance of the parallel combination?

$$\frac{1}{R} = \frac{1}{R_1} + \frac{1}{R_2} + \frac{1}{R_3} = \frac{1}{35\ \Omega} + \frac{1}{55\ \Omega} + \frac{1}{85\ \Omega}, \text{ so}$$

$R = 17\ \Omega$

b. What is the current through each resistor?

$$V = IR, \text{ so } I_1 = \frac{V}{R_1} = \frac{35\text{ V}}{35\ \Omega} = 1.0\text{ A}$$

$$I_2 = \frac{V}{R_2} = \frac{35\text{ V}}{55\ \Omega} = 0.64\text{ A}$$

$$I_3 = \frac{V}{R_3} = \frac{35\text{ V}}{85\ \Omega} = 0.41\text{ A}$$

10. A 110 V household circuit that contains a 1800 W microwave, a 1000 W toaster, and a 800 W coffee maker is connected to a 20 A fuse. Will the fuse melt if the microwave and the coffee maker are both on?

$P = IV$, so

$$I = \frac{P}{V} = \frac{1800\text{ W}}{110\text{ V}} = 16.4\text{ A} \quad \text{(microwave)}$$

$$I = \frac{P}{V} = \frac{800\text{ W}}{110\text{ V}} = \underline{7.27\text{ A}} \quad \text{(coffee maker)}$$

Total current of 23.7 A is greater than 20 A so the fuse will melt.

Supplemental Problems

23

11. Resistors R_1, R_2, and R_3 have resistances of 15.0 Ω, 9.0 Ω, and 8.0 Ω respectively. R_1 and R_2 are connected in series and their combination is in parallel with R_3 to form a load across a 6.0 Volt battery.

a. Draw the circuit diagram.

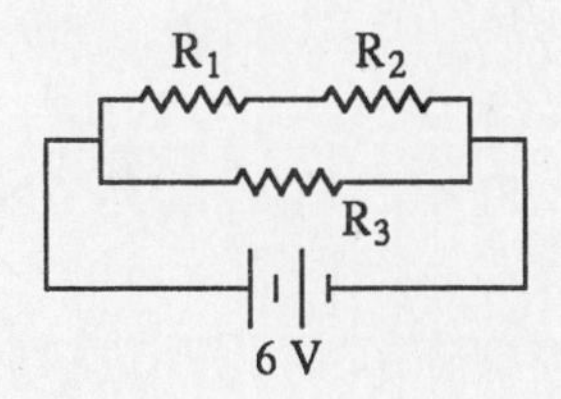

b. What is the total resistance of the load?

$R_1 + R_2 = 15.0\ \Omega + 9.0\ \Omega = 24.0\ \Omega$

$$\frac{1}{R_T} = \frac{1}{R_{12}} + \frac{1}{R_3} = \frac{1}{24.0\ \Omega} + \frac{1}{8.0\ \Omega}, \text{ so}$$

$R_T = 6.0\ \Omega$

c. What is the magnitude of the circuit current?

$$V = IR, \text{ so } I = \frac{V}{R} = \frac{6.0\text{ V}}{6.0\ \Omega} = 1.0\text{ A}$$

d. What is the current in R_3?

$$V = IR, \text{ so } I_3 = \frac{V}{R_3} = \frac{6.0\text{ V}}{8.0\ \Omega} = 0.75\text{ A}$$

e. What is the potential difference across R_2?

$I_T = I_2 + I_3$, so
$I_2 = I_T - I_3 = 1.0\text{ A} - 0.75\text{ A}$
$= 0.25\text{ A}$ and
$V_2 = I_2R_2 = (0.25\text{ A})(9.0\ \Omega) = 2.3\text{ V}$

12. A 15.0 Ω resistor is connected in series to a 120 Volt generator and two 10.0 Ω resistors that are connected in parallel to each other.

a. Draw the circuit diagram.

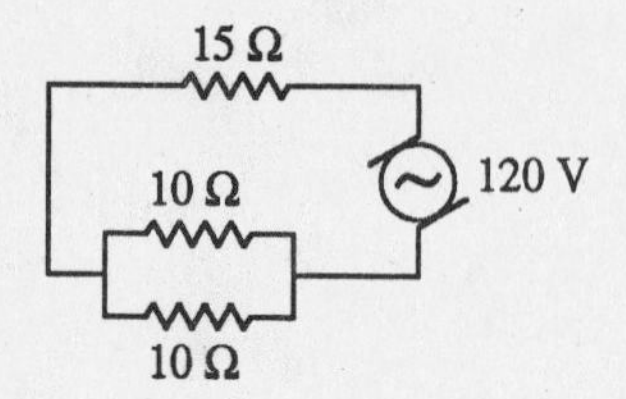

b. What is the total resistance of the load?

$$\frac{1}{R_{12}} = \frac{1}{R_1} + \frac{1}{R_2} = \frac{1}{10.0\ \Omega} + \frac{1}{10.0\ \Omega} = \frac{1}{5.0\ \Omega},$$

so $R_{12} = 5.0\ \Omega$

$R_T = R_3 + R_{12} = 15.0\ \Omega + 5.0\ \Omega = 20.0\ \Omega$

c. What is the magnitude of the circuit current?

$V = IR$, so $I = \frac{V}{R} = \frac{120\ \text{V}}{20.0\ \Omega} = 6.00\ \text{A}$

d. What is the current in one of the 10.0 Ω resistors?

The current would divide equally, so 3.00 A.

e. What is the potential difference across 15.0 Ω resistor?

$V = IR = (6.00\ \text{A})(15.0\ \Omega) = 90.0\ \text{V}$

13. How would you change the resistance of a voltmeter to allow the voltmeter to measure a larger potential difference?

Increase the resistance.

14. How would you change the shunt in an ammeter to allow the ammeter to measure a larger current?

Decrease the resistance of the shunt.

Supplemental Problems

15. An ohmmeter is made by connecting a 6.0 V battery in series with an adjustable resistor and an ideal ammeter. The ammeter deflects full–scale with a current of 1.0 mA. The two leads are touched together and the resistance is adjusted so 1.0 mA current flows.

a. What is the resistance of the adjustable resistor?

$V = IR$, so

$$R = \frac{V}{I} = \frac{6.0\ \text{V}}{1.0 \times 10^{-3}\ \text{A}} = 6.0 \times 10^3\ \Omega$$

b. The leads are now connected to an unknown resistance. What external resistance would produce a reading of 0.50 mA, half full–scale?

$$R = \frac{V}{I} = \frac{6.0\ \text{V}}{0.50 \times 10^{-3}\ \text{A}} = 1.2 \times 10^4\ \Omega \text{ and}$$

$R_T = R_I + R_e$, so

$R_e = R_T - R_I = 1.2 \times 10^4\ \Omega - 6.0 \times 10^3\ \Omega$
$= 6 \times 10^3\ \Omega$

c. What external resistance would produce a reading of 0.25 mA, quarter–scale?

$$R = \frac{V}{I} = \frac{6.0\ \text{V}}{0.25 \times 10^{-3}\ \text{A}} = 2.4 \times 10^4\ \Omega \text{ and}$$

$R_e = R_T - R_I = 2.4 \times 10^4\ \Omega - 6.0 \times 10^3\ \Omega$
$= 1.8 \times 10^4\ \Omega$

d. What external resistance would produce a reading of 0.75 mA, three–quarter full–scale?

$$R = \frac{V}{I} = \frac{6.0\ \text{V}}{0.75 \times 10^{-3}\ \text{A}} = 8.0 \times 10^3\ \Omega \text{ and}$$

$R_e = R_T - R_I = 8.0 \times 10^3\ \Omega - 6.0 \times 10^3\ \Omega$
$= 2.0 \times 10^3\ \Omega$

Chapter 24: Magnetic Fields

Practice Problems

page 496

1. A student holds a bar magnet in each hand. If both hands are brought close together, will the force be attractive or repulsive if the magnets are held so that

   a. the two N–poles are brought close together?

   repulsive

   b. an N–pole and an S–pole are brought together?

   attractive

2. Figure 24–7 shows five disk magnets floating above each other. The N–pole of the top–most disk faces up. Which poles are on the top side of the other magnets?

   south, north, south, north

3. In the Chapter 1 opening photo, page 2, assume the N–pole is the bottom face of the floating magnet. Which is the direction of the induced field in the superconducting disk?

   The top face of the disk is the N–pole, so the direction of the field is up out of the N–pole.

4. Figure 24–3 shows a magnet attracting a nail to it which, in turn, has attracted many small tacks to it. If the N–pole of the permanent magnet is the top face, which end of the nail is the N–pole?

   The bottom (the point).

page 499

5. A long, straight, current–carrying wire runs from north to sourth.

   a. A compass needle placed above the wire points with its N–pole toward the east. In what direction is the current flowing?

   from south to north

Practice Problems

   b. If a compass is put underneath the wire, in which direction will the needle point?

   west

6. Suppose you measure the strength of the magnetic field 1 cm from a current carrying–wire.

   a. Compare the strength 2 cm away to the strength of the field at 1 cm.

   Since magnetic field strength varies inversely with the distance from the wire, it will be half as strong.

   b. Now compare the strength of the field 3 cm from the wire.

   It is one–third as strong.

7. The loop in figure 24–11b has current running in a clockwise direction (from left to right above the cardboard). If a compass is placed on the cardboard beneath the loop, in which direction will the N–pole point?

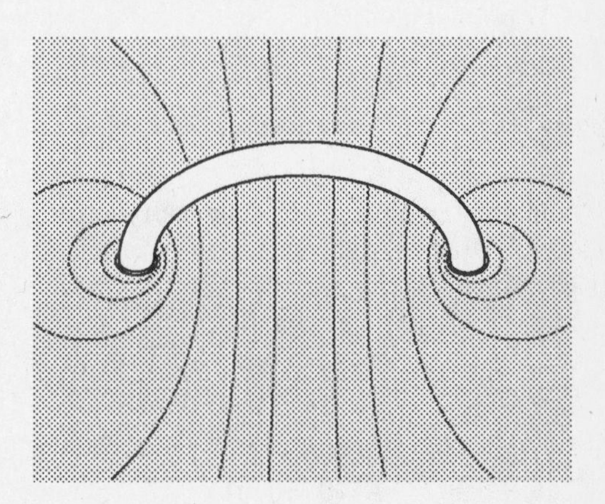

   It will point toward the top of the page.

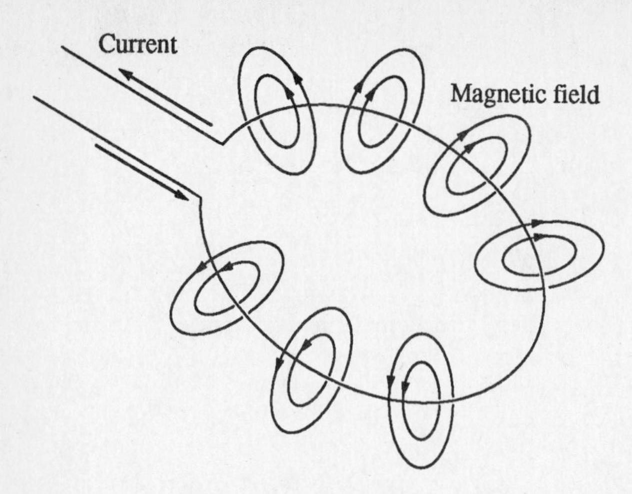

8. A student makes a magnet by winding wire around a large nail as in Figure 24–14. The magnet is connected to the battery as shown. Which end of the nail, pointed end or head, will be the N-pole?

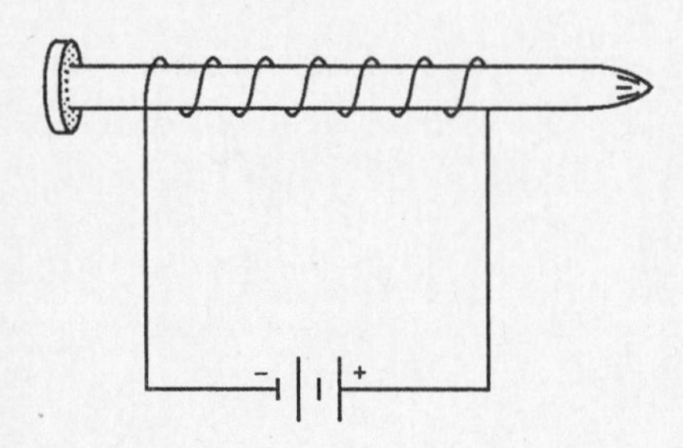

The pointed end.

page 504

9. A straight wire 0.10 m long carrying a current of 2.0 A is at right angles to a magnetic field. The force on the wire is 0.04 N. What is the strength of the magnetic field?

$F = BIL$,

$$B = \frac{F}{IL} = \frac{0.04\ \text{N}}{(2.0\ \text{A})(0.10\ \text{m})} = 0.2\ \text{T}$$

10. A wire 0.50 m long carrying a current of 8.0 A is at right angles to a 0.40 T magnetic field. How strong a force acts on the wire?

$F = BIL = (0.40\ \text{N/A} \cdot \text{m})(8.0\ \text{A})(0.50\ \text{m})$
$= 1.6\ \text{N}$

Practice Problems

page 505

11. A wire 75 cm long carrying a current of 6.0 A is at right angles to a uniform magnetic field. The magnitude of the force acting on the wire is 0.60 N. What is the strength of the magnetic field?

$$B = \frac{F}{IL} = \frac{0.60\ \text{N}}{(6.0\ \text{A})(0.75\ \text{m})} = 0.13\ \text{T}$$

12. A copper wire 40 cm long carries a current of 6.0 A and weighs 0.35 N. A certain magnetic field is strong enough to balance the force of gravity on the wire. What is the strength of the magnetic field?

$F = BIL$, F = weight of wire.

$$B = \frac{F}{IL} = \frac{0.35\ \text{N}}{(6.0\ \text{A})(0.40\ \text{m})} = 0.15\ \text{T}$$

page 508

13. An electron passes through a magnetic field at right angles to the field at a velocity of 4.0×10^6 m/s. The strength of the magnetic field is 0.50 T. What is the magnitude of the force acting on the electron?

$F = Bqv$
$= (0.50\ \text{T})(1.6 \times 10^{-19}\ \text{C})(4.0 \times 10^6\ \text{m/s})$
$= 3.2 \times 10^{-13}\ \text{N}$

page 509

14. A stream of doubly–ionized particles (missing two electrons and thus carrying a net charge of two elementary charges) moves at a velocity of 3.0×10^4 m/s perpendicular to a magnetic field of 9.0×10^{-2} T. What is the magnitude of the force acting on each ion?

$F = Bqv$
$= (9.0\times10^{-2}\ \text{T})(2)(1.6\times10^{-19}\ \text{C})(3.0\times10^4\ \text{m/s})$
$= 8.6 \times 10^{-16}\ \text{N}$

15. Triply–ionized particles in a beam carry a net positive charge of three elementary charge units. The beam enters a 4.0×10^{-2}–T magnetic field. The particles have a velocity of 9.0×10^6 m/s. What is the magnitude of the force acting on each particle?

$F = Bqv$
$E = (4.0 \times 10^{-2}\text{T})(3)(1.6 \times 10^{-19}\text{C})(9.0\times 10^6\text{m/s})$
$= 1.7 \times 10^{-13}\ \text{N}$

Practice Problems

16. Doubly–ionized helium atoms (alpha particles) are traveling at right angles to a magnetic field at a speed of 4.0×10^{-2} m/s. The field strength is 5.0×10^{-2} T. What force acts on each particle?

$F = Bqv$
$= (5.0\times10^{-2}\text{T})(2)(1.6\times10^{-19}\text{C})\cdot(4.0\times10^{-2}\text{ m/s})$
$= 6.4 \times 10^{-22}$ N

Chapter Review Problems

page 511–513

1. A wire 1.50 m long carrying a current of 10.0 A is at right angles to a uniform magnetic field. The force acting on the wire is 0.60 N. What is the induction of the magnetic field?

$F = BIL$, so

$$B = \frac{F}{IL} = \frac{0.60\text{ N}}{10.0\text{ A}\times 1.50\text{ m}} = 0.040\text{ N/A}\cdot\text{m}$$

$= 0.040$ T

2. The repulsive force between two ceramic magnets was measured and found to depend on distance as given in the table below.

Separation, *d* (mm)	Force, *F* (N)
10	3.93
12	0.40
14	0.13
16	0.057
18	0.030
20	0.018
22	0.011
24	0.0076
26	0.0053
28	0.0038
30	0.0028

Chapter Review Problems

a. Plot the force as a function of distance.

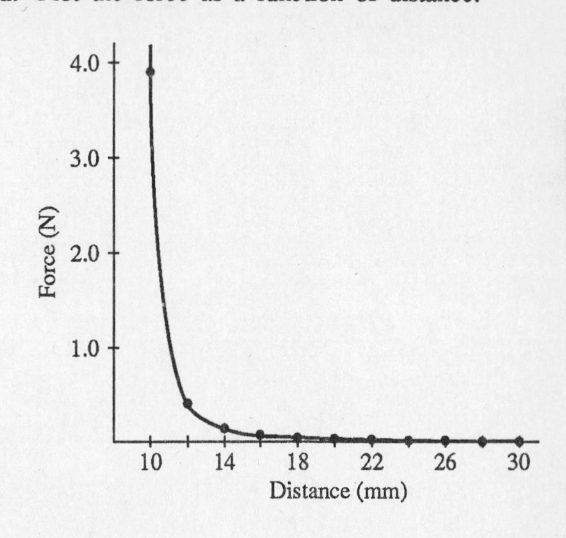

b. Does this force follow an inverse square law?

No.

3. A conventional current is in a wire as shown in Figure 24–28. Copy the wire segment and sketch the magnetic field the current generates.

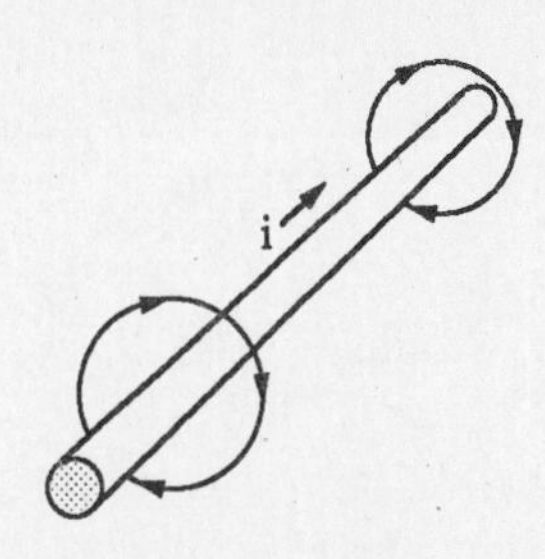

4. The current is coming straight out of the page in Figure 24–29. Copy the figure and sketch the magnetic field the current generates.

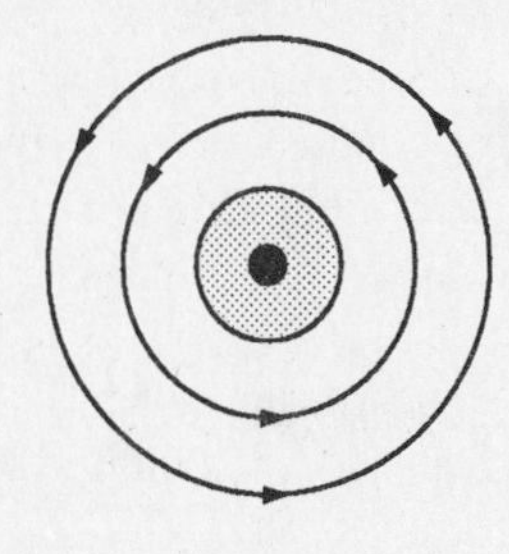

Chapter Review Problems

5. Figure 24–30 shows the end view of an electromagnet with the current as shown.

a. What is the direction of the magnetic field inside the loop?

down

b. What is the direction of the magnetic field outside the loop?

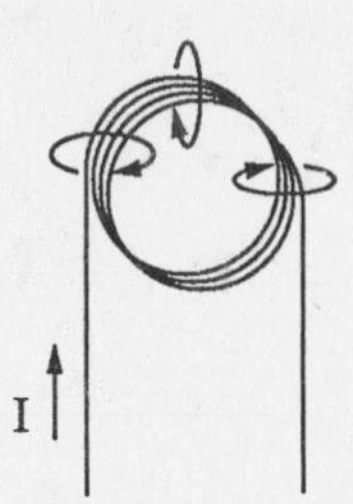

up

6. A current–carrying wire is placed between the poles of a magnet as shown in Figure 24–31. What is the direction of the force on the wire?

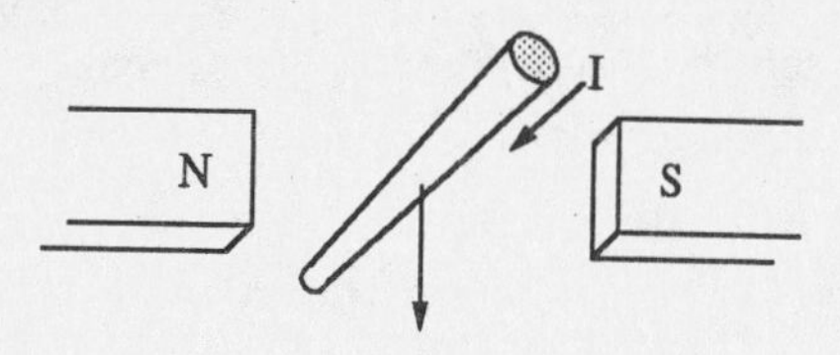

7. A room contains a strong, uniform magnetic field. A loop of fine wire in the room has current flowing through it. You rotate the loop until there is no tendency for it to rotate as a result of the field. What is the direction of the magnetic field relative to the plane of the coil?

The magnetic field is perpendicular to the plane of the coil. The right–hand rule would be used to find the direction of the field produced by the coil. The field in the room is in the same direction.

8. A wire 0.50 m long carrying a current of 8.0 A is at right angles to a uniform magnetic field. The force on the wire is 0.40 N. What is the strength of the magnetic field?

$F = BIL$, so

$$B = \frac{F}{IL} = \frac{0.40\text{ N}}{8.0\text{ A} \times 0.50\text{ m}} = 0.10\text{ N/A}\cdot\text{m}$$

$$= 0.10\text{ T}$$

9. The current through a wire 0.80 m long is 5.0 A. The wire is perpendicular to a 0.60–T magnetic field. What is the magnitude of the force on the wire?

$$F = BIL = (0.60\text{ N/A}\cdot\text{m})(5.0\text{ A})(0.80\text{ m})$$
$$= 2.4\text{ N}$$

10. A wire 25 cm long is at right angles to a 0.30–T uniform magnetic field. The current through the wire is 6.0 A. What is the magnitude of the force on the wire?

$$F = BIL = (0.30\text{ N/A}\cdot\text{m})(6.0\text{ A})(0.25\text{ m})$$
$$= 0.45\text{ N}$$

11. A wire 35 cm long is parallel to a 0.53–T uniform magnetic field. The current through the wire is 4.5 A. What force acts on the wire?

$$F = BIL = (0.53\text{ T})(4.5\text{ A})(0.35\text{ m}) = 0.83\text{ N}$$

12. A wire 625 m long is in a 0.40–T magnetic field. A 1.8–N force acts on the wire. What current is in the wire?

$F = BIL$, so

$$I = \frac{F}{BL} = \frac{1.8\text{ N}}{(0.40\text{ T})(625\text{ m})} = 0.0072\text{ A}$$

$$= 7.2\text{ mA}$$

13. The force on a wire 0.80 m long that is perpendicular to Earth's magnetic field is 0.12 N. What current flows through the wire?

$F = BIL$, so

$$I = \frac{F}{BL} = \frac{0.12\text{ N}}{(5.0 \times 10^{-5}\text{ T})(0.80\text{ m})} = 3000\text{ A}$$

$$= 3.0\text{ kA}$$

14. The force acting on a wire at right angles to a 0.80–T magnetic field is 3.6 N. The current flowing through the wire is 7.5 A. How long is the wire?

$F = BIL$, so

$$L = \frac{F}{BI} = \frac{3.6\text{ N}}{(0.80\text{ T})(7.5\text{ A})} = 0.60\text{ m}$$

15. A power line carries a 225–A current from east to west parallel to the surface of Earth.

a. What is the magnitude of the force acting on each meter of the wire due to Earth's magnetic field?

$F = BIL$, so

$\frac{F}{L} = IB = (225\ \text{A})(5.0 \times 10^{-5}\ \text{T})$

$= 0.011\ \text{N/m}$

b. What is the direction of the force?

The force would be north.

c. In your judgment, would this force be important in designing towers to hold these power lines?

No; the force is much smaller than the weight of the wires.

16. The magnetic field in a loudspeaker is 0.15 T. The wire consists of 250 turns wound on a 2.5–cm diameter cylindrical form. The resistance of the wire is 8.0 ohms. Find the force exerted on the wire when 15 V is placed across the wire.

$I = \frac{V}{R} = \frac{15\ \text{V}}{8.0\ \Omega} = 1.9\ \text{A}$ and

$L = (\#\text{ of turns})(\text{circumference})$
$= (250)(\pi d) = 250\ \pi(0.025\ \text{m})$
$= 20\ \text{m}$
$F = BIL = (0.15\ \text{T})(1.9\ \text{A})(20\ \text{m}) = 5.7\ \text{N}$

17. A wire carrying 15 A of current has a length of 25 cm between a magnetic field of 0.85 T. The force on a current–carrying wire in a uniform magnetic field can be found by $F = BIL \sin \theta$. Find the force on the wire if it makes an angle with the magnetic field lines of

a. 90°.

$F = BIL \sin \theta$
$= (0.85\ \text{T})(15\ \text{A})(0.25\ \text{m})(\sin 90)$
$= 3.2\ \text{N}$

Chapter Review Problems

b. 45°.

$F = BIL \sin \theta$
$= (0.85\ \text{T})(15\ \text{A})(0.25\ \text{m})(\sin 45)$
$= 2.3\ \text{N}$

c. 0°.

$\sin 0 = 0$, so $F = 0$

18. A galvanometer deflects full scale for a 50.0 μA current.

a. What must be the total resistance of the series resistor and the galvanometer to make a voltmeter with 10.0 V full–scale deflection?

$V = IR$, so

$R = \frac{V}{I} = \frac{10.0\ \text{V}}{50.0 \times 10^{-6}\ \text{A}} = 2.00 \times 10^{5}\ \Omega$

$= 200\ \text{k}\Omega$

b. If the galvanometer has a resistance of 1.0 kΩ, what should be the resistance of the series (multiplier) resistor?

Total resistance = 200 kΩ,
so series resistor is
200 kΩ – 1.0 kΩ = 199 kΩ

19. The galvanometer in the previous problem is used to make an ammeter that deflects full–scale for 10 mA.

a. What is the potential difference across the galvanometer, 1.0 kΩ resistance, when 50 × μA flows through it?

$V = IR = (50 \times 10^{-6}\ \text{A})(1.0 \times 10^{3}\ \Omega)$
$= 5.0 \times 10^{-2}\ \text{V}$

b. What is the equivalent resistance of parallel resistors that have the potential difference calculated in part a for a circuit with a total of 10 mA current?

$V = IR$, so $R = \frac{V}{I} = \frac{5.0 \times 10^{-2}\ \text{A}}{1.0 \times 10^{-2}\ \text{A}} = 5.0\ \Omega$

Chapter Review Problems

c. What resistor should be placed in parallel with the galvanometer to make the resistance calculated in part **b**?

$$\frac{1}{R} = \frac{1}{R_1} + \frac{1}{R_2}, \text{ so}$$

$$\frac{1}{R_1} = \frac{1}{R} - \frac{1}{R_2} = \frac{1}{5.0\ \Omega} - \frac{1}{1.0 \times 10^3\ \Omega}$$

so $R_1 = 5.0\ \Omega$

20. A beam of electrons moves at right angles to a 6.0×10^{-2}–T magnetic field. The electrons have a velocity of 2.5×10^6 m/s. What is the magnitude of the force on each electron?

$$F = Bqv$$
$$= (6.0 \times 10^{-2}\ \text{T})(1.6 \times 10^{-19}\ \text{C})(2.5 \times 10^6\ \text{m/s})$$
$$= 2.4 \times 10^{-14}\ \text{N}$$

21. A beta particle (high–speed electron) is traveling at right angles to a 0.60–T magnetic field. It has a speed of 2.5×10^7 m/s. What size force acts on the particle?

$$F = Bqv$$
$$= (0.60\ \text{T})(1.6 \times 10^{-19}\ \text{C})(2.5 \times 10^7\ \text{m/s})$$
$$= 2.4 \times 10^{-12}\ \text{N}$$

22. The mass of an electron is 9.11×10^{-31} kg. What is the acceleration of the beta particle described in the previous problem?

$F = ma$, so

$$a = \frac{F}{m} = \frac{2.4 \times 10^{-12}\ \text{N}}{9.11 \times 10^{-31}\ \text{kg}} = 2.6 \times 10^{18}\ \text{m/s}^2$$

23. A magnetic field of 16 T acts in a direction due west. An electron is traveling due south at 8.1×10^5 m/s. What is the magnitude and direction of the force acting on the electron?

$$F = Bqv$$
$$= (16\ \text{T})(1.6 \times 10^{-19}\ \text{C})(8.1 \times 10^5\ \text{m/s})$$
$$= 2.1 \times 10^{-12}\ \text{N, upward (right–hand rule)}$$

24. In a nuclear research laboratory, a proton moves in a particle accelerator through a magnetic field of intensity 0.10 T at a speed of 3.0×10^7 m/s.

a. If the proton is moving perpendicular to the field, what force acts on it?

$$F = Bqv$$
$$= (0.10\ \text{T})(1.6 \times 10^{-10}\ \text{C})(3.0 \times 10^7\ \text{m/s})$$
$$= 4.8 \times 10^{-13}\ \text{N}$$

b. If the proton continues to move in a direction that is consistently perpendicular to the field, what is the radius of curvature of its path?
The mass of the proton is 1.67×10^{-27} kg.

$$F = \frac{mv^2}{r}, \text{ so}$$

$$r = \frac{mv^2}{F}$$

$$= \frac{(1.67 \times 10^{-27}\ \text{kg})(3.0 \times 10^7\ \text{m/s})^2}{4.8 \times 10^{-13}\ \text{N}}$$

$$= 3.1\ \text{m}$$

25. An electron is accelerated from rest through a potential difference of 20 000 V, which exists between the plates P_1 and P_2, the figure below. The electron then passes through a small opening into a magnetic field of uniform field strength B. As indicated, the magnetic field is directed into the page.

P_1 P_2

Electron

a. State the direction of the electric field between the plates as either P_1 to P_2 or P_2 to P_1.

From P_2 to P_1.

Chapter Review Problems

b. In terms of the information given, calculate the electron's speed at plate P_2.

$$E = (20\ 000\ \text{J/C})(1.6 \times 10^{-19}\ \text{C})$$
$$= 3.2 \times 10^{-15}\ \text{J}$$

$$E = \frac{1}{2}mv^2$$

$$v = \sqrt{\frac{2E}{m}} = \sqrt{\frac{(2)(3.2 \times 10^{-15}\ \text{J})}{(9.1 \times 10^{-31}\ \text{kg})}}$$
$$= 8.4 \times 10^7\ \text{m/s}$$

c. Describe the motion of the electron through the magnetic field.

clockwise

26. A muon, a particle with the same charge as an electron, is traveling at 4.21×10^7 m/s at right angles to a magnetic field. The muon experiences a force of 5.00×10^{-12} N. How strong is the field?

$F = Bqv$, so

$$B = \frac{F}{qv} = \frac{(5.00 \times 10^{-12}\ \text{N})}{(4.21 \times 10^7\ \text{m/s})(1.60 \times 10^{-19}\ \text{C})}$$
$$= 0.742\ \text{T}$$

27. The mass of a muon is 1.88×10^{-28} kg. What acceleration does the muon described in the previous problem experience?

$F = ma$, so

$$a = \frac{F}{m} = \frac{(5.00 \times 10^{-12}\ \text{N})}{(1.88 \times 10^{-28}\ \text{kg})} = 2.66 \times 10^{16}\ \text{m/s}^2$$

28. A singly–ionized particle experiences a force of 4.1×10^{-13} N when it travels at right angles through a 0.61–T magnetic field. What is the velocity of the particle?

$F = Bqv$, so

$$v = \frac{F}{Bq} = \frac{4.1 \times 10^{-13}\ \text{N}}{(0.61\ \text{T})(1.6 \times 10^{-19}\ \text{C})}$$
$$= 4.2 \times 10^6\ \text{m/s}$$

29. A force of 5.78×10^{-16} N acts on an unknown particle traveling at a 90° angle through a magnetic field. If the velocity of the particle is 5.65×10^4 m/s and the field is 3.20×10^{-2} T,how many elementary charges does the particle carry?

$F = Bqv$, so

$$q = \frac{F}{Bv} = \frac{5.78 \times 10^{-16}\ \text{N}}{(3.2 \times 10^{-2}\ \text{T})(5.65 \times 10^4\ \text{m/s})}$$
$$= 3.20 \times 10^{-19}\ \text{C}$$

$$(3.20 \times 10^{-19}\ \text{C})\left[\frac{\text{el charge}}{1.90 \times 10^{-19}\ \text{C}}\right] = 2\ \text{charges}$$

Supplemental Problems (Appendix B)

1. Assume the current in the wire shown in Figure 24–28 goes in the opposite direction. Copy the wire segment and sketch the new magnetic field the current generated.

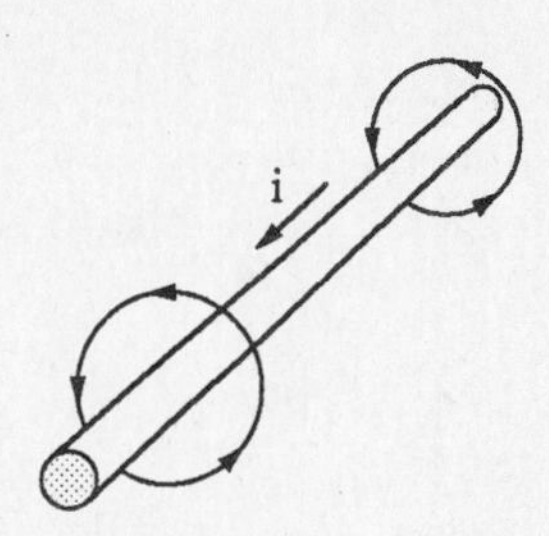

2. Assume the current shown in Figure 24–29 goes into the page instead of out of the page. Copy the figure with the new current and sketch the magnetic field.

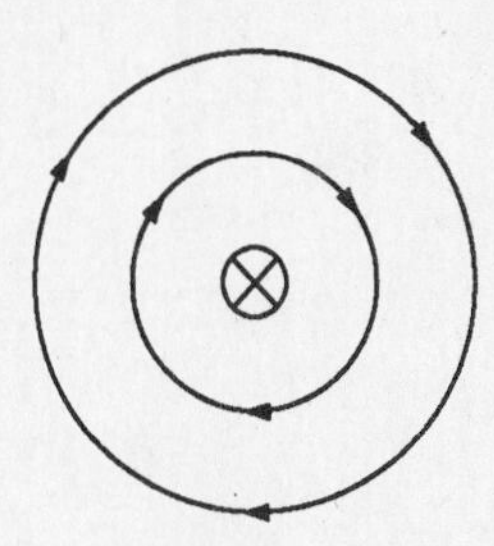

3. What happens to the strength of a magnetic field around a wire if the current in the wire is doubled?

   It doubles, since magnetic field strength is proportional to current.

4. What happens to the magnetic field inside the coil of Figure 24–30 if the current shown was reversed?

   The direction of the magnetic field is also reversed.

5. What is the direction of the force on a current carrying wire in a magnetic field if the current is toward the left on a page and the magnetic field is down the page?

   Out of the page.

6. A 0.25 m long wire is carrying 1.25 A while the wire is perpendicular to a 0.35–T magnetic field. What is the force on the wire?

   $F = BIL = (0.35\text{ T})(1.25\text{ A})(0.25\text{ m}) = 0.11\text{ N}$

7. A 3.0–cm long wire lies perpendicular to a magnetic field with a magnetic induction of 0.40 T. Calculate the force on the wire if the current in the wire is 5.0 A.

   $F = BIL = (0.40\text{ T})(5.0\text{ A})(0.030\text{ m}) = 0.060\text{ N}$

8. What is the force on a 3.5 m long wire that is carrying a 12–A current if the wire is perpendicular to Earth's magnetic field?

   $$F = BIL = (5.0 \times 10^{-5}\text{ T})(12\text{ A})(3.5\text{ m}) = 2.1 \times 10^{-3}\text{ N} = 2.1\text{ mN}$$

9. A wire 0.50 m long is put into a uniform magnetic field. The force exerted upon the wire when the current in the wire is 20 A is 3.0 N. What is the magnetic induction acting on the wire?

   $F = BIL$, so

   $$B = \frac{F}{IL} = \frac{3.0\text{ N}}{(20\text{ A})(0.50\text{ m})} = 0.30\text{ T}$$

10. What is the size of the current in a 35–cm long wire that is perpendicular to a magnetic field of 0.085 T if the force on the wire is 125 mN?

    $F = BIL$, so

    $$I = \frac{F}{BL} = \frac{125 \times 10^{-3}\text{ N}}{(0.085\text{ T})(0.35\text{ m})} = 4.2\text{ A}$$

11. A galvanometer has a full–scale deflection when the current is 50.0 μA. If the galvanometer has a resistance of 1.0 kΩ, what should the resistance of the multiplier resistor be to make a voltmeter with a full–scale deflection of 30.0 V?

    $V = IR$, so

    $$R = \frac{V}{I} = \frac{30.0\text{ V}}{50.0 \times 10^{-6}\text{ A}} = 6.00 \times 10^{5}\ \Omega = 6.00 \times 10^{2}\text{ k}\Omega$$

    $R_T = R_g + R_m$, so

    $R_m = R_T - R_g = 600\text{ k}\Omega - 1\text{ k}\Omega = 599\text{ k}\Omega$

12. A charged particle is moving to the right in a magnetic field whose direction is up the page. Show by diagram the direction of the force exerted by the magnetic field upon the particle if the particle is a positive proton.

    Out of the page.

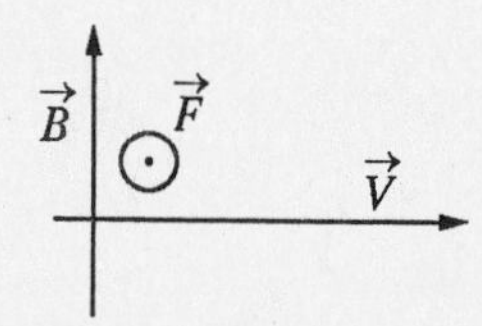

13. An electron beam moving horizontally away from you is deflected toward the right after passing through a certain region of space that contains a constant magnetic field. What is the direction of the magnetic field?

    An electron beam moving away from you is the same as a positive beam moving toward you. The magnetic field is either up or down the page if the force is to the right. The right–hand rule shows the magnetic field must be down the page.

Supplemental Problems

14. A beam of electrons moving left at 3.0×10^7 m/s passes at right angles to a uniform magnetic field that is down and in which the magnetic induction is 2.0×10^{-4} T. What force acts upon each electron in the beam?

$F = Bqv$
$= (2.0 \times 10^{-4}\ \text{T})(1.60 \times 10^{-19}\ \text{C})(3.0 \times 10^7\ \text{m/s})$
$= 9.6 \times 10^{-16}$ N

The right–hand rule gives a direction of out of the page, but the force on an electron is in the opposite direction, into the page. So the force is 9.6×10^{-16} N into the page.

15. The electrons in a beam in a cathode ray tube are moving horizontally at 5.0×10^7 m/s and pass through a vertical magnetic field of 3.5×10^{-3} T. What size force acts on each of the electrons in the beam?

$F = Bqv$
$= (3.5 \times 10^{-3}\ \text{T})(1.60 \times 10^{-19}\ \text{C})(5.0 \times 10^7\ \text{m/s})$
$= 2.8 \times 10^{-14}$ N

16. An ion of oxygen having 2 elementary negative electric charges is moving at right angles to a uniform magnetic field for which $B = 0.30$ T. If its velocity is 2.0×10^7 m/s, what force is acting on the ion?

$F = Bqv$
$= (0.30\ \text{T})(2)(1.60 \times 10^{-19}\ \text{C})(2.0 \times 10^7\ \text{m/s})$
$= 1.9 \times 10^{-12}$ N

Chapter 25: Electromagnetic Induction

Practice Problems

page 518

1. A straight wire 0.5 m long is moved straight up through a 0.4 T magnetic field pointed in the horizontal direction at a speed of 20 m/s.

   a. What *EMF* is induced in the wire?

   $$\begin{aligned} EMF &= BLv \\ &= (0.4\ \text{N/A}\cdot\text{m})(0.5\ \text{m})(20\ \text{m/s}) \\ &= 4\text{V} \end{aligned}$$

   b. The wire is part of a circuit of total resistance 6.0 Ω. What is the current in the circuit?

   $$I = \frac{V}{R} = \frac{4\ \text{V}}{6.0\ \Omega} = 0.7\ \text{A}$$

2. A straight wire 25 m long is mounted on an airplane flying at 125 m/s. The wire moves perpendicularly through Earth's magnetic field ($B = 5.0 \times 10^{-5}$ T). What *EMF* is induced in the wire?

   $$\begin{aligned} EMF &= BLv \\ &= (5.0 \times 10^{-5}\ \text{T})(25\ \text{m})(125\ \text{m/s}) \\ &= 0.16\ \text{V} \end{aligned}$$

3. A permanent horseshoe magnet is mounted so that the magnetic field lines are vertical. If a student passes a straight wire between the poles and pulls it toward herself, the current flow through the wire is from right to left. Which is the N–pole of the magnet?

   Using the right–hand rule, the north pole is at the bottom.

4. A straight wire 30.0 m long moves at 2.0 m/s perpendicularly through a 1.0 T magnetic field.

   a. What *EMF* is induced in the wire?

   $$\begin{aligned} EMF = BLv &= (1.0\ \text{T})(30.0\ \text{m})(2.0\ \text{m/s}) \\ &= 60\ \text{V} \end{aligned}$$

Practice Problems

   b. The total resistance of the circuit of which the wire is a part is 15.0 Ω. What is the current?

   $$I = \frac{V}{R} = \frac{60\ \text{V}}{15.0\ \Omega} = 4.0\ \text{A}$$

page 521

5. A generator in a power plant develops a maximum voltage of 170 V.

   a. What is the effective voltage?

   $$V_{eff} = (0.707)V_{max} = (0.707)(170\ \text{V}) = 120\ \text{V}$$

   b. A 60–W light bulb is placed across the generator. A maximum current of 0.70 A flows through the bulb. What effective current flows through the bulb?

   $$I_{eff} = (0.707)I_{max} = (0.707)(0.70\ \text{A}) = 0.49\ \text{A}$$

   c. What is the resistance of the light bulb when it is working?

   $$R = \frac{V_{eff}}{I_{eff}} = \frac{120\ \text{V}}{0.49\ \text{A}} = 240\ \text{ohms}$$

6. The effective voltage of a particular AC household outlet is 117 V.

   a. What is the maximum voltage across a lamp connected to the outlet?

   $$V_{max} = \frac{V_{eff}}{0.707} = \frac{117\ \text{V}}{0.707} = 165\ \text{V}$$

   b. The effective current through the lamp is 5.5 A. What is the maximum current in the lamp?

   $$I_{max} = \frac{I_{eff}}{0.707} = \frac{5.5\ \text{A}}{0.707} = 7.8\ \text{A}$$

7. An AC generator delivers a peak voltage of 425 V.

   a. What is the effective voltage in a circuit placed across the generator?

   $$V_{eff} = (0.707)V_{max} = (0.707)(425\ V) = 300\ V \text{ or } 3.00 \times 10^2\ V$$

   b. The resistance of the circuit is $5.0 \times 10^2\ \Omega$. What is the effective current?

   $$I_{eff} = V_{eff}/R = (300\ V)/(5.0 \times 10^2\ \Omega) = 0.60\ A$$

8. If the average power dissipated by an electric light is 100 W, what is the peak power?

   Since $P = V_{eff}I_{eff} = (0.707\ V_{max})(0.707\ I_{max})$

   $$= \frac{1}{2}P_{max},$$

   $$P_{max} = 2P = 2(100\ W) = 200\ W$$

page 527

9. A step–down transformer has 7500 turns on its primary and 125 turns on its secondary. The voltage across the primary is 7200 V.

   a. What voltage is across the secondary?

   $$\frac{V_S}{V_P} = \frac{N_S}{N_P}$$

   $$V_S = \frac{V_P N_S}{N_P} = \frac{(7200\ V)(125)}{7500} = 120\ V$$

   b. The current in the secondary is 36 A. What current flows in the primary?

   $$V_P I_P = V_S I_S$$

   $$I_P = \frac{V_S I_S}{V_P} = \frac{(120\ V)(36\ A)}{7200\ V} = 0.60\ A$$

Practice Problems

10. The secondary of a step–down transformer has 500 turns. The primary has 15 000 turns.

   a. The *EMF* of the primary is 3600 V. What is the *EMF* of the secondary?

   $$V_S = \frac{V_P N_S}{N_P} = \frac{(3600\ V)(500)}{15000} = 120\ V$$

   b. The current in the primary is 3.0 A. What current flows in the secondary?

   $$I_S = \frac{V_P I_P}{V_S} = \frac{(3600\ V)(3.0\ A)}{120\ V} = 90\ A$$

page 528

11. An ideal step–up transformer's primary circuit has 500 turns. Its secondary circuit has 15 000 turns. The primary is connected to an AC generator having an *EMF* of 120 V.

   a. Calculate the *EMF* of the secondary.

   $$\frac{V_P}{V_S} = \frac{N_P}{N_S}$$

   $$V_S = \frac{V_P N_S}{N_P} = \frac{(120\ V)(15000)}{500} = 3.60 \times 10^3\ V$$

   b. Find the current in the primary if the current in the secondary is 3.0 A.

   $$V_P I_P = V_S I_S$$

   $$I_P = \frac{V_S I_S}{V_P} = \frac{(3600\ V)(3.0\ A)}{120\ V} = 90\ A$$

   c. What power is drawn by the primary? What power is supplied by the secondary?

   $$V_P I_P = (120\ V)(90\ A) = 1.1 \times 10^4\ W$$
   $$V_S I_S = (3600\ V)(3.0\ A) = 1.1 \times 10^4\ W$$

Practice Problems

12. A step–up transformer has 300 turns on its primary and 90 000 (9.000×10^4) turns on its secondary. The *EMF* of the generator to which the primary is attached is 60.0 V.

a. What is the *EMF* in the secondary?

$$V_S = \frac{V_P N_S}{N_P}$$

$$= \frac{(60.0 \text{ V})(90\,000)}{300}$$

$$= 1.80 \times 10^4 \text{ V}$$

b. The current flowing in the secondary is 0.50 A. What current flows in the primary?

$$I_P = \frac{V_S I_S}{V_P}$$

$$= \frac{(1.80 \times 10^4 \text{ V})(0.50 \text{ A})}{60.0 \text{ V}}$$

$$= 1.5 \times 10^2 \text{ A}$$

Chapter Review Problems

pages 532–533

1. A wire segment 31 m long, moves straight up through a 4.0×10^{-2}–T magnetic field at a speed of 15.0 m/s. What *EMF* is induced in the wire?

$$EMF = BLv$$
$$= (4.0 \times 10^{-2} \text{ T})(31 \text{ m})(15.0 \text{ m/s})$$
$$= 19 \text{ V}$$

2. A wire 20.0 m long moves at 4.0 m/s perpendicularly through a 0.50–T magnetic field. What *EMF* is induced in the wire?

$$EMF = BLv = (0.50 \text{ T})(20.0 \text{ m})(4.0 \text{ m/s})$$
$$= 40 \text{ V}$$

Chapter Review Problems

3. An airplane traveling at 950 km/h passes over a region where Earth's magnetic field is 4.5×10^{-5} T and is nearly vertical. What voltage is induced between the plane's wing tips, which are 75 m apart?

$$EMF = BLv$$
$$= (4.5 \times 10^{-5} \text{ T})(75 \text{ m})\left[950 \frac{\text{km}}{\text{h}}\right]\left[\frac{1000 \text{ m}}{\text{km}}\right]\left[\frac{\text{h}}{3600 \text{ s}}\right]$$
$$= 0.89 \text{ V}$$

4. A straight wire 0.75 m long moves upward through a horizontal 0.30–T magnetic field at a speed of 16 m/s.

a. What *EMF* is induced in the wire?

$$EMF = BLv$$
$$= (0.30 \text{ T})(0.75 \text{ m})(16 \text{ m/s})$$
$$= 3.6 \text{ V}$$

b. The wire is part of a circuit with a total resistance of 11 Ω. What current flows in the circuit?

$$V = IR, \text{ so } I = \frac{V}{R} = \frac{3.6 \text{ V}}{11 \ \Omega} = 0.33 \text{ A}$$

5. A 40–cm wire is moved perpendicular with a velocity of 1.3 m/s through a magnetic field of 0.32 T. If this wire is connected across a circuit of 10–Ω resistance, how much current if flowing?

$$EMF = BLv = (0.32 \text{ T})(0.40 \text{ m})(1.3 \text{ m/s})$$
$$= 0.17 \text{ V}$$

$$I = \frac{V}{R} = \frac{0.17 \text{ V}}{10 \ \Omega} = 17 \text{ mA}$$

6. Jennifer connects both ends of a copper wire of total resistance 0.10 Ω to the terminals of a galvanometer. The galvanometer has resistance of 875 Ω. Jennifer then moves a 10.0–cm segment upward at 1.0 m/s through a 2.0×10^{-2} T magnetic field. What current will the galvanometer indicate?

$$EMF = BLv$$
$$= (2.0 \times 10^{-2} \text{ T})(0.100 \text{ m})(1.0 \text{ m/s})$$
$$= 2.0 \times 10^{-3} \text{ V}$$

$$I = \frac{V}{R} = \frac{(2.0 \times 10^{-3} \text{ V})}{(875 \ \Omega)} = 2.3 \ \mu\text{A}$$

Chapter Review Problems

7. A 0.045–T magnetic field is at an angle of 60° above the horizontal. A wire 2.5 m long moves horizontally at 2.4 m/s.

   a. What the vertical component of the magnetic field?

   The vertical component of magnetic field is $B \sin 60° = (0.045 \text{ T})(\sin 60°) = 0.039 \text{ T}$.

   b. What *EMF* is induced in the wire?

   $$EMF = B_v Lv = (0.039 \text{ T})(2.5 \text{ m})(2.4 \text{ m/s}) = 0.23 \text{ V}$$

8. An *EMF* of 0.0020 V is induced in a wire 10 cm long when it is moving perpendicularly across a uniform magnetic field at a speed of 4.0 m/s. What is the size of the magnetic field?

   $EMF = BLv$, so

   $$B = \frac{EMF}{Lv} = \frac{0.0020 \text{ V}}{(0.10 \text{ m})(4.0 \text{ m/s})} = 0.0050 \text{ T}$$

9. What speed would a 0.20–m length of wire have to move across a 2.5–T magnetic field to induce an *EMF* of 10 V?

   $EMF = BLv$, so

   $$v = \frac{EMF}{BL} = \frac{10 \text{ V}}{(2.5 \text{ T})(0.20 \text{ m})} = 20 \text{ m/s}$$

10. An AC generator develops a maximum *EMF* of 565 V. What effective *EMF* does the generator deliver to an external circuit?

    $$V_{eff} = 0.707(V_{max}) = 0.707(565 \text{ V}) = 399 \text{ V}$$

11. An AC generator develops a maximum voltage of 150 V. It delivers a maximum current of 30.0 A to an external circuit.

    a. What is the effective voltage of the generator?

    $$V_{eff} = 0.707(V_{max}) = 0.707(150 \text{ V}) = 106 \text{ V}$$

    b. What effective current does it deliver to the external circuit?

    $$I_{eff} = 0.707(I_{max}) = 0.707(30.0 \text{ A}) = 21.2 \text{ A}$$

    c. What is the effective power dissipated in the circuit?

    $$P_{eff} = I_{eff}V_{eff} = (21.2 \text{ A})(106 \text{ V}) = 2.25 \times 10^3 \text{ W} = 2.25 \text{ kW}$$

12. An electric stove is connected to a 240–V AC source.

    a. Find the maximum voltage across one of the stove's elements when it is operating.

    $V_{eff} = (0.707)V_{max}$, so

    $$V_{max} = \frac{V_{eff}}{0.707} = \frac{240 \text{ V}}{0.707} = 340 \text{ V}$$

    b. The resistance of the operating element is 11 Ω. What effective current flows through it?

    $$V = IR, \text{ so } I = \frac{V}{R} = \frac{240 \text{ V}}{11 \text{ }\Omega} = 22 \text{ A}$$

13. A generator at Hoover Dam can supply 375 MW, 375×10^6 W, of electrical power. Assume that the turbine and generator are 85% efficient.

    a. Find the rate which falling water must supply energy to the turbine.

    $$eff = \frac{P_{out}}{P_{in}} \times 100\%, \text{ so}$$

    $$P_{in} = P_{out} \times \frac{100\%}{eff} = 375 \text{ MW}\left[\frac{100\%}{85\%}\right] = 441 \text{ MW input}$$

    b. The energy of the water comes from a change in potential energy, *mgh*. What is the needed change in potential energy each second?

    $$441 \text{ MW} = 441 \text{ MJ/s} = 4.41 \times 10^8 \text{ J each second}$$

25

c. If the water falls 22 m, what is the mass of water that must pass through the turbine each second to supply this power?

$PE = mgh$, so

$$m = \frac{PE}{gh} = \frac{(4.41 \times 10^8\ \text{J})}{(9.8\ \text{m/s}^2)(22\ \text{m})}$$

$$= 2.0 \times 10^6\ \text{kg each second}$$

14. The primary transformer has 150 turns. It is connected to a 120–V source. Calculate the number of turns on the secondary needed to supply these voltages.

a. 625 V

$$\frac{V_s}{V_p} = \frac{N_s}{N_p},\ \text{so}$$

$$N_s = \left[\frac{V_s}{V_p}\right]N_p = \left[\frac{625\ \text{V}}{120\ \text{V}}\right]150 = 781\ \text{turns}$$

b. 35 V

$$N_s = \left[\frac{V_s}{V_p}\right]N_p = \left[\frac{35\ \text{V}}{120\ \text{V}}\right](150) = 44\ \text{turns}$$

c. 6.0 V

$$N_s = \left[\frac{V_s}{V_p}\right]N_p = \left[\frac{6.0\ \text{V}}{120\ \text{V}}\right](150) = 7.5\ \text{turns}$$

15. A step–up transformer has 80 turns on its primary coil. It has 1200 turns on its secondary coil. The primary coil is supplied with an alternating current at 120 V.

a. What voltage is across the secondary coil?

$$\frac{V_p}{V_s} = \frac{N_p}{N_s},\ \text{so}$$

$$V_s = \frac{V_p N_s}{N_p} = \frac{(120\ \text{V})(1200)}{80}$$

$$= 1.8 \times 10^3\ \text{V}$$
$$= 1.8\ \text{kV}$$

b. The current in the secondary coil is 2.0 A. What current flows in the primary circuit?

$$V_p I_p = V_s I_s$$

$$I_p = \frac{V_s I_s}{V_p} = \frac{(1.80 \times 10^3\ \text{V})(2.0\ \text{A})}{120\ \text{V}} = 30\ \text{A}$$

c. What is the power input and output of the transformer?

$$V_p I_p = (120\ \text{V})(30\ \text{A}) = 3.6 \times 10^3\ \text{W}$$
$$= 3.6\ \text{kW}$$
$$V_s I_s = (1800\ \text{V})(2.0\ \text{A}) = 3.6 \times 10^3\ \text{W}$$
$$= 3.6\ \text{kW}$$

16. A portable computer requires an effective voltage of 9.0 volts from the 120–V line.

a. If the primary of the transformer has 475 turns, how many does the secondary have?

$$\frac{V_s}{V_p} = \frac{N_s}{N_p},\ \text{so}$$

$$N_s = \frac{V_s N_p}{V_p} = \frac{(9.0\ \text{V})(475)}{(120\ \text{V})} = 36\ \text{turns}$$

b. A 125–mA current flows through the computer. What current flows through the transformer's primary?

$$V_p I_p = V_s I_s$$

$$I_p = \frac{V_s I_s}{V_p} = \frac{(9.0\ \text{V})(125\ \text{mA})}{(120\ \text{V})} = 9.4\ \text{mA}$$

17. In a hydroelectric plant, electricity is generated at 1200 V. It is transmitted at 240 000 V.

a. What is the ratio of the turns on the primary to the turns on the secondary of a transformer connected to one of the generators?

$$\frac{N_p}{N_s} = \frac{V_p}{V_s} = \frac{1200\ \text{V}}{240\ 000\ \text{V}} = \frac{1}{200},\ 1\ \text{to}\ 200$$

b. One of the plant generators can deliver 40.0 A to the primary of its transformer. What current is flowing in the secondary?

$$V_p I_p = V_s I_s,\ \text{so}$$

$$I_s = \frac{V_p I_p}{V_s} = \frac{(1200\ \text{V})(40.0\ \text{A})}{240\ 000\ \text{V}} = 0.200\ \text{A}$$

18. A hair dryer uses 10 A at 120 V. It is used with a transformer in England, where the line voltage is 240 V.

a. What should be the ratio of the turns of the transformer?

$$\frac{V_p}{V_s} = \frac{N_p}{N_s} = \frac{(240\text{ V})}{(120\text{ V})} = \frac{2}{1}\text{, 2 to 1}$$

b. What current will it draw from the 240–V line?

$V_pI_p = V_sI_s$, so

$$I_p = \frac{V_sI_s}{V_p} = \frac{(120\text{ V})(10\text{ A})}{(240\text{ V})} = 5.0\text{ A}$$

19. A step–up transformer is connected to a generator that is delivering 125 V and 95 A. The ratio of the turns on the secondary to the turns on the primary is 1000 to 1.

a. What voltage is across the secondary?

$\frac{V_s}{V_p} = \frac{N_s}{N_p}$, so

$$V_s = \left[\frac{N_s}{N_p}\right]V_p = 1000(125\text{ V})$$

$$= 1.25 \times 10^5\text{ V} = 125\text{ kV}$$

b. What current flows in the secondary?

$\frac{I_s}{I_p} = \frac{V_p}{V_s}$, so

$$I_s = \left[\frac{V_p}{V_s}\right]I_p = \left[\frac{N_p}{N_s}\right]I_p = \left[\frac{1}{1000}\right](95\text{ A})$$

$$= 0.095\text{ A} = 95\text{ mA}$$

20. A 150-W transformer has an input voltage of 9.0 V and an output current of 5.0 A.

a. Is this a step–up or step–down transformer?

A step–up transformer.

Chapter Review Problems

b. What is the ratio of output voltage to input voltage?

$P = V_sI_s$, so

$$V_s = \frac{P}{I_s} = \frac{(150\text{ W})}{(5.0\text{ A})} = 30\text{ V}$$

$$\frac{30\text{ V}}{9\text{ V}} = \frac{10}{3}\text{ or 10 to 3}$$

21. A transformer has input voltage and current of 12 V and 3.0 A respectively, and an output current of 0.75 A. If there are 1200 turns on the secondary side of the transformer, how many turns are on the primary side?

$V_pI_p = V_sI_s$, so

$$V_s = \frac{V_pI_p}{I_s} = \frac{(12\text{ V})(3.0\text{ A})}{(0.75\text{ A})} = 48\text{ V}$$

$\frac{N_s}{N_p} = \frac{V_s}{V_p}$, so

$$N_p = \frac{N_sV_p}{V_s} = \frac{(1200)(12\text{ V})}{(48\text{ V})} = 300\text{ turns}$$

22. Scott connects a transformer to a 24–V source and measures 8.0 V at the secondary. If the primary and secondary were reversed, what would the new output voltage be?

The turns ratio is $\frac{N_s}{N_p} = \frac{V_s}{V_p} = \frac{8.0\text{ V}}{24\text{ V}} = \frac{1}{3}$.

Reversed it would be $\frac{3}{1}$.

Thus, the voltage would now be found by

$\frac{N_s}{N_p} = \frac{V_s}{V_p}$, so

$$V_s = \left[\frac{N_s}{N_p}\right]V_p = 3(24\text{ V}) = 72\text{ V}$$

Supplemental Problems (Appendix B)

1. A north–south wire is moved toward the east through a magnetic field that is pointing down, into Earth. What is the direction of the induced current?

North.

2. A wire 1.0 m long is moved at right angles to Earth's magnetic field where the magnetic induction is 5.0×10^{-5} T at a speed of 4.0 m/s. What is the *EMF* induced in the wire?

$$EMF = B\ell v = (5.0 \times 10^{-5}\ \text{T})(1.0\ \text{m})(4.0\ \text{m/s})$$
$$= 2.0 \times 10^{-4}\ \text{V} = 0.20\ \text{mV}$$

3. An *EMF* of 2.0 mV is induced in a wire 0.10 m long when it is moving perpendicularly across a uniform magnetic field at a velocity of 4.0 m/s. What is the magnetic induction of the field?

$EMF = B\ell v$, so

$$B = \frac{EMF}{\ell v} = \frac{2.0 \times 10^{-3}\ \text{V}}{(0.10\ \text{m})(4.0\ \text{m/s})} = 5.0 \times 10^{-3}\ \text{T}$$
$$= 5.0\ \text{mT}$$

4. With what speed must a 0.20–m long wire cut across a magnetic field for which B is 2.5 T if it is to have an *EMF* of 10 V induced in it?

$EMF = B\ell v$, so

$$v = \frac{EMF}{B\ell} = \frac{10\ \text{V}}{(2.5\ \text{T})(0.20\ \text{m})} = 20\ \text{m/s}$$

5. At what speed must a wire conductor 50 cm long be moved at right angles to a magnetic field of induction 0.20 T to induce an *EMF* of 1.0 V in it?

$EMF = B\ell v$, so

$$v = \frac{EMF}{B\ell} = \frac{1.0\ \text{V}}{(0.20\ \text{T})(0.50\ \text{m})} = 10\ \text{m/s}$$

6. A wire 0.40 m long cuts perpendicularly across a magnetic field for which B is 2.0 T at a velocity of 8.0 m/s.

a. What *EMF* is induced in the wire?

$$EMF = B\ell v = (2.0\ \text{T})(0.40\ \text{m})(8.0\ \text{m/s})$$
$$= 6.4\ \text{V}$$

b. If the wire is in a circuit having a resistance of 6.4 Ω, what is the size of the current through the wire?

$$V = IR,\ \text{so}\ I = \frac{V}{R} = \frac{6.4\ \text{V}}{6.4\ \Omega} = 1.0\ \text{A}$$

Supplemental Problems

7. A coil of wire which has a total length of 7.50 m is moved perpendicularly to Earth's magnetic field at 5.50 m/s. What is the size of the current in the wire if the total resistance of the wire is 5.0×10^{-2} Ω?

$EMF = B\ell v$ and $V = IR$, but $EMF = V$, so $IR = B\ell v$, and

$$I = \frac{B\ell v}{R} = \frac{(5.0 \times 10^{-5}\ \text{T})(7.50\ \text{m})(5.50\ \text{m/s})}{5 \times 10^{-2}\ \Omega}$$
$$= 4.1 \times 10^{-2}\ \text{A} = 41\ \text{mA}$$

8. A house lighting circuit is rated at 120 V. What is the maximum voltage that can be expected from this circuit?

$V_{eff} = 0.707\ V_{max}$, so

$$V_{max} = \frac{V_{eff}}{0.707} = \frac{120\ \text{V}}{0.707} = 170\ \text{V}$$

9. A toaster draws 2.5 A of alternating current. What is the maximum current that this toaster can draw?

$I_{eff} = 0.707\ I_{max}$, so

$$I_{max} = \frac{I_{eff}}{0.707} = \frac{2.5\ \text{A}}{0.707} = 3.5\ \text{A}$$

10. The insulation of a capacitor will break down if the instantaneous voltage exceeds 575 V. What is the largest effective alternating voltage that may be applied to the capacitor?

$$V_{eff} = 0.707\ V_{max} = 0.707(575\ \text{V}) = 406\ \text{V}$$

11. A magnetic circuit breaker will open its circuit if the instantaneous current reaches 21.25 A. What is the largest effective current the circuit will carry?

$$I_{eff} = 0.707\ I_{max} = 0.707(21.25\ \text{A}) = 15.0\ \text{A}$$

12. The peak value of the alternating voltage applied to a 144–Ω resistor is 1.00×10^2 V. What power must the resistor be able to handle?

$P = IV$ and $V = IR$, so $I = \frac{V}{R}$; therefore,

$$P_{max} = \left[\frac{V}{R}\right]V = \frac{V^2}{R} = \frac{(100\ \text{V})^2}{144\ \Omega} = 69.4\ \text{W}$$

The resistor must be able to handle peak voltage.

13. Steve drops a magnet, S–pole down, through a vertical copper pipe.

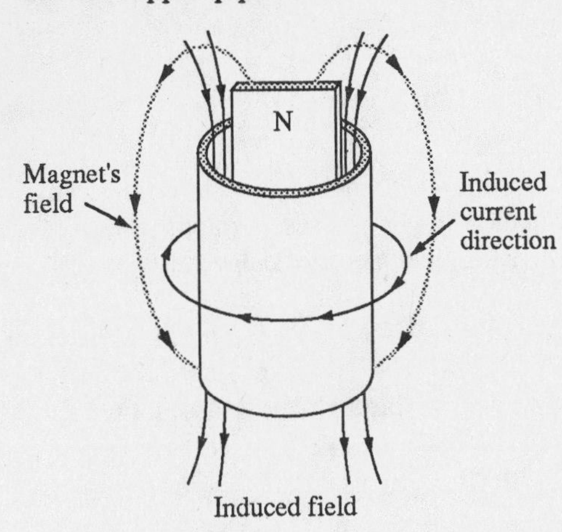

a. What is the direction of the induced current in the copper pipe as the bottom of the magnet passes?

Clockwise around the pipe, as viewed from above.

b. The induced current produces a magnetic field. What is the direction of the induced magnetic field?

Down the pipe, at the location of the S–pole of the magnet (or opposite the magnet's field).

14. The electricity received at an electrical substation has a potential difference 240 000 V. What should the ratio of the turns of the step–down transformer be to have an output of 440 V?

$$\frac{N_s}{N_p} = \frac{V_s}{V_p} = \frac{440\ \text{V}}{240\ 000\ \text{V}} = \frac{1}{545}$$

1 to 545

Supplemental Problems

15. The CRT in a television uses a step–up transformer to change 120 V to 48 000 V. The secondary side of the transformer has 20 000 turns and an output of 1.0 mA.

a. How many turns does the primary side have?

$$\frac{N_s}{N_p} = \frac{V_s}{V_p}, \text{ so } N_sV_p = N_pV_s, \text{ and}$$

$$N_p = \frac{N_sV_p}{V_s} = \frac{(20\ 000)(120\ \text{V})}{48\ 000\ \text{V}} = 50 \text{ turns}$$

b. What is the input current?

$$V_sI_s = V_pI_p, \text{ so}$$

$$I_p = \frac{V_sI_s}{V_p} = \frac{(48\ 000\ \text{V})(1.0 \times 10^{-3}\ \text{A})}{(120\ \text{V})}$$

$$= 0.40\ \text{A}$$

25

Chapter 26: Electric and Magnetic Fields

Practice Problems

page 539

1. Protons passing without deflection through a 0.6–T magnetic field are balanced by a 4.5×10^3–N/C electric field. What is the speed of the moving protons?

$Bqv = Eq$,

$$v = \frac{E}{B} = \frac{4.5 \times 10^3 \text{ N/C}}{0.6 \text{ T}} = 8 \times 10^3 \text{ m/s}$$

2. A proton moves at a speed of 7.5×10^3 m/s as it passes through a 0.6–T magnetic field. Find the radius of the circular path. The charge carried by the proton is equal to that of the electron, but it is positive.

$Bqv = \frac{mv^2}{r}$,

$$r = \frac{mv}{Bq} = \frac{(1.7 \times 10^{-27} \text{ kg})(7.5 \times 10^3 \text{ m/s})}{(0.6 \text{ T})(1.6 \times 10^{-19} \text{ C})}$$

$$= 1 \times 10^{-4} \text{ m}$$

3. Electrons move through a 6.0×10^{-2} T magnetic field balanced by a 3.0×10^3 N/C electric field. What is the speed of the electrons?

$Bqv = Eq$,

$$v = \frac{E}{B} = \frac{3.0 \times 10^3 \text{ N/C}}{6.0 \times 10^{-2} \text{ T}} = 5.0 \times 10^4 \text{ m/s}$$

4. Calculate the radius of the circular path the electrons in Practice Problem 3 follow in the absence of the electric field.

$Bqv = \frac{mv^2}{r}$,

$$r = \frac{mv}{Bq} = \frac{(9.11 \times 10^{-31} \text{ kg})(5.0 \times 10^4 \text{ m/s})}{(6.0 \times 10^{-2} \text{ T})(1.6 \times 10^{-19} \text{ C})}$$

$$= 4.7 \times 10^{-6} \text{ m}$$

Practice Problems

page 541

5. A stream of singly–ionized lithium atoms is not deflected as it passes through a 1.5×10^{-3}–T magnetic field perpendicular to a 6.0×10^2–V/m electric field.

a. What is the speed of the lithium atoms as they pass through the crossed fields?

$Bqv = Eq$,

$$v = \frac{E}{B} = \frac{6.0 \times 10^2 \text{ N/C}}{1.5 \times 10^{-3} \text{ T}} = 4.0 \times 10^5 \text{ m/s}$$

b. The lithium atoms move into a 0.18–T magnetic field. They follow a circular path of radius 0.165 m. What is the mass of a lithium atom?

$$Bqv = \frac{mv^2}{r}$$

$$m = \frac{Bqr}{v}$$

$$= \frac{(0.18 \text{ T})(1.6 \times 10^{-19} \text{ C})(0.165 \text{ m})}{4.0 \times 10^5 \text{ m/s}}$$

$$= 1.2 \times 10^{-26} \text{ kg}$$

page 542

6. A mass spectrometer gives data for a beam of doubly–ionized argon atoms. The values are $B = 5.0 \times 10^{-2}$ T, $q = 2(1.6 \times 10^{-19}$ C), $r = 0.106$ m, and $V = 66.0$ V. Find the mass of an argon atom.

$$m = \frac{B^2r^2q}{2V}$$

$$= \frac{(5.0 \times 10^{-2} \text{ T})^2(0.106 \text{ m})^2(2)(1.6 \times 10^{-19} \text{ C})}{2(66.0 \text{ V})}$$

$$= 6.8 \times 10^{-26} \text{ kg}$$

Practice Problems

7. A beam of singly–ionized oxygen atoms is sent through a mass spectrometer. The values are $B = 7.2 \times 10^{-2}$ T, $q = 1.6 \times 10^{-19}$ C, r = 0.085 m, and $V = 110$ V. Find the mass of an oxygen atom.

$$m = \frac{B^2r^2q}{2V}$$

$$= \frac{(7.2 \times 10^{-2}\ \text{T})^2(0.085\ \text{m})^2(1.6 \times 10^{-19}\ \text{C})}{2(110\ \text{V})}$$

$$= 2.7 \times 10^{-26}\ \text{kg}$$

8. The Example Problem found the mass of a neon isotope. Another neon isotope has a mass of 22 proton masses. How far on the film from the first isotope would these ions land?

Use $r = \frac{1}{B}\sqrt{\frac{2Vm}{q}}$ to find the ratio of radii of the two isotopes. If M represents the number of proton masses, then $\frac{r_{22}}{r_{20}} = \sqrt{\frac{M_{22}}{M_{20}}}$, so

$r_{22} = r_{20}\left[\frac{22}{20}\right]^{.5} = 0.056$ m. Separation then is $2(0.056\ \text{m} - 0.053\ \text{m}) = 6$ mm.

26

Chapter Review Problems

pages 552–553

1. A beam of ions passes through a pair of crossed electric and magnetic fields. E is 6.0×10^6 N/C and B 3.0×10^{-3} T. What is the speed of the ions?

$$v = \frac{E}{B} = \frac{6.0 \times 10^5\ \text{N/C}}{3.0 \times 10^{-3}\ \text{T}} = 2.0 \times 10^8\ \text{m/s}$$

2. Electrons moving at 3.6×10^4 m/s pass through an electric field of intensity 5.8×10^3 N/C. How large a magnetic field must the electrons also experience for their path to be undeflected?

$$v = \frac{E}{B}, \text{ so } B = \frac{E}{v} = \frac{(5.8 \times 10^3\ \text{N/C})}{(3.6 \times 10^4\ \text{m/s})} = 0.16\ \text{T}$$

3. The electrons in a beam are moving at 2.8×10^8 m/s in an electric field of 1.4×10^4 N/C. What value must the magnetic field have if the electrons pass through the crossed field undeflected?

$$v = \frac{E}{B}, \text{ so } B = \frac{E}{v} = \frac{(1.4 \times 10^4\ \text{N/C})}{(2.8 \times 10^8\ \text{m/s})} = 5.0 \times 10^{-5}\ \text{T} = 50\ \mu\text{T}$$

4. A proton moves across 0.36–T magnetic field in a circular path of radius 0.2 m. What is the speed of t proton?

$$\frac{q}{m} = \frac{v}{Br}, \text{ so } v = \frac{Brq}{m} = \frac{(0.36\ \text{T})(0.2\ \text{m})(1.6 \times 10^{-19}\ \text{C})}{(1.7 \times 10^{-27}\ \text{kg})} = 7 \times 10^6\ \text{m/s}$$

5. Electrons move across a 4.0–mT magnetic field. They follow a circular path of radius 2.0 cm.

a. What is their speed?

$$\frac{q}{m} = \frac{v}{Br}, \text{ so } v = \frac{Brq}{m} = \frac{(4.0 \times 10^{-3}\ \text{T})(2.0 \times 10^{-2}\ \text{m})(1.6 \times 10^{-19}\ \text{C})}{(9.11 \times 10^{-31}\ \text{kg})}$$

$$= 1.4 \times 10^7\ \text{m/s}$$

b. An electric field is applied perpendicularly to the magnetic field. The electrons then follow a straight–line path. Find the magnitude of the electric field.

$$v = \frac{E}{B}, \text{ so } E = Bv = (4.0 \times 10^{-3}\ \text{T})(1.4 \times 10^7\ \text{m/s}) = 5.6 \times 10^4\ \text{N/C}$$

Chapter Review Problems

6. What energy must be given to an electron to transfer it across difference in potential of 4.0×10^5 V?

$$v = \frac{E}{B}, \text{ so } E = qV = (1.6 \times 10^{-19}\text{ C})(4.0 \times 10^5\text{ V}) = 6.4 \times 10^{-14}\text{ J}$$

7. A proton enters a 6.0×10^{-2} T magnetic field with a speed of 5.4×10^4 m/s. What is the radius of the circular path it follows?

$$r = \frac{mv}{qB} = \frac{(1.7 \times 10^{-27}\text{ kg})(5.4 \times 10^4\text{ m/s})}{(1.6 \times 10^{-19}\text{ C})(6.0 \times 10^{-2}\text{ T})} = 9.6 \times 10^{-3}\text{ m}$$

8. A proton enters a magnetic field of induction 6.4×10^{-2} T with a speed of 4.5×10^4 m/s. What is the circumference of the circular path that it follows?

$$r = \frac{mv}{Bq} = \frac{(1.7 \times 10^{-27}\text{ kg})(4.5 \times 10^4\text{ m/s})}{(6.4 \times 10^{-2}\text{ T})(1.6 \times 10^{-19}\text{ C})} = 7.5 \times 10^{-3}\text{ m}$$

$$C = 2\pi r = 2\pi(7.5 \times 10^{-3}\text{ m}) = 4.7 \times 10^{-2}\text{ m}$$

9. An alpha particle has a mass of approximately 6.6×10^{-27} kg and bears a double elementary positive charge. Such a particle is observed to move through a 2.0–T magnetic field along a path of radius 0.15

a. What speed does it have?

$$r = \frac{mv}{qB}, \text{ so } v = \frac{Bqr}{m} = \frac{(2.0\text{ T})(2)(1.6 \times 10^{-19}\text{ C})(0.15\text{ m})}{6.6 \times 10^{-27}\text{ kg}} = 1.5 \times 10^7\text{ m/s}$$

b. What is its kinetic energy?

$$KE = \frac{1}{2}mv^2 = \frac{(6.6 \times 10^{-27}\text{ kg})(1.5 \times 10^7\text{ m/s})^2}{2} = 7.4 \times 10^{-13}\text{ J}$$

c. What potential difference would be required to give it this kinetic energy?

$$KE = qV, \text{ so } V = \frac{KE}{q} = \frac{7.4 \times 10^{-13}\text{ J}}{2(1.6 \times 10^{-19}\text{ C})} = 2.3 \times 10^6\text{ V} = 2.3\text{ MV}$$

10. A 3.0×10^{-2} T magnetic field in a mass spectrometer causes an isotope of sodium to move in a circular path with a radius of 0.081 m. If the ions have a single positive charge and are moving with a speed of 1.0×10^4 m/s, what is the isotope's mass?

$$r = \frac{mv}{qB}, \text{ so } m = \frac{Brq}{v} = \frac{(3.0 \times 10^{-2}\text{ T})(0.081\text{ m})(1.6 \times 10^{-19}\text{ C})}{1.0 \times 10^4\text{ m/s}} = 3.9 \times 10^{-26}\text{ kg}$$

11. An alpha particle, a doubly ionized helium atom, has a mass of 6.7×10^{-27} kg and is accelerated by a voltage of 1.0 kV. If a uniform magnetic field of 6.5×10^{-2} T is maintained on the alpha particle, what will be the particle's radius of curvature?

$$r = \frac{1}{B}\sqrt{\frac{2Vm}{q}} = \frac{1}{(6.5 \times 10^{-2}\text{ T})}\sqrt{\frac{(2)(1.0 \times 10^3\text{ V})(6.7 \times 10^{-27}\text{ kg})}{(2)(1.6 \times 10^{-19}\text{ C})}} = 0.10\text{ m}$$

Chapter Review Problems

12. An electron is accelerated by 4.5–kV potential difference. How strong of a magnetic field must be experienced by the electron if its path is a circle of radius 5.0 cm?

$$r = \frac{1}{B}\sqrt{\frac{2Vm}{q}}, \text{ so } B = \frac{1}{r}\sqrt{\frac{2Vm}{q}} = \frac{1}{(0.050 \text{ m})}\sqrt{\frac{(2)(4.5 \times 10^3 \text{ V})(9.11 \times 10^{-31} \text{ kg})}{(1.6 \times 10^{-19} \text{ C})}} = 4.5 \times 10^{-3} \text{ T}$$

13. A mass spectrograph yields the following data for a beam of doubly ionized sodium atoms: $B = 8.0 \times 10^{-2}$ T, $q = 2(1.60 \times 10^{-19}$ C), $r = 0.077$ m, and $V = 156$ V. Calculate the mass of a sodium atom.

$$\frac{q}{m} = \frac{2V}{B^2r^2}, \text{ so m} = \frac{qB^2r^2}{2V} = \frac{(2)(1.6 \times 10^{-19} \text{ C})(8.0 \times 10^{-2} \text{ T})^2(0.077 \text{ m})^2}{(2)(156 \text{ V})} = 3.9 \times 10^{-26} \text{ kg}$$

14. In a mass spectrograph, ionized silicon atoms have radii of curvature of 16.23 cm and 17.97 cm. If the smaller radius corresponds to an atomic mass of 28 units, what is the atomic mass of the other silicon isotope?

$$\frac{(28 \text{ u})(17.97 \text{ cm})}{16.23 \text{ cm}} = 31 \text{ u}$$

$$\frac{q}{m} = \frac{2v}{B^2r^2}, \text{ so } m \text{ is proportional to } r^2. \quad \frac{m_2}{m_1} = \frac{r_2^2}{r_1^2}, \text{ so } m_2 = m_1\left[\frac{r_2}{r_1}\right]^2 = (28 \text{ units})\left[\frac{17.97 \text{ cm}}{16.23 \text{ cm}}\right]^2 = 34 \text{ units}$$

15. A mass spectrograph is used to analyze a molecule with a mass of 175 × 10³ proton masses. The operat wants to know whether the carbon inthe molecule has mass 12 or 13 proton masses. What percent differentiation is needed?

One proton mass out of 175 × 10³ is 1/1750 of one percent, or about one two–thousandth of one percent differentiation ability.

16. The difference in potential between the cathode and anode of a spark plug is 1.0 × 10⁴ V.

a. What energy does an electron give up as it passes between the electrodes?

$$E = qV = (1.6 \times 10^{-19} \text{ C})(1.0 \times 10^4 \text{J/C}) = 1.6 \times 10^{-15} \text{ J}$$

b. One–fourth of the energy given up by the electron is converted to electromagnetic radiation. The frequency of the wave is related to the energy by the equation $E = hf$, where h is Planck's constant, 6.6×10^{-34} J/Hz. What is the frequency of the waves?

$$E = hf, \text{ so } f = \frac{E}{h} = \frac{(1.6 \times 10^{-15} \text{ J})}{(4)(6.6 \times 10^{-34} \text{ J/Hz})} = 6.1 \times 10^{17} \text{ Hz}$$

17. Television Channel 6 broadcasts on a frequency of 85 MHz.

a. What is the wavelength of the electromagnetic wave broadcast on Channel 6?

$$c = f\lambda, \text{ so } \lambda = \frac{c}{f} = \frac{(3.0 \times 10^8 \text{ m/s})}{(85 \times 10^6 \text{ Hz})} = 3.5 \text{ m.}$$

b. What is the length of an antenna that will detect Channel 6 most easily?

$$Length = \frac{\lambda}{2} = \frac{3.5 \text{ m}}{2} = 1.8 \text{ m}$$

Practice Problems

18. The radio waves reflected by the parabolic dish are 2.0 cm long. How long is the antenna that detects t waves?

The antenna is 1 cm long.

Supplemental Problems (Appendix B)

1. A beam of electrons travels through a set of crossed electric and magnetic fields. What is the speed of the electrons if the magnetic field is 85 mT and the electric field is 6.5×10^4 N/C?

$$v = \frac{E}{B} = \frac{6.5 \times 10^4 \text{ N/C}}{85 \times 10^{-3} \text{ T}}$$

$$= 7.6 \times 10^5 \text{ m/s}$$

2. Electrons moving at 8.5×10^7 m/s pass through crossed magnetic and electric fields undeflected. What is the size of the magnetic field if the electric field is 4.0×10^4 N/C?

$$v = \frac{E}{B}, \text{ so}$$

$$B = \frac{E}{v} = \frac{4.0 \times 10^4 \text{ N/C}}{8.5 \times 10^7 \text{ m/s}}$$

$$= 4.7 \times 10^{-4} \text{ T} = 0.47 \text{ mT}$$

3. What effect does increasing the magnetic induction of the field have on the radius of the particle's path for a given particle moving at a fixed speed?

It decreases the radius.

4. An electron is moving at 2.0×10^8 m/s in a constant magnetic field. How strong should the magnetic field be to keep the electron moving in a circle of radius 0.50 m?

$$\frac{q}{m} = \frac{v}{Br}, \text{ so}$$

$$B = \frac{mv}{qr} = \frac{(9.11 \times 10^{-3} \text{ kg})(2.0 \times 10^8 \text{ m/s})}{(1.60 \times 10^{-19} \text{ C})(0.50 \text{ m})}$$

$$= 2.3 \times 10^{-3} \text{ T} = 2.3 \text{ mT}$$

Supplemental Problems (Appendix B)

5. A positively charged ion having two elementary charges and a velocity of 5.0×10^7 m/s is moving across a magnetic field for which $B = 4.0$ T. If the mass of the ion is 6.8×10^{-27} kg, what is the radius of the circular path it travels?

$$\frac{q}{m} = \frac{v}{Br}, \text{ so}$$

$$r = \frac{mv}{qB} = \frac{(6.8 \times 10^{-27} \text{ kg})(5.0 \times 10^7 \text{ m/s})}{2(1.6 \times 10^{-19} \text{ C})(4.0 \text{ T})}$$

$$= 0.27 \text{ m}$$

6. A beam of electrons moving at 2.0×10^8 m/s passes at right angles to a uniform magnetic field of 41 mT. What is the radius of the circular path in which this beam will travel through the magnetic field?

$$\frac{q}{m} = \frac{v}{Br}, \text{ so}$$

$$r = \frac{mv}{qB} = \frac{(9.11 \times 10^{-31} \text{ kg})(2.0 \times 10^8 \text{ m/s})}{(1.6 \times 10^{-19} \text{ C})(41 \times 10^{-3} \text{ T})}$$

$$= 0.028 \text{ m} = 2.8 \text{ cm}$$

7. An unknown particle is accelerated by a potential difference of 150 V. The particle then enters a magnetic field of 50.0 mT and follows a curved path with a radius of 9.80 cm. What is the ratio of q/m?

$$\frac{q}{m} = \frac{2V}{B^2 r^2}$$

$$= \frac{2(150 \text{ V})}{(50.0 \times 10^{-3} \text{ T})^2 (9.8 \times 10^{-2} \text{ m})^2}$$

$$= 1.25 \times 10^7 \text{ C/kg}$$

Supplemental Problems

8. A beam of doubly-ionized oxygen atoms is accelerated by a potential difference of 232 V. The oxygen then enters a magnetic field of 75.0 mT, and follows a curved path with a radius of 8.3 cm. What is the mass of the oxygen atom?

$$\frac{q}{m} = \frac{2V}{B^2 r^2}, \text{ so}$$

$$m = \frac{qB^2 r^2}{2V}$$

$$= \frac{2(1.6 \times 10^{-19}\ \text{C})(75.0 \times 10^{-3}\ \text{T})^2(8.3 \times 10^{-2}\ \text{m})^2}{2(232\ \text{V})}$$

$$= 2.7 \times 10^{-26}\ \text{kg}$$

9. If the atomic mass unit is equal to 1.67×10^{-27} kg, how many atomic mass units are in the oxygen atom in the previous problem?

$$2.7 \times 10^{-26}\ \text{kg}\left[\frac{1\text{u}}{1.67 \times 10^{-27}\ \text{kg}}\right] = 16\text{u}$$

10. A hydrogen ion is accelerated through an accelerating potential of 1.00×10^2 V and then through a magnetic field of 50.0 mT to standardize the mass spectrometer. What is the radius of curvature if the mass of the ion is 1.67×10^{-27} kg?

$$r = \frac{1}{B}\sqrt{\frac{2Vm}{q}}$$

$$= \frac{1}{50.0 \times 10^{-3}\ \text{T}}\sqrt{\frac{2(100\ \text{V})(1.67 \times 10^{-27}\ \text{kg})}{1.60 \times 10^{-19}\ \text{C}}}$$

$$= 2.89 \times 10^{-2}\ \text{m} = 2.89\ \text{cm}$$

Supplemental Problems

11. What is the change in the radius of curvature if a doubly-ionized neon atom, mass $= 3.34 \times 10^{-26}$ kg, is sent through the mass spectrometer in the previous problem?

$$r = \frac{1}{B}\sqrt{\frac{2Vm}{q}}$$

$$= \frac{1}{50.0 \times 10^{-3}\ \text{T}}\sqrt{\frac{2(100\ \text{V})(3.34 \times 10^{-26}\ \text{kg})}{2(1.60 \times 10^{-19}\ \text{C})}}$$

$$= 9.14 \times 10^{-2}\ \text{m}$$

$$\text{diff} = 9.14 \times 10^{-2}\ \text{m} - 2.89 \times 10^{-2}\ \text{m}$$

$$= 6.25 \times 10^{-2}\ \text{m} = 6.25\ \text{cm}$$

12. Microwaves for a microwave oven are produced in a special tube, the klystron tube, which has a microwave antenna attached to it. What length antenna would produce 3.0–cm microwaves?

$$\frac{1}{4}\lambda = \frac{1}{4}(3.0\ \text{cm}) = 0.75\ \text{cm}$$

13. An FM radio station broadcasts on a frequency of 94.5 MHz. What is the antenna length that would give the best reception for this radio station?

$$c = f\lambda, \text{ so } \lambda = \frac{c}{f}$$

$$= \frac{3.00 \times 10^8\ \text{m/s}}{94.5 \times 10^6\ \text{Hz}} = 3.17\ \text{m}$$

$$\frac{1}{4}\lambda = \frac{1}{4}(3.17\ \text{m}) = 0.794\ \text{m}$$

Chapter 27 Quantum Theory

Practice Problems

page 561

1. The stopping potential to prevent current through a photocell is 3.2 V. Calculate the kinetic energy in joules of the photoelectrons as they are emitted.

$KE = -qV_0 = -(-1.6 \times 10^{-19}\ \text{C})(3.2\ \text{J/C}) = 5.1 \times 10^{-19}\ \text{J}$

2. The stopping potential for a photoelectric cell is 5.7 V. Calculate the kinetic energy in electron volts of the photoelectrons as they are emitted.

$$KE = -qV_0 = \frac{-(-1.6 \times 10^{-19}\ \text{C})(5.7\ \text{J/C})}{(1.6 \times 10^{-19}\ \text{J/eV})} = 5.7\ \text{eV}$$

3. The threshold wavelength of zinc is 310 nm (310×10^{-9} m).

a. Find the threshold frequency of zinc.

$c = f_0\lambda$

$$f_0 = \frac{c}{\lambda} = \frac{3.00 \times 10^8\ \text{m/s}}{310 \times 10^{-9}\ \text{m}} = 9.68 \times 10^{14}\ \text{Hz}$$

b. What is the work function in eV of zinc?

$$hf_0 = (6.6 \times 10^{-34}\ \text{J/Hz})(9.67 \times 10^{14}\ \text{Hz}) = (6.4 \times 10^{-19}\ \text{J})\left[\frac{\text{eV}}{1.6 \times 10^{-19}\ \text{J}}\right] = 4.0\ \text{eV}$$

c. Zinc in a photocell is irradiated by ultraviolet light of 240 nm wavelength. What is the kinetic energy of the photoelectrons in eV?

$$KE_{\text{max}} = \frac{hc}{\lambda} - hf_0 = \frac{\left[(6.6 \times 10^{-34}\ \text{J/Hz})(3.00 \times 10^8\ \text{m/s})\left[\frac{\text{eV}}{1.6 \times 10^{-19}}\right]\right]}{(240 \times 10^{-9}\ \text{m})} - 4.0\ \text{eV}$$

$$= 5.2\ \text{eV} - 4.0\ \text{eV} = 1.2\ \text{eV}$$

4. The work function for cesium is 1.96 eV.

a. Find the threshold wavelength for cesium.

$E = \text{work function} = hf_0 = \dfrac{1240\ \text{eV}\cdot\text{nm}}{\lambda_0}$ where λ_0 has units of nm and E has units of eV.

$$\lambda_0 = \frac{(1240\ \text{eV}\cdot\text{nm})}{E} = \frac{(1240\ \text{eV}\cdot\text{nm})}{(1.96\ \text{eV})} = 633\ \text{nm}.$$

b. What is the kinetic energy in eV of photoelectrons ejected when 425–nm violet light falls on the cesium?

$$KE_{\text{max}} = hf - hf_0 = E_{\text{photon}} - hf_0 = \frac{1240\ \text{eV}\cdot\text{nm}}{\lambda} - hf_0 = \frac{(1240\ \text{eV}\cdot\text{nm})}{(425\ \text{nm})} - 1.96\ \text{eV}$$

$$= 2.92\ \text{eV} - 1.96\ \text{eV} = 0.96\ \text{eV}$$

Practice Problems

page 567

5. **a.** Find the speed of an electron accelerated by a potential difference of 250 V.

$$\frac{1}{2}mv^2 = qV_0,$$

$$v^2 = \frac{2qV_0}{m} = \frac{2(1.60 \times 10^{-19}\text{ C})(250\text{ J/C})}{(9.11 \times 10^{-31}\text{ kg})} = 8.78 \times 10^{13}\text{ m}^2/\text{s}^2,$$

$$v = 9.4 \times 10^6\text{ m/s}$$

b. What is the de Broglie wavelength of this electron?

$$\lambda = \frac{h}{mv} = \frac{(6.6 \times 10^{-34}\text{ J}\cdot\text{s})}{(9.11 \times 10^{-31}\text{ kg})(9.4 \times 10^6\text{ m/s})} = 7.7 \times 10^{-11}\text{ m}$$

6. A 7.0–kg bowling ball rolls down the alley with a velocity of 8.5 m/s.

a. What is the de Broglie wavelength of the bowling ball?

$$\lambda = \frac{h}{mv} = \frac{6.6 \times 10^{-34}\text{ J}\cdot\text{s}}{(7.0\text{ kg})(8.5\text{ m/s})} = 1.1 \times 10^{-35}\text{ m}$$

b. Why does the bowling ball show little wave behavior?

The wavelength is too small to show observable effects.

7. An X ray of wavelength 5.0×10^{-12} m is traveling in a vacuum.

a. Calculate the momentum associated with this X ray.

$$p = \frac{h}{\lambda} = \frac{6.6 \times 10^{-34}\text{ J}\cdot\text{s}}{5.0 \times 10^{-12}\text{ m}} = 1.3 \times 10^{-22}\text{ kg}\cdot\text{m/s}$$

b. Why does the X ray show little particle behavior?

Its momentum is too small to affect objects of ordinary size.

8. **a.** In what ways are electrons and photons the same?

They have momentum and energy, and they show wave behavior.

b. In what ways are they different?

An electron has mass and charge, a photon does not.

27

Chapter Review Problems

pages 570–571

1. A home uses about 4×10^{11} J of energy each year. In many parts of the United States, there are about 3000 h of sunlight each year.

   a. How much energy from the sun falls on one square meter each year?

   Earth receives about 1000 J per square meter each second, so

   $$E = \left(1000 \frac{\text{J}}{\text{m}^2 \cdot \text{s}}\right)\left(\frac{3600\ \text{s}}{\text{h}}\right)\left(\frac{3000\ \text{h}}{\text{yr}}\right)$$

   $= 1 \times 10^{10}$ J/m² per year

   b. If the solar energy can be converted to useful energy with an efficiency of 20%, how large an area of converters would produce the energy needed by the house?

   $$Area = \frac{4 \times 10^{11}\ \text{J}}{(0.2)(1 \times 10^{10}\ \text{J/m}^2)} = 2 \times 10^2\ \text{m}^2$$

2. The stopping potential of a certain metal is 5.0 V. What is the maximum kinetic energy of the photoelectrons in

   a. electron volts?

   $KE = -qV_0 = -(-1$ elem charge$)(5.0$ V$)$
   $= 5.0$ eV

   b. joules?

   $$\frac{5.0\ \text{eV}}{1}\left[\frac{1.6 \times 10^{-19}\ \text{J}}{1\ \text{eV}}\right] = 8.0 \times 10^{-19}\ \text{J}$$

3. To block the current in a photocell, a stopping potential of 3.8 V is used. Find the kinetic energy of the photoelectrons in J.

   $KE = qV$
   $= (1.6 \times 10^{-19}\ \text{C})(3.8\ \text{J/C})$
   $= 6.1 \times 10^{-19}$ J

4. What potential difference is needed to stop electrons having a maximum kinetic energy of 4.8×10^{-19} J?

   $$KE = -qV_0,\ \text{so}\ V_0 = \frac{KE}{-q} = \frac{4.8 \times 10^{-19}\ \text{J}}{-(-1.6 \times 10^{-19}\ \text{C})}$$

   $= 3.0$ V

5. The threshold frequency of sodium is 4.4×10^{14} Hz. How much work must be done to free an electron from the surface of the sodium?

   Work $= hf_0$
   $= (6.626 \times 10^{-34}\ \text{J/Hz})(4.4 \times 10^{14}\ \text{Hz})$
   $= 2.9 \times 10^{-19}$ J

6. If light with a frequency of 1.00×10^{15} Hz falls on the sodium in the previous problem, what is the maximum kinetic energy of the photoelectrons?

   $KE = hf - hf_0$
   $= (6.626 \times 10^{-34}\ \text{J/Hz})(1.00 \times 10^{15}\ \text{Hz})$
   $- 2.9 \times 10^{-19}$ J
   $= 3.7 \times 10^{-19}$ J

7. Barium has a work function of 2.48 eV. What is the longest wavelength of light that will emit electrons from barium?

   Work function $= 2.48\ \text{eV} = hf_0 = \frac{hc}{\lambda_0}$, so

   $$\lambda_0 = \frac{hc}{2.48\ \text{eV}}$$

   $$= \frac{(6.63 \times 10^{-34}\ \text{J}\cdot\text{s})(3.00 \times 10^8\ \text{m/s})}{(2.48\ \text{eV})\left(\frac{1.60 \times 10^{-19}\ \text{J}}{\text{eV}}\right)}$$

   $= 5.01 \times 10^{-7}$ m
   $= 501$ nm

8. A photocell is used by a photographer to measure the light falling on the subject to be photographed. What should be the work function of the cathode if the photocell is to be sensitive to red light, $\lambda = 680$ nm, as well as the other colors?

   $$W = \frac{1240}{\lambda_0}\ \text{eV}\cdot\text{nm}$$

   $$= \frac{1240}{680\ \text{nm}}\ \text{ev}\cdot\text{nm}$$

   $= 1.8$ eV

9. The threshold frequency of tin is 1.2×10^{15} Hz.

   a. What is the threshold wavelength?

   $c = f\lambda$, so

   $$\lambda = \frac{c}{f} = \frac{3.0 \times 10^8\ \text{m/s}}{1.2 \times 10^{15}\ \text{Hz}} = 2.5 \times 10^{-7}\ \text{m}$$

Chapter Review Problems

b. What is the work function of tin?

$W = hf_0$
$= (6.6 \times 10^{-34}\ \text{J/Hz})(1.2 \times 10^{15}\ \text{Hz})$
$= 8.0 \times 10^{-19}\ \text{J}$

c. Electromagnetic radiation of 167 nm wavelength falls on tin. What is the kinetic energy of the ejected electrons in eV?

$$KE_{max} = \frac{hc}{\lambda} - hf_0$$

$$= \frac{(6.6 \times 10^{-34}\ \text{J/Hz})(3.0 \times 10^{8}\ \text{m/s})}{(167 \times 10^{-9}\ \text{m})}$$

$$- 8.0 \times 10^{-19}\ \text{J}$$
$$= 0.39 \times 10^{-18}\ \text{J}$$

$$(0.39 \times 10^{-18}\ \text{J})\left[\frac{\text{eV}}{1.60 \times 10^{-19}\ \text{J}}\right] = 2.4\ \text{eV}$$

10. The threshold frequency of a given metal is 6.7×10^{14} Hz. Calculate the kinetic energy, in eV, of the electrons ejected when the surface is illuminated with light of wavelengths:

a. 350 nm.

$c = f\lambda$, so $f = \frac{c}{\lambda}$.

$$f = \frac{c}{\lambda} = \frac{3.00 \times 10^{8}\ \text{m/s}}{350 \times 10^{-9}\ \text{m}} = 8.57 \times 10^{14}\ \text{Hz}$$

$KE = hf - hf_0$
$= (6.626 \times 10^{-34}\ \text{J}\cdot\text{s})(8.57 \times 10^{14}\ \text{Hz})$
$- (6.626 \times 10^{-34}\ \text{J}\cdot\text{s})(6.7 \times 10^{14}\ \text{Hz})$
$= 5.68 \times 10^{-19}\ \text{J} - 4.4 \times 10^{-19}\ \text{J}$
$= 1.3 \times 10^{-19}\ \text{J}$

$$(1.3 \times 10^{-19}\ \text{J})\left[\frac{\text{eV}}{1.60 \times 10^{-19}\ \text{J}}\right] = 0.81\ \text{eV}$$

b. 550 nm.

$$f = \frac{c}{\lambda} = \frac{3.00 \times 10^{8}\ \text{m/s}}{550 \times 10^{-9}\ \text{m}} = 5.45 \times 10^{14}\ \text{Hz}$$

No electrons are ejected because this is below the threshold frequency.

11. The work function of iron is 4.7 eV.

a. What is the threshold wavelength of iron?

$$E = \frac{1240}{\lambda}, \text{ so } \lambda = \frac{1240}{E} = \frac{1240}{7.4\ \text{eV}}$$

$= 2.6 \times 10^{2}$ nm

b. Iron is exposed to radiation of wavelength 150 nm. What is the maximum kinetic energy of the ejected electrons in eV?

$$KE = \frac{1240}{\lambda} - 4.7 = \frac{1240}{150} - 4.7 = 3.6\ \text{eV}$$

12. Suppose a 5.0 g object, such as a nickel, vibrates while connected to a spring. Its maximum velocity is 1.0 cm/s.

a. Find a maximum kinetic energy of the vibrating object.

$$KE = \frac{1}{2}mv^2$$

$$= \left[\frac{1}{2}\right](5.0 \times 10^{-3}\ \text{kg})(1.0 \times 10^{-2}\ \text{m/s})^2$$
$$= 2.5 \times 10^{-7}\ \text{J}$$

b. The object emits energy in the form of light of frequency 5.0×10^{14} Hz and its energy is reduced by one step. Find the energy lost by the object.

$E = hf = (7 \times 10^{-34}\ \text{J/Hz})(5.0 \times 10^{14}\ \text{Hz})$
$= 3.3 \times 10^{-19}\ \text{J}$

c. How many step reductions would this object have to make to lose all its energy?

$$\frac{2.5 \times 10^{-7}\ \text{J}}{3.3 \times 10^{-19}\ \text{J/step}} = 7.6 \times 10^{11}\ \text{steps}$$

13. What is the momentum of a photon of yellow light whose wavelength is 600 nm?

$$P = \frac{h}{\lambda} = \frac{6.626 \times 10^{-34}}{6.00 \times 10^{-7}\ \text{m}}$$

$= 1.10 \times 10^{-27}$ kg m/s

14. Find the de Broglie wavelength of a deuteron of mass 3.3×10^{-27} kg that moves with a speed of 2.5×10^{4} m/s.

$$\lambda = \frac{h}{mv} = \frac{6.6 \times 10^{-34}\ \text{J/Hz}}{(3.3 \times 10^{-27}\ \text{kg})(2.5 \times 10^{4}\ \text{m/s})}$$

$= 8.0 \times 10^{-12}$ m

15. What is the de Broglie wavelength of a proton moving with a speed of 1.00×10^6 m/s? The mass of a proton is 1.67×10^{-27} kg.

$$\lambda = \frac{h}{mv} = \frac{6.63 \times 10^{-34}\ \text{J/Hz}}{(1.67 \times 10^{-27}\ \text{kg})(1.00 \times 10^6\ \text{m/s})}$$
$$= 3.97 \times 10^{-13}\ \text{m}$$

16. An electron is accelerated across a potential difference of 54 V.

a. Find the maximum velocity of the electron.

$$KE_{max} = \frac{1}{2}mv^2 = -qV, \text{ so}$$
$$v = \sqrt{\frac{2qV}{m}}$$
$$= \sqrt{\frac{(2)(1.6 \times 10^{-19}\ \text{C})(54\ \text{V})}{9.1 \times 10^{-31}\ \text{kg}}}$$
$$= 4.4 \times 10^6\ \text{m/s}$$

b. Calculate the de Broglie wavelength of the electron.

$$\lambda = \frac{h}{mv} = \frac{6.6 \times 10^{-34}\ \text{J/Hz}}{(9.1 \times 10^{-31}\ \text{kg})(4.4 \times 10^6\ \text{m/s})}$$
$$= 1.7 \times 10^{-10}\ \text{m} = 0.17\ \text{nm}$$

17. A neutron is held in a trap with a kinetic energy of only 0.025 eV.

a. What is the velocity of the neutron?

$$KE = \frac{1}{2}mv^2$$
$$= 0.025\ \text{eV}\left[\frac{1.60 \times 10^{-19}\ \text{J}}{\text{eV}}\right]$$
$$= 4.0 \times 10^{-21}\ \text{J}$$
$$v = \sqrt{\frac{2KE}{m}} = \sqrt{\frac{(2)(4.0 \times 10^{-21}\ \text{J})}{1.67 \times 10^{-27}\ \text{bg}}}$$
$$= 2.2 \times 10^3\ \text{m/s}$$

b. Find the de Broglie wavelength of the neutron.

$$\lambda = \frac{h}{mv}$$
$$= \frac{6.6 \times 10^{-34}\ \text{J/Hz}}{(1.67 \times 10^{-27}\ \text{kg})(2.2 \times 10^3\ \text{m/s})}$$
$$= 1.8 \times 10^{-10}\ \text{m}$$

18. The kinetic energy of the hydrogen atom electron is 13.65 eV.

a. Find the velocity of the electron.

$$KE = \frac{1}{2}mv^2, \text{ so}$$
$$v = \sqrt{\frac{2KE}{m}}$$
$$= \sqrt{\frac{(2)(13.65\ \text{eV})(1.60 \times 10^{-19}\ \text{J/eV})}{9.11 \times 10^{-31}\ \text{kg}}}$$
$$= 2.19 \times 10^6\ \text{m/s}$$

b. Calculate the de Broglie wavelength of this electron.

$$\lambda = \frac{h}{mv}$$
$$= \frac{6.63 \times 10^{-34}\ \text{J/Hz}}{(9.11 \times 10^{-31}\ \text{kg})(2.19 \times 10^6\ \text{m/s})}$$
$$= 3.32 \times 10^{-10}\ \text{m}$$

c. Compare your answer with the radius of the hydrogen atom, 5.19 nm.

$$5.19\ \text{nm} = 51.9 \times 10^{-10}\ \text{m}$$
$$\frac{3.3 \times 10^{-10}}{51.9 \times 10^{-10}} = \frac{1}{16} \text{ the radius of the atom}$$

19. An electron has a de Broglie wavelength of 400 nm, the shortest wavelength of visible light.

a. Find its velocity.

$$\lambda = \frac{h}{mv}, \text{ so}$$
$$v = \frac{h}{m\lambda}$$
$$= \frac{(6.63 \times 10^{-34}\ \text{J/Hz})}{(9.11 \times 10^{-31}\ \text{kg})(400 \times 10^{-9}\ \text{m})}$$
$$= 1.83 \times 10^3\ \text{m/s}$$

b. Calculate the energy of this electron in eV.

$$KE = \frac{1}{2}mv^2$$

$$= \frac{1}{2}(9.11 \times 10^{-31} \text{ kg})(1.82 \times 10^3 \text{ m/s})^2$$

$$= (1.51 \times 10^{-24} \text{ J})\left[\frac{\text{eV}}{1.60 \times 10^{-19} \text{ J}}\right]$$

$$= 9.43 \times 10^{-6} \text{ eV}$$

20. An electron microscope is useful because the de Broglie wavelength of electrons can be made smaller than the wavelength of visible light. What energy, in eV, has to be given to an electron for it to have a de Broglie wavelength of 20 nm?

$$\lambda = \frac{h}{mv}, \text{ so}$$

$$v = \frac{h}{m\lambda}$$

$$= \frac{6.6 \times 10^{-34} \text{ J/Hz}}{(9.1 \times 10^{-31} \text{ kg})(20 \times 10^{-9} \text{ m})}$$

$$= 3.6 \times 10^4 \text{ m/s}$$

$$KE = \frac{1}{2}mv^2$$

$$= \frac{(9.1 \times 10^{-31} \text{ kg})(3.6 \times 10^4 \text{ m/s})^2}{2(1.6 \times 10^{-19} \text{ J/eV})}$$

$$= 3.8 \times 10^{-3} \text{ eV}$$

21. An electron has a de Broglie wavelength of 0.18 nm.

a. How large a potential difference did it experience if it started from rest?

$$v = \frac{h}{m\lambda}$$

$$= \frac{6.6 \times 10^{-34} \text{ J}\cdot\text{s}}{(9.1 \times 10^{-31} \text{ kg})(1.8 \times 10^{-10} \text{ m})}$$

$$= 4.0 \times 10^6 \text{ m/s}$$

Chapter Review Problems

$$KE = \frac{1}{2}mv^2$$

$$= \frac{1}{2}(9.1 \times 10^{-31} \text{ kg})(4.0 \times 10^6)^2$$

$$= 7.4 \times 10^{-18} \text{ J}$$

$$KE = qV$$

$$V = \frac{KE}{q}$$

$$= \frac{7.4 \times 10^{-18} \text{ J}}{1.6 \times 10^{-19} \text{ C}}$$

$$= 46 \ V$$

b. If a proton has a de Broglie wavelength of 0.18 nm, how large of a potential difference did it experience if it started from rest?

$$v = \frac{h}{m\lambda}$$

$$= \frac{6.6 \times 10^{-34} \text{ J}\cdot\text{s}}{(1.7 \times 10^{-27} \text{ kg})(1.8 \times 10^{-10} \text{ m})}$$

$$= 2.2 \times 10^3 \text{ m/s}$$

$$KE = \frac{1}{2}mv^2$$

$$= \frac{1}{2}(1.7 \times 10^{-27} \text{ kg})(2.2 \times 10^3 \text{ m/s})^2$$

$$= 4.1 \times 10^{-21} \text{ J}$$

$$V = \frac{KE}{q} = \frac{4.1 \times 10^{-21} \text{ J}}{1.6 \times 10^{-19} \text{ C}}$$

$$= 2.6 \times 10^{-2} \ V$$

Supplemental Problems (Appendix B)

1. Consider an incandescent light bulb on a dimmer control. What happens to the color of the light given off by the bulb as the dimmer control is turned down?

The light becomes more red.

2. What would the change in frequency of the vibration of an atom be according to Planck's theory if it gave off 5.44×10^{-19} J? Assume n = 1.

$E = nhf$, so

$$f = \frac{E}{nh} = \frac{5.44 \times 10^{-19}\ \text{J}}{(1)(6.627 \times 10^{-34}\ \text{J/Hz})}$$

$$= 8.21 \times 10^{14}\ \text{Hz}$$

3. What is the maximum kinetic energy of photoelectrons ejected from a metal that has a stopping potential of 3.8 V?

$KE = qV = (1\text{e})(3.8\ \text{V}) = 3.8\ \text{eV}$

4. The stopping potential needed to return all the electrons ejected from a metal is 7.3 V. What is the maximum kinetic energy of the electrons in J?

$$7.3\ \text{eV}\left[\frac{1.60 \times 10^{-19}\ \text{J}}{1\text{eV}}\right] = 1.2 \times 10^{-18}\ \text{J}$$

5. What is the potential difference needed to stop photoelectrons that have a maximum kinetic energy of 8.0×10^{-19} J?

$$8.0 \times 10^{-19}\ \text{J}\left[\frac{1\text{eV}}{1.60 \times 10^{-19}\ \text{J}}\right] = 5.0\ \text{eV, so}$$

5.0 V.

6. The threshold frequency of a certain metal is 8.0×10^{14} Hz. What is the work function of the metal?

$$E = hf_0 = (6.627 \times 10^{-34}\ \text{J/Hz})(8.0 \times 10^{14}\ \text{Hz}) = 5.3 \times 10^{-19}\ \text{J}$$

7. If light with a frequency of 1.6×10^{15} Hz falls on the metal in the previous problem, what is the maximum kinetic energy of the photo–electrons?

$$\begin{aligned} KE &= hf - hf_0 \\ &= (6.627 \times 10^{-34}\ \text{J/Hz})(1.6 \times 10^{15}\ \text{Hz}) - 5.3 \times 10^{-19}\ \text{J} \\ &= 1.06 \times 10^{-18}\ \text{J} - 5.3 \times 10^{-19}\ \text{J} \\ &= 5.3 \times 10^{-19}\ \text{J} \end{aligned}$$

8. The threshold frequency of a certain metal is 3.00×10^{14} Hz. What is the maximum kinetic energy of the ejected photoelectrons when the metal is illuminated by light with a wavelength of 650 nm?

$c = f\lambda$, so

$$f = \frac{c}{\lambda} = \frac{3.00 \times 10^{8}\ \text{m/s}}{650 \times 10^{-9}\ \text{m}}$$

$$= 4.62 \times 10^{14}\ \text{Hz}$$

$$\begin{aligned} KE &= hf - hf_0 \\ &= (6.627 \times 10^{-34}\ \text{J/Hz})(4.62 \times 10^{14}\ \text{Hz}) - (6.627 \times 10^{-34}\ \text{J/Hz})(3.00 \times 10^{14}\ \text{Hz}) \\ &= 3.06 \times 10^{-19}\ \text{J} - 1.99 \times 10^{-19}\ \text{J} \\ &= 1.07 \times 10^{-19}\ \text{J} \end{aligned}$$

9. What is the momentum of a photon of violet light that has a wavelength of 4.00×10^{2} nm?

$$P = \frac{h}{\lambda} = \frac{6.627 \times 10^{-34}\ \text{J/Hz}}{4.00 \times 10^{-2}\ \text{m}}$$

$$= 1.66 \times 10^{-27}\ \text{kg}\cdot\text{m/s}$$

10. What is the momentum of a photon of red light that has a wavelength of 7.00×10^{2} nm?

$$P = \frac{h}{\lambda} = \frac{6.627 \times 10^{-34}\ \text{J/Hz}}{7.00 \times 10^{-7}\ \text{m}}$$

$$= 9.47 \times 10^{-28}\ \text{kg}\cdot\text{m/s}$$

11. What is the wavelength associated with an electron moving at 3.0×10^{6} m/s?

$$\lambda = \frac{h}{mv}$$

$$= \frac{6.627 \times 10^{-34}\ \text{J/Hz}}{(9.11 \times 10^{-31}\ \text{kg})(3.0 \times 10^{6}\ \text{m/s})}$$

$$\begin{aligned} &= 2.4 \times 10^{-10}\ \text{m} \\ &= 0.24\ \text{nm} \end{aligned}$$

Supplemental Problems (Appendix B)

12. What velocity would an electron need to have a wavelength of 3.0×10^{-10} m associated with it?

$$\lambda = \frac{h}{mv}, \text{ so}$$

$$v = \frac{h}{m\lambda} = \frac{6.627 \times 10^{-34} \text{ J/Hz}}{(9.11 \times 10^{-31} \text{ kg})(3.0 \times 10^{-10} \text{ m})}$$

$$= 2.4 \times 10^{6} \text{ m/s}$$

13. An electron is accelerated across a potential difference of 5.0×10^{3} V in the CRT of a television.

a. What is the velocity of the electron if it started from rest?

$$\frac{1}{2}mv^2 = qV, \text{ so}$$

$$v = \sqrt{\frac{qV}{\frac{1}{2}m}} = \sqrt{\frac{(1.60 \times 10^{-19} \text{ C})(5.0 \times 10^{3})}{\frac{1}{2}(9.11 \times 10^{-31} \text{ kg})}}$$

$$= 4.2 \times 10^{7} \text{ m/s}$$

b. What is the wavelength associated with the electron?

$$\lambda = \frac{h}{mv}$$

$$= \frac{6.627 \times 10^{-34} \text{ J/Hz}}{(9.11 \times 10^{-31} \text{ kg})(4.2 \times 10^{7} \text{ m/s})}$$

$$= 1.7 \times 10^{-11} \text{ m} = 0.017 \text{ nm}$$

Chapter 28: The Atom

Practice Problems

page 583

1. According to the Bohr model, how many times larger is the orbit of hydrogen in the second level than in the first?

   Four times as large since orbit radius is proportional to n^2, where n is the integer labeling the level.

2. The discussion on page 582 shows how to calculate the radius of the innermost orbit of the hydrogen atom. Note that all factors in the equation are constants with the exception of n^2. Use the solution to the Example Problem to find the radius of the orbit of the second, third and fourth allowable energy levels in the hydrogen atom.

   $r_n = n^2k$, where $k = 5.3 \times 10^{-11}$ m
   $r_2 = (2)^2(5.3 \times 10^{-11} \text{ m}) = 2.1 \times 10^{-10}$ m
   $r_3 = (3)^2(5.3 \times 10^{-11} \text{ m}) = 4.8 \times 10^{-10}$ m
   $r_4 = (4)^2(5.3 \times 10^{-11} \text{ m}) = 8.5 \times 10^{-10}$ m

3. Calculate the energies of the second, third and fourth energy levels in the hydrogen atom.

   $$E_n = \frac{-13.6 \text{ eV}}{n^2}$$

   $$E_2 = \frac{-13.6 \text{ eV}}{(2)^2} = -3.4 \text{ eV}$$

   $$E_3 = \frac{-13.6 \text{ eV}}{(3)^2} = -1.5 \text{ eV}$$

   $$E_4 = \frac{-13.6 \text{ eV}}{(4)^2} = -0.85 \text{ eV}$$

4. Calculate the energy difference between E_3 and E_2 in the hydrogen atom. Do the same for E_4 and E_3.

   Using the results of Practice Exercise 3,
   $E_3 - E_2 = (-1.5 \text{ eV}) - (-3.4 \text{ eV}) = 1.9$ eV
   $E_4 - E_3 = (-0.85 \text{ eV}) - (-1.5 \text{ eV}) = 0.7$ eV

Chapter Review Problems

pages 593

1. A hydrogen nucleus is 2.5×10^{-15} m in diameter, while the distance between the nucleus and the first electron is about 5×10^{-9} m. Suppose you used a baseball to represent the nucleus. How far away would the electron be?

   baseball diameter = 7.5 cm
   distance to electron
   $$= \frac{0.075 \text{ m}}{(2.5 \times 10^{-15} \text{ m})(5 \times 10^{-9} \text{ m})}$$
   = 200 km
   about 200 km

2. A mercury atom drops from 8.82 eV about its ground state to 6.67 eV above its ground state.

   a. What is the energy of the photon emitted by the mercury atom?

   $E = 8.82 \text{ eV} - 6.67 \text{ eV} = 2.15$ eV

   b. What is the frequency of the photon?

   $$E = hf = 2.15 \text{ eV}\left[\frac{1.60 \times 10^{-19} \text{ J}}{\text{eV}}\right]$$
   $$= 3.44 \times 10^{-19} \text{ J, so}$$
   $$f = \frac{E}{h} = \frac{3.44 \times 10^{-19} \text{ J}}{6.63 \times 10^{-34} \text{ J}\cdot\text{s}} = 5.19 \times 10^{14} \text{ Hz}$$

3. A mercury atom is in an excited state when its energy level is 6.67 eV above the ground state. A photon of energy 2.15 eV strikes the mercury atom and is absorbed by it. To what energy level is the mercury atom raised? See Figure 28–23.

   $E = 6.67 \text{ eV} + 2.15 \text{ eV} = 8.82$ eV which is E_9.

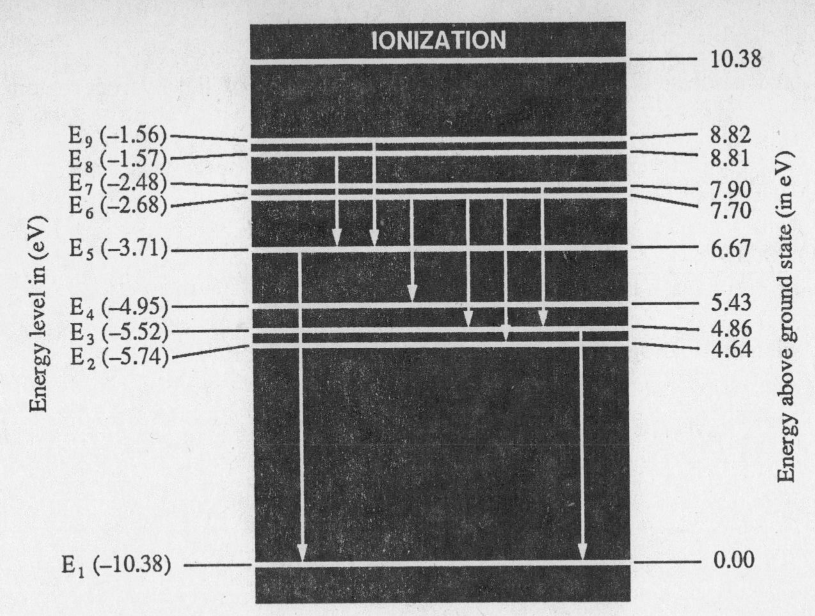

4. A mercury atom is in an excited state at the E_6 energy level. (See Figure 28–23)

   a. How much energy would be needed to ionize the atom?

   $E_6 = 7.70$ eV
   10.38 eV − 7.70 eV = 2.68 eV

   b. How much energy would be released if the electron dropped down to the E_2 energy level instead?

   $E_2 = 4.64$ eV
   7.70 eV − 4.64 eV = 3.06 eV

5. A mercury atom is in an excited state which has an energy level of −4.95 eV. It absorbs a photon that raises it to the next higher energy level. (See Figure 28–23.)

   $E_4 = -4.95$ eV
   $E_5 = -3.71$ eV

   a. What is the energy of the photon?

   $E_5 - E_4 = -3.71 \text{ eV} - (-4.95 \text{ eV}) = 1.24 \text{ eV}$

   b. What is the photon's frequency?

$$E = hf, \text{ so } f = \frac{E}{h} = \frac{1.24 \text{ eV}\left[\frac{1.60 \times 10^{-19} \text{ J}}{\text{eV}}\right]}{6.626 \times 10^{-34} \text{ J}\cdot\text{s}} = 2.99 \times 10^{14} \text{ Hz}$$

6. A photon with an energy of 14.0 eV enters a hydrogen atom in the ground state and ionizes it. With what kinetic energy will the electron be ejected from the atom?

   It takes 13.6 eV to ionize the atom, so 14.0 eV − 13.6 eV = 0.4 eV kinetic energy.

7. Calculate the radius of the orbital associated with the energy levels E_5 and E_6 of the hydrogen atom.

$$r_5 = \frac{h^2}{4\pi^2 Kmq^2}n^2 = \frac{(6.262 \times 10^{-34}\ \text{J}\cdot\text{s})^2}{4\pi^2\left[9.0 \times 10^9\ \frac{\text{Nm}^2}{\text{C}^2}\right](9.11 \times 10^{-31}\ \text{kg})(1.60 \times 10^{-19}\ \text{C})^2}(5)^2 = 1.32 \times 10^{-9}\ \text{m}$$

$$r_6 = \frac{(6.262 \times 10^{-34}\ \text{J}\cdot\text{s})}{4\pi^2(9.0 \times 10^9\ \text{Nm}^2/\text{C}^2)(9.11 \times 10^{-31}\ \text{kg})(1.60 \times 10^{-19}\ \text{C})^2}(6)^2 = 1.91 \times 10^{-9}\ \text{m}$$

8. What energies are associated with the hydrogen atom energy levels E_2, E_3, E_4, E_5 and E_6?

$$E_2 = \frac{-13.6\ \text{eV}}{n^2} = \frac{-13.6\ \text{eV}}{(2)^2} = -3.40\ \text{eV}$$

$$E_3 = \frac{-13.6\ \text{eV}}{(3)^2} = -1.51\ \text{eV}$$

$$E_4 = \frac{-13.6\ \text{eV}}{(4)^2} = -0.85\ \text{eV}$$

$$E_5 = \frac{-13.6\ \text{eV}}{(5)^2} = -0.54\ \text{eV}$$

$$E_6 = \frac{-13.6\ \text{eV}}{(6)^2} = -0.38\ \text{eV}$$

9. Using the values calculated in Problem 8, calculate the following energy differences for a hydrogen atom.

a. $E_6 - E_5$

$(-0.38\ \text{eV}) - (-0.54\ \text{eV}) = 0.16\ \text{eV}$

b. $E_6 - E_3$

$(-0.38\ \text{eV}) - (-1.50\ \text{eV}) = 1.13\ \text{eV}$

c. $E_4 - E_2$

$(-0.85\ \text{eV}) - (-3.40\ \text{eV}) = 2.55\ \text{eV}$

d. $E_5 - E_2$

$(-0.54\ \text{eV}) - (-3.40\ \text{eV}) = 2.86\ \text{eV}$

e. $E_5 - E_3$

$(-0.54\ \text{eV}) - (-1.50\ \text{eV}) = 0.97\ \text{eV}$

Chapter Review Problems

10. Use the values from Problem 9 to determine the frequencies of the photons emitted when the hydrogen atom makes the level changes listed.

a. $E = hf$

$hf = E_6 - E_5 = 0.16 \text{ eV}$

$$f = \frac{(0.16 \text{ eV})(1.6 \times 10^{-19} \text{ J/eV})}{6.6 \times 10^{-34} \text{ J/Hz}}$$

$= 3.9 \times 10^{13} \text{ Hz}$

b. $hf = E_6 - E_3 = 1.13 \text{ eV}$

$$f = \frac{(1.12 \text{ eV})(1.6 \times 10^{-19} \text{ J/eV})}{6.6 \times 10^{-34} \text{ J/Hz}}$$

$= 2.70 \times 10^{14} \text{ Hz}$

c. $hf = E_4 - E_2 = 2.55 \text{ eV}$

$$f = \frac{(2.55 \text{ eV})(1.6 \times 10^{-19} \text{ J/eV})}{6.6 \times 10^{-34} \text{ J/Hz}}$$

$= 6.14 \times 10^{14} \text{ Hz}$

d. $hf = E_5 - E_2 = 2.86 \text{ eV}$

$$f = \frac{(2.86 \text{ eV})(1.6 \times 10^{-19} \text{ J/eV})}{6.6 \times 10^{-34} \text{ J/Hz}}$$

$= 6.89 \times 10^{14} \text{ Hz}$

e. $hf = E_5 - E_3 = 0.96 \text{ eV}$

$$f = \frac{(0.96 \text{ eV})(1.6 \times 10^{-19} \text{ J/eV})}{6.6 \times 10^{-34} \text{ J/Hz}}$$

$= 2.3 \times 10^{14} \text{ Hz}$

11. Determine the wavelengths of the photons having the frequencies calculated in Problem 10.

a. $c = f\lambda$, so

$$\lambda = \frac{c}{f} = \frac{3.00 \times 10^8 \text{ m/s}}{3.9 \times 10^{13} \text{ Hz}} = 7.7 \times 10^{-6} \text{ m}$$

b. $$\lambda = \frac{c}{f} = \frac{3.00 \times 10^8 \text{ m/s}}{2.70 \times 10^{14} \text{ Hz}} = 1.11 \times 10^{-6} \text{ m}$$

c. $$\lambda = \frac{c}{f} = \frac{3.00 \times 10^8 \text{ m/s}}{6.14 \times 10^{14} \text{ Hz}} = 4.89 \times 10^{-7} \text{ m}$$

$= 489 \text{ nm}$

d. $$\lambda = \frac{c}{f} = \frac{3.00 \times 10^8 \text{ m/s}}{6.89 \times 10^{14} \text{ Hz}} = 4.35 \times 10^{-7} \text{ m}$$

$= 435 \text{ nm}$

e. $$\lambda = \frac{c}{f} = \frac{3.00 \times 10^8 \text{ m/s}}{2.3 \times 10^{14} \text{ Hz}} = 1.3 \times 10^{-6} \text{ m}$$

$= 13 \text{ nm}$

12. Determine the frequency and wavelength of the photon emitted when an electron drops from

a. E_3 to E_2 in an excited hydrogen atom.

$E_3 - E_2 = -1.5 \text{ eV} - (-3.4 \text{ eV})$

$$= 1.9 \text{ eV}\left[\frac{1.60 \times 10^{-19} \text{ J}}{\text{eV}}\right]$$

$= 3.0 \times 10^{-19} \text{ J}$

$E = hf$, so

$$f = \frac{E}{h} = \frac{3.0 \times 10^{-19} \text{ J}}{6.64 \times 10^{-34} \text{ J}\cdot\text{s}}$$

$= 4.6 \times 10^{14} \text{ Hz}$

$c = f\lambda$, so

$$\lambda = \frac{c}{f} = \frac{3.00 \times 10^8 \text{ m/s}}{4.6 \times 10^{14} \text{ Hz}}$$

$= 6.5 \times 10^{-7} \text{ m}$

b. E_4 to E_3 in an excited hydrogen atom.

$E_4 - E_3 = -0.85 \text{ eV} - (-1.50 \text{ eV})$

$$= 0.65 \text{ eV}\left[\frac{1.60 \times 10^{-19} \text{ J}}{\text{eV}}\right]$$

$= 1.0 \times 10^{-19} \text{ J}$

$E = hf$, so

$$f = \frac{E}{h} = \frac{1.0 \times 10^{-19} \text{ J}}{6.64 \times 10^{-34} \text{ J}\cdot\text{s}}$$

$= 1.5 \times 10^{14} \text{ Hz}$

$c = f\lambda$, so

$$\lambda = \frac{c}{f} = \frac{3.00 \times 10^8 \text{ m/s}}{1.5 \times 10^{14} \text{ Hz}}$$

$= 2.0 \times 10^{-6} \text{ m}$

13. What is the difference between the energies of the E_4 and E_1 energy levels of the hydrogen atom?

$E_4 - E_1 = (-0.85 \text{ eV}) - (-13.6 \text{ eV})$

$= 12.8 \text{ eV}$

14. By what amount does the mass of a hydrogen atom decrease when its electron makes a down transition from E_4 to E_1, in an excited hydrogen atom?

$$E_1 = \frac{-2.17 \times 10^{-18}\ \text{J}}{1^2} = -2.17 \times 10^{-18}\ \text{J}$$

$$E_4 = \frac{-2.17 \times 10^{-18}\ \text{J}}{4^2} = -1.36 \times 10^{-19}\ \text{J}$$

$$E_4 - E_1 = 2.03 \times 10^{-18}\ \text{J}$$

$$E = mc^2, \text{ so } m = \frac{E}{c^2}$$

$$= \frac{2.03 \times 10^{-18}\ \text{J}}{(3.0 \times 10^8\ \text{m/s})^2} = 2.26 \times 10^{-35}\ \text{kg}$$

15. From what energy level did an electron fall if it emits a photon of 9.38×10^{-8} m wavelength when it reaches ground state within a hydrogen atom?

$$c = f\lambda, \text{ so}$$

$$f = \frac{c}{\lambda} = \frac{3.00 \times 10^8\ \text{m/s}}{9.38 \times 10^{-8}\ \text{m}}$$

$$= 3.20 \times 10^{15}\ \text{Hz}$$

$$E_N - E_1 = (6.64 \times 10^{-34}\ \text{J/Hz})(3.20 \times 10^{15}\ \text{Hz})$$

$$= 2.11 \times 10^{-18}\ \text{J}$$

$$E_N = (-2.17 \times 10^{-18}\ \text{J}) + 2.11 \times 10^{-18}\ \text{J}$$

$$E_N = -6 \times 10^{-20}\ \text{J}$$

$$\frac{-2.17 \times 10^{-18}\ \text{J}}{N^2} = -6 \times 10^{-20}\ \text{J}$$

$$N^2 = 36$$

$$N = 6$$

16. For a hydrogen atom in the $n = 3$ Bohr orbital, find

a. the radius of the orbital.

$$r = \frac{h^2}{4\pi^2 Kmq^2} n^2$$

when $n = 1$, $r = 5.30 \times 10^{-11}$ m

when $n = 3$, $r = 4.77 \times 10^{-10}$ m

Chapter Review Problems

b. the electric force acting on the electron.

$$F = \frac{Kq^2}{r^2}$$

$$= \frac{(8.99 \times 10^9\ \text{N}\cdot\text{m}^2/\text{C}^2)(1.6 \times 10^{-19}\ \text{C})^2}{(4.8 \times 10^{-10}\ \text{m})^2}$$

$$= 1.01 \times 10^{-9}\ \text{N}$$

c. the centripetal acceleration of the electron.

$$F = ma, \text{ so}$$

$$a = \frac{F}{m} = \frac{1.01 \times 10^{-9}\ \text{N}}{9.11 \times 10^{-31}\ \text{kg}}$$

$$= 1.11 \times 10^{21}\ \text{m/s}^2$$

d. the orbital speed of the electron. Compare this speed with the speed of light.

$$a = \frac{v^2}{r}, \text{ so}$$

$$v = \sqrt{ar} = \sqrt{(1.1 \times 10^{21}\ \text{m/s}^2)(4.8 \times 10^{-10}\ \text{m})}$$

$$= 7.28 \times 10^5\ \text{m/s or } 0.2\% \text{ of } c$$

17. A hydrogen atom has the electron in the $n = 2$ level.

a. If a photon with a wavelength of 332 nm strikes the atom, will the atom be ionized?

$$E = \frac{13.65\ \text{eV}}{n^2} = \frac{13.65}{4}\ \text{eV} = 3.4\ \text{eV}$$

Yes, the atom is ionized.

$$E = hf = \frac{hc}{\lambda} = 6.0 \times 10^{-19}\ \text{J} = 3.7\ \text{eV}$$

b. When the atom is ionized, assume the electron receives the excess energy from the ionization. What will be the kinetic energy of the electron in joules?

$$3.7\ \text{eV} - 3.4\ \text{eV} = 0.3\ \text{eV} = 5 \times 10^{-20}\ \text{J}$$

Chapter Review Problems

18. How many orders of magnitude larger is the electrical force between the electron and proton in a hydrogen atom than the gravitational force between them?

$r = 5.3 \times 10^{-11}$ m

$$F_E = \frac{Kq_1q_2}{r^2}$$

$$= \frac{(9 \times 10^9 \text{ N}\cdot\text{m}^2/\text{C}^2)(1.6 \times 10^{-19}\text{ C})^2}{(5.3 \times 10^{-11}\text{ m})^2}$$

$$= 8.2 \times 10^{-8}\text{ N} \approx 10^{-7}\text{ N}$$

$$F_G = \frac{Gm_1m_2}{r^2}$$

$$= \frac{G(1.67 \times 10^{-27}\text{ kg})(9.1 \times 10^{-31}\text{ kg})}{(5.3 \times 10^{-11}\text{ m})^2}$$

$$= 3.6 \times 10^{-47}\text{ N} \approx 10^{-47}\text{ N}$$

$$\frac{10^{-7}}{10^{-47}} = 10^{40}\text{, i.e. 40 orders of magnitude.}$$

NOTE: $\dfrac{F_E}{F_G} = \dfrac{K\frac{q_1q_2}{r^2}}{\frac{Gm_1m_2}{r^2}}$; the r^2 divides out.

19. Gallium arsenide lasers are used in CD (compact disk) players. If the temperature is chosen so the laser emits at 840 nm, what is the difference, in eV, between the two lasing energy levels?

$c = f\lambda$, so

$$f = \frac{c}{\lambda} = \frac{3.00 \times 10^8\text{ m/s}}{840 \times 10^{-9}\text{ m}} = 3.57 \times 10^{14}\text{ Hz}$$

$$E = hf = \frac{(6.64 \times 10^{-34}\text{ J/Hz})(3.57 \times 10^{14}\text{ Hz})}{1.60 \times 10^{-19}\text{ eV/J}}$$

$$= 1.48\text{ eV}$$

20. The carbon dioxide laser emits very high power infrared radiation. What is the energy difference, in eV, between the two lasing energy levels?

$c = f\lambda$, so

$$f = \frac{c}{\lambda} = \frac{3.00 \times 10^{-8}\text{ m/s}}{10\,600 \times 10^{-9}\text{ m}} = 2.83 \times 10^{13}\text{ Hz}$$

$$E = hf = \frac{(6.64 \times 10^{-34}\text{ J/Hz})(2.83 \times 10^{13}\text{ Hz})}{1.60 \times 10^{-19}\text{ eV/J}}$$

$$= 0.117\text{ eV}$$

Supplemental Problems (Appendix B)

1. A calcium atom drops from 5.16 eV above the ground state to 2.93 eV above ground state. What is the frequency of the photon emitted by the atom?

$E = hf$, so

$$f = \frac{E}{h} = \frac{(5.16\text{ eV} - 2.93\text{ eV})\frac{1.60 \times 10^{-19}\text{ J}}{1\text{eV}}}{6.627 \times 10^{-34}\text{ J/Hz}}$$

$$= 5.38 \times 10^{14}\text{ Hz}$$

2. A calcium atom is in an excited state when the energy level is 2.93 eV, E_2, above the ground state. A photon of energy 1.20 eV strikes the calcium atom and is absorbed by it. To what energy level is the calcium atom raised? Refer to the diagram below.

$$E_2 = 2.93\text{ eV} + 1.20\text{ eV} = 4.13\text{ eV} = E_3$$

3. A calcium atom is in an excited state at the E_6 energy level. How much energy is released when the atom dropped down to the E_2 energy level?

$$E_6 - E_2 = 5.16\text{ eV} - (-2.93\text{ eV}) = 2.23\text{ eV}$$

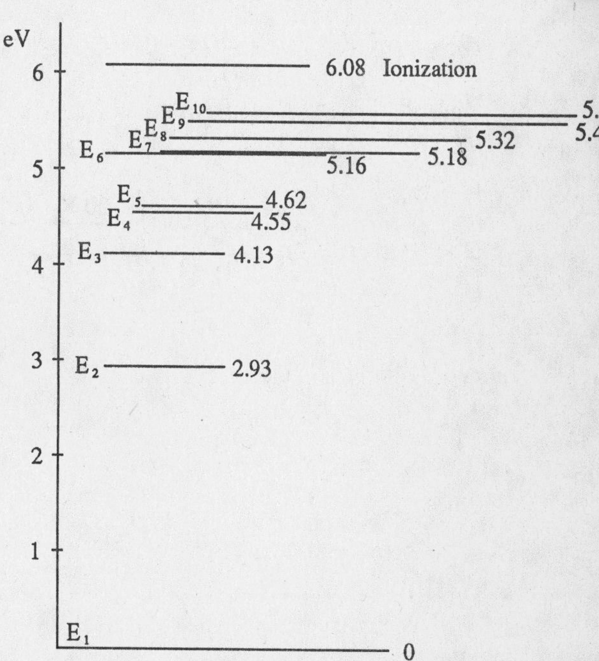

Energy Level Diagram for Calcium Atom

4. A photon of orange light, wavelength of 600 nm, enters a calcium atom in the E_6 excited state and ionizes the atom. What kinetic energy will the electron have as it is ejected from the atom?

$$E = \frac{hc}{\lambda} = \frac{(6.627 \times 10^{-34}\ \text{J/Hz})(3.00 \times 10^{8}\ \text{m/s})}{600 \times 10^{-9}\ \text{m}} = 3.314\ \text{J}\left[\frac{1\text{eV}}{1.60 \times 10^{-19}\ \text{J}}\right] = 2.07\ \text{eV}$$

Energy needed to ionize 6.08 eV

E_6 − 5.16 eV

= 0.92 eV

Photon energy − ionization energy = kinetic energy

2.07 eV − 0.92 eV = 1.15 eV

5. Calculate the radius of the orbital associated with the energy level E_4 of the hydrogen atom.

$$r = \frac{h^2}{4\pi^2 Kmq^2}n^2 = \frac{(6.626 \times 10^{-34}\ \text{J}\cdot\text{s})^2}{4\pi^2(9.00 \times 10^{9}\ \text{N}\cdot\text{m}^2/\text{C}^2)(9.11 \times 10^{-31}\ \text{kg})(1.60 \times 10^{-19}\ \text{C})^2}(4)^2$$

$$= 8.48 \times 10^{-10}\ \text{m} = 0.848\ \text{nm}$$

6. Calculate the energy associated with the E_7 and the E_2 energy levels of the hydrogen atom.

$$E_7 = -13.6\ \text{eV}\left[\frac{1}{n^2}\right] = -13.6\ \text{eV}\left[\frac{1}{7^2}\right] = -0.278\ \text{eV}$$

$$E_2 = -13.6\ \text{eV}\left[\frac{1}{n^2}\right] = -13.6\ \text{eV}\left[\frac{1}{2^2}\right] = -3.40\ \text{eV}$$

7. Calculate the difference in energy levels in the previous problem.

$E_7 - E_2 = -0.278\ \text{eV} - (-3.40\ \text{eV}) = 3.12\ \text{eV}$

8. What frequency photon is emitted from the hydrogen atom when the atom releases the energy found in the previous problem?

$$E = hf,\ \text{so}\ f = \frac{E}{h} = \frac{(3.12\ \text{eV})\left[\frac{1.60 \times 10^{-19}\ \text{J}}{\text{eV}}\right]}{6.627 \times 10^{-34}\ \text{J/Hz}} = 7.53 \times 10^{14}\ \text{Hz}$$

Chapter 29: Solid State Electronics

Practice Problems

page 598

1. Zinc, density 7.13 g/cm^3, atomic mass 65.37 g/mole, has two free electrons per atom. How many free electrons are there in each cubic centimeter of zinc?

$$\text{free } \frac{e^-}{cm^3}$$

$$= \frac{(2\ e^-/\text{atom})(6.02 \times 10^{23}\ \text{atoms/mole})(7.13 g/cm^3)}{(65.37\ g/\text{mole})}$$

$= 1.31 \times 10^{23}$ free e^-/cm^3.

page 601

2. In pure germanium, density 5.23 g/cm^3, atomic mass 72.6 g/mole, there are 2×10^{16} free electrons/cm^3 at room temperature. How many free electrons are there per atom?

$$\text{atoms}/cm^3$$

$$= \frac{(6.02 \times 10^{23}\ \text{atoms/mole})(5.23\ g/cm^3)}{(72.6\ g/\text{mole})}$$

$= 4.34 \times 10^{22}$ atoms/cm^3,

$$\text{free } e^-/\text{atom} = \frac{(2 \times 10^{16}\ \text{free } e^-/cm^3)}{(4.34 \times 10^{22}\ \text{atoms}/cm^3)}$$

$= 5 \times 10^{-7}$

page 603

3. If you wanted to have 5×10^3 as many electrons from As doping as thermally–free electrons in the germanium semiconductor described in Problem 2, how many As atoms should there be per Ge atom?

There were 5×10^{-7} free e^-/Ge atom, so we need 5×10^3 as many As dopant atoms, or 2×10^{-3} As atom/Ge atom.

page 607

4. What battery voltage would be needed to have a current of 2.5 mA in the diode above?

At I = 2.5 mA, V_d = 0.6 V, so

$V = V_d + IR$

$= 0.6\ V + (2.5 \times 10^{-3}\ A)(470\ \Omega)$

$= 1.8\ V$

Practice Problems

5. A Ge diode has a voltage drop of 0.4 V when 12 mA flows through it. If the same 470–Ω resistor is used, what battery voltage is needed?

$V = V_d + IR$

$= 0.4\ V + (1.2 \times 10^{-2}\ A)(470\ \Omega)$

$= 6.0\ V$

Chapter Review Problems

pages 612–613

1. The forbidden gap in silicon is 1.1 eV. Electromagnetic light waves striking the silicon cause electrons to move from the valence band to the conduction band. What is the longest wavelength of radiation that could excite an electron in this way? Chapter 27 gives $E = \frac{1240\ eV \cdot nm}{\lambda}$, where the energy must be in eV and the wavelength must be in nm.

$$E = \frac{1240\ eV \cdot nm}{\lambda}, \text{ so}$$

$$\lambda = \frac{(1240\ eV \cdot nm)}{E} = 1.1 \times 10^3\ nm$$

$= 1.1\ \mu m$ (infrared).

2. A light–emitting diode (LED) produces green light with a wavelength of 550 nm when an electron moves from the conduction band to the valence band. Find the energy width of the forbidden gap in this diode. See previous problem for additional information.

$$E = \frac{(1240\ eV \cdot nm)}{\lambda} = \frac{(1240\ eV \cdot nm)}{(550\ nm)}$$

$= 2.25\ eV$

29

3. How many free electrons exist in a cubic centimeter of sodium? Its density is 0.971 g/cm³, atomic weight is 22.99 g/mole, and there is one free electron per atom.

$$\frac{\text{free e}^-}{\text{cm}^3} = \left[\frac{1\text{e}^-}{\text{atom}}\right]\left[\frac{6.02\times 10^{23}\ \text{atom}}{\text{mole}}\right]\left[\frac{\text{mole}}{22.99\ \text{g}}\right]\cdot\left[\frac{0.971\ \text{g}}{\text{cm}^3}\right]$$

$$= 2.54\times 10^{22}\ \frac{\text{free e}^-}{\text{cm}^3}$$

4. At 0°C, thermal energy frees 1.1×10^{12} e⁻/cm³ in pure silicon. The density of silicon is 2.33 g/cm³ and the atomic weight of silicon is 28.09 g/mole. What is the fraction of atoms that have free electrons?

$$\frac{\text{free e}^-}{\text{atom}} = \frac{\left[\frac{\text{free e}^-}{\text{cm}^3}\right]}{\left[\frac{\text{atoms}}{\text{cm}^3}\right]}$$

$$= \frac{1.1\times 10^{12}\ \text{e}^-/\text{cm}^3}{\left[6.02\times 10^{23}\ \frac{\text{atom}}{\text{mole}}\right]\left[\frac{\text{mole}}{28.09\ \text{g}}\right]\left[\frac{2.33\ \text{g}}{\text{cm}^3}\right]}$$

$$= \frac{1.1\times 10^{12}\ \frac{\text{e}^-}{\text{cm}^3}}{4.99\times 10^{22}\ \frac{\text{atom}}{\text{cm}^3}} = 2.2\times 10^{-11}\ \frac{\text{e}^-}{\text{atom}}$$

5. Use a periodic table to determine which of the following elements could be added to germanium to make a p-type semiconductor: B, C, N, P, Si, Al, Ge, Ga, As, In, Sn, Sb.

B, Al, Ga, In (Group 3)

6. Which of the elements listed in the previous problem would produce an n-type semiconductor?

N, P, As, Sb (Group 5)

7. Which element or elements could be used as the second dopant when making a diode if the first dopant was boron?

N, P, As or Sb (all Group 5, n-types)

Chapter Review Problems

8. The potential drop across a glowing LED is about 1.2 V. In Figure 29–16, the potential drop across the resistor is the difference between the battery voltage and LED potential drop, 6.0 V – 1.2 V = 4.8 V. What is the current through

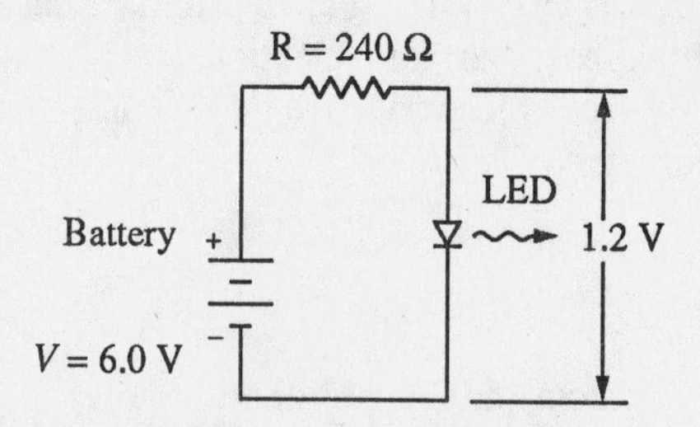

a. the LED?

$$I = \frac{V}{R} = \frac{(4.8\ \text{V})}{(240\ \Omega)} = 0.020\ \text{A} = 20\ \text{mA}$$

b. the resistor?

20 mA. The current is the same through both.

9. Jon wanted to raise the current through the LED in the previous problem to 30 mA so that it would glow brighter. Assume that the potential drop across the LED is still 1.2 V. What resistor should be used?

$$V = IR,\ \text{so}\ R = \frac{V}{I} = \frac{(4.8\ \text{V})}{(0.030\ \text{A})} = 160\ \Omega.$$

10. Figure 29–17 shows a battery, diode, and bulb connected in series so that the bulb lights. Note that the diode is forward-biased. Describe whether the bulb in each of the pictured circuits is lighted.

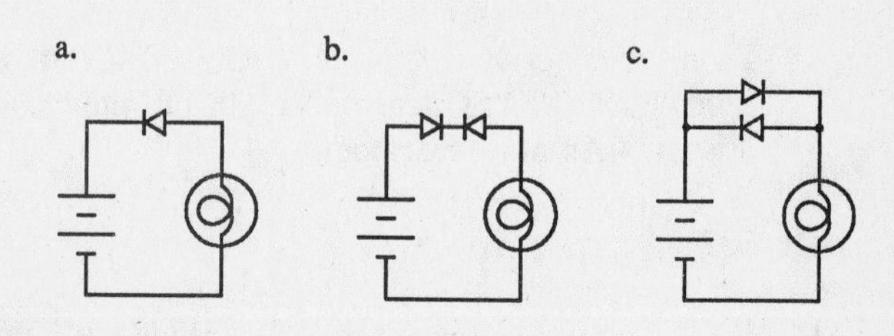

a. No (diode reverse-biased).
b. No (no current through second reverse-biased diode).
c. Yes (current through forward-biased diode).

11. For each pictured circuit tell whether lamp L_1, lamp L_2, both, or neither is lighted.

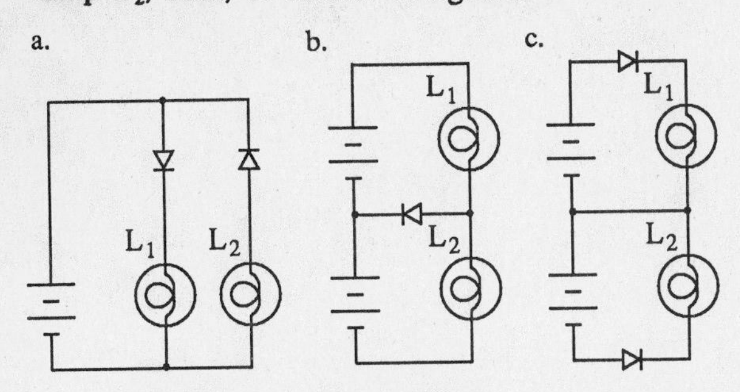

a. L_1 is on, L_2 is off.

b. Both lamps are on (current for L_1 goes through both L_2, lighting it, and through diode).

c. Only L_1 is on (lower diode blocks current for L_2).

12. Draw a circuit having one 6.0 V battery, two LEDs and two resistors. One LED should have a current of 30 mA, the other 20 mA.

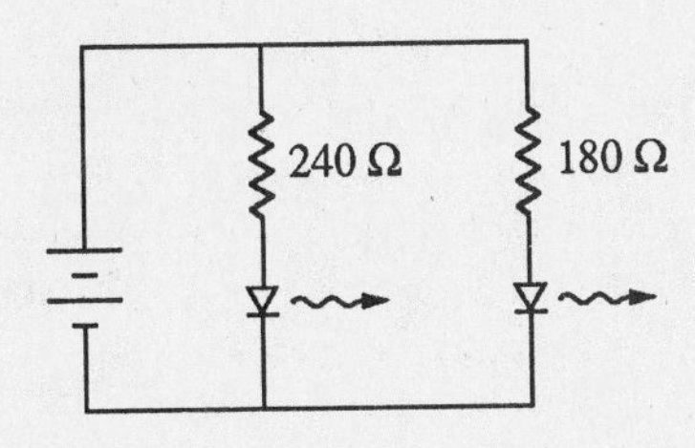

13. A silicon diode whose I/V characteristics are shown in Figure 29–12 is connected to a battery through a 270–Ω resistor. The battery forward–biases the diode and its voltage is adjusted until the diode current is 15 mA. What is the battery voltage?

The diode voltage drop is 0.7 V. The voltage drop across the resistor is $(270\ \Omega)(1.5 \times 10^{-2}\ \text{A}) = 4.1$ V. Thus the battery voltage is 4.8 V.

14. What bulbs are lighted in the circuit of Figure 29–18 when

Chapter Review Problems

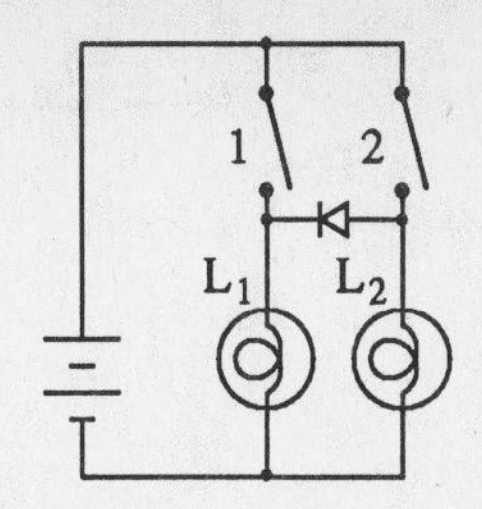

a. switch 1 is closed and switch 2 is open?

Light 1 only.

b. switch 2 is closed and switch 1 is open?

Both lights 1 and 2.

Supplemental Problems (Appendix B)

1. An LED, light–emitting diode, produces infrared radiation, wavelength 800 nm, when an electron jumps from the conduction band to the valence band. Find the energy width of the forbidden gap in this diode.

$$E = \frac{hc}{\lambda} = \frac{(6.627 \times 10^{-34}\ \text{J/Hz})(3.00 \times 10^{8}\ \text{m/s})}{800 \times 10^{-9}\ \text{m}}$$

$$= 2.49 \times 10^{-19}\ \text{J}$$

$$2.49 \times 10^{-19}\ \text{J}\left[\frac{1\ \text{eV}}{1.60 \times 10^{-19}\ \text{J}}\right] = 1.55\ \text{eV}$$

2. How many free electrons exist in 1.00 cm³ of lithium? Its density is 0.534 g/cm³, atomic weight is 6.941 g/mole, and there is one free electron per atom.

$$\left[\frac{1\ \text{free e}^-}{1\ \text{atom}}\right]\left[\frac{6.02 \times 10^{23}\ \text{atom}}{1\ \text{mole}}\right]\left[\frac{1\ \text{mole Li}}{6.941\ \text{g}}\right] \cdot \left[\frac{0.534\ \text{g}}{1\ \text{cm}^3}\right]$$

$$= 4.63 \times 10^{22}\ \text{e}^-/\text{cm}^3$$

3. The voltage drop across a diode is 0.70 V when it is connected in series to a 210–Ω resistor and a battery, and there is a 11 mA current. If the LED has an equivalent resistance of 70 Ω, what potential difference must be supplied by the battery?

$R = R_r + R_D = 210\ \Omega + 70\ \Omega = 280\ \Omega$, and
$V = IR = (11 \times 10^{-3}\ \text{A})(280\ \Omega) = 3.1$ V

Supplemental Problems

4. What resistor would replace the 210-Ω resistor in the previous problem if the current were changed to 30 mA?

   $V = IR$, so $R = \frac{V}{I} = \frac{3.1\ \text{V}}{30 \times 10^{-3}\ \text{A}} = 103\ \Omega$

   $R = R_r + R_D$, so

   $R_r = R - R_D = 103\ \Omega - 70\ \Omega = 33\ \Omega$

5. What would the new current in the previous problem be if the leads on the battery were reversed?

   Zero. The diode would stop the current.

Chapter 30: The Nucleus

Practice Problems

page 618

1. An isotope of oxygen has a mass number of 15. The atomic number of oxygen is 8. How many neutrons are in the nuclei of this isotope?

   $A - Z = 15 - 8 = 7$ neutrons

2. Three isotopes of uranium have mass numbers of 234, 235, and 238 respectively. The atomic number of uranium is 92. How many neutrons are in the nuclei of each of these isotopes?

   $A - Z =$ *neutrons*
   $234 - 92 = 142$ neutrons
   $235 - 92 = 143$ neutrons
   $238 - 92 = 146$ neutrons

3. How many neutrons are in an atom of the mercury isotope $^{200}_{80}Hg$?

   $A - Z = 200 - 80 = 120$ neutrons

4. Write the symbols for the three isotopes of hydrogen in Figure 30–2 with 0, 1, and 2 neutrons in the nucleus.

   $^{1}_{1}H$, $^{2}_{1}H$, $^{3}_{1}H$

page 621

5. Write the nuclear equation for the transmutation of a radioactive uranium isotope, $^{234}_{92}U$, into a thorium isotope, $^{230}_{90}Th$, by the emission of an α particle.

   $^{234}_{92}U \rightarrow {}^{230}_{90}Th + {}^{4}_{2}He$

6. Write the nuclear equation for the transmutation of a radioactive thorium isotope, $^{230}_{90}Th$, into a radioactive radium isotope, $^{226}_{88}Ra$, by the emission of an α particle.

   $^{230}_{90}Th \rightarrow {}^{226}_{88}Ra + {}^{4}_{2}He$

Practice Problems

7. Write the nuclear equation for the transmutation of radioactive radium isotope, $^{226}_{88}Ra$, into a radon isotope, $^{222}_{86}Rn$, by the emission of an α particle.

   $^{226}_{88}Ra \rightarrow {}^{222}_{86}Rn + {}^{4}_{2}He$

8. A radioactive lead isotope, $^{214}_{82}Pb$, can change to a radioactive bismuth isotope, $^{214}_{83}Bi$, by the emission of a β particle and an antineutrino. Write the nuclear equation.

   $^{214}_{82}Pb \rightarrow {}^{214}_{83}Bi + {}^{0}_{-1}e + {}^{0}_{0}\bar{\nu}$

page 622

9. A sample of 1.0 g of tritium, $^{3}_{1}H$, is produced. What will be the mass of tritium remaining after 24.6 years?

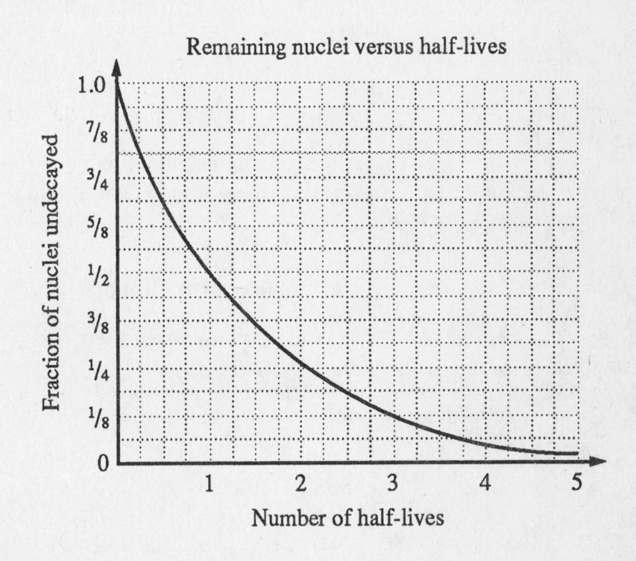

Practice Problems

TABLE 30–1

Half-Life of Selected Isotopes			
Element	Isotope	Half-Life	Radiation Produced
hydrogen	$^{3}_{1}H$	12.3 years	β
carbon	$^{14}_{6}C$	5730 years	β
iodine	$^{131}_{53}I$	80.7 days	β, γ
lead	$^{212}_{82}Pb$	10.6 hours	β, γ
polonium	$^{194}_{94}Po$	0.7 second	α
polonium	$^{210}_{84}Po$	138 days	α
uranium	$^{227}_{92}U$	1.1 minutes	α
uranium	$^{235}_{92}U$	7.1×10^8 years	α, γ
uranium	$^{238}_{92}U$	4.51×10^9 years	α, γ
plutonium	$^{236}_{94}Pu$	2.85 years	α, γ
plutonium	$^{242}_{94}Pu$	3.79×10^5 years	α

24.6 years = 2(12.3 years) which is 2 half–lives. Since $\frac{1}{2} \times \frac{1}{2} = \frac{1}{4}$ there will be

$$(1.0 \text{ g})\left[\frac{1}{4}\right] = 0.25 \text{ g remaining}$$

10. The isotope $^{238}_{93}Np$ has a half–life of 2.0 days. If 4.0 g are produced on Monday, what will be the mass of the neptunium remaining on Tuesday of the next week?

Amount remaining = (original amount)$\left[\frac{1}{2}\right]^N$ where N is the number of half–lives elapsed. Since N = 8 days/2.0 days = 4, Amount remaining = $(4.0 \text{ g})\left[\frac{1}{2}\right]^4 = 0.25$ g

11. A sample of $^{210}_{84}Po$ is purchased for a physics class on September 1. Its activity is 2×10^6 decays per second. The sample is used in an experiment on June 1. What activity can be expected?

The half–life of $^{210}_{84}Po$ is 138 days.

There are 273 days or about 2 half–lives between September 1 and June 1.
So the activity is

$$= \left[2 \times 10^6 \frac{\text{decays}}{\text{s}}\right]\left[\frac{1}{2}\right]\left[\frac{1}{2}\right] = 5 \times 10^5 \frac{\text{decays}}{\text{s}}$$

Practice Problems

12. Tritium, $^{3}_{1}H$, was once used in some watches to produce a fluorescent glow so the watch could be read in the dark. If the brightness of the glow is proportional to the activity of the tritium, what would be the brightness of the watch, in comparison to its original brightness, when the watch is six years old?

From Table 30–1, 6 years is approximately 0.5 half–life for tritium. Since Figure 30–4 indicates that approximately $\frac{11}{16}$ of the original nuclei remain after 0.5 half–life, the brightness will be about $\frac{11}{16}$ of the original.

page 631

13. The mass of a proton is 1.67×10^{-27} kg.

a. Find the energy equivalent of the proton's mass in joules.

$$E = mc^2$$
$$= (1.67 \times 10^{-27} \text{ kg})(3.00 \times 10^8 \text{ m/s})^2$$
$$= 1.50 \times 10^{-10} \text{J}$$

b. Convert this value to eV.

$$E = \frac{1.50 \times 10^{-10}\text{J}}{1.60 \times 10^{-19}\text{J/eV}}$$
$$= 9.38 \times 10^8 \text{ eV}$$
$$= 938 \text{ MeV}$$

c. Find the smallest total γ ray energy that could result in a proton–antiproton pair.

The pair will be (2)(938 MeV) = 1.88 GeV

Chapter Review Problems

pages 636–637

1. An atom of an isotope of magnesium has an atomic mass of about 24 u. The atomic number of magnesium is 12. How many neutrons are in the nucleus of this atom?

12 neutrons $^{24}_{12}Mg$

Chapter Review Problems

2. An atom of an isotope of nitrogen has an atomic mass of about 15 u. The atomic number of nitrogen is 7. How many neutrons are in the nucleus of this isotope?

8 neutrons $^{15}_{7}N$

3. List the number of neutrons in an atom of each of these isotopes.

a. $^{112}_{48}Cd$ 112 − 48 = 64

b. $^{209}_{83}Bi$ 209 − 83 = 126

c. $^{208}_{83}Bi$ 208 − 83 = 125

d. $^{80}_{35}Br$ 80 − 35 = 45

e. $^{1}_{1}H$ 1 − 1 = 0

f. $^{40}_{18}Ar$ 40 − 18 = 22

4. Find the symbol for the elements that are shown by the following symbols, where X replaces the symbol for the element.

a. $^{18}_{9}X$ F

b. $^{241}_{95}X$ Am

c. $^{21}_{10}X$ Ne

d. $^{7}_{3}X$ Li

5. A radioactive bismuth isotope, $^{214}_{83}Bi$, emits a β particle. Write the complete nuclear equation and show the element formed.

$^{214}_{83}Bi \rightarrow ^{214}_{84}Po + ^{0}_{-1}e$

6. A radioactive polonium isotope, $^{210}_{84}Po$, emits an α particle. Write the complete nuclear equation and show the element formed.

$^{210}_{84}Po \rightarrow ^{206}_{82}Pb + ^{4}_{2}He$

7. An unstable chronium isotope, $^{56}_{24}Cr$, emits a β particle. Write a complete equation and show the element formed.

$^{56}_{24}Cr \rightarrow ^{56}_{25}Mn + ^{0}_{-1}e$

8. During a reaction, two deuterons, $^{2}_{1}H$, combine to from a helium isotope, $^{3}_{2}He$. What other particle is produced?

$^{2}_{1}H + ^{2}_{1}H \rightarrow ^{3}_{2}He + ^{1}_{0}n$

9. One the sun, the nuclei of four ordinary hydrogen atoms combine to form a helium isotope, $^{4}_{2}He$. What type of particle is missing from the following equation for this reaction?

$$4^{1}_{1}H \rightarrow ^{4}_{2}He + 2?$$

$4^{1}_{1}H \rightarrow ^{4}_{2}He + 2^{0}_{1}e$

10. Write a complete nuclear equation for the transmutation of a uranium isotope, $^{227}_{92}U$, into a thorium isotope, $^{223}_{90}Th$.

$^{227}_{92}U \rightarrow ^{223}_{90}Th + ^{4}_{2}He$

11. $^{238}_{92}U$ decays by α emission and two successive β emissions back into uranium again. Show the three nuclear decay equations and predict the atomic mass number of the uranium formed.

$^{238}_{92}U \rightarrow ^{234}_{90}Th + ^{4}_{2}He$

$^{234}_{90}Th \rightarrow ^{234}_{91}Pa + ^{0}_{-1}e$

$^{234}_{91}Pa \rightarrow ^{234}_{92}U + ^{0}_{-1}e$

$A = 234$

12. In an accident in a research laboratory, a radioactive isotope with a half-life of three days is spilled. As a result, the radiation is eight times the maximum permissible amount. How long must workers wait before they can enter the room?

For the activity to fall $\frac{1}{8}$ its present amount you must wait three half-lives, or 9 days.

13. If the half-life of an isotope is two years, what fraction of the isotope remains after six years?

$$\left[\frac{1}{2}\right]^3 = \frac{1}{8}$$

14. The half-life of strontium-90 is 28 years. After 280 years, how would the intensity of a sample of strontium-90 compare to the original intensity of the sample?

280 years is 10 half-lives. $\left[\frac{1}{2}\right]^{10}$ is equal to 9.8×10^{-4} or approximately 0.098%.

15. A Geiger counter registers an initial reading of 3200 counts for a radioactive substance and 100 counts 30 hours later. What is the half-life of this substance?

3200 counts to 100 counts represents 5 half-lives.

$$\frac{30\ \text{h}}{5} = 6\ \text{h}$$

16. A 14-g sample of ${}^{14}_{6}\text{C}$ contains Avogadro's number, 6.02×10^{23}, nuclei. A 5.0-g sample of ${}^{14}_{6}\text{C}$ will have how many nondecayed nuclei after 11 460 years?

$$\frac{(6.02 \times 10^{23}\ \text{nuclei})}{14\ \text{g}} = \frac{N}{5.0\ \text{g}}$$

$$N = \frac{(6.02 \times 10^{23}\ \text{nuclei})(5\ \text{g})}{14\ \text{g}}$$

$$= 2.1 \times 10^{23}\ \text{nuclei}$$

After 2 half-lives only $\frac{1}{4}$ of the nuclei are nondecayed.

$$\left[\frac{1}{4}\right](2.1 \times 10^{23}\ \text{nuclei}) = 5.4 \times 10^{22}\ \text{nuclei}$$

Chapter Review Problems

17. A 1.00 μg sample of radioactive material contains 6.0×10^{14} nuclei. After 48 hours 0.25 μg of the material remains.

a. What is the half-life of the material?

48 h is two half-lives, therefore 24 h is one half-life.

b. How could one determine the activity of the sample at 24 hours using this information?

Determine the slope (at 24 hours) of the line of a graph of remaining nuclei versus time.

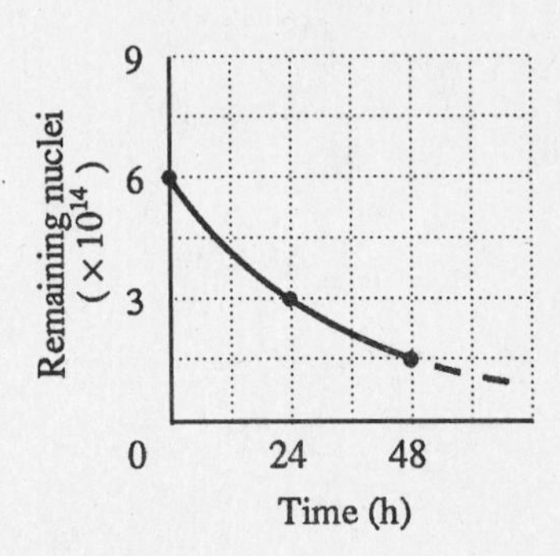

The slope is 9×10^{12} nuclei/hour.

18. The synchrotron at FermiLab has a diameter of 2.0 km. Protons circling in it move at approximately the speed of light.

a. How long does it take a proton to complete one revolution?

$v = \frac{d}{t}$, so

$$t = \frac{d}{v} = \frac{\pi(2.0 \times 10^3\ \text{m})}{(3.0 \times 10^8\ \text{m/s})} = 2.1 \times 10^{-5}\ \text{s}$$

b. The protons enter the ring at an energy of 8.0 GeV. They gain 2.5 MeV each revolution. How many revolutions must they travel before they reach 400 GeV energy?

$$\frac{(400 \times 10^9\ \text{eV}) - (8.0 \times 10^9\ \text{eV})}{2.5 \times 10^6\ \text{eV/revolution}}$$

$= 1.6 \times 10^5$ revolutions

Chapter Review Problems

c. How long does it take the protons to be accelerated to 400 GeV?

$t = (1.6 \times 10^5 \text{ rev})(2.1 \times 10^{-5} \text{ s/rev})$
$= 3.4 \text{ s}$

d. How far do the protons travel during this acceleration?

$d = vt = (3.0 \times 10^8 \text{ m/s})(3.4 \text{ s})$
$= 1.0 \times 10^9$ m, or about 1 million km

19. What would be the charge of a particle composed of three *u* quarks?

Each u quark has a charge of $+\frac{2}{3}$.

$\text{uuu} = 3\left[+\frac{2}{3}\right] = +2$ elementary charges

20. The charge of an antiquark is opposite that of a quark. A pion is composed of a *u* quark and an *anti–d* quark. What would be the charge of this pion?

$\text{u} + \bar{\text{d}} = +\frac{2}{3} + \left[-\left[-\frac{1}{3}\right]\right] = +1$ elementary charge

21. Find the charges of the following pions made of

a. *u* and *anti–u* quark pair.

$\text{u} + \bar{\text{u}} = +\frac{2}{3} + \left[-\left[+\frac{2}{3}\right]\right] = 0$ charge

b. *d* and *anti–u* quarks.

$\text{d} + \bar{\text{u}} = -\frac{1}{3} + \left[-\left[+\frac{2}{3}\right]\right] = -1$ charge

c. *d* and *anti–d* quarks.

$\text{d} + \bar{\text{d}} = -\frac{1}{3} + \left[-\left[-\frac{1}{3}\right]\right] = 0$ charge

Supplemental Problems

1. What particles, and how many of each, make up an atom of ${}^{109}_{47}\text{Ag}$?

47 electrons, 47 protons, 62 neutrons

Supplemental Problems

30

2. A calcium ion has 20 protons and 20 neutrons. Write its isotopic symbol.

${}^{40}_{20}\text{Ca}$

3. What is the isotopic symbol of a zinc atom composed of 30 protons and 34 neutrons?

${}^{64}_{30}\text{Zn}$

4. Write the complete nuclear equation for the alpha decay of ${}^{210}_{84}\text{Po}$.

${}^{210}_{84}\text{Bi} \rightarrow {}^{4}_{2}\text{He} + {}^{206}_{82}\text{Pb}$

5. Write the complete nuclear equation for the beta decay of ${}^{14}_{6}\text{C}$.

${}^{14}_{6}\text{C} \rightarrow {}^{0}_{-1}e + {}^{14}_{7}\text{N} + {}^{0}_{0}\bar{\upsilon}$

6. Complete the nuclear reaction:

${}^{225}_{89}\text{Ac} \rightarrow {}^{4}_{2}\text{He} +$ ______.

${}^{225}_{89}\text{Ac} \rightarrow {}^{4}_{2}\text{He} + {}^{221}_{87}\text{Fr}$

7. Complete the nuclear reaction:

${}^{227}_{88}\text{Ra} \rightarrow {}^{0}_{-1}e +$ ______ + ______.

${}^{227}_{88}\text{Ra} \rightarrow {}^{0}_{-1}e + {}^{227}_{89}\text{Ac} + {}^{0}_{0}\bar{\upsilon}$

8. Complete the nuclear reaction:

${}^{65}_{29}\text{Cu} + {}^{1}_{0}n \rightarrow$ ____ $\rightarrow {}^{1}_{1}p +$ ____.

${}^{65}_{29}\text{Cu} + {}^{1}_{0}n \rightarrow {}^{66}_{29}\text{Cu} \rightarrow {}^{1}_{1}p + {}^{65}_{28}\text{Ni}$

9. Complete the nuclear equation:

${}^{235}_{92}\text{U} + {}^{1}_{0}n \rightarrow {}^{96}_{40}\text{Zr} + 3({}^{1}_{0}n) +$ ______.

${}^{235}_{92}\text{U} + {}^{1}_{0}n \rightarrow {}^{96}_{40}\text{Zr} + 3({}^{1}_{0}n) + {}^{137}_{52}\text{Te}$

10. An isotope has a half-life of 3.0 days. What percent of the original material will be left after

a. 6.0 days?

$\frac{6.0 \text{ dy}}{3.0 \text{ dy}} = 2$ half-lives, so $\left[\frac{1}{2}\right]^2 = \frac{1}{4}$, so 25% is left.

b. 9.0 days?

$\frac{9.0 \text{ dy}}{3.0 \text{ dy}} = 3$ half-lives, so $\left[\frac{1}{2}\right]^3 = \frac{1}{8}$, so 12.5% is left.

c. 12 days?

$\frac{12 \text{ dy}}{3.0 \text{ dy}} = 4$ half-lives, so $\left[\frac{1}{2}\right]^4 = \frac{1}{16}$, so 6.3% is left.

11. $^{211}_{86}Rn$ has a half-life of 15 h. What fraction of a sample would be left after 60 h?

$\frac{60 \text{ h}}{15 \text{ h}} = 4$ half-lives, so $\left[\frac{1}{2}\right]^4 = \frac{1}{16}$ is left.

12. $^{209}_{84}Po$ has a half-life of 103 years. How long would it take for a 100 g sample to decay so only 3.1 g of Po-209 was left?

$\frac{100 \text{ g}}{3.1 \text{ g}} = 32 = 2^5$, so 5 half-lives or 515 years.

13. The positron, $^{0}_{+1}e$, is the antiparticle to the electron and is the particle ejected from the nucleus in some nuclear reactions. Complete the nuclear reaction:
$^{17}_{9}F \rightarrow {}^{0}_{+1}e +$ _____ + _____.

$^{17}_{9}F \rightarrow {}^{0}_{+1}e + {}^{17}_{8}O + {}^{0}_{0}\upsilon$

14. Complete the nuclear reaction:

$^{22}_{11}Na \rightarrow {}^{0}_{+1}e +$

$^{22}_{11}Na \rightarrow {}^{0}_{+1}e + {}^{22}_{10}Ne + {}^{0}_{0}\upsilon$

15. Find the charge of a π+ meason made of a *u* and *anti–d* quark pair.

$u + \bar{d} = +\frac{2}{3} + -\left[-\frac{1}{3}\right] = +1$

16. Baryons are particles that are made of three quarks. Find the charge on each of the following baryons.

a. Neutron; *d*, *d*, *u* quark triplet.

$d + d + u = \left[-\frac{1}{3}\right] + \left[-\frac{1}{3}\right] + \left[\frac{2}{3}\right] = 0$

b. Antiproton; *anti–u*, *anti–u*, *anti–d* quark triplet.

$\bar{u} + \bar{u} + \bar{d} = -\left[\frac{2}{3}\right] + -\left[\frac{2}{3}\right] + -\left[-\frac{1}{3}\right] = -1$

Chapter 31: Nuclear Applications

Practice Problems

page 642

1. The carbon isotope, $^{12}_{6}C$, has a nuclear mass of 12.0000 u.

a. Calculate its mass defect.

$$\begin{array}{rrl} 6 \text{ protons} = (6)(1.007825 \text{ u}) = & 6.046950 & \text{u} \\ 6 \text{ neutrons} = (6)(1.008665 \text{ u}) = & \underline{6.051990} & \text{u} \\ \text{total} & 12.098940 & \text{u} \\ \text{mass of carbon nucleus} & -\underline{12.000000} & \text{u} \\ \text{mass defect} & -0.098940 & \text{u} \end{array}$$

b. Calculate its binding energy in MeV.

$-(0.098940 \text{ u})(931.49 \text{ MeV/u})$
$= -92.162 \text{ MeV}$

2. The isotope of hydrogen that contains 1 proton and 1 neutron is called deuterium. The mass of its nucleus is 2.0140 u.

a. What is its mass defect?

$$\begin{array}{rrl} 1 \text{ proton} = & 1.007825 & \text{u} \\ 1 \text{ neutron} = & \underline{1.008665} & \text{u} \\ & 2.016490 & \text{u} \\ \text{mass of deuterium nucleus} = & -\underline{2.0140} & \text{u} \\ \text{mass defect} & -0.0025 & \text{u} \end{array}$$

b. What is the binding energy of deuterium in MeV?

$-(0.0025 \text{ u})(931.49 \text{ MeV/u}) = -2.3 \text{ MeV}$

3. A nitrogen isotope, $^{15}_{7}N$, has 7 protons and 8 neutrons. Its nucleus has a mass of 15.00011 u.

a. Calculate the mass defect of this nucleus.

$$\begin{array}{rrl} 7 \text{ protons} = 7(1.007825 \text{ u}) = & 7.054775 & \text{u} \\ 8 \text{ neutrons} = 8(1.008665 \text{ u}) = & \underline{8.069320} & \text{u} \\ \text{total} & 15.124095 & \text{u} \\ \text{mass of nitrogen nucleus} & -\underline{15.00011} & \text{u} \\ \text{mass defect} & -0.123985 & \text{u} \\ = & -0.12399 & \text{u} \end{array}$$

Practice Problems

b. Calculate the binding energy of the nucleus.

$-(0.12399 \text{ u})(931.49 \text{ MeV/u}) = -115.50 \text{ MeV}$

4. An oxygen isotope, $^{16}_{8}O$, has a nuclear mass of 15.99491 u.

a. What is the mass defect of this isotope?

$$\begin{array}{rrl} 8 \text{ protons} = (8)(1.007825 \text{ u}) = & 8.062600 & \text{u} \\ 8 \text{ neutrons} = (8)(1.008665 \text{ u}) = & \underline{8.069320} & \text{u} \\ \text{total} & 16.131920 & \text{u} \\ \text{mass of oxygen nucleus} & -\underline{15.99491} & \text{u} \\ \text{mass defect} & -0.13701 & \text{u} \end{array}$$

b. What is the binding energy of its nucleus?

$-(0.13701 \text{ u})(931.49 \text{ MeV/u}) = -127.62 \text{ MeV}$

page 645

5. Use Table C–5 of the Appendix to complete the following nuclear equations.

a. $^{14}_{6}C \rightarrow ? + ^{0}_{-1}e$

$^{14}_{6}C \rightarrow ^{14}_{7}N + ^{0}_{-1}e$

b. $^{55}_{24}Cr \rightarrow ? + ^{0}_{-1}e$

$^{55}_{24}Cr \rightarrow ^{55}_{25}Mn + ^{0}_{-1}e$

6. Write the nuclear equation for the transmutation of a uranium isotope, $^{238}_{92}U$, into a thorium isotope, $^{234}_{90}Th$, by emission of an alpha particle.

$^{238}_{92}U \rightarrow ^{234}_{90}Th + ^{4}_{2}He$

7. A radioactive polonium isotope, $^{214}_{84}Po$, undergoes alpha decay and becomes lead. Write the nuclear equation.

$^{214}_{84}Po \rightarrow ^{210}_{82}Pb + ^{4}_{2}He$

Practice Problems

8. Write the nuclear equations for the beta decay of these isotopes.

a. $^{210}_{82}Pb$

$^{210}_{82}Pb \rightarrow ^{210}_{83}Bi + ^{0}_{-1}e$

b. $^{210}_{83}Bi$

$^{210}_{83}Bi \rightarrow ^{210}_{84}Po + ^{0}_{-1}e$

c. $^{234}_{90}Th$

$^{234}_{90}Th \rightarrow ^{234}_{91}Pa + ^{0}_{-1}e$

d. $^{239}_{93}Np$

$^{239}_{93}Np \rightarrow ^{239}_{94}Pu + ^{0}_{-1}e$

page 652

9. a. Calculate the mass defect for the deuterium–tritium fusion reaction used in the Tokamak, $^{2}_{1}H + ^{3}_{1}H \rightarrow ^{4}_{2}He + ^{1}_{0}n$.

Input masses 2.014102 u + 3.016049 u
= 5.030151 u.
Output masses 4.002603 u + 1.008665 u
= 5.011268 u.
Difference is –0.018883 u

b. Find the energy equivalent of the mass defect.

–(0.018883 u)(931.49 MeV/u)
= –17.589 MeV

10. Calculate the energy released for the overall reaction in the sun where four protons produce one $^{4}_{2}He$, two positrons, and two neutrinos.

Practice Problems

Positron mass

$= (9.109 \times 10^{-31}\ kg)\left[\frac{1u}{1.661 \times 10^{-27}\ kg}\right]$

= 0.000548 u

Input mass: 4 protons = 4(1.007825 u)
= 4.031300 u

Output mass:

$^{4}_{2}He$ + 2 positrons = 4.002603 u + 2(0.000548 u)
= 4.003699

Mass difference = 0.027601 u

Energy released = (0.027601 u)(931.49 MeV/u)
= 25.710 MeV

Chapter Review Problems

pages 654–655

1. A carbon isotope, $^{13}_{6}C$, has a nuclear mass of 13.00335 u.

a. What is the mass defect of this isotope?

6 protons = (6)(1.007825 u) = 6.046950 u
7 neutrons = (7)(1.008665 u) = 7.060655 u

total 13.107605 u
mass of carbon nucleus – 13.00335 u

mass defect –0.10426 u

b. What is the binding energy of its nucleus?

–(0.10426 u)(931 MeV/u) = –97.1 MeV

2. A nitrogen isotope, $^{14}_{7}N$, has a nuclear mass of approximately 14.00307 u.

a. What is the mass defect of the nucleus?

7 protons = (7)(1.007825 u) = 7.054775 u
7 neutrons = (7)(1.008665 u) = 7.060655 u

total 14.11543 u
mass of nitrogen nucleus – 14.00307 u

mass defect –0.11236 u

b. What is the binding energy of this nucleus?

$-(0.11236\ u)(931\ MeV/u) = -105\ MeV$

c. What is the binding energy per nucleon?

$$Energy = \frac{-105\ MeV}{14\ nucleons}$$

$$= -7.5\ MeV/nucleon$$

3. A nitrogen isotope, $^{12}_{7}N$, has a nuclear mass of 12.0188 u.

a. What is the binding energy per nucleon?

7 protons	= (7)(1.007825 u) =	7.054775 u
5 neutrons	= (5)(1.008665 u) =	5.043325 u
	total	12.098100 u
	mass of nitrogen–12 nucleus	– 12.0188 u
	mass defect	–0.0793 u

binding energy
$-(0.0793\ u)(931\ MeV/u) = -73.8\ MeV$

$$\text{binding energy per nucleon} = \frac{-73.8\ MeV}{12\ nucleons}$$

$$= -6.15\ MeV$$

b. Does it require more energy to separate a nucleon from a $^{14}_{7}N$ nucleus or from a $^{12}_{7}N$ nucleus? Refer to the previous problem.

It requires more energy to remove a nucleon from nitrogen – 14, 7.5 MeV.

4. The two positively–charged protons in a helium nucleus are separated by about 2.0×10^{-15} m. Use Coulomb's law to find the electric force of repulsion between the two protons. The result will give you an indication of the strength of the strong nuclear force.

$$F = K\frac{qq'}{d^2}$$

$$= \frac{K(1.6 \times 10^{-19}\ C)(1.6 \times 10^{-19}\ C)}{(2.0 \times 10^{-15}\ m)^2}$$

$$= 58\ N$$

Chapter Review Problems

5. A $^{232}_{92}U$ nucleus, mass = 232.0372 u, decays to $^{228}_{90}Th$, mass = 228.0287 u, by emitting an α particle, mass = 4.0026 u, with a kinetic energy of 5.3 MeV. What must be the kinetic energy of the recoiling thorium nucleus?

mass defect
= (232.0372 u) – (228.0287 u + 4.0026 u)
= 0.0059 u

total *KE* = (0.0059 u)(931 MeV/u)
= 5.5 MeV

KE for thorium nucleus
= (5.5 MeV) – (5.3 MeV)
= 0.2 MeV

6. The binding energy for $^{4}_{2}He$ is 28.3 MeV. Calculate the mass of a helium nucleus in atomic mass units.

$$\text{Mass defect } \frac{28.3\ MeV}{931\ MeV/u} = 0.0304\ u$$

2 protons	= (2)(1.007825 u) =	2.015650 u
2 neutrons	= (2)(1.008665 u) =	2.017330 u
	mass	4.032980 u
	minus mass defect	– 0.0304 u
		4.0026 u

7. The radioactive nucleus indicated in each equation disintegrates by emitting a positron. Complete each nuclear equation.

a. $^{21}_{11}Na \rightarrow ? + ^{0}_{+1}e + ?$

$^{21}_{11}Na \rightarrow ^{21}_{10}Ne + ^{0}_{+1}e + ^{0}_{0}\upsilon$

b. $^{49}_{24}Cr \rightarrow ? + ^{0}_{+1}e + ?$

$^{49}_{24}Cr \rightarrow ^{49}_{23}V + ^{0}_{+1}e + ^{0}_{0}\upsilon$

8. Complete the nuclear equations for these transmutations.

a. $^{30}_{15}P \rightarrow ? + ^{0}_{+1}e + ?$

$^{30}_{15}P \rightarrow ^{30}_{14}Si + ^{0}_{+1}e + ^{0}_{0}\upsilon$

Chapter Review Problems

b. ${}^{205}_{82}Pb \rightarrow\ ?\ + {}^{0}_{+1}e + ?$

${}^{205}_{82}Pb \rightarrow {}^{205}_{81}Tl + {}^{0}_{+1}e + {}^{0}_{0}\upsilon$

9. A mercury isotope, ${}^{200}_{80}Hg$, is bombarded the deuterons, ${}^{2}_{1}H$. The mercury nucleus absorbs the dueteron and then emits an alpha particle.

a. What element is formed by this reaction?

Gold.

b. Write the nuclear equation for the reaction.

${}^{200}_{80}Hg + {}^{2}_{1}H \rightarrow {}^{198}_{79}Au + {}^{4}_{2}He$

10. When bombarded by protons, a lithium isotope, ${}^{7}_{3}Li$, absorbs a proton and then ejects two alpha particles. Write the nuclear equation for this reaction.

${}^{7}_{3}Li + {}^{1}_{1}H \rightarrow 2{}^{4}_{2}He$

11. Each of the nuclei given below can abosorb an alpha particle. Assume that no secondary particles are emitted by the nucleus. Complete each equation.

a. ${}^{14}_{7}N + {}^{4}_{2}He \rightarrow\ ?$

${}^{14}_{7}N + {}^{4}_{2}He \rightarrow {}^{18}_{9}F$

b. ${}^{27}_{13}Al + {}^{4}_{2}He \rightarrow\ ?$

${}^{27}_{13}Al + {}^{4}_{2}He \rightarrow {}^{31}_{15}P$

12. In each of these reactions, a neutron is absorbed by a nucleus. The nucleus then emits a proton. Complete the equations.

a. ${}^{65}_{29}Cu + {}^{1}_{0}n \rightarrow\ ?\ + {}^{1}_{1}H$

${}^{65}_{29}Cu + {}^{1}_{0}n \rightarrow {}^{65}_{28}Ni + {}^{1}_{1}H$

b. ${}^{14}_{7}N + {}^{1}_{0}n \rightarrow\ ?\ + {}^{1}_{1}H$

${}^{14}_{7}N + {}^{1}_{0}n \rightarrow {}^{14}_{6}C + {}^{1}_{1}H$

13. When a boron isotope, ${}^{10}_{5}B$, is bombarded with neutrons, it absorbs a neutron and then emits an alpha particle.

a. What element is also formed?

Lithium.

b. Write the nuclear equation for this reaction.

${}^{10}_{5}B + {}^{1}_{0}n \rightarrow {}^{7}_{3}Li + {}^{4}_{2}He$

14. When a boron isotope, ${}^{11}_{5}B$, is bombarded with protons, it absorbs a proton and emits a neutron.

a. What element is formed?

Carbon.

b. Write the nuclear equation for this reaction.

${}^{11}_{5}B + {}^{1}_{1}p \rightarrow {}^{11}_{6}C + {}^{1}_{0}n$

c. The isotope formed is radioactive, decaying by emitting a positron. Write the complete nuclear equation for this reaction.

${}^{11}_{6}C \rightarrow {}^{11}_{5}B + {}^{0}_{1}e + {}^{0}_{0}\upsilon$

15. The isotope most commonly used in *PET* scanners is ${}^{18}_{9}F$.

a. What element is formed by the positron emission of this element?

Oxygen.

b. Write the equation for this reaction.

${}^{18}_{9}F \rightarrow {}^{18}_{8}O + {}^{0}_{1}e + {}^{0}_{0}\upsilon$

c. The half–life of ${}^{18}_{9}F$ is 110 min. A solution containing 10.0 mg of this isotope is injected into a patient at 8:00 a.m. How much remains at 3:30 p.m.?

The time is about 4 half–lives, so

$\frac{1}{16}(10.0\ mg)$ or 0.63 mg remains.

Chapter Review Problems

16. The basements of many homes contain the rock granite or are built over granite. Granite contains small amounts of radioactive uranium and thorium. Uranium–238 goes through a series of decays before reaching a stable lead isotope. $^{238}_{92}U$ emits an alpha, leaving an isotope that decays by emitting a beta. The next decay is again a β, followed by three α decays. The result is the gas radon that can seep into the basement. Write the equations for these decays.

$^{238}_{92}U \rightarrow ^{234}_{90}Th + ^{4}_{2}He$

$^{234}_{90}Th \rightarrow ^{234}_{91}Pa + ^{0}_{-1}e + ^{0}_{0}\bar{\upsilon}$

$^{234}_{91}Pa \rightarrow ^{234}_{92}U + ^{0}_{-1}e + ^{0}_{0}\bar{\upsilon}$

$^{234}_{92}U \rightarrow ^{230}_{90}Th + ^{4}_{2}He$

$^{230}_{90}Th \rightarrow ^{226}_{88}Ra + ^{4}_{2}He$

$^{226}_{88}Ra \rightarrow ^{222}_{86}Rn + ^{4}_{2}He$

17. The first atomic bomb released an energy equivalent of 20 kilotons of TNT. One kiloton of TNT is the equivalent of 5.0×10^{12} J. What was the mass of the uranium–235 that was fissioned to produce this energy?

$Energy = (20 \text{ kilotons})(5.0 \times 10^{12} \text{ J/kiloton})$
$= 1.0 \times 10^{14}$ J

$$\frac{1.0 \times 10^{14} \text{ J}}{1.6 \times 10^{-19} \text{ J/eV}} = 6.3 \times 10^{32} \text{ eV}$$

$$\frac{(6.3 \times 10^{32} \text{ eV})}{(2.0 \times 10^{2} \text{ MeV/atom})(10^{6} \text{ eV/MeV})}$$

$= 3.1 \times 10^{24}$ atoms

$$\frac{3.1 \times 10^{24} \text{ atoms}}{6.02 \times 10^{23} \text{ atoms/mole}} = 5.2 \text{ moles}$$

$(5.2 \text{ moles})(0.235 \text{ kg/mole}) = 1.2$ kg

18. Complete the following fission reaction.
$^{239}_{94}Pu + ^{1}_{0}n \rightarrow ^{137}_{52}Te + \ ? \ + 3^{1}_{0}n$

$^{239}_{94}Pu + ^{1}_{0}n \rightarrow ^{137}_{52}Te + ^{100}_{42}Mo + 3^{1}_{0}n$

19. Complete the following fission reaction.
$^{235}_{92}U + ^{1}_{0}n \rightarrow ^{92}_{36}Kr + \ ? \ + 3^{1}_{0}n$

$^{235}_{92}U + ^{1}_{0}n \rightarrow ^{92}_{36}Kr + ^{141}_{56}Ba + 3^{1}_{0}n$

20. Plutonium is formed in two steps. First U–238 absorbs a neutron which then becomes unstable U–239. The U–239 emits a beta particle forming a new element and this new element emits a second beta particle forming plutonium. Complete the following reaction.

$^{238}_{92}U + ^{1}_{0}n \rightarrow \left[^{239}_{92}U\right] \rightarrow$

$^{238}_{92}U + ^{1}_{0}n \rightarrow \left[^{239}_{92}U\right] \rightarrow ^{239}_{93}Np + ^{0}_{-1}e + ^{0}_{0}\bar{\upsilon}$

$^{239}_{93}Np \rightarrow ^{239}_{94}Pu + ^{0}_{-1}e + ^{0}_{0}\bar{\upsilon}$

21. Complete each of the following fusion reactions.

a. $^{2}_{1}H + ^{2}_{1}H \rightarrow \ ? \ + ^{1}_{0}n$

b. $^{2}_{1}H + ^{2}_{1}H \rightarrow \ ? \ + ^{1}_{1}H$

c. $^{2}_{1}H + ^{3}_{1}H \rightarrow \ ? \ + ^{1}_{0}n$

$^{2}_{1}H + ^{2}_{1}H \rightarrow ^{3}_{2}He + ^{1}_{0}n$

$^{2}_{1}H + ^{2}_{1}H \rightarrow ^{3}_{1}H + ^{1}_{1}H$

$^{2}_{1}H + ^{3}_{1}H \rightarrow ^{4}_{2}He + ^{1}_{0}n$

22. One fusion reaction is $^{2}_{1}H + ^{2}_{1}H \rightarrow ^{4}_{2}He$.

a. What energy is released in this reaction?

$(2)(2.01410 \text{ u}) - (4.00263 \text{ u}) = 0.02557$ u
$(0.02557 \text{ u})(931 \text{ MeV/u}) = 23.8$ MeV

b. Deuterium exists as a diatomic, two–atom, molecule. One mole of deuterium contains 6.02×10^{23} molecules. Find the amount of energy released, in joules, in the fusion of one mole of deuterium molecules.

$(23.8 \text{ MeV/molecule})$
$\times (6.02 \times 10^{23} \text{ molecules/mole})$
$\times (1.6 \times 10^{-19} \text{ J/eV})(10^{6} \text{ eV/MeV})$
$= 2.29 \times 10^{12}$ J/mole

c. When one mole of deuterium burns, it releases 2.9 × 10^6 J. How many moles of dueterium molecules would have to burn to release just the energy released by the fusion of one mole of deuterium molecules?

$$\frac{2.29 \times 10^{12}\ \text{J}}{2.9 \times 10^{6}\ \text{J/mole}} = 7.9 \times 10^{5}\ \text{moles}$$

23. The energy released in the fission of one atom of $^{235}_{92}U$ is 2.00 × 10^2 MeV. One mole of uranium atoms, 6.02 × 10^{23} atoms, has a mass of 0.235 kg.

a. How many atoms are in 1.00 kg $^{235}_{92}U$?

$$\frac{(6.02 \times 10^{23}\ \text{atoms/mole})(1.00\ \text{kg})}{(0.235\ \text{kg/mole})} = 2.56 \times 10^{24}\ \text{atoms.}$$

b. How much energy would be released if all the atoms in 1.00 kg of $^{235}_{92}U$ underwent fission?

$$(2.56 \times 10^{24}\ \text{atoms/kg})(2.0 \times 10^{2}\ \text{MeV/atom})(1.6 \times 10^{-19}\ \text{J/ev})(10^{6}\ \text{eV/MeV}) = 8.2 \times 10^{13}\ \text{J}$$

c. A typical large nuclear reactor produces fission energy at a rate of 3600 MW. How many kilograms of $^{235}_{92}U$ are used each second?

$$\frac{3.6 \times 10^{9}\ \text{J/s}}{8.2 \times 10^{13}\ \text{J/kg}} = 4.4 \times 10^{-5}\ \text{kg/s}$$

d. How much $^{235}_{92}U$ would be used in one year?

$$(4.4 \times 10^{-5}\ \text{kg/s})(3.15 \times 10^{7}\ \text{s/y}) = 1.4 \times 10^{3}\ \text{kg/y}$$

Supplementary Problems (Appendix B)

1. The carbon isotope, $^{12}_{6}C$, has a nuclear mass of 12.000 000 u.

a. What is the mass defect of this isotope?

$^{12}_{6}C$	$6(^1_1p) = 6(1.007\ 825\ \text{u}) =$	6.046 950 u
	$6(^1_0n) = 6(1.008\ 665\ \text{u}) =$	6.051 990 u
	total mass of nucleus	12.098 940 u
	$^{12}_{6}C$	− 12.000 000 u
	mass defect	− 0.098 940 u

b. What is the binding energy of its nucleus?

$$\begin{aligned} E &= (931.5\ \text{MeV/u})(0.098\ 940\ \text{u}) \\ &= 92.16\ \text{MeV} \end{aligned}$$

2. The sulfur isotope, ${}^{32}_{16}S$, has a nuclear mass of 31.972 07 u.

a. What is the mass defect of this isotope?

$$16({}^{1}_{1}p) = 16(1.007\ 825\ \text{u}) = 16.125\ 20\ \text{u}$$
$$16({}^{1}_{0}n) = 16(1.008\ 665\ \text{u}) = \underline{16.138\ 64}\ \text{u}$$
$$32.263\ 84\ \text{u}$$
$${}^{32}_{16}S = 31.972\ 07\ \text{u}$$
$$\underline{32.263\ 84}$$
$$\text{mass defect} \quad -0.291\ 77\ \text{u}$$

b. What is the binding energy of its nucleus?

$$E = (931.5\ \text{MeV/u})(0.291\ 77\ \text{u}) = 271.8\ \text{MeV}$$

3. The sodium isotope, ${}^{22}_{11}Na$, has a nuclear mass of 21.994 44 u.

a. What is the mass defect of this isotope?

$$11({}^{1}_{1}p) = 11(1.007\ 825\ \text{u}) = 11.086\ 08\ \text{u}$$
$$11({}^{1}_{0}n) = 11(1.008\ 665\ \text{u}) = \underline{11.095\ 32}\ \text{u}$$
$$22.181\ 40\ \text{u}$$
$$-{}^{22}_{11}Na = 21.994\ 44\ \text{u}$$
$$\underline{22.181\ 40}$$
$$\text{mass defect} \quad -0.186\ 96\ \text{u}$$

b. What is the binding energy of its nucleus?

$$E = (931.5\ \text{MeV/u})(0.18696\ \text{u}) = 174.2\ \text{MeV}$$

c. What is the binding energy per nucleon?

$$\frac{174.2\ \text{MeV}}{22\ \text{nucleons}} = 7.916\ \text{MeV/nucleon}$$

4. The binding energy for ${}^{7}_{3}Li$ is 39.25 MeV. Calculate the mass of the lithium-7 nucleus in atomic mass units.

$$3({}^{1}_{1}p) = 3(1.007\ 825\ \text{u}) = 3.023\ 475$$

u

$$3({}^{1}_{0}n) = 4(1.008\ 665\ \text{u}) = \underline{4.034\ 660}$$

u

$$\text{mass defect} = \frac{39.25\ \text{MeV}}{931.5\ \text{MeV/u}} = -\underline{0.042\ 14}\ \text{u}$$
$$7.016\ 00$$

u

5. Write the complete nuclear equation for the positron decay of ${}^{132}_{55}Cs$.

$${}^{132}_{55}Cs \rightarrow {}^{0}_{+1}e + {}^{132}_{54}Xe + {}^{0}_{0}\nu$$

6. Complete the nuclear reaction:
${}^{14}_{7}N + {}^{1}_{0}n \rightarrow\ ?\ {}^{1}_{1}p +\ ?$

$${}^{14}_{7}N + {}^{1}_{0}n \rightarrow {}^{15}_{7}N \rightarrow {}^{1}_{1}p + {}^{14}_{6}C$$

7. Complete the nuclear reaction:
${}^{65}_{29}Cu + {}^{1}_{0}n \rightarrow\ ?\ \rightarrow {}^{1}_{1}p +\ ?$

$${}^{65}_{29}Cu + {}^{1}_{0}n \rightarrow {}^{66}_{29}Cu \rightarrow {}^{1}_{1}p + {}^{65}_{28}Ni$$

8. When a magnesium isotope, ${}^{24}_{12}Mg$, is bombarded with neutrons, it absorbs a neutron and then emits a proton. Write the complete nuclear equation for this reaction.

$${}^{24}_{12}Mg + {}^{1}_{0}n \rightarrow {}^{25}_{12}Mg \rightarrow {}^{1}_{1}p + {}^{24}_{11}Na$$

9. When oxygen-17 is bombarded by neutrons, it absorbs a neutron and then emits an alpha particle. The resulting nucleus is unstable and it will emit a beta particle. Write the complete nuclear equation for this reaction.

$${}^{17}_{8}O + {}^{1}_{0}n \rightarrow {}^{18}_{8}O \rightarrow {}^{4}_{2}He + {}^{14}_{6}C \rightarrow {}^{0}_{-1}e + {}^{14}_{7}N + {}^{0}_{0}\bar{\nu}$$

10. Complete the following fission reaction:
${}^{239}_{94}Pu + {}^{1}_{0}n \rightarrow {}^{137}_{52}Te + 3({}^{1}_{0}n) +\ ?$

$${}^{239}_{94}Pu + {}^{1}_{0}n \rightarrow {}^{137}_{52}Te + 3({}^{1}_{0}n) + {}^{100}_{42}Mo$$

11. Complete the following fission reaction:
$^{233}_{92}U + ^{1}_{0}n \rightarrow ^{134}_{55}Cs + 2(^{1}_{0}n) + ?$

$^{233}_{92}U + ^{1}_{0}n \rightarrow ^{134}_{55}Cs + 2(^{1}_{0}n) + ^{98}_{37}Rb$

12. Complete the following fission reaction:
$^{235}_{92}U + ^{1}_{0}n \rightarrow ^{90}_{38}Sr + 10(^{1}_{0}n) + ?$

$^{235}_{92}U + ^{1}_{0}n \rightarrow ^{90}_{38}Sr + 10(^{1}_{0}n) + ^{136}_{54}Xe$

13. Strontium–90 has a mass of 89.907 747 u, xenon–136 has a mass of 135.907 221 u and uranium–235 has a mass of 235.043 915 u.

a. Compute the mass defect in the previous problem.

Sr–90 = 89.907 747 u
Xe–136 = 135.907 221 u
$10(^{1}_{0}n)$ = 10(1.008 665 u) = 10.086 65 u

= 235.901 62 u
$^{1}_{0}n$ = 1.008 665 u
U–235 = 235.043 915 u

= 236.052 580 u

mass defect = 235.90162 u – 236.05258 u
= – 0.150 96 u

b. Compute the amount of energy released.

E = (931.5 MeV/u)(0.15096 u)
= 140.6 MeV

14. One of the simplest fusion reactions involves the production of deuterium, $^{2}_{1}H$ 2.014 102 u,

from a neutron and a proton. Write the complete fusion reaction and find the amount of energy released.

$^{1}_{1}p + ^{1}_{0}n \rightarrow ^{2}_{1}H$

$1(^{1}_{1}p)$ = 1(1.007 825 u) = 1.007 825
$1(^{1}_{0}n)$ = 1(1.008 665 u) = 1.008 665

2.016 490
$^{2}_{1}H$ = 2.014 102

2.016 490

mass defect = – 0.002 388

E = (931.5 MeV/u)(0.002388 u)
= 2.224 MeV

15. The fusion reactions most likely to succeed in a fusion reactor are listed below. Complete each fusion reaction.

a. $^{2}_{1}H + ^{2}_{1}H \rightarrow ^{3}_{1}H + ?$

$^{2}_{1}H + ^{2}_{1}H \rightarrow ^{3}_{1}H + ^{1}_{1}H$

b. $^{2}_{1}H + ^{2}_{1}H \rightarrow ^{3}_{2}He + ?$

$^{2}_{1}H + ^{2}_{1}H \rightarrow ^{3}_{2}He + ^{1}_{0}n$

c. $^{2}_{1}H + ^{3}_{1}H \rightarrow ^{4}_{2}He + ?$

$^{2}_{1}H + ^{3}_{1}H \rightarrow ^{4}_{2}He + ^{1}_{0}n$

d. $^{3}_{1}H + ^{3}_{1}H \rightarrow ^{4}_{2}He + 2?$

$^{3}_{1}H + ^{3}_{1}H \rightarrow ^{4}_{2}He + 2(^{1}_{0}n)$

PROBLEM CORRELATION, Chapters 2-4

CONCEPTS	CHAPTER REVIEW			PROBLEMS APPENDIX
	Reviewing Concepts	Applying Concepts	Problems	
2.1 The Measure of Science				
The Metric System	1,2,3	1		
Scientific Notation			1	1
Prefixes Used with SI Units	4	2,3,4	2,**3**	2
Arithmetic Operations in Scientific Notation		7	4	3
2.2 Not All Is Certain				
Uncertainties of Measurement				
Accuracy and Precision	5,6	5,6		
Significant Digits	7,8		5,6,7	4,5
Operations Using Significant Digits			8,9,10,11,12,13,14,15	6,7,8
2.3 Displaying Data				
Graphing Data	11,12	11		
Linear, Quadratic, and Inverse Relationships	9,10,13,14,15	8,9,12	**16**,17,**18,19**	**9,10**
2.4 Manipulating Equations				
Solving Equations Using Algebra			21	11,**12**
Units in Equations	16	10	20,22,23,24,**25**, **26**,27,28,**29**	**13**,14,15
3.1 How Far and How Fast?				
Position and Distance	1,2	1,2	1	1
Average Velocity	3,4	3,4	2,3,5,6,7	2,3,**4**
Finding Displacement From Velocity and Time		5	4,9,10,**11,12**	5,6,**7**
Position-Time Graphs			13,14	**8**,9
The Slope of a Position-Time Graph	5,6	6,7,8,9	**15,16**,17,18, 19,**20**	10,11
3.2 New Meanings For Old Words				
Position and Negative Velocities	7			
Instantaneous Velocity	8		21,22	12
Velocity-Time Graphs	9,10,11	10,11	23,24,**25,26,27**	**13,14**
Relativity of Velocity			8	15
4.1 What Is Acceleration?				
Average Acceleration	1,2		1,2	1
Average and Instantaneous Acceleration	3,4,5	1,2,4	3,4,6,**7**	2,**3**
Velocity of an Object With Constant Acceleration		3	5,8,9	4,5
4.2 Displacement During Constant Acceleration				
Displacement When Velocity and Time Are Known			10,11	6,7
Displacement When Acceleration and Time Are Known			12,13,14,21	8,9
Displacement When Velocity and Acceleration Are Known	6,7		16,17,18,19,20,22, 23,24,**25,26**,27,**28**,29	10,11,12,13
Acceleration Due to Gravity	8,9,10	5,6,7,8,9	**15**,30,31,32,**33,34**, 35,36,37	14,**15,16**

PROBLEM CORRELATION, Chapters 5-7

CONCEPTS	CHAPTER REVIEW			PROBLEMS APPENDIX
	Reviewing Concepts	Applying Concepts	Problems	
5.1 Newton's Laws of Motion				
Force	1	1		
Newton's First Law	2,3			
Newton's Second Law		2,3	1,4,5,**6,7,8**	1,2,**3,4**
Newton's Third Law	4	4	9,10	5
5.2 Using Newton's Laws				
Mass and Weight	5,6	5	11,12,13	6,7
Two Kinds of Mass				
Friction	7	6,7,8,9	14,15,**16**	8,9
Net Force and Acceleration	8,9,10		17,18,19,**20,21**,22,23, 24,25,**26,27,28,29**	10,**11,12,13**
Fall of Bodies in Air	11	10,11		
Other Kinematics			2,**3**	
6.1 Graphical Method of Vector Addition				
Vector Addition in One Dimension		1,2,3,4	1,2,3,4	4,**5**
Vector Addition in Two Dimensions	1,2,3,4,6	5	5	6,7
Addition of Several Vectors	5		6,7	
Independence of Vector Quantities				
6.2 Analytical Method of Vector Addition				
Adding Perpendicular Vectors		6	**8,9,10**,11,**13,14,15**,16 17,18,19,**20**	1,2,3,8,9,**10**
Components of Vectors	7	7,8,11	21,22,**23,24**	11,12,13,14,**15**
Adding Vectors at Any Angle			**12**,25,26,27,**28**	16,**17**
6.3 Applications of Vectors				
Equilibrium	8,9,10,11	9,10	29,30,31,32,**33**	**18,19,20,21**
Gravitational Force and Inclined Planes	12	12,13	34,**35,36,37**	
7.1 Projectile Motion				
Independence of Motion in Two Dimensions	1,2	1	**1**	1
Objects Launched Horizontally	3	2,3	2,3,4,**5,6,7**	**2**,3,4,5
Objects Launched at an Angle		4,5	**8,9,10,11,12**	6,7,**8**,9
7.2 Periodic Motion				
Circular Motion	4,5,6,7	6,7	13,14,15,16,17, **18,19,20**	**10,11,12**,13
Changing Circular Motion: Torque	8	8,9		14
Simple Harmonic Motion	9,10,11,12	10,11	21,**22**	15,**16**

PROBLEM CORRELATION, Chapters 8-11

CONCEPTS	CHAPTER REVIEW			PROBLEMS APPENDIX
	Reviewing Concepts	Applying Concepts	Problems	
8.1 Motion in the Heavens and on Earth				
Kepler's Laws of Planetary Motion	1,2,3	1	1,**2,3**,4,**5**	1,2,**3**
Universal Gravitation	4,5	2,3	6,7,8,9,10,11,12, **13**,14,**15,16**	4,5,6,7,8,9,**10**,11
Newton's Use of His Law of Universal Gravitation	**6,7,8**	4,5	17,**18,19**	12
Weighing Earth				
8.2 Using the Law of Universal Gravitation				
Motion of Planets and Satellites	9,10,11	6,7,8	20,**21**	13
Weight and Weightlessness	12,13	9,10,11	22,23,**24,25**	14
Gravitational Field	14	12,13	26,27,28	15,16
Einstein's Theory of Gravity	15			
9.1 Impulse and Change in Momentum				
Momentum and Impulse	1,2,4	1,2,3,4	1,2,3,4,5,6,7,8, 9,**10**,11,**12,13, 14,15**	1,2,3,**4**,5,6
Angular Momentum				
9.2 The Conservation of Momentum				
Newton's Third Law and Momentum	3,5			7
Law of Conservation of Momentum	6,8	6,8,9,10,11	16,17,18,19,20,21, 22,23,24,**25,26**,27 **28,33**	8,9,10,**11**,12,**13**
Internal and External Forces	7,9,10	5,7		
Conservation of Momentum in Two Dimensions			**29,30,31,32**	**14,15**
10.1 Work and Energy				
Work	1,2,3	1,2	**1,2,3,4,5,6,7,**	1,2,3,4
Work and Direction of Force		3,4,5	8,9,10,11,12,13, **14,15,16,**	**5,6**,7,**8**
Power	4,5	6	17,18,19,**20,21**,22, 23,24,**25,26,27,** 28	9,10,**11,12**
10.2 Machines				
Simple and Complex Machines	6			
Energy Conservation and Mechanical Advantage	7	7,8,9	29,30,31,**32**,33,34	13,**14**
Compound Machines			**35,36**	**15**
11.2 Energy In Its Many Forms				
Forms of Energy	1,2,3			
Doing Work to Change Kinetic Energy	4,5,6	1,2,3,4,5,6	1,2,3,4,**5,6**,7, 8,9,10,**11**	1,2,3,4,**5**
Potential Energy	7,8,9,10,11, 12,13	7,8	12,13,14,15,16, 17,18,**19**	6,7,8,9,**10**
11.2 Conservation of Energy				
Systems	14,15,16,	9,10,11,12,13, 15,16	20,21,22,23,**24,25, 26**,27,28	11,12,**13,14**
Analyzing Collisions	17,18,19	14	29,30,**31**,32,33	**15**

PROBLEM CORRELATION, Chapters 12-15

CONCEPTS	CHAPTER REVIEW			PROBLEMS APPENDIX
	Reviewing Concepts	Applying Concepts	Problems	
12.1 Temperature and Thermal Energy				
What Makes a Hot Body Hot?	1			
Thermal Energy Transfer				
Thermal Energy and Temperature	2,3,4	1		
Equilibrium and Thermometry	6			
Temperature Scales: Celsius and Kelvin	5	2	1,2,3	1,2
Heat and Thermal Energy	7,8,9,10	3,4,5	4,5,6,7,8,11	3,4,5,6,7
Calorimetry: Measuring Specific Heat		6	9,10,13,**14**,15	**8,9,10**
12.2 Change of State and Laws of Thermodynamics				
Change of State	11,12	7,8	**16,17,18,19,21,22**	11,**12,13**
The First Law of Thermodynamics	13	9	20,23,24,25	**14,15**
The Second Law of Thermodynamics	14			
13.1 The Fluid State				
Pressure	1	1,2	3,4,5	1,2,3,**4,5**
Fluids at Rest—Hydrostatics	2,3,4	3,4	**1,2**,6,7,8,9,10, 11,12,13,**14**,15	6,7,8,**9,10**
Fluids in Motion—Hydrodynamics	5			
Liquids vs Gases	6			
Surface Tension	7,8	5		
Evaporation and Condensation	9,10,11	6,7		
Plasma	12,13			
13.2 The Solid State				
Solid Bodies	14	8		
Elasticity of Solids	15			
Thermal Expansion of Matter	16	9,10,11,12	16,17,**18,19,20**	11,12,13,**14,15**
14.1 Wave Properties				
Types of Waves	1,2,3,4,5	1		
The Measure of a Wave: Frequency, Wavelength, and Velocity	6,7,8,9	2,3,4	1,2,3,4,5,**6**,7,8, 9,10,**11,12**,13	1,2,3,4,5,**6, 7,8**,9,10
Amplitude of a Wave	10,11,12	5		
14.2 Wave Interference				
Waves at Boundaries Between Media	13,14,15,16	6,7	**14**	
Superposition of Waves	17	8	15	
Standing Waves	18,19,20		16	
Reflection of Waves	21			11
Refraction of Waves				
Diffraction and Interference of Waves	22	9		
15.1 Properties of Sound				
Sound Waves	1,2,3,4	1,2,3	1,2,3,4,5,**6**,7,8, 9,10	1,2,3,4,5,6,**7,8**
The Doppler Shift	5,6	4,5	11,12	**9,10**
Pitch and Loudness		6,7,8	13,14,15	11,12,**14**
15.2 The Sound of Music				
Sources of Sound				
Resonance	7,8,9,10	9	16,17,18	13
Detection of Sound			**19**	
The Quality of Sound	11	10,11	20,21,22,23,**24, 25,26**	15,16,17

PROBLEM CORRELATION, Chapters 16-19

CONCEPTS	CHAPTER REVIEW			PROBLEMS APPENDIX
	Reviewing Concepts	Applying Concepts	Problems	
16.1 Light Fundamentals				
The Facts of Light	1,2,3		1	1
The Speed of Light	4	1	2,3,4,5,6,7	2,3,4,5,6,7,8
Sources of Light	5,6,7,8,9	2,3,4	8,9,10,11,12,13, 14,15	9,10,11
16.2 Light and Matter				
Color	10,11,12,13,14	5,6,7,10,11,13, 14,15		12,13,14,15,16
Formation of Color in Thin Films		8,12,16		
Polarization of Light	15,16	9		
17.1 How Light Behaves at a Boundary				
The Law of Reflection	1,2,3	1,2	1,2	1
Refraction of Light	4,5,6	3,4		
Snell's Law	7,8,9	5,6,7	3,4,5,6,7,8,9,10, 11,12,13,14,15	2,3,4,5,6,7,8,12
Index of Refraction and the Speed of Light		8,9	16,17,18,19	9,10,11
17.2 Applications of Reflected and Refracted Light				
Total Internal Reflection	10,11	10,11,12,13	20,21,22,23,24	13,14,15,16
Effects of Refraction	12	14		
Dispersion of Light	13,14	15,16,17	25,26,27,28	17,18
18.1 Mirrors				
Objects and Their Images in Plane Mirrors	1,2		1,2,3	1
Concave Mirror			4	2
Spherical Aberrations and Parabolic Mirrors	3	2		
Real vs Virtual Images	4,5,6,7			
Real Images Formed by Concave Mirrors	8	3,4,5	5,6,7	3,4,5,6,7,8
Virtual Images Formed by Concave Mirrors	9	1	8,9,10	9
Virtual Images Formed by Convex Mirrors	11	6,7,8,10	11	10,11
18.2 Lenses				
Types of Lenses		9		
Real Images Formed by Convex Lenses	10,12,13	12	12,13,14,15,16	12,13,14,15,16
Virtual Images Formed by Convex Lenses		11		18
Virtual Images Formed by Concave Lenses				
Chromatic Aberration		13		
Optical Instruments			17,18	17
19.1 When Light Waves Interfere				
The Two-Slit Interference Pattern	1			
Measuring the Wavelength of a Light Wave	2,3	1,2	1,2,3,4,5	1,2,3,4,5
Single-Slit Diffraction	5	3,4,5	6,7,8,9	6,7,8,9
19.2 Applications of Diffraction				
Diffraction Gratings	6,7,8,9	7,8,9	10,11,12,13,14	10,11,12,13
Resolving Power of Lenses	4,10	6	15,16,17,18,19	14

PROBLEM CORRELATION, Chapters 20-23

CONCEPTS	CHAPTER REVIEW			PROBLEMS APPENDIX
	Reviewing Concepts	Applying Concepts	Problems	
20.1 Electrical Charges				
Charged Objects				
A Microscopic View of Charging	1,2,5,6	1,2		
Conductors and Insulators	3,4	3,4		
20.2 Electrical Forces				
Forces on Charged Bodies		5,8		
Separation of Charge and Charging by Induction	7,8	6,7,14,15		
Coulomb's Law		9,10,11,12	1	**1,2,3,4**
The Unit of Charge: The Coulomb		13	2,3,4,5,6,7,8,9, 10,11,12,13,**14,** **15,16,17,18,19**	5,6,7,8,9,10, 11,12,**13,14**
Using Electric Forces on Neutral Bodies				
21.1 Creating and Measuring Electric Fields				
The Electric Field	2,3	1	1,2,3,4,**5,6,9**	1,2,3,4,5
Picturing the Electric Field	1,4,5	3	7,8	6
21.2 Uses of the Electric Field				
Energy and the Electric Potential	6,7	2,4	10,11,12,13,**14**	7,8,**9**
The Electric Potential in a Uniform Field	8,9	5	15,16	10,11,12
Millikan's Oil Drop Experiment		6,7	17,**18**	**13**
Sharing of Charge	10,11	8		
Electric Fields Near Conductors	12			
Storing Charges: The Capacitor	13	9,10	19,20,21,**22,23,24**	14,15,16
22.1 Current and Circuits				
Producing Electric Current				
Electric Circuits	1	1		
Rates of Charge Flow and Energy Transfer	2,4		1,2,3,4,5,6,**7**	**1,2,3,4,5**
Resistance and Ohm's Law	3,5,6	2,3,4,5,6,7,8	8,9,10,11,12,13, 14,15,**16**,17,**18**	6,7,8,9,10,11
Diagramming Circuits	7,8	9	**19,20**	
22.2 Using Electrical Energy				
Energy Transfer in Electric Circuits	9,10	10	21,22,23,24,25,**26**	12,13,**14**
Transmission of Electric Power	11			
The Kilowatt Hour			27,**28,29**	15,**16**
23.1 Simple Circuits				
Series Circuits	1	1	1,2,3,4,5,6,7,8,9	1,2,3,**4**
Voltage Drops in a Series Circuit		2	10,11	**5**
Parallel Circuits	2,3,4,6	3,4,5,6,7,8,9	**12**,13,14,15	6,7,**8,9**
23.2 Applications of Circuits				
Safety Devices	5,7,8	10	16	10
Combined Series Parallel Circuits			17,18,19,**20**	11,12
Ammeters and Voltmeters	9,10			13,14,**15**

PROBLEM CORRELATION, Chapters 24-27

CONCEPTS	CHAPTER REVIEW			PROBLEMS APPENDIX
	Reviewing Concepts	Applying Concepts	Problems	
24.1 Magnets: Permanent and Temporary				
General Properties of Magnets	1,2,3,6	1,2		
Magnetic Fields; Permanent Magnets	4,5	3,4	**2**	
Electromagnetism	7		3,4	1,2,3
Magnetic Field Near a Coil	8,9	5	5	4
A Microscopic Picture	10,11	6		
24.2 Forces Caused by Magnetic Fields				
Forces on Currents in Magnetic Fields	12	7,8,9	**6,7**	5
Measuring the Force on a Wire Due to a Magnetic Field	13		**1,8,9,10,11,12** 13,14,15,**16,17**	6,7,8,9,10,**11**
Galvanometers	14	10	18,19	
Electric Motors				
The Force on a Single-Charged Particle		11,12,13	20,21,22,23,**24,25,** 26,27,28,**29**	12,13,14,15,16
25.1 Creating Electric Current From Changing Magnetic Fields				
Faraday's Discovery	1,2	1,8,10,15		1
Electromotive Force	3	2,3,14	1,2,3,4,**5,6,7**,8, 9	2,3,4,5,6,**7**
Electric Generators	4,5,6			
Alternating Current Generator	7,8,9	5,6,7	**10,11,12,13**	8,9,10,11,**12**
25.2 Effects of Changing Magnetic Fields: Induced EMF				
Lenz's Law	10,11,12	4,9,16,17		**13**
Self–Inductance	13,14	18		
Transformers	15	11,12,13	14,15,16,17,18,19, **20,21,22**	14,**15**
26.1 Action of Electric and Magnetic Fields on Matter				
Mass of the Electron	1	1,2,3	1,2,3,4,5	1,2,3,4,5,6,7, 8,9,10,**11**
The Mass Spectrometer	2	4,5,6	**6**,7,8,**9**,10,11,12, 13,**14,15,**	
26.2 Electric and Magnetic Fields in Space				
Electromagnetic Waves	3,5,6			
Production of Electromagnetic Waves	7	7	**16**	12
Reception of Electromagnetic Waves	4,8,9	8,9	**17**,18	13
X Rays				
27.1 Waves Behave Like Particles				
Radiation From Incandescent Bodies	1,2	1,2	**1**	1,2
Photoelectric Effect	3,4,5,6	3,4	2,3,4,5,6,7,8,9, 10,**11,12**	3,4,5,6,7,8
The Compton Effect	7,8,10		13	9,10
27.2 Particles Behave Like Waves				
Matter Waves	9	5,6,7	14,15,16,17,18, **19,20,21**	11,12,**13**
Particles and Waves				

PROBLEM CORRELATION, Chapters 28-31

CONCEPTS	CHAPTER REVIEW			PROBLEMS APPENDIX
	Reviewing Concepts	Applying Concepts	Problems	
28.1 The Bohr Model				
The Nuclear Model	1		1	
Atomic Spectra		1,2		
The Bohr Model of the Atom	2,3	3,4,5	2,3,4,5	1,2,3,**4**
Predictions of the Bohr Model	4,5	6,7	6,7,8,9,10,11,12,13, **14,15,16**,17,**18**	5,6,7,8
28.2 The Present Model of the Atom				
A Quantum Model of the Atom		8		
Lasers	6,7,8	9	**19,20**	
29.1 Conduction in Solids				
Band Theory of Solids	1		1,2	1
Conductors			3,4	2
Insulators		2,3		
Semiconductors	2	1,4		
Doped Semiconductors	3	5,6,7	**5,6**	
29.2 Electronic Devices				
Diodes	4	8,9	**7**,8,9,10,11,12,13,14	3,4,5
Transistors and Integrated Circuits	5,6	10		
30.1 Radioactivity				
Description of the Nucleus	1	3	1,2	
Isotopes		2	3,4	1,2,3
Radioactive Decay	2,3,4,5	1,4,5		
Nuclear Reactions and Equations	6		5,6,7,8,9,10,**11**	4,5,6,7,**8,9**,10,11,**12**
Half-Life		6,7	12,13,14,**15,16,17**	
30.2 The Building Blocks of Matter				
Nuclear Bombardment				
Linear Accelerators	7			
The Synchrotron			**18**	
Particle Detectors	8			
The Fundamental Particles	9		19	
Particles and Antiparticles	10,11	8	20,21	**13,14**
The Quark Model of Nucleons				15,16
31.1 Holding the Nucleus Together				
The Strong Nuclear Force	1			
Binding Energy of the Nucleus	2	1,2	1,2,3,4,**5,6**	1,2,3,**4**,13
31.2 Using Nuclear Energy				
Artificial Radioactivity	3	3	7,8,9,10,11,12, 13,14,**15,16**	5,6,7,8,**9**
Nuclear Fission	4,5,6		**17**,18,19,20	10,11,12
Nuclear Reactors	7,8,9	4,6,7	**23**	
Nuclear Fusion	10,11	5	21,**22**	**14,15**
Controlled Fusion	12	8		